W9-CPF-783

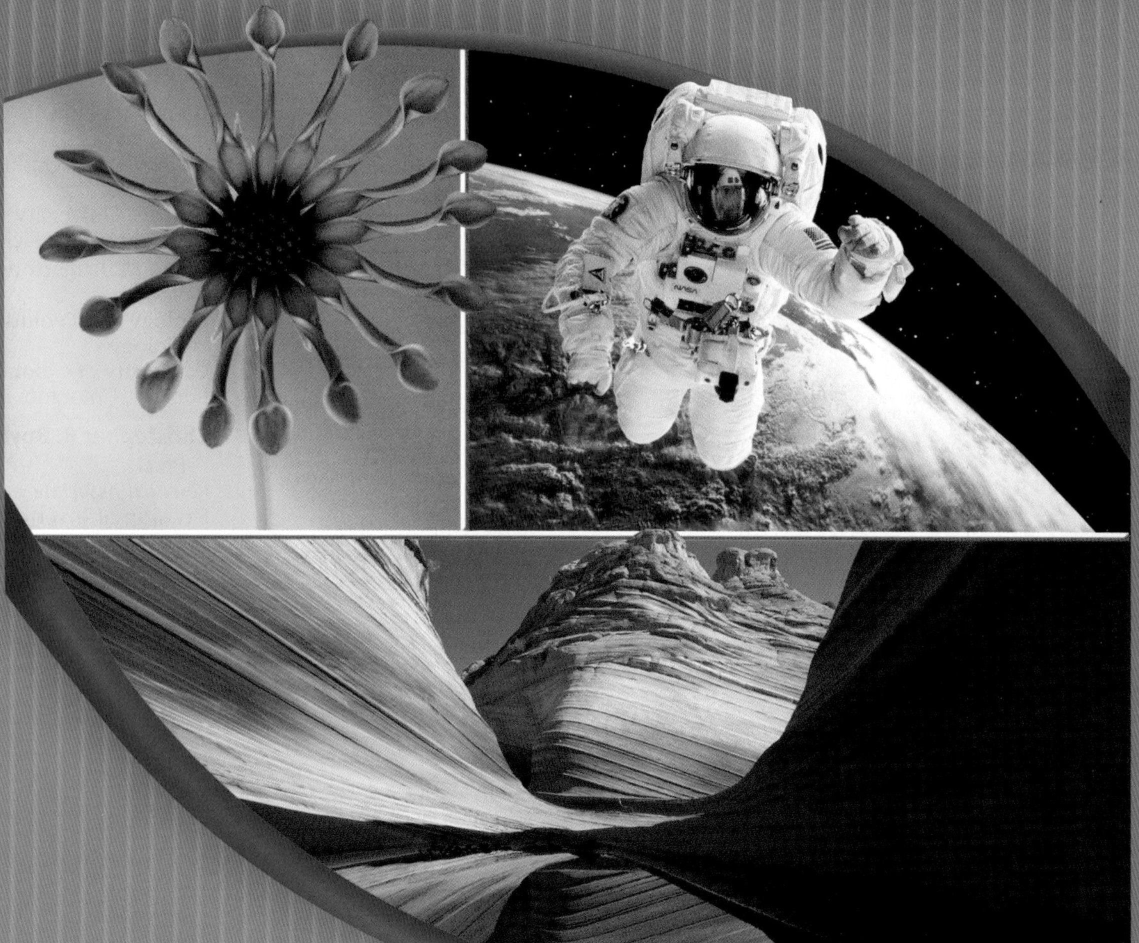

HOLT, RINEHART AND WINSTON
A Harcourt Education Company
Orlando • **Austin** • New York • San Diego • Toronto • London

Acknowledgments

Contributing Authors

Katy Z. Allen
Science Writer
Wayland, Massachusetts

Kathleen Meehan Berry
Science Chairman
Canon-McMillan School District
Canonsburg, Pennsylvania

Linda Ruth Berg, Ph.D.
Adjunct Professor
Natural Sciences
St. Petersburg College
St. Petersburg, Florida

Christie Borgford, Ph.D.
Assistant Professor of Chemistry
Department of Chemistry
The University of Alabama
Birmingham, Alabama

Barbara Christopher
Science Writer and Editor
Austin, Texas

Mapi Cuevas, Ph.D.
Professor of Chemistry
Department of Natural Sciences
Santa Fe Community College
Gainesville, Florida

Leila Dumas
Former Physics Teacher
Austin, Texas

Jennie Dusheck
Science Writer
Santa Cruz, California

Robert H. Fronk, Ph.D.
Professor
Science and Mathematics Education Department
Florida Institute of Technology
Melbourne, Florida

Mary Kay Hemenway, Ph.D.
Research Associate and Senior Lecturer
Department of Astronomy
The University of Texas at Austin
Austin, Texas

Kathleen Kaska
Former Life and Earth Science Teacher and Science Department Chair

William G. Lamb, Ph.D.
Winningstad Chair in the Physical Sciences
Oregon Episcopal School
Portland, Oregon

Karen J. Meech, Ph.D.
Astronomer
Institute for Astronomy
University of Hawaii
Honolulu, Hawaii

Robert J. Sager, M.S., J.D., L.G.
Coordinator and Professor of Earth Science
Pierce College
Lakewood, Washington

Mark F. Taylor, Ph.D.
Associate Professor of Biology
Biology Department
Baylor University
Waco, Texas

Indiana Teacher Consultants

Amy Bethke
Science Teacher
Baker Middle School
Michigan City, Indiana

Kathy Bartley
High School Math and Science Teacher
Highland High School
Highland, Indiana

Richard Bishop
Science Teacher
Clifford Pierce Middle School
Merrillville, Indiana

Jayme Herbert
Seventh and Eighth Grade Teacher
South Dearborn Middle School
Aurora, Indiana

Christina L. Hilton
Science Teacher
Science Department Curriculum Coordinator
Greenfield-Central High School
Greenfield, Indiana

Bruce A. Starek
Department Chairperson, Science Teacher
Baker Middle School
Michigan City, Indiana

Inclusion Specialists

Karen Clay
Inclusion Specialist Consultant
Boston, Massachusetts

Ellen McPeek Glisan
Special Needs Consultant
San Antonio, Texas

Safety Reviewer

Jack Gerlovich, Ph.D.
Associate Professor
School of Education
Drake University
Des Moines, Iowa

Academic Reviewers

Glenn Adelson
Instructor
Biology Undergraduate Program
Harvard University
Cambridge, Massachusetts

David M. Armstrong, Ph.D.
Professor
Ecology and Evolutionary Biology
University of Colorado
Boulder, Colorado

Christopher B. Boyko, Ph.D.
Research Associate
Division of Invertebrate Zoology
American Museum of Natural History
New York, New York

Acknowledgments
continued on page 764

Printed in the United States of America

ISBN 0-03-038142-8

2 3 4 5 6 7 048 08 07 06 05

Contents in Brief

Contents

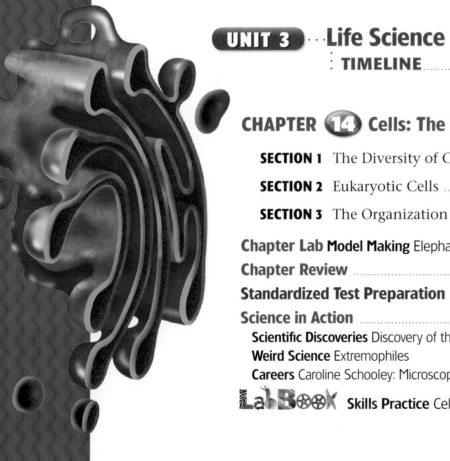

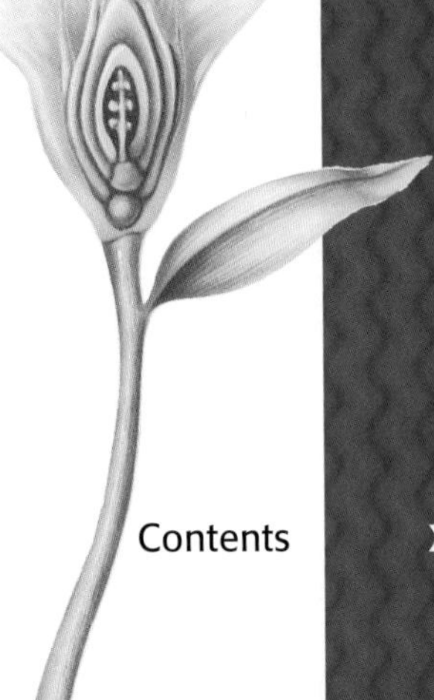

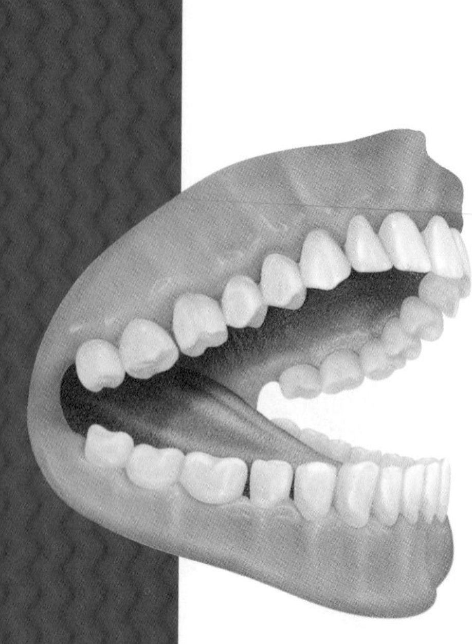

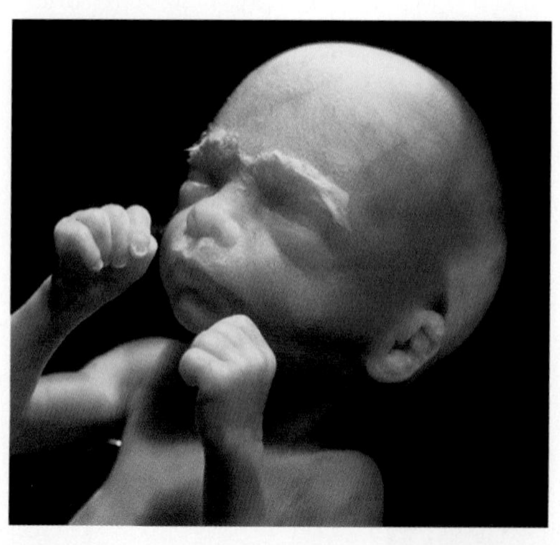

Chapter Labs and LabBook

The more labs, the better!

Take a minute to browse the variety of exciting **labs** in this textbook. Labs appear within the chapters and in a special LabBook in the back of the textbook. All labs are designed to help you experience science firsthand. But please don't forget to be safe. Read the Safety First! section before starting any of the labs.

Start your engines with an activity!

Get motivated to learn by doing the two activities at the beginning of each chapter. The **Pre-Reading Activity** helps you organize information as you read the chapter. The **Start-up Activity** helps you gain scientific understanding of the topic through hands-on experience.

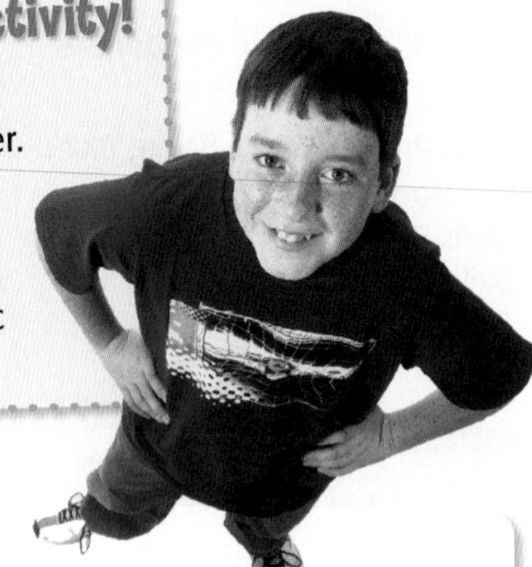

PRE-READING ACTIVITY

FOLDNOTES

Graphic Organizer

START-UP ACTIVITY

READING STRATEGY

Remembering what you read doesn't have to be hard!

A **Reading Strategy** at the beginning of every section provides tips to help you remember and/or organize the information covered in the section.

Quick Lab

School to Home

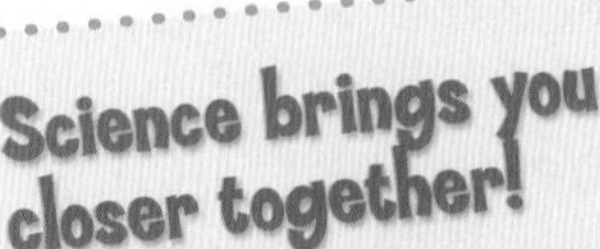

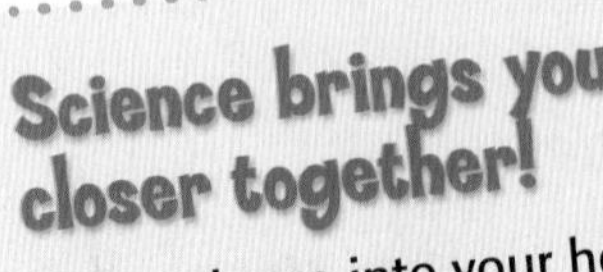

Science brings you closer together!

Bring science into your home by doing **School-to-Home Activities** with a parent or another adult in your household.

Internet Activity

Get caught in the Web!

Go to **go.hrw.com** for **Internet Activities** related to each chapter. To find the Internet Activity for a particular chapter, just type in the keyword listed below.

Math Practice

Science and math go hand in hand.

The **Math Focus** and **Math Practice** items show you many ways that math applies directly to science and vice versa.

Connection to...

One subject leads to another.

You may not realize it at first, but different subjects are related to each other in many ways. Each **Connection** explores a topic from the viewpoint of another discipline. In this way, all of the subjects you learn about in school merge to improve your understanding of the world around you.

Science in Action

Science moves beyond the classroom!

Read **Science in Action** articles to learn more about science in the real world. These articles will give you an idea of how interesting, strange, helpful, and action-packed science is. At the end of each chapter, you will find three short articles. And if your thirst is still not quenched, go to **go.hrw.com** for in-depth coverage.

Careers

People in Science

Science, Technology, and Society

Scientific Debate

Scientific Discoveries

Weird Science

Science Fiction

How to Use Your Textbook

Your Roadmap for Success with Holt Science and Technology

Reading Warm-Up

A Reading Warm-Up at the beginning of every section provides you with the section's objectives and key terms. The objectives tell you what you'll need to know after you finish reading the section.

Key terms are listed for each section. Learn the definitions of these terms because you will most likely be tested on them. Each key term is highlighted in the text and is defined at point of use and in the margin. You can also use the glossary to locate definitions quickly.

STUDY TIP Reread the objectives and the definitions to the key terms when studying for a test to be sure you know the material.

Get Organized

A Reading Strategy at the beginning of every section provides tips to help you organize and remember the information covered in the section. Keep a science notebook so that you are ready to take notes when your teacher reviews the material in class. Keep your assignments in this notebook so that you can review them when studying for the chapter test.

SECTION 1

READING WARM-UP

Objectives

- Describe how moving water shapes the surface of the Earth by the process of erosion.
- Explain how water moves through the water cycle.
- Describe a watershed.
- Explain three factors that affect the rate of stream erosion.
- Identify four ways that rivers are described.

Terms to Learn

erosion, water cycle, tributary, watershed, divide, channel, load

READING STRATEGY

Reading Organizer As you read this section, create an outline of the section. Use the headings from the section in your outline.

The Active River

If you had fallen asleep with your toes dangling in the Colorado River 6 million years ago and you had woken up today, your toes would be hanging about 1.6 km (about 1 mi) above the river!

The Colorado River carved the Grand Canyon, shown in **Figure 1,** by washing billions of tons of soil and rock from its riverbed. The Colorado River made the Grand Canyon by a process that can take millions of years.

Rivers: Agents of Erosion

Six million years ago, the area now known as the Grand Canyon was nearly as flat as a pancake. The Colorado River cut down into the rock and formed the Grand Canyon over millions of years through a process called erosion. **Erosion** is the process by which soil and sediment are transported from one location to another. Rivers are not the only agents of erosion. Wind, rain, ice, and snow can also cause erosion.

Because of erosion caused by water, the Grand Canyon is now about 1.6 km deep and 446 km long. In this section, you will learn about stream development, river systems, and the factors that affect the rate of stream erosion.

Reading Check **Describe the process that created the Grand Canyon.** *(See the Appendix for answers to Reading Checks.)*

erosion the process by which wind, water, ice, or gravity transports soil and sediment from one location to another

Figure 1 *The Grand Canyon is located in northwestern Arizona. The canyon formed over millions of years as running water eroded the rock layers. (In some places, the canyon is now 29 km wide.)*

94 Chapter 4 The Flow of Fresh Water

Be Resourceful—Use the Web

SCILINKS®

Internet Connect boxes in your textbook take you to resources that you can use for science projects, reports, and research papers. Go to scilinks.org, and type in the SciLinks code to get information on a topic.

go.hrw.com

Visit go.hrw.com Find worksheets, Current Science® magazine articles online, and other materials that go with your textbook at **go.hrw.com.** Click on the textbook icon and the table of contents to see all of the resources for each chapter.

The Water Cycle

Have you ever wondered how rivers keep flowing? Where do rivers get their water? Learning about the water cycle, shown in **Figure 2,** will help you answer these questions. The **water cycle** is the continuous movement of Earth's water from the ocean to the atmosphere to the land and back to the ocean. The water cycle is driven by energy from the sun.

water cycle the continuous movement of water from the ocean to the atmosphere to the land and back to the ocean

Figure 2 The Water Cycle

Condensation takes place when water vapor cools and changes into water droplets that form clouds in the atmosphere. Water loses energy during condensation.

Precipitation is rain, snow, sleet, or hail that falls from clouds onto the Earth's land and oceans.

Evaporation takes place when water from the oceans and the Earth's surface changes into water vapor. Energy from the sun causes evaporation. Water gains energy during evaporation.

Percolation ward mover through por spaces in so

SECTION **Review**

Summary

- Rivers cause erosion by removing and transporting soil and rock from the riverbed.
- The water cycle is the movement of Earth's water from the ocean to the atmosphere to the land and back to the ocean.
- A river system is made up of a network of streams and rivers.
- A watershed is a region that collects runoff water that then becomes part of a river or a lake.
- A stream with a high gradient has more energy for eroding soil and rock.
- When a stream's discharge increases, its erosive energy also increases.
- A stream with a load of large particles has a higher rate of erosion than a stream with a dissolved load.
- A developing river can be described as youthful, mature, old, or rejuvenated.

Using Key Terms

1. Use each of the following terms in a separate sentence: *erosion, water cycle, tributary, watershed, divide, channel,* and *load.*

Understanding Key Ideas

2. Which of the following drains a watershed?
   a. a divide
   b. a drainage basin
   c. a tributary
   d. a water system
3. Describe how the Grand Canyon was formed.
4. Draw the water cycle. In your drawing, label *condensation, precipitation,* and *evaporation.*
5. What are three factors that affect the rate of stream erosion?
6. Which stage of river development is characterized by flat flood plains?

Critical Thinking

7. **Making Inferences** How does the water cycle help develop river systems?
8. **Making Comparisons** How do youthful rivers, mature rivers, and old rivers differ?

Interpreting Graphics

Use the pie graph below to answer the questions that follow.

Distribution of Water in the World

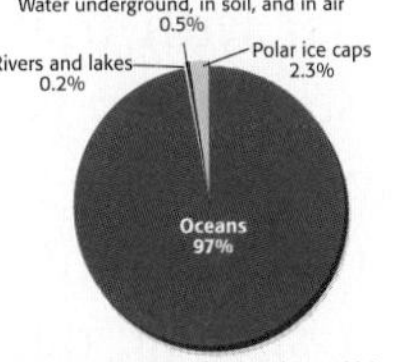

9. Where is most of the water in the world found?
10. In what form is the majority of the world's fresh water?

SCILINKS.
NSTA
Developed and maintained by the National Science Teachers Association
For a variety of links related to this chapter, go to www.scilinks.org
Topic: Rivers and Streams
SciLinks code: HSM1316

101

Use the Illustrations and Photos

Art shows complex ideas and processes. Learn to analyze the art so that you better understand the material you read in the text.

Tables and graphs display important information in an organized way to help you see relationships.

A picture is worth a thousand words. Look at the photographs to see relevant examples of science concepts that you are reading about.

Answer the Section Reviews

Section Reviews test your knowledge of the main points of the section. Critical Thinking items challenge you to think about the material in greater depth and to find connections that you infer from the text.

STUDY TIP When you can't answer a question, reread the section. The answer is usually there.

Do Your Homework

Your teacher may assign worksheets to help you understand and remember the material in the chapter.

STUDY TIP Don't try to answer the questions without reading the text and reviewing your class notes. A little preparation up front will make your homework assignments a lot easier. Answering the items in the Chapter Review will help prepare you for the chapter test.

Holt Online Learning

Visit Holt Online Learning

If your teacher gives you a special password to log onto the Holt Online Learning site, you'll find your complete textbook on the Web. In addition, you'll find some great learning tools and practice quizzes. You'll be able to see how well you know the material from your textbook.

Visit CNN Student News

You'll find up-to-date events in science at **cnnstudentnews.com.**

Exploring, inventing, and investigating are essential to the study of science. However, these activities can also be dangerous. To make sure that your experiments and explorations are safe, you must be aware of a variety of safety guidelines. You have probably heard of the saying, "It is better to be safe than sorry." This is particularly true in a science classroom where experiments and explorations are being performed. Being uninformed and careless can result in serious injuries. Don't take chances with your own safety or with anyone else's.

The following pages describe important guidelines for staying safe in the science classroom. Your teacher may also have safety guidelines and tips that are specific to your classroom and laboratory. Take the time to be safe.

Safety Rules!

Start Out Right

Always get your teacher's permission before attempting any laboratory exploration. Read the procedures carefully, and pay particular attention to safety information and caution statements. If you are unsure about what a safety symbol means, look it up or ask your teacher. You cannot be too careful when it comes to safety. If an accident does occur, inform your teacher immediately regardless of how minor you think the accident is.

If you are instructed to note the odor of a substance, wave the fumes toward your nose with your hand. Never put your nose close to the source.

Safety Symbols

All of the experiments and investigations in this book and their related worksheets include important safety symbols to alert you to particular safety concerns. Become familiar with these symbols so that when you see them, you will know what they mean and what to do. It is important that you read this entire safety section to learn about specific dangers in the laboratory.

Eye protection

Clothing protection

Hand safety

Heating safety

Electric safety

Chemical safety

Animal safety

Sharp object

Plant safety

Eye Safety

Wear safety goggles when working around chemicals, acids, bases, or any type of flame or heating device. Wear safety goggles any time there is even the slightest chance that harm could come to your eyes. If any substance gets into your eyes, notify your teacher immediately and flush your eyes with running water for at least 15 minutes. Treat any unknown chemical as if it were a dangerous chemical. Never look directly into the sun. Doing so could cause permanent blindness.

Avoid wearing contact lenses in a laboratory situation. Even if you are wearing safety goggles, chemicals can get between the contact lenses and your eyes. If your doctor requires that you wear contact lenses instead of glasses, wear eye-cup safety goggles in the lab.

Safety Equipment

Know the locations of the nearest fire alarms and any other safety equipment, such as fire blankets and eyewash fountains, as identified by your teacher, and know the procedures for using the equipment.

Neatness

Keep your work area free of all unnecessary books and papers. Tie back long hair, and secure loose sleeves or other loose articles of clothing, such as ties and bows. Remove dangling jewelry. Don't wear open-toed shoes or sandals in the laboratory. Never eat, drink, or apply cosmetics in a laboratory setting. Food, drink, and cosmetics can easily become contaminated with dangerous materials.

Certain hair products (such as aerosol hair spray) are flammable and should not be worn while working near an open flame. Avoid wearing hair spray or hair gel on lab days.

Sharp/Pointed Objects 

Use knives and other sharp instruments with extreme care. Never cut objects while holding them in your hands. Place objects on a suitable work surface for cutting.

Be extra careful when using any glassware. When adding a heavy object to a graduated cylinder, tilt the cylinder so that the object slides slowly to the bottom.

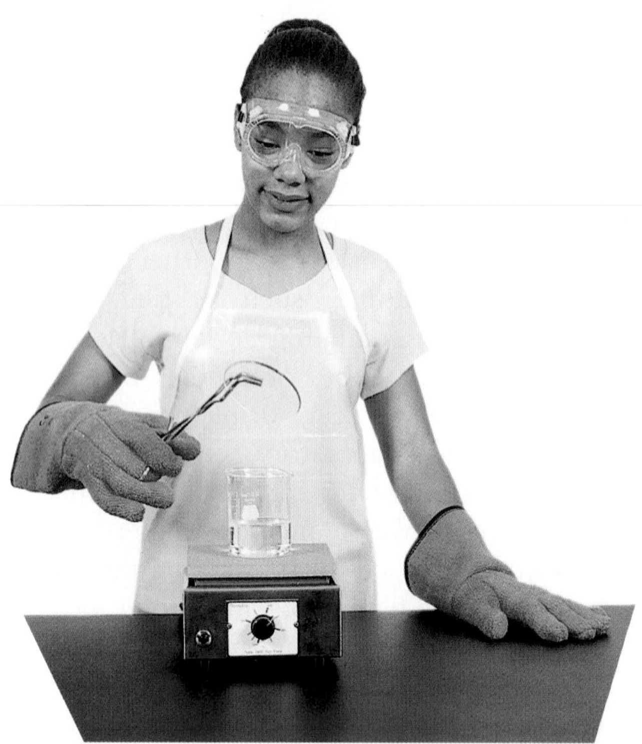

Chemicals

Wear safety goggles when handling any potentially dangerous chemicals, acids, or bases. If a chemical is unknown, handle it as you would a dangerous chemical. Wear an apron and protective gloves when you work with acids or bases or whenever you are told to do so. If a spill gets on your skin or clothing, rinse it off immediately with water for at least 5 minutes while calling to your teacher.

Never mix chemicals unless your teacher tells you to do so. Never taste, touch, or smell chemicals unless you are specifically directed to do so. Before working with a flammable liquid or gas, check for the presence of any source of flame, spark, or heat.

Heat

Wear safety goggles when using a heating device or a flame. Whenever possible, use an electric hot plate as a heat source instead of using an open flame. When heating materials in a test tube, always angle the test tube away from yourself and others. To avoid burns, wear heat-resistant gloves whenever instructed to do so.

Electricity

Be careful with electrical cords. When using a microscope with a lamp, do not place the cord where it could trip someone. Do not let cords hang over a table edge in a way that could cause equipment to fall if the cord is accidentally pulled. Do not use equipment with damaged cords. Be sure that your hands are dry and that the electrical equipment is in the "off" position before plugging it in. Turn off and unplug electrical equipment when you are finished.

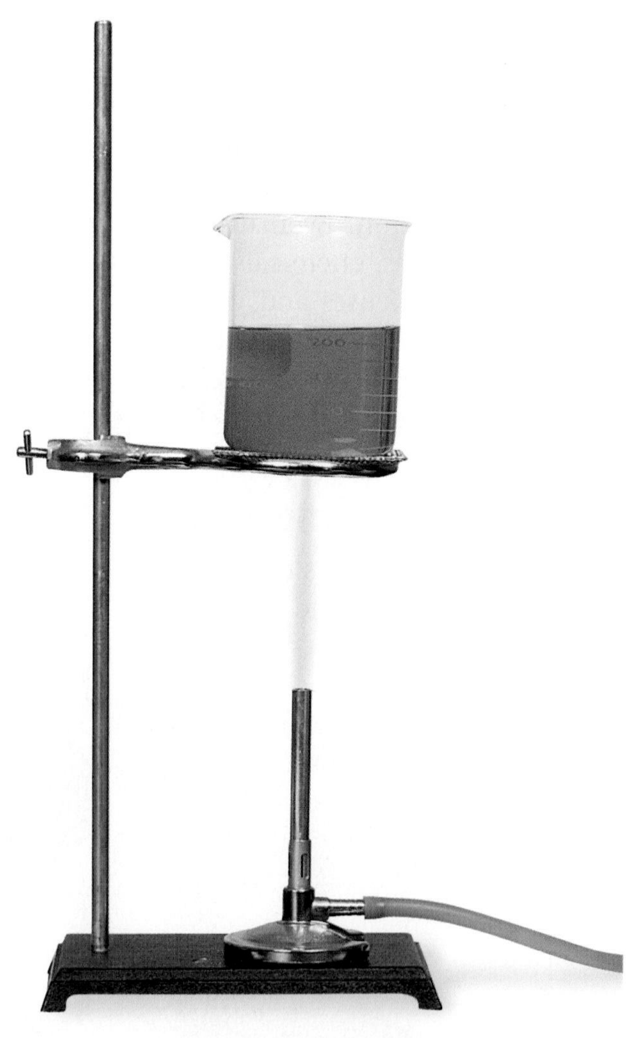

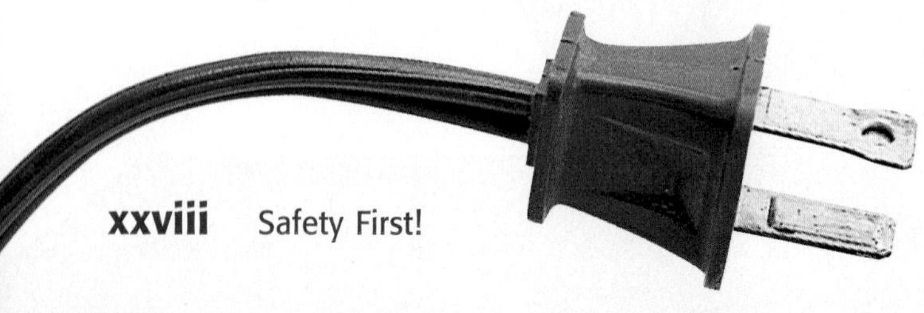

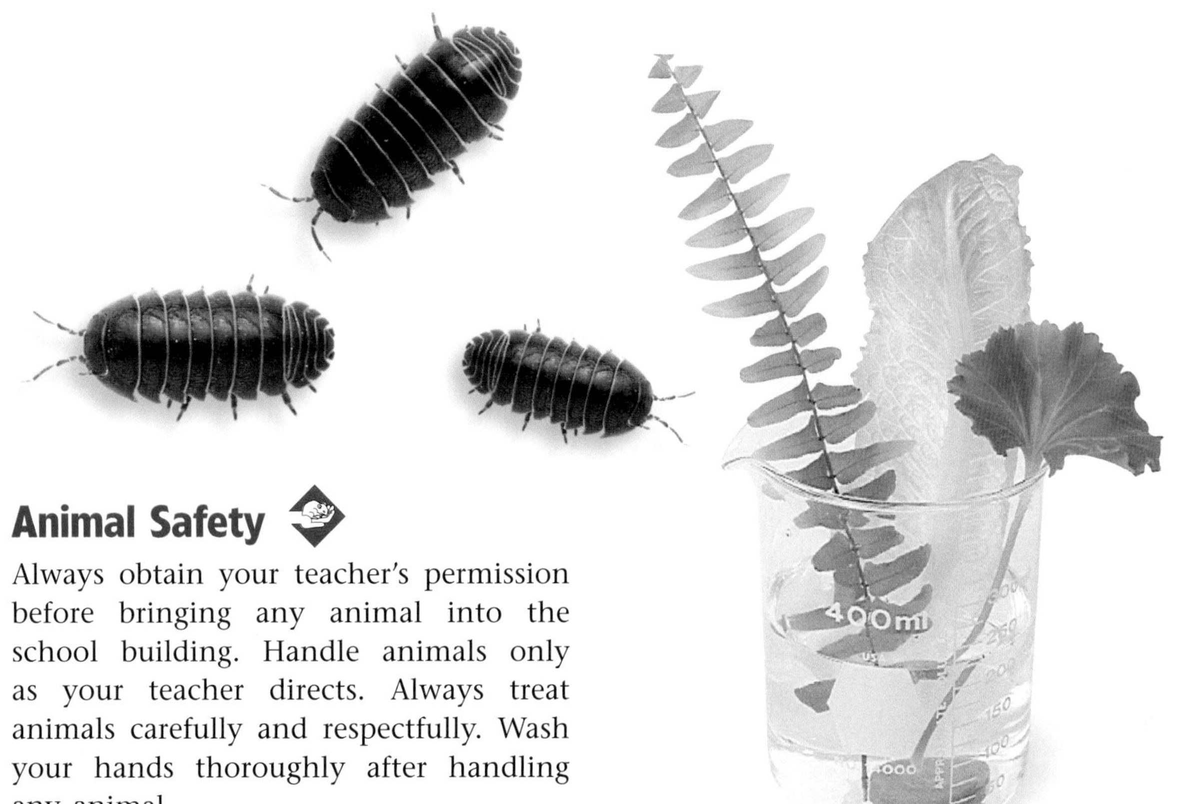

Animal Safety

Always obtain your teacher's permission before bringing any animal into the school building. Handle animals only as your teacher directs. Always treat animals carefully and respectfully. Wash your hands thoroughly after handling any animal.

Plant Safety

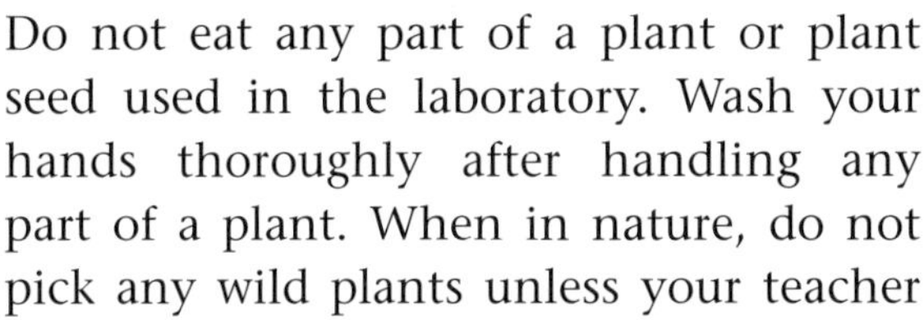

Do not eat any part of a plant or plant seed used in the laboratory. Wash your hands thoroughly after handling any part of a plant. When in nature, do not pick any wild plants unless your teacher instructs you to do so.

Glassware

Examine all glassware before use. Be sure that glassware is clean and free of chips and cracks. Report damaged glassware to your teacher. Glass containers used for heating should be made of heat-resistant glass.

1

Science in Our World

About the 

What is that man doing? Ricardo Alonso, a geologist in Argentina, is measuring the footprints left by a dinosaur millions of years ago. Taking measurements is just one way that scientists collect data to answer questions and test hypotheses.

PRE-READING ACTIVITY

FOLDNOTES **Key-Term Fold** Before you read the chapter, create the FoldNote entitled "Key-Term Fold" described in the **Study Skills** section of the Appendix. Write a key term from the chapter on each tab of the key-term fold. Under each tab, write the definition of the key term.

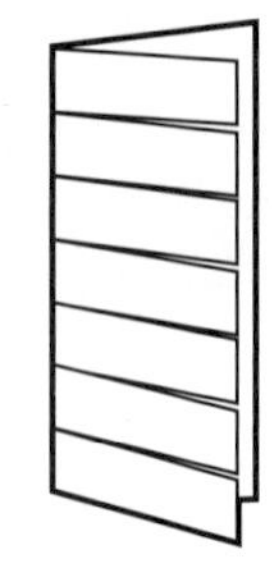

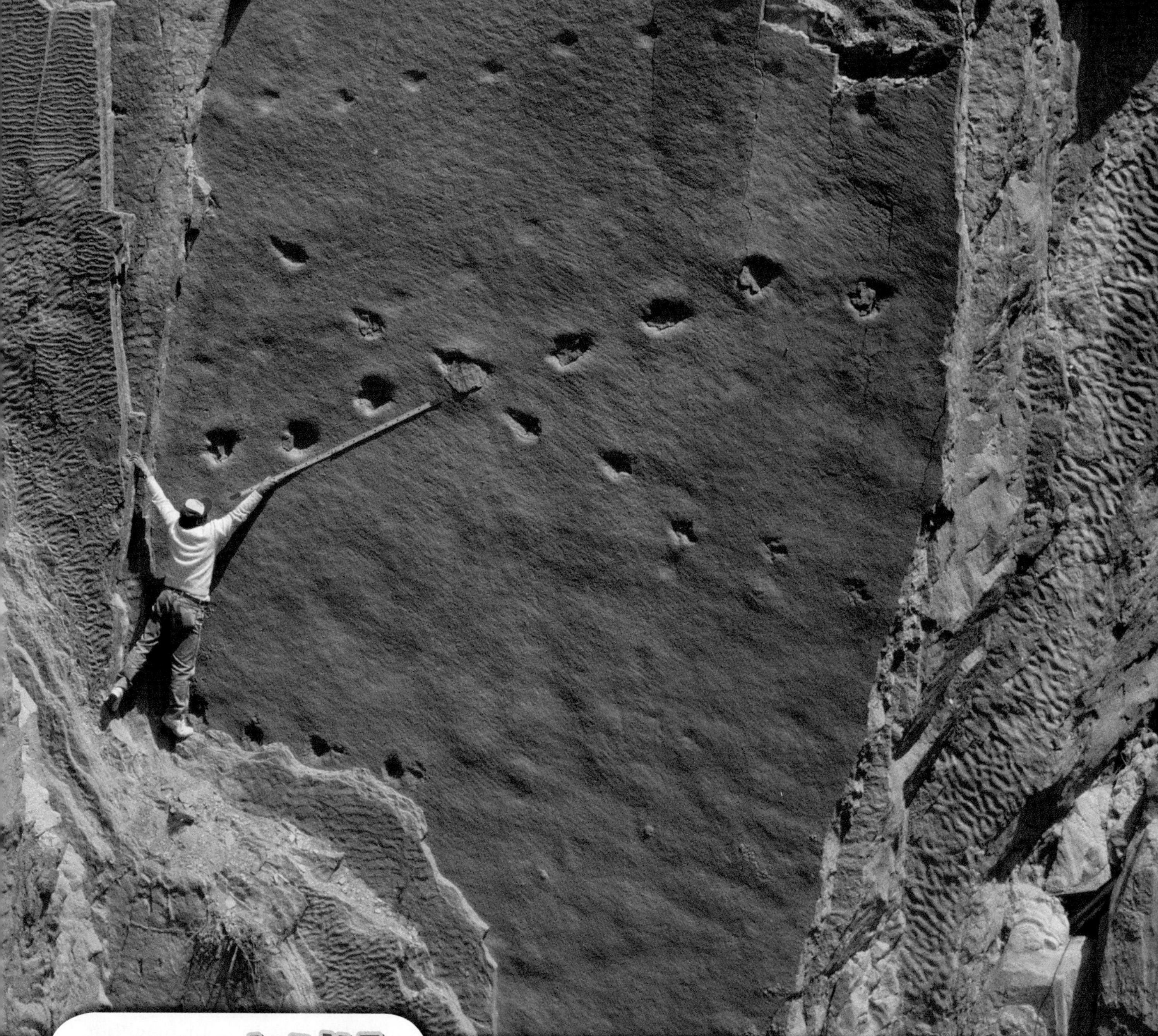

START-UP ACTIVITY

Mission Impossible?

In this activity, you will do some creative thinking to solve what might seem like an impossible problem.

Procedure

1. Examine an **index card.** Your mission is to fit yourself through the card. You can only tear and fold the card. You cannot use tape, glue, or anything else to hold the card together.
2. Brainstorm with a partner ways to complete your mission. Then, record your plan.
3. Test your plan. Did it work? If necessary, get **another index card** and try again. Record your new plan and the results.
4. Share your plans and results with your classmates.

Analysis

1. Why was it helpful to come up with a plan in advance?
2. How did testing your plan help you complete your mission?
3. How did sharing your ideas with your classmates help you complete your mission? What did your classmates do differently?

SECTION 1

Science and Scientists

You are on a hike in the mountains when you see something strange. You pick it up. It looks like a shell. You are curious. How could a shell be up on this mountain?

READING WARM-UP

Objectives

- Describe three ways to answer questions about science.
- Identify three benefits of science.
- Describe five jobs that use science.

Terms to Learn

science

READING STRATEGY

Reading Organizer As you read this section, create an outline of the section. Use the headings from the section in your outline.

Congratulations! You just completed the first steps of being a scientist. How did you do it? You observed the world around you. Then, you asked a question about your observations. And that's part of what science is all about.

Science Starts with a Question

Science is the knowledge gained by observing the natural world. Asking a question can help you gather knowledge. The world around you is full of amazing things that can lead you to ask questions, such as those in **Figure 1.**

Reading Check What is science? (*See the Appendix for answers to Reading Checks.*)

science the knowledge obtained by observing natural events and conditions in order to discover facts and formulate laws or principles that can be verified or tested

In Your Own Neighborhood

Take a look around your school and around your neighborhood. Most of the time, you take things that you use or see every day for granted. However, one day you might look at something in a new way. That's when a question hits you! You might sit under the tree in front of your school every day. At some point, you may wonder how the leaves change color.

The World and Beyond

Do you think that you might get tired of asking questions about things in your neighborhood? Then just remember that the world is a big place. You could ask questions about deserts, forests, or sandy beaches. Many different plants and animals live in each of these places, and the environment is full of rocks, soil, and water.

But the Earth is not the final place to look for questions. You can look outward to the moon, sun, and planets in our solar system. And beyond that, you have the rest of the universe! There seems to be enough questions to keep scientists busy for a long time.

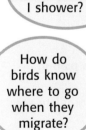

How do birds know where to go when they migrate?

How are a frog and a lizard different?
Why does the mirror fog when I shower?

Figure 1 *Part of science is asking questions about the world around you.*

Science Educator

A *science educator* is a person who teaches others about science. Learning about science can help people understand how the world works. With education, people can be aware of the effects of their actions. As a result, people can act in ways that are healthy for themselves and others around them. Many science educators teach at schools. Others work at zoos, at aquariums, or in national parks, as shown in **Figure 9.**

Reading Check Where do science educators work?

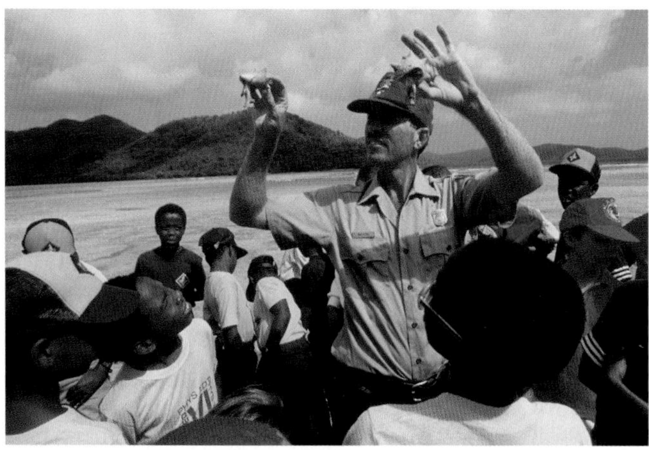

Figure 9 *Some science educators work as park rangers in national parks.*

SECTION Review

Summary

- Science is the knowledge gained by observing the natural world.
- Scientists answer questions by using research, observation, and experimentation to collect data. Often, there is more than one good way to analyze and interpret data.
- Knowledge gained through science helps people protect lives, resources, and the environment.
- People use science in many types of jobs. Some people who use science in their jobs are environmental scientists, cartographers, engineers, zoologists, and science educators.

Using Key Terms

1. In your own words, write a definition for the term *science*.

Understanding Key Ideas

2. How do scientists investigate their questions?
3. What are three ways that knowledge gained through scientific discoveries can benefit the world around you?
4. Which of the following careers does NOT rely on science?
   a. environmental science
   b. cartography
   c. zoology
   d. None of the above
5. What are some resources that you can use to do research?

Math Skills

6. If recycling 1 metric ton of paper saves 4,500 kWh of energy, how much energy is saved by recycling 2.75 metric tons of paper?
7. Imagine that you are a cartographer who needs to draw a map that has the following scale: 1 cm = 1 m. How long would the line representing a wall that is 8.5 m long be?

Critical Thinking

8. **Consumer Focus** Your family usually buys the leading brand of toothpaste. A 5 oz tube of this toothpaste costs $3.00. You notice that a 5 oz tube of another brand costs $2. Which brand is cheaper? What other information would you need in order to decide which brand was a better value?
9. **Applying Concepts** Imagine that you were camping during a meteor shower. You were amazed at what you saw, and you wanted to know what causes a shooting star. Name two ways that you could investigate the cause of a shooting star.

For a variety of links related to this chapter, go to www.scilinks.org

Topic: Recycling; Careers in Science
SciLinks code: HSM1277; HSM0225

SECTION 2

Scientific Methods

Standing by a river, several long-necked dinosaurs quietly chew on plants. Through the trees, they see an allosaurus (AL oh SAWR uhs), the most common meat-eating dinosaur of the Jurassic period.

This scene is not based on imagination alone. Even though scientists have never seen a dinosaur, they have been studying dinosaurs for years! How can that be? Scientists gather bits of information about dinosaurs and their environment from fossils. Then, they re-create what the Earth might have been like long ago. They use imagination and scientific methods.

What Are Scientific Methods?

When scientists observe the natural world, they often think of a question or problem. But scientists don't just guess at answers. **Scientific methods** are the ways in which scientists answer questions and solve problems.

As scientists look for answers, they often use the same steps. But there is more than one way to use the steps. Look at **Figure 1.** Scientists may use all of the steps or just some of the steps during an investigation. They may even repeat some of the steps or do the steps in a different order. It all depends on what works best to answer their question.

READING WARM-UP

Objectives

- Identify the steps used in scientific methods.
- Formulate testable hypotheses.
- Explain how scientific methods are used to answer questions and solve problems.

Terms to Learn

scientific methods
observation
hypothesis
data

READING STRATEGY

Reading Organizer As you read this section, make a flowchart of the possible steps in scientific methods.

scientific methods a series of steps followed to solve problems

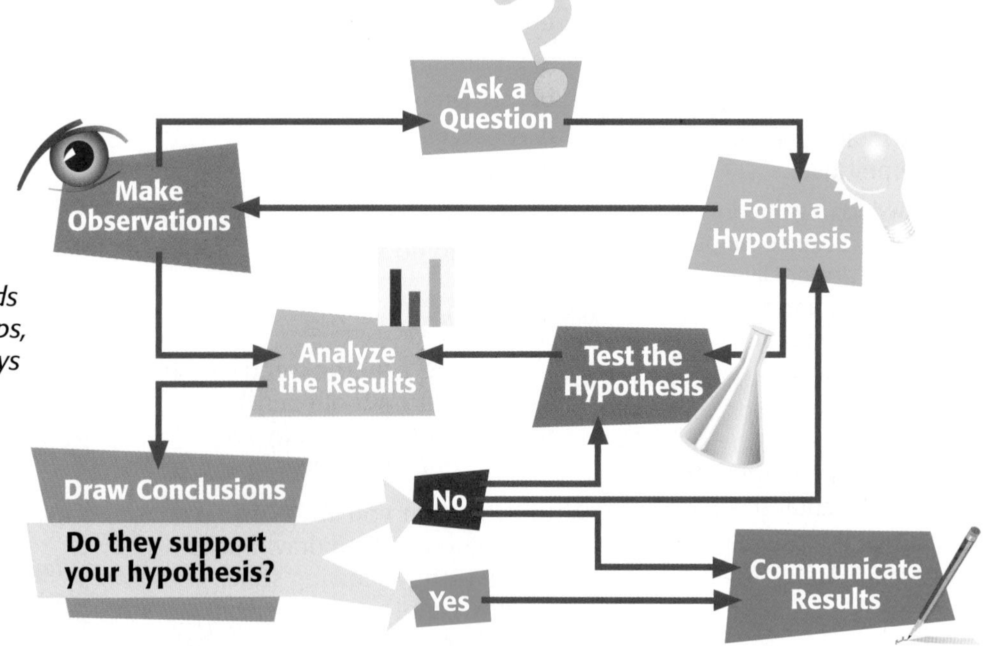

Figure 1 *Scientific methods often involve the same steps, but the steps are not always used in the same order.*

Ask a Question

Asking a question helps focus the purpose of an investigation. Scientists often ask a question after making observations. An **observation** is the act of using the senses to gather information. Observations can be made at any point in an investigation.

observation the process of obtaining information by using the senses

There are many kinds of observations. Observations may describe the hardness or softness of a rock. They may describe the color of a substance. Even the patterns in behavior of an animal can be described by observations. Measurements are observations that are made with tools, such as metersticks, stopwatches, and thermometers. Observations lead to answers only when they are accurate and carefully recorded.

A Dinosaur-Sized Question

In 1979, two people on a hike found dinosaur bones in the area of northwestern New Mexico shown in **Figure 2.** Soon after, David D. Gillette, a scientist who studies fossils, went to see the bones. After observing the bones, Gillette may have asked, "What kind of dinosaur did these bones come from?" Gillette would have to use scientific methods to come up with an answer that he could trust.

Reading Check **Why do scientists use scientific methods to answer questions?** (*See the Appendix for answers to Reading Checks.*)

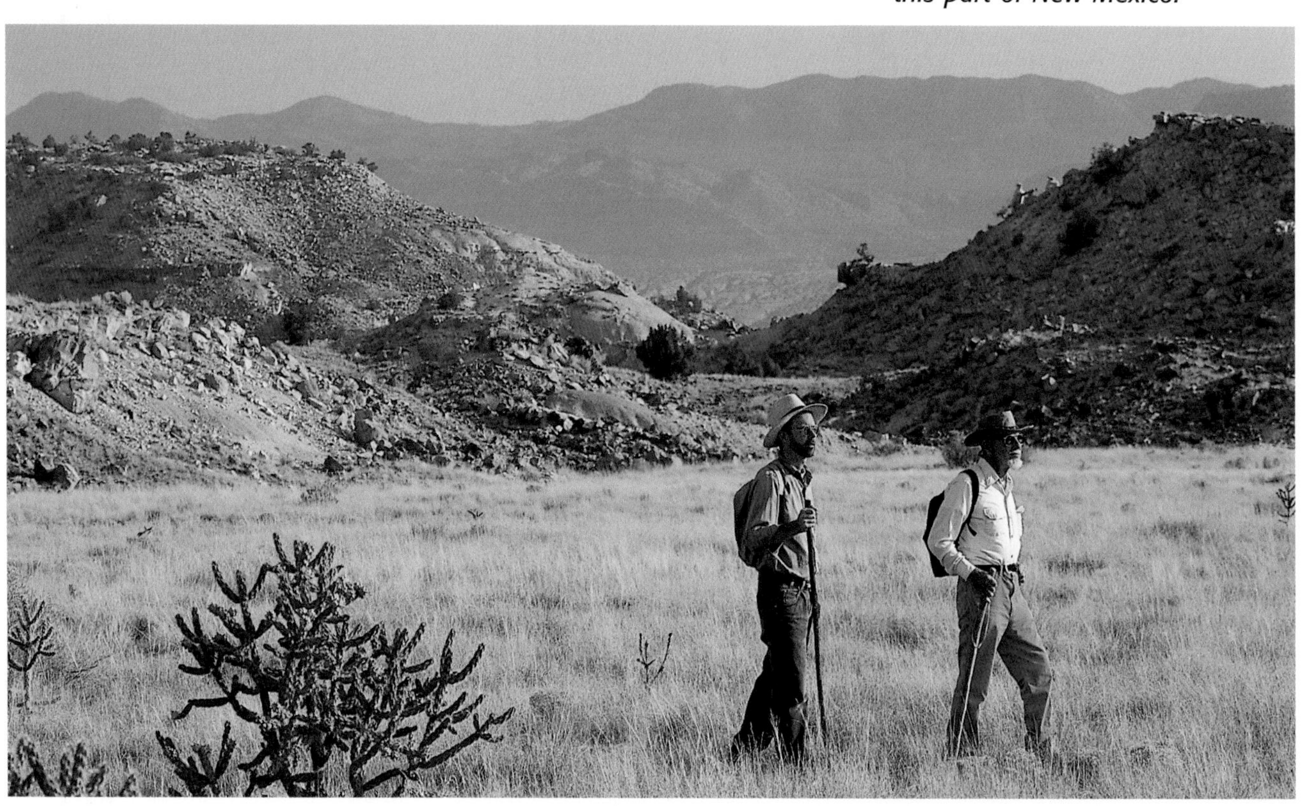

Figure 2 *Bones were found in this part of New Mexico.*

Form a Hypothesis

hypothesis an explanation that is based on prior scientific research or observations and that can be tested

When scientists want to investigate a question, they form a hypothesis. A **hypothesis** is a possible explanation or answer to a question. It is sometimes called an educated guess. The hypothesis is a scientist's best answer to the question. But a hypothesis can't be just any answer. Someone must be able to test the hypothesis to see if it is true.

From his observations and previous knowledge about dinosaurs, Gillette formed a hypothesis about the bones. He said that the bones, seen in **Figure 3,** came from a kind of dinosaur not yet known to scientists. This hypothesis was Gillette's best testable explanation. To test it, Gillette would have to do a lot of research.

Make Predictions

Before scientists test a hypothesis, they often make predictions. To make a prediction, you say what you think will happen in your experiment or investigation. Predictions are usually stated in an if-then format. For example, Gillette could make the following prediction: If the bones are from a dinosaur not yet known to science, then at least some of the bones will not match any dinosaur bones that have been studied before. Sometimes, scientists make many predictions about one experiment. After predictions are made, scientists can do experiments to see which predictions, if any, support the hypothesis.

Figure 3 *Gillette and his team had to dig out the bones carefully before studying them.*

Test the Hypothesis

A hypothesis must be tested for scientists to learn whether an idea can be supported scientifically. Scientists test hypotheses by gathering data. **Data** are any pieces of information gathered through experimentation. The data can help scientists tell if the hypotheses are valid.

data any pieces of information acquired through observation or experimentation

To test his hypothesis, Gillette took hundreds of measurements of the bones, as shown in **Figure 4.** He compared his measurements with those of bones from known dinosaurs. He visited museums and talked with other scientists. After gathering all of these data, Gillette was ready for the next step toward answering his question.

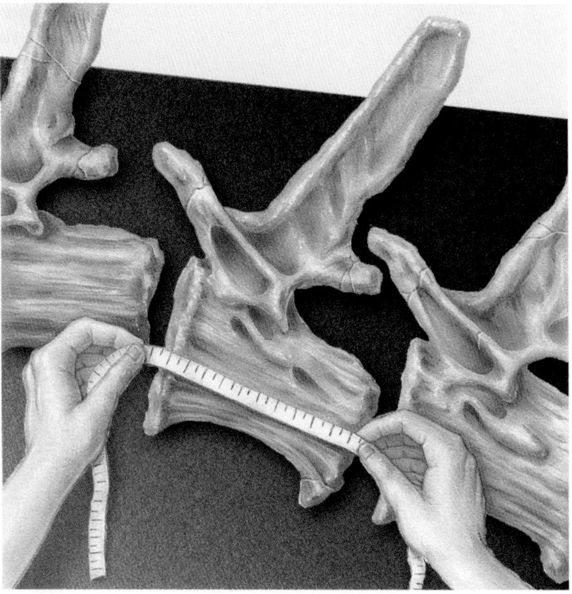

Figure 4 *To test his hypothesis, Gillette took hundreds of measurements of the bones.*

Under Control

To test a hypothesis, a scientist may conduct a controlled experiment. A *controlled experiment* tests only one factor at a time. The one factor that is changed in a controlled experiment is called a *variable.* By changing only the variable, scientists can see the results of just that one change.

Not all investigations are made by doing controlled experiments. Sometimes, it is not possible to use a controlled experiment to test something. Also, some scientists depend on observations more than they depend on experiments to test their hypotheses. By observing nature, scientists can often collect large amounts of data about their hypotheses. When large amounts of data support a hypothesis, the hypothesis is probably valid.

Reading Check **What is a variable?**

Laguna Colorada In some parts of the world, lake water doesn't look blue. In parts of Bolivia, the lakes may be green, yellow, or red! One Bolivian lake, Laguna Colorada, is a deep-red body of water surrounded by a white stretch of flat land. The land around the lake is white because of all of the salty minerals in the rock there. Some of the lakes are colored by minerals. Others are colored by the microorganisms that live there. How could you find out why Laguna Colorada is red?

Analyze the Results

After they finish their tests, scientists must analyze the results. Analyzing the results helps scientists construct reasonable explanations based on the evidence that has been collected. Scientists often make tables and graphs to arrange their data. **Figure 5** shows how Gillette organized his data. When Gillette analyzed his results, he found that the bones of the mystery dinosaur did not match the bones of any known dinosaur. The bones were either too large or too different in shape.

Reading Check **What are two ways that scientists can organize their data?**

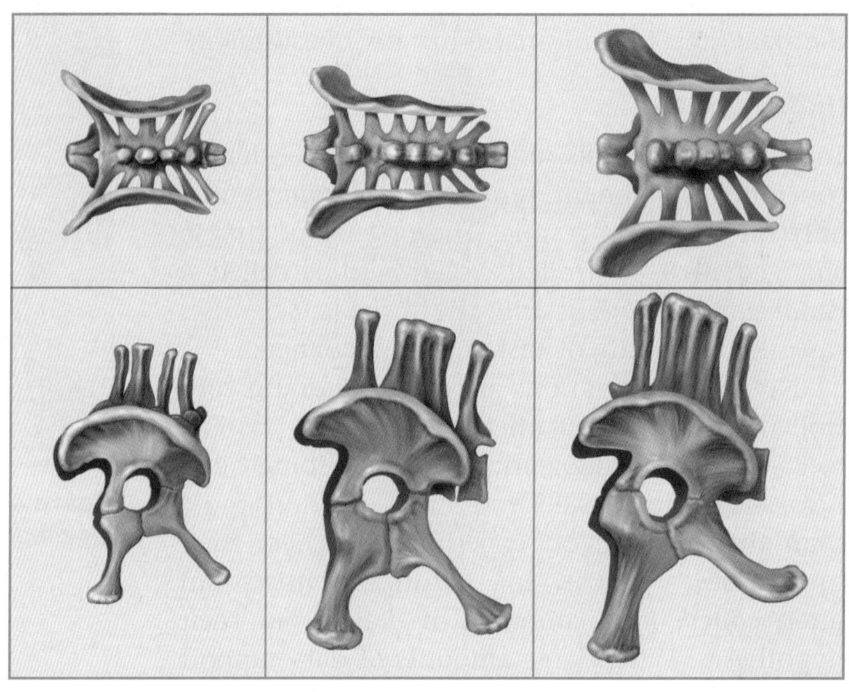

Figure 5 *By organizing his measurements in a chart, Gillette could analyze his results more easily.*

Figure 6 *This model of the skeleton of* Seismosaurus hallorum *is based on Gillette's research. The bones shown in the darker color are the bones that have been found so far.*

Mapping a Sphere

1. Examine a **soccer ball,** and notice the patterns on the ball.
2. Place different **stickers** on each pentagon of the ball.
3. Now, try mapping the images from the soccer ball onto a **flat piece of paper.**
4. What problems came up when you tried to represent a sphere on a flat piece of paper?
5. Use your experience to draw a conclusion about why maps of the entire Earth are often represented on a globe. Then, explain why flat maps of the entire Earth are often distorted.

Draw Conclusions

After analyzing the results of their tests, scientists must conclude if the results support the hypothesis. Proving that a hypothesis is not true can be as valuable as proving that it is true. If the hypothesis is not supported, scientists may repeat the investigation to check for mistakes. Or, scientists may look at the original question in a new way, ask new questions, and form new hypotheses. New questions and hypotheses can lead to new investigations and discoveries.

From all of his work, Gillette concluded that the bones found in New Mexico, shown in the model in **Figure 6,** were indeed from a yet unknown dinosaur. The dinosaur was about 45 m (148 ft) long and had a mass of almost 100 metric tons. The creature certainly fit the name that Gillette gave it—*Seismosaurus hallorum,* the "earth shaker."

For another activity related to this chapter, go to **go.hrw.com** and type in the keyword **HZ5WESW.**

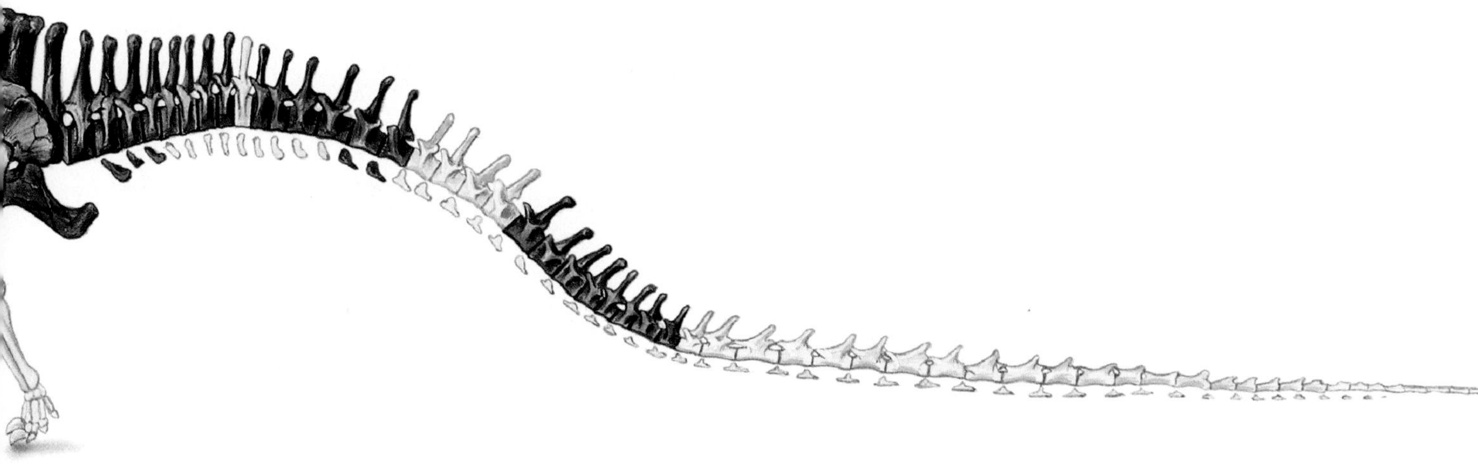

Communicate Results

After finishing an investigation, scientists communicate their results. By doing so, scientists share what they have learned. Scientists communicate by writing reports for scientific journals and by giving talks. They can also put their results on the Internet. In fact, scientists use computers to prepare research reports as well as to share data with other scientists.

Science depends on sharing information. Sharing allows other scientists to repeat experiments to see if they get the same results. Also, by sharing, scientists can compare hypotheses and form consistent explanations. Sometimes, new data lead scientists to change their hypotheses.

Gillette shared his discovery of *Seismosaurus hallorum* at a press conference at the New Mexico Museum of Natural History and Science. He later sent a report that described his investigation to the *Journal of Vertebrate Paleontology.*

Reading Check Name three ways that scientists share results.

Case Closed?

All of the bones that Gillette found have been dug up from the ground. But as **Figure 7** shows, the fun is not over yet! The work on *Seismosaurus hallorum* continues. The remains of one of the largest dinosaurs ever discovered are still being studied. Like so many other investigations, Gillette's work led to new questions to be answered.

CONNECTION TO Physics

Defining Technology As technologies are developed, scientists are able to investigate questions in new ways. How would you define the word *technology*? Consider the pros and cons of the following definitions: 1) artifact or hardware; 2) methodology or technique; 3) system of production; or 4) social-technical system. Can you find evidence to support the use of any of these definitions? Give an example of a technology that fits each definition.

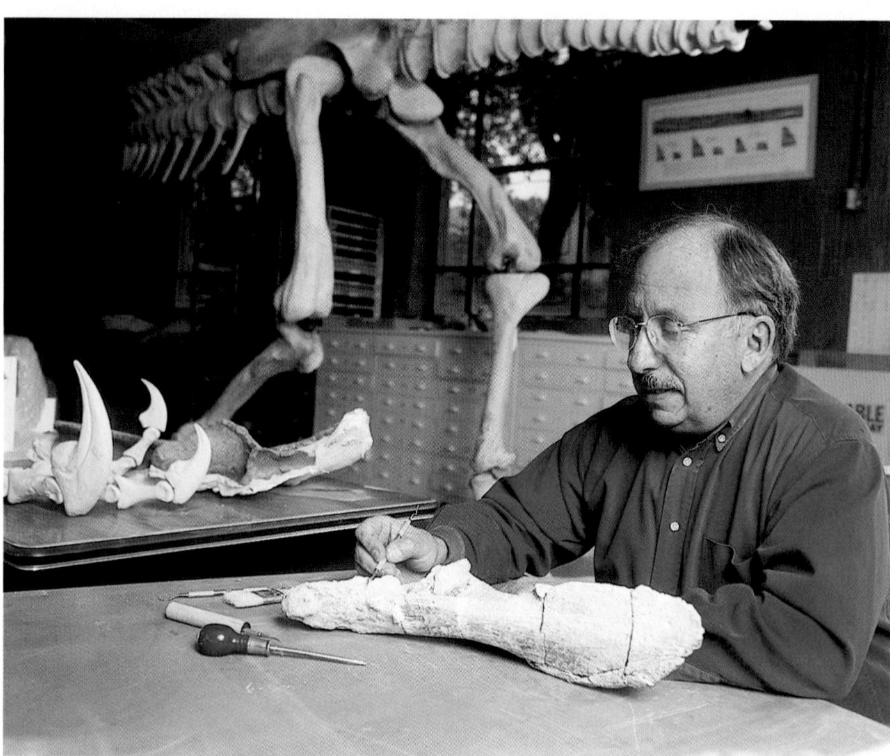

Figure 7 *David Gillette continues to study the bones of* Seismosaurus hallorum *for new views into the past.*

SECTION
Review

Summary

- Scientific methods are the ways in which scientists follow steps to answer questions and solve problems.
- Any information gathered through the senses is an observation. Observations often lead to the formation of questions and hypotheses.
- A hypothesis is a possible explanation or answer to a question. A well-formed hypothesis can be tested by experiments.
- A controlled experiment tests only one factor at a time in order to determine the effects of changes to just that one factor.
- After testing a hypothesis, scientists analyze the results and draw conclusions about whether the hypothesis is supported.
- Communicating results allows others to check the results, add to their knowledge, form new hypotheses, and design new experiments.

Using Key Terms

1. Use the following terms in the same sentence: *scientific methods, observations, hypothesis,* and *data*.

Understanding Key Ideas

2. Which of the following statements about the steps of scientific methods is true?
   - **a.** Steps must always be used in the same order.
   - **b.** All steps must be used.
   - **c.** Steps are repeated sometimes.
   - **d.** The steps must support the hypothesis.
3. The following statements could have been made during Gillette's field investigation. Which statement is a testable hypothesis?
   - **a.** Dinosaur bones were found in New Mexico.
   - **b.** The bones are from a known dinosaur.
   - **c.** One of the ribs is 2 m long.
   - **d.** The first step in studying the bones is to dig them out of the ground.
4. What is an observation? Write down one observation about the room that you are in at this moment.
5. What is a controlled experiment?

Critical Thinking

6. **Analyzing Processes** How could two scientists working to answer the same question draw different conclusions?
7. **Applying Concepts** What are two ways that you could analyze data about temperature changes over many years? What are the benefits and limitations of each method?

Interpreting Graphics

8. The table below shows how long one bacterium takes to divide into two bacteria. Plot the data on a graph. Put temperature on the *x*-axis and the time to double on the *y*-axis. Do not graph values for which there is no growth. What temperature allows the bacteria to grow the fastest?

Temperature (°C)	Time to double (min)
10	130
20	60
25	40
30	29
37	17
40	19
45	32
50	no growth

SCILINKS®
NSTA
Developed and maintained by the National Science Teachers Association
For a variety of links related to this chapter, go to www.scilinks.org
Topic: Scientific Methods
SciLinks code: HSM1359

SECTION 3

Scientific Models

Imagine you are studying volcanoes. How do you think baking soda, vinegar, and some clay could help you?

READING WARM-UP

Objectives

- Use models to represent the natural world.
- Identify the limitations of models.
- Describe theories and laws.

Terms to Learn

model
theory
law

READING STRATEGY

Paired Summarizing Read this section silently. In pairs, take turns summarizing the material. Stop to discuss ideas that seem confusing.

You might not think these things alone could help you. But you could use them to build a model of a volcano. Then they might help you understand volcanoes a little better.

Types of Scientific Models

A **model** is a representation of an object or system. Models often use familiar objects or ideas that stand for other things. That's how a model can be a tool for understanding the natural world. A model uses something familiar to help you understand something that is not familiar. Models can be used to explain the past and the present. They can even be used to predict future events. However, keep in mind that models have limitations. Three major kinds of scientific models are physical, mathematical, and conceptual models.

model a pattern, plan, representation, or description designed to show the structure or workings of an object, system, or concept

Physical Models

Model airplanes, maps, and dolls are physical models. Some physical models, such as a doll, look like the thing they model. However, a limitation of a doll as the model of a baby is that the doll doesn't act like a baby. Other models, such as the one shown in **Figure 1,** look and act at least somewhat like the real thing.

Figure 1 *The model volcano looks a little bit like the real volcano, but it has its limitations. The model lava is not formed in the same way or at the same temperature as the real lava.*

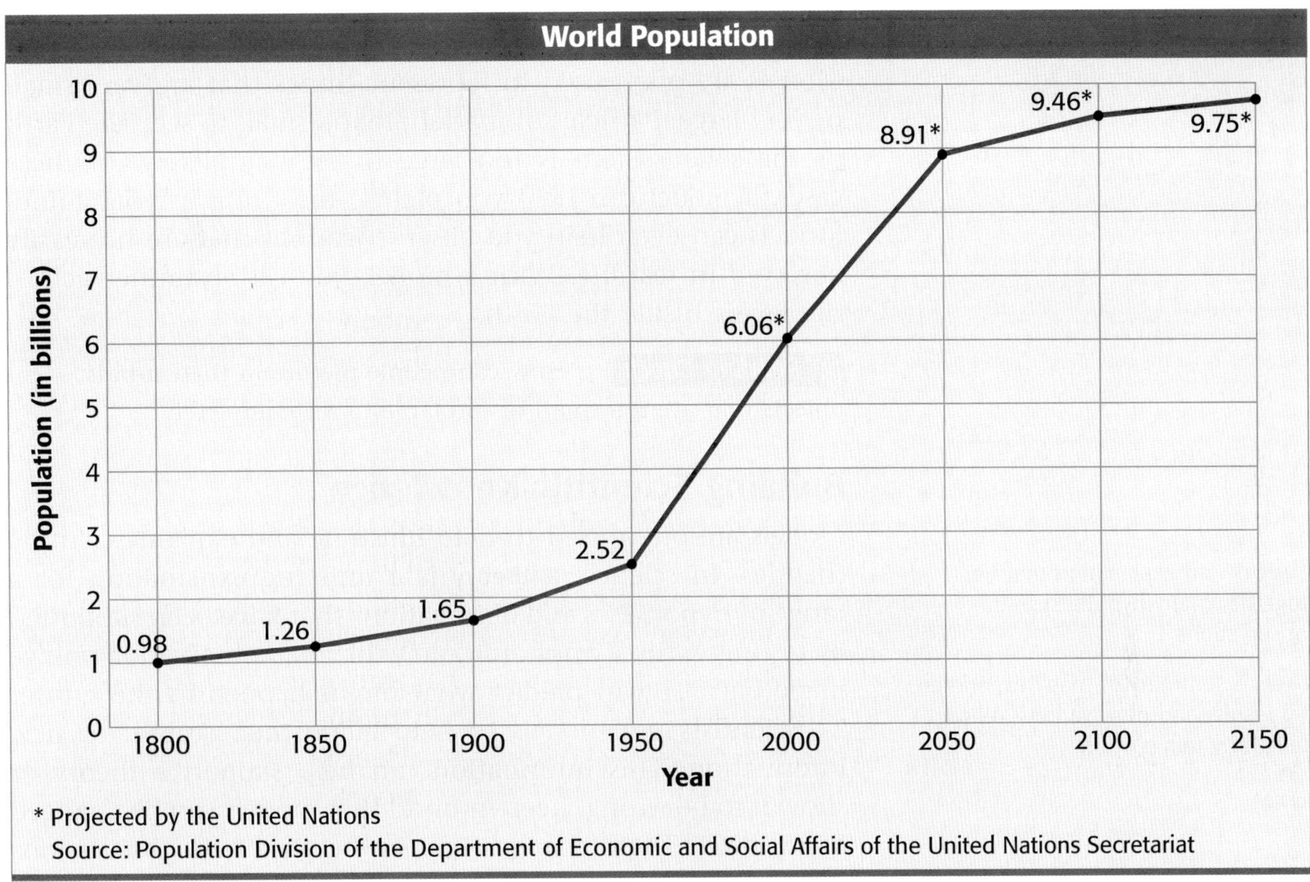

Figure 2 *This graph shows human population growth predicted by a mathematical model run on a computer.*

Mathematical Models

A mathematical model is made up of mathematical equations and data. Simple mathematical models allow you to calculate things such as how far a car will go in an hour. Other models are so complex that only computers can handle them. Look at **Figure 2.** Scientists use a mathematical model to help predict how fast the number of people on Earth will grow and how many resources people will use. Some of these very complex models have many variables. Using the most correct data does not make the prediction correct. A change in a variable that was not predicted could cause the model to fail.

Conceptual Models

The third kind of model is a conceptual model. Some conceptual models are systems of ideas. Others are based on making comparisons with familiar things to help illustrate or explain an idea. One example of a conceptual model is the system that scientists use to classify living things. By using a system of ideas, scientists can group living things by what they have in common. This type of model allows scientists to better understand each group of living things.

Reading Check **What are three kinds of models?** (*See the Appendix for answers to Reading Checks.*)

CONNECTION TO Language Arts

Analogies Many writers use analogies. An analogy points to similarities between two things that are otherwise unlike each other. Do you think scientists use analogies? What could be some strengths and weaknesses of using analogies to describe events and objects in scientific explorations?

Just the Right Size

Models are often used to represent things that are very small or very large. Particles of matter are too small to see. The Earth or the solar system is too large to see completely. In these cases, a model can help you picture the thing in your mind. Models can even help you observe features that are not easily observed in real life. With a model, you can examine each of the layers inside the Earth.

Reading Check **How can people picture in their minds objects that are too small or too large to see completely?**

Building Scientific Knowledge

theory an explanation that ties together many hypotheses and observations

law a summary of many experimental results and observations; a law tells how things work

Models are often used to help illustrate and explain scientific theories. In science, a **theory** is a unifying explanation for a range of hypotheses and observations that have been supported by testing. A theory not only can explain an observation you've made but also can predict what might happen in the future.

Scientists use models to help guide their search for new information. This information can help support a theory or show it to be wrong. Keep in mind that models can be changed or replaced. These changes happen because new observations cause scientists to change their theories. You can compare an old model with a current one in **Figure 3.**

Figure 3 Scientists' model of Earth changed as new information was gathered.

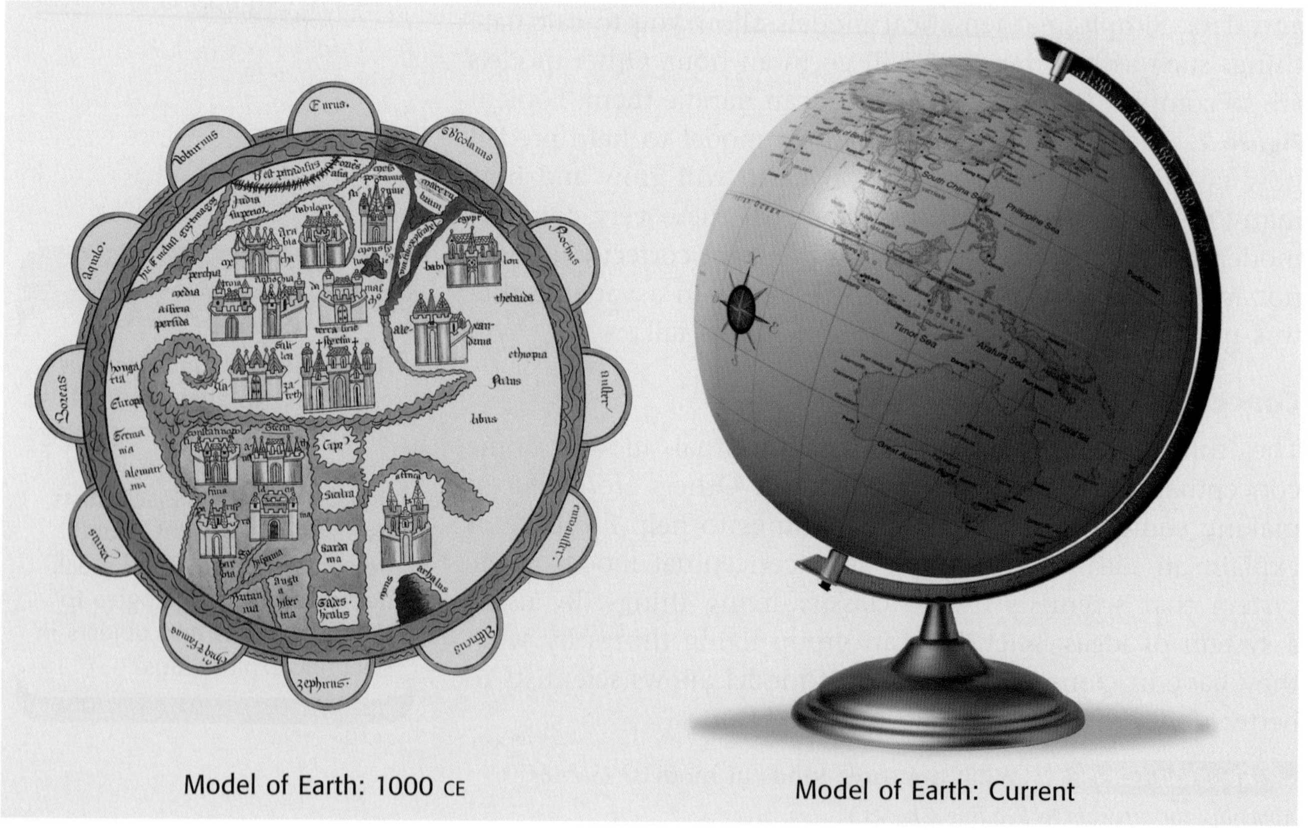

Scientific Laws

What happens when a theory and its models correctly predict the results of many different experiments? A scientific law could be formed. In science, a **law** is a summary of many experimental results and observations. A law tells you how things work.

A law tells you to expect the same thing to happen every time. Look at **Figure 4.** Every object in the universe is attracted to every other object. This fact is summed up by the *law of universal gravitation.* This law says that you can always expect two objects to be attracted to one another. It also helps you calculate the size of the attraction. The size of the attraction depends on the masses of the objects and the distance between them. However, the law does not explain why there is an attraction.

Force of attraction on small book

Force of attraction on large book

Figure 4 *Each of these books has a different attraction between it and Earth. The attraction is larger between the more massive book and Earth.*

SECTION Review

Summary

- Three main types of models are physical, mathematical, and conceptual.
- A model is a representation of an object or system. Models often use familiar things to represent unfamiliar things that may be difficult to observe.
- Scientific knowledge is built as scientists form laws and revise scientific hypotheses, models, and theories.

Using Key Terms

In each of the following sentences, replace the incorrect term with the correct term from the word bank.

theory model law

1. A conclusion is an explanation that matches many hypotheses but may still change.
2. A hypothesis tells you exactly what to expect in a situation.
3. A variable represents an object or a system.

Understanding Key Ideas

4. What are the three main types of models?
5. How do scientists form theories and laws?

Math Skills

6. If Jerry is 2.1 m tall, how tall is a scale model of Jerry that is 10% of his size?

Critical Thinking

7. **Applying Concepts** Draw a map showing the way from your school to your home. What type of model have you made? Identify any symbols that you used to represent things on your map. What are some limitations of your model?
8. **Forming Hypotheses** How could you use a solar system model to hypothesize why the moon appears to change shape?

SCILINKS
NSTA
Developed and maintained by the National Science Teachers Association
For a variety of links related to this chapter, go to www.scilinks.org
Topic: Using Models
SciLinks code: HSM1588

SECTION 4

Tools, Measurement, and Safety

READING WARM-UP

Objectives

- Describe three kinds of tools.
- Explain the importance of the International System of Units.
- Describe how to measure length, area, mass, volume, and temperature.
- Identify lab safety symbols, and demonstrate safe practices during lab investigations.

Terms to Learn

meter
area
mass
volume
temperature

READING STRATEGY

Reading Organizer As you read this section, make a concept map by using the terms above.

Would you use a hammer to tighten a bolt on a bicycle? You probably wouldn't. To be successful in many tasks, you need the correct tools.

Tools for Science

Scientists use many tools. A *tool* is anything that helps you do a task. If you observe a jar of pond water, you may see a few creatures swimming around. But a microscope can help you see many creatures that you couldn't see before. And a graduated cylinder can help you measure the water in the jar. Different tools help scientists gather specific kinds of data.

Tools for Seeing

Microscopes help you make careful observations of things that are too small to see with just your eyes. The compound light microscope in **Figure 1** is made up of three main parts—a tube that has lenses at each end, a stage, and a light. When you place what you want to see on the stage, light passes through it. The lenses magnify the image.

Reading Check **Name the three main parts of a compound light microscope.** (*See the Appendix for answers to Reading Checks.*)

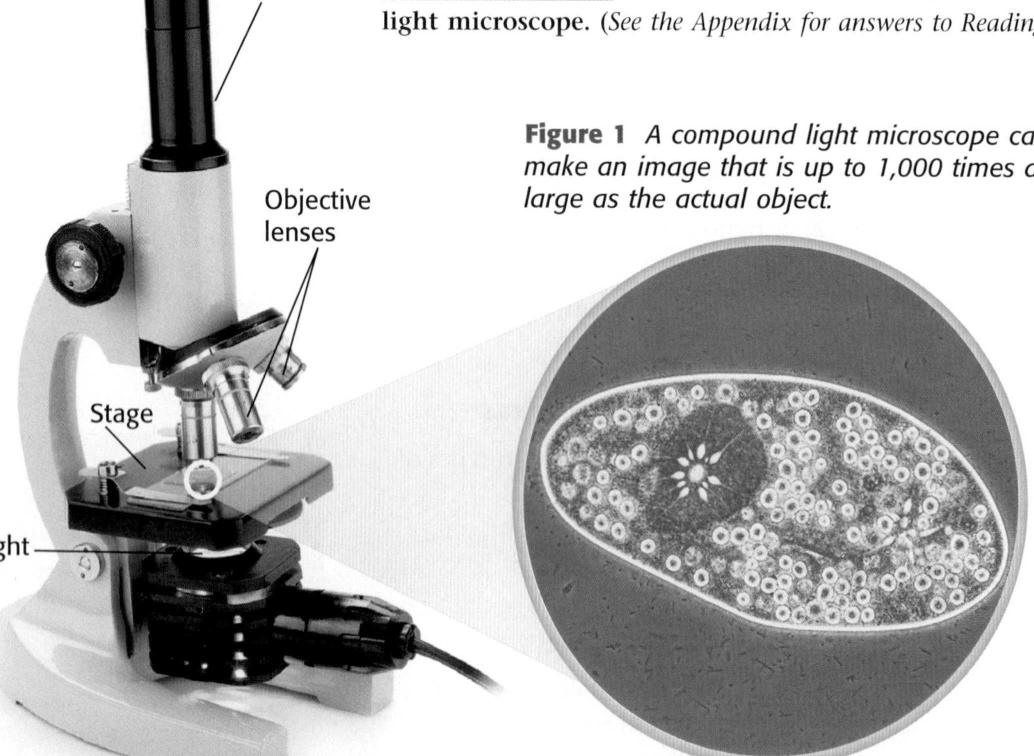

Figure 1 *A compound light microscope can make an image that is up to 1,000 times as large as the actual object.*

Figure 2 Measurement Tools

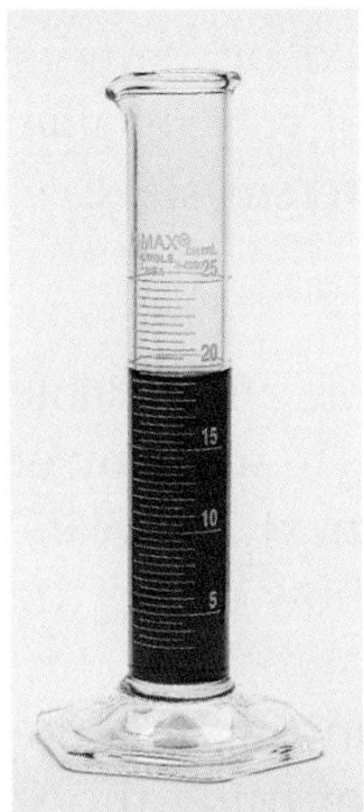

You can use a **graduated cylinder** to measure volume.

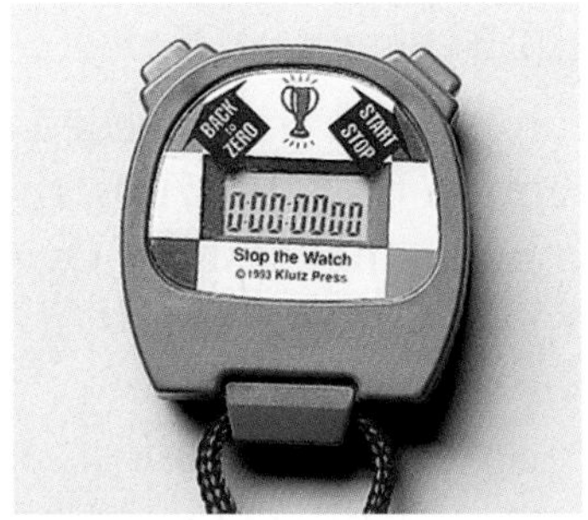

You can use a **stopwatch** to measure time.

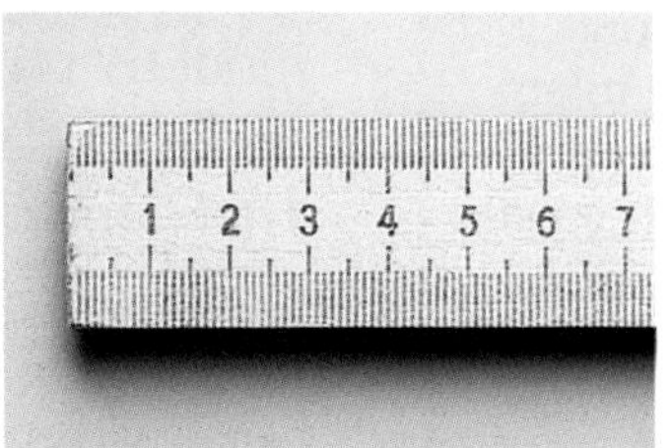

You can use a **meterstick** to measure length.

You can use a **spring scale** to measure force.

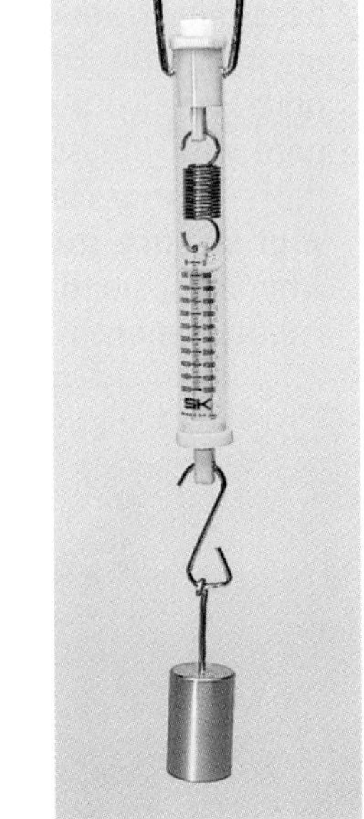

You can use a **thermometer** to measure temperature.

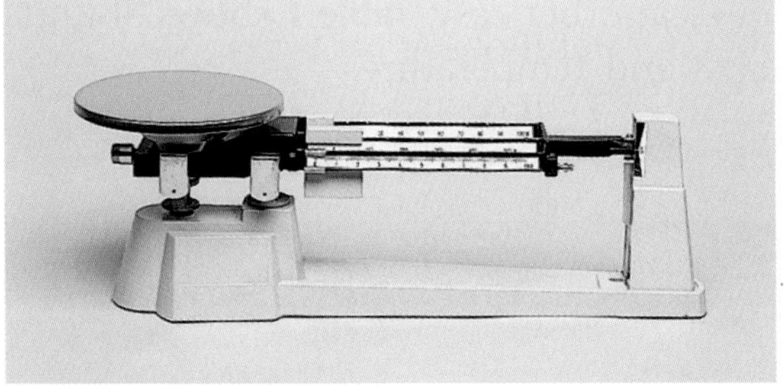

You can use a **balance** to measure mass.

Tools for Measuring

You might remember that one way to collect data during an experiment is to take measurements. To have the best measurements possible, you need to use the proper tools. Stopwatches, metersticks, and balances are some of the tools you can use to make measurements. Thermometers, spring scales, and graduated cylinders are also helpful tools. **Figure 2** explains what characteristics these tools can be used to measure.

Tools for Analyzing

After you collect data, you need to analyze them. Perhaps you need to find the average of your data. Calculators are handy tools that help you do calculations quickly. Or you might show your data in a graph or a figure. A computer that has the correct software can help you make neat, colorful figures. In fact, computers have become invaluable tools for collecting, storing, and analyzing data. Of course, even a pencil and graph paper are tools that you can use to graph your data.

See for Yourself

1. Use a **metric ruler** to measure the length and width of one of your fingernails. Draw and describe the details of your fingernail.
2. Look at the same fingernail through a **magnifying lens.** Now, draw the details of your fingernail as seen with magnification.
3. How does using a magnifying lens change what details you can see?

Units of Measurement

Measure the width of your desk, but do not use a ruler. Pick an object to use as your unit of measurement. It could be a pencil, your hand, or anything else. Find how many units wide your desk is. Compare your measurement with those of your classmates. In your **science journal,** explain why using standard units of measurement is important.

ACTIVITY

Measurement

Hundreds of years ago, different countries used different systems of measurement. At one time in England, the standard for an inch was three grains of barley placed end to end. Other modern standardized units were originally based on parts of the body, such as the foot. Such systems were not very reliable. Their units were based on objects that had different sizes.

The International System of Units

In time, people realized that they needed a simple and reliable measurement system. In the late 1700s, the French Academy of Sciences set out to make that system. Over the next 200 years, the metric system was formed. This system is now called the *International System of Units* (SI).

Today, most scientists and almost all countries use the International System of Units. One advantage of using the SI measurements is that they help all scientists share and compare their observations and results. Another advantage of the SI is that all units are based on the number 10. This feature makes changing from one unit to another easy. **Table 1** shows SI units for length, volume, mass, and temperature.

Table 1 **Common SI Units and Conversions**

Length	**meter (m)** kilometer (km) decimeter (dm) centimeter (cm) millimeter (mm) micrometer (µm) nanometer (nm)	1 km = 1,000 m 1 dm = 0.1 m 1 cm = 0.01 m 1 mm = 0.001 m 1 µm = 0.000001 m 1 nm = 0.000000001 m
Volume	**cubic meter (m^3)** cubic centimeter (cm^3) liter (L) milliliter (mL)	1 cm^3 = 0.000001 m^3 1 L = 1 dm^3 = 0.001 m^3 1 mL = 0.001 L = 1 cm^3
Mass	**kilogram (kg)** gram (g) milligram (mg)	1 g = 0.001 kg 1 mg = 0.000001 kg
Temperature	**Kelvin (K)** Celsius (°C)	0°C = 273 K 100°C = 373 K

Length

How long is your arm? The student in **Figure 3** could describe the length of her arm by using the **meter** (m), the basic SI unit of length. Remember that SI units are based on the number 10. If you divide 1 m into 100 parts, each part equals 1 cm. In other words, 1 cm is one-hundredth of a meter. To describe the length of microscopic objects, micrometers (µm) or nanometers (nm) are used. To describe the length of larger objects, kilometers (km) are used.

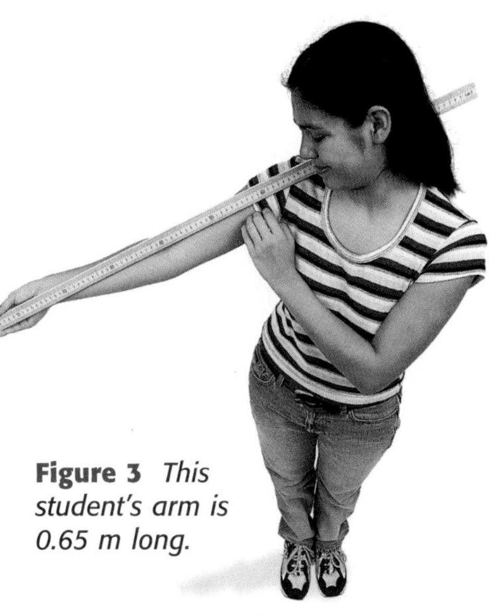

Figure 3 *This student's arm is 0.65 m long.*

Area

How much carpet would it take to cover the floor of your classroom? To answer this question, you must find the area of the floor. **Area** is a measure of how much surface an object has. Area is based on two measurements. To calculate the area of a square or rectangle, first measure the length and width. Then, use the following equation:

$$area = length \times width$$

The units for area are square units, such as square meters (m^2), square centimeters (cm^2), and square kilometers (km^2).

Reading Check What does area measure?

Mass

How many sacks of grain can a mule carry? The answer depends on the strength of the mule and the mass of the sacks of grain. **Mass** is the amount of matter that makes up an object. Scientists often use a balance to measure mass, as shown in **Figure 4.** The kilogram (kg) is the basic unit for mass. The kilogram is used to describe the mass of things such as sacks of grain. Many common objects are not so large, however. The mass of smaller objects, such as an apple, can be described by using grams. One thousand grams equals 1 kg. The mass of large objects, such as an elephant, is given in metric tons. A metric ton equals 1,000 kg.

meter the basic unit of length in the SI (symbol, m)

area a measure of the size of a surface or a region

mass a measure of the amount of matter in an object

Figure 4 *This boy is using a balance to measure the mass of an apple.*

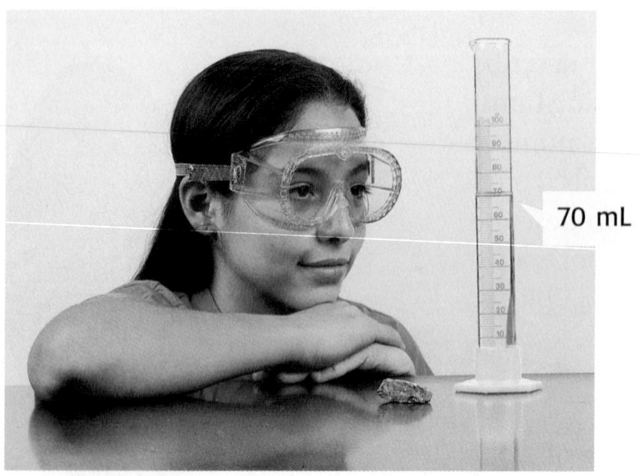

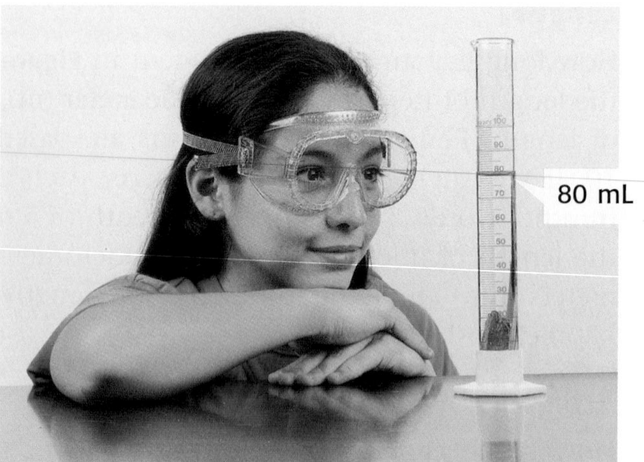

Figure 5 *Adding the rock changes the water level from 70 mL to 80 mL. So, the rock displaces 10 mL of water. Because 1 mL = 1 cm^3, the volume of the rock is 10 cm^3.*

Volume

Suppose that some hippos born in a zoo are being moved to Africa. How many hippos will fit into a cage? The answer depends on volume. **Volume** is the amount of space that something occupies or, as in the case of the cage, the amount of space that something contains.

volume a measure of the size of a body or region in three-dimensional space

temperature a measure of how hot (or cold) something is

The volume of a liquid is often given in liters (L). Liters are based on the meter. A cubic meter (1 m^3) is equal to 1,000 L. So, 1,000 L will fit into a box measuring 1 m on each side. A milliliter (mL) will fit into a box measuring 1 cm on each side. So, 1 mL = 1 cm^3. Graduated cylinders are used to measure liquid volume in milliliters.

The volume of a large, solid object is given in cubic meters (m^3). The volumes of smaller objects can be given in cubic centimeters (cm^3) or cubic millimeters (mm^3). To calculate the volume of a box-shaped object, multiply the object's length by its width and then by its height. To find the volume of an irregularly shaped object, measure the volume of liquid that the object displaces. This process is shown in **Figure 5.**

Figure 6 *This thermometer shows the relationship between degrees Fahrenheit and degrees Celsius.*

8F 8C
212°F Water boils — 100°C Water boils
98.6°F Normal body temperature — 37°C Normal body temperature
32°F Water freezes — 0°C Water freezes
220 200 180 160 140 120 100 80 60 40 20 0
110 100 90 80 70 60 50 40 30 20 10 0 −10 −20

Temperature

How hot is a lava flow? To answer this question, scientists need to measure temperature. **Temperature** is a measure of how hot (or cold) something is. You probably use degrees Fahrenheit (°F) to describe temperature. Scientists often use degrees Celsius (°C). However, the kelvin (K), the SI base unit for temperature, is also used. The thermometer in **Figure 6** shows how two of these units are related.

Safety Rules!

Science can be exciting, fun, and safe if you follow your teacher's instructions. You should get your teacher's permission before starting any science investigation. Read lab procedures carefully, and pay special attention to safety information. **Figure 7** shows the safety symbols used in this book. Be sure you know these symbols and their meanings. You should also read the safety information at the beginning of this book. If you still have safety-related questions, ask your teacher for help.

Reading Check **What should you do if you don't understand what a safety symbol means?**

Figure 7 **Safety Symbols**

Eye Protection

Clothing Protection

Hand Safety

Heating Safety

Electric Safety

Sharp Object

Chemical Safety

Animal Safety

Plant Safety

SECTION Review

Summary

- Scientists use tools that help them see, measure and analyze. Microscopes, metersticks, and computers are a few tools that scientists use in their investigations.
- Scientists use the International System of Units so that they can share and compare their observations and results.
- Scientists have determined standard ways to measure length, area, mass, volume, and temperature.
- Students and anyone doing science investigations should follow safety instructions and should be able to understand safety icons.

Using Key Terms

Complete each of the following sentences by choosing the correct term from the word bank.

area	mass
volume	temperature

1. The measure of the surface of an object is called ____.
2. Scientists use kilograms when measuring an object's ____.
3. The ____ of a liquid is usually described in liters.

Understanding Key Ideas

4. SI units are
   - **a.** always based on standardized measurements of body parts.
   - **b.** almost always based on the number 10.
   - **c.** used to measure only length.
   - **d.** used only in France.
5. What are three units that are used to measure temperature?
6. If you were going to measure the mass of a fly, which SI unit would be most appropriate?
7. Describe three kinds of tools, and give an example of each kind of tool.

Math Skills

8. What is the area of a garden that is 12 m long and 8 m wide?
9. What is the volume of a box if the sides of the box are each 1 m in length?

Critical Thinking

10. **Predicting Consequences** Give an example of what could happen if you do not follow safety rules about animal safety.
11. **Applying Concepts** During an experiment, you must mix chemicals in a glass beaker. What should you wear to protect yourself during this experiment?

SCILINKS®
NSTA
Developed and maintained by the National Science Teachers Association
For a variety of links related to this chapter, go to www.scilinks.org
Topic: Tools of Science; SI Units
SciLinks code: HSM1535; HSM1390

Using Scientific Methods

Model-Making Lab

Using Scientific Methods

Geologists often use a technique called core sampling to learn what underground rock layers look like. This technique involves drilling several holes in the ground in different places and taking samples of the underground rock or soil. Geologists then compare the samples from each hole at each depth to construct a diagram that shows the bigger picture.

In this activity, you will model the process geologists use to diagram underground rock layers. You will first use modeling clay to form a rock-layer model. You will then exchange models with a classmate, take core samples, and draw a diagram of your classmate's rock layers.

OBJECTIVES

Design a model to demonstrate core sampling.

Create a diagram of a classmate's model by using the core sample method.

MATERIALS

- knife, plastic
- modeling clay, three or four colors
- pan or box, opaque
- pencil, unsharpened
- pencils or markers, three or four colors
- PVC pipe, 1/2 in.

SAFETY

- Form a plan for your rock layers. Make a sketch of the layers. Your sketch should include the colors of clay in several layers of varying thicknesses. Note: Do not let the classmates who will be using your model see your plan.
- In the pan or box, mold the clay into the shape of the lowest layer in your sketch.
- Repeat the procedure described in the second bullet for each additional layer of clay. Exchange your rock-layer model with a classmate.

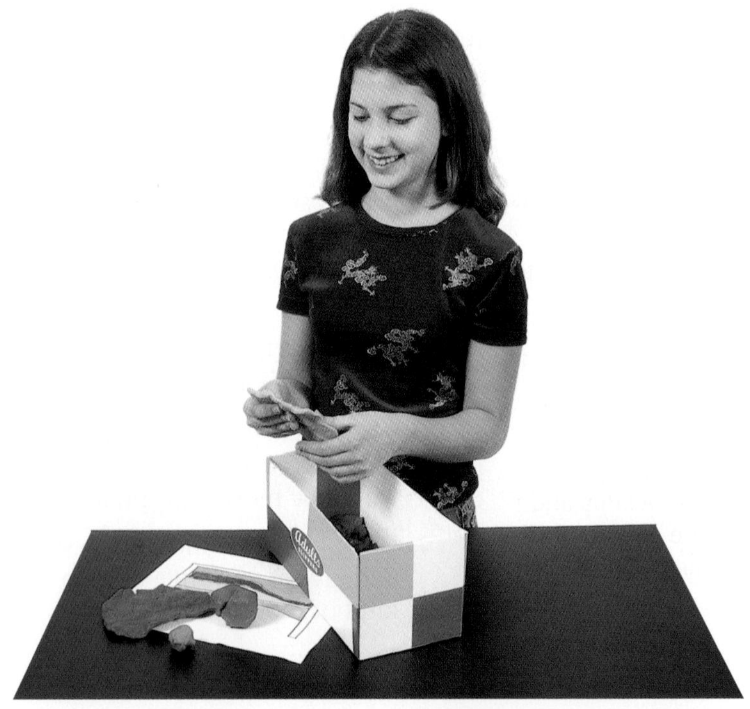

Ask a Question

1. Can unseen features be revealed by sampling parts of the whole?

Form a Hypothesis

2. Form a hypothesis about whether taking core samples from several locations will give a good indication of the entire hidden feature.

Test the Hypothesis

3. Choose three places on the surface of the clay to drill holes. The holes should be far apart and in a straight line. (Do not remove the clay from the pan or box.)
4. Slowly push the PVC pipe through all the layers of clay. Slowly remove the pipe.
5. Gently push the clay out of the pipe with an unsharpened pencil. This clay is a core sample.
6. Draw the core sample, and record your observations. Be sure to use a different color of pencil or marker for each layer.
7. Repeat steps 4–6 for the next two core samples. Make sure your drawings are side by side and in the same order as the samples in the model.

Analyze the Results

1. **Examining Data** Look at the pattern of rock layers in each of your core samples. Think about how the rock layers between the core samples might look. Then, make a diagram of the rock layers.
2. **Organizing Data** Complete your diagram by coloring the rest of each rock layer.

Draw Conclusions

3. **Evaluating Models** Use the plastic knife to cut the clay model along a line connecting the three holes. Remove one side of the model so that you can see the layers. How well does your rock-layer diagram match the model? Explain your answer.
4. **Evaluating Methods** What are some limitations of your diagram as a model of the rock layers?
5. **Drawing Conclusions** Do your conclusions support your hypothesis? Explain your answer.

Applying Your Data

List two ways that the core-sampling method could be improved.

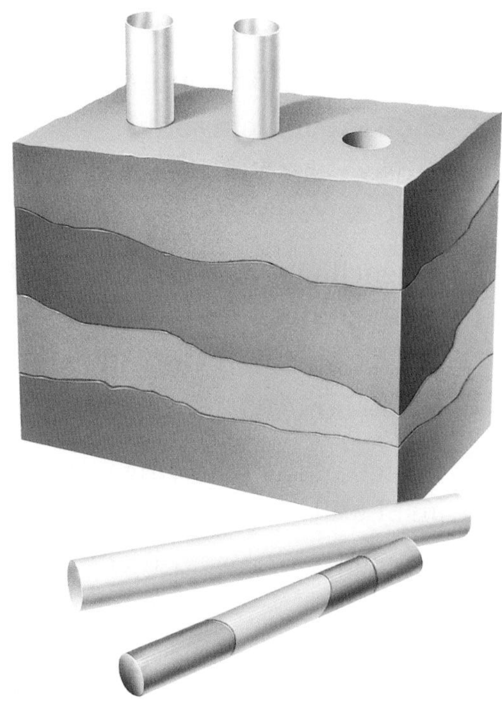

Chapter Review

USING KEY TERMS

Complete each of the following sentences by choosing the correct term from the word bank.

models	science
scientific methods	hypothesis

1. The process of gathering knowledge about the natural world is called ___.

2. An explanation that is based on prior scientific research or observations and that can be tested is called a ___.

3. ___ are a series of steps followed to solve problems.

UNDERSTANDING KEY IDEAS

Multiple Choice

4. A good way to investigate answers to scientific questions is to
   - **a.** do research only.
   - **b.** make observations only.
   - **c.** do experiments only.
   - **d.** do research, make observations, and do experiments.

5. A pencil measures 14 cm long. How many millimeters long is it?
   - **a.** 1.4 mm
   - **b.** 140 mm
   - **c.** 1,400 mm
   - **d.** 1,400,000 mm

6. Which of the following units is NOT an SI unit?
   - **a.** meter
   - **b.** foot
   - **c.** liter
   - **d.** degree Celsius

7. Which of the following statements describes a limitation of models?
   - **a.** Models are large enough to be seen.
   - **b.** Models do not act exactly like the things that they model.
   - **c.** Models are smaller than the thing that they model.
   - **d.** Models use familiar things to model unfamiliar things.

8. What kind of model is a map?
   - **a.** physical model
   - **b.** conceptual model
   - **c.** mathematical model
   - **d.** hypothesis model

Short Answer

9. How could a hypothesis that is proven to be false lead to new scientific investigations?

10. How and why do scientists use models?

11. What are three types of models? Give an example of each type.

12. What problems could occur if scientists did not communicate the results of their investigations?

13. What problems could occur if the International System of Units were not used?

14. Which safety symbols would you expect to see for an experiment that requires the use of acid?

Careers

Sue Hendrickson

Paleontologist Could you imagine having a job in which you spent all day digging in the dirt? This is just one of Sue Hendrickson's job descriptions. But Hendrickson does not dig up flowers. Hendrickson is a paleontologist, and she digs up dinosaurs! Her most famous discovery is the bones of a *Tyrannosaurus rex*. *T. rex* is one of the largest meat-eating dinosaurs. It lived between 65 million and 85 million years ago. Walking tall at 6 m, *T. rex* was approximately 12.4 m long and weighed between 5 and 7 tons. Hendrickson's discovery is the most complete set of bones ever found of the *T. rex*. The dinosaur was named Sue to honor Hendrickson for her important find. From these bones, Hendrickson and other scientists have been able to learn more about the dinosaur, including how it lived millions of years ago. For example, Hendrickson and her team of scientists found the remains of Sue's last meal, part of a duck-billed, plant-eating dinosaur of the genus *Edmontosaurus* that weighed approximately 3.5 tons!

Math Activity

ACTIVITY

The *T. rex* named Sue weighed 7 tons and the *Edmontosaurus* dinosaur weighed 3.5 tons. How much smaller is *Edmontosaurus* than Sue? Express your answer as a percentage.

To learn more about these Science in Action topics, visit go.hrw.com and type in the keyword **HZ5WESF.**

Current Science

Check out Current Science® articles related to this chapter by visiting go.hrw.com. Just type in the keyword HZ5CS01.

TIMELINE

Earth Science

In this unit, you will start your own investigation of the planet Earth and of the regions of space beyond it. As you can imagine, it is not easy to study something as large as the Earth or as far away as Venus. Yet Earth scientists study these planets and more. The timeline shown here identifies a few of the events that have helped shape our understanding of the Earth.

1669

Nicolaus Steno accurately describes the process by which living organisms become fossils.

1904

Roald Amundsen determines the position of the magnetic north pole.

1922

Roy Chapman Andrews discovers fossilized dinosaur eggs in the Gobi Desert. They are the first such eggs to be found.

fossilized dinosaur eggs in the Gobi Desert

1962

By reaching an altitude of over 95 km, the *X-15* becomes the first fixed-wing plane to reach space.

1758

Halley's comet makes a reappearance, which confirms Edmond Halley's 1705 prediction. The comet reappeared 16 years after Halley's death.

1799

The Rosetta stone is discovered in Egypt. It enables scholars to decipher Egyptian hieroglyphics.

1896

The first modern Olympic Games are held in Athens, Greece.

1943

The volcano Paricutín grows more than 200 m tall during its first two weeks of eruption.

Paricutín Volcano

1960

The first weather satellite, *TIROS I,* is launched by the United States.

1970

The first Earth Day is celebrated in the United States on April 22.

1990

The Hubble Space Telescope is launched into orbit. Three years later, faulty optics are repaired during a space walk.

1994

China begins construction of Three Gorges Dam, the world's largest dam. Designed to control the Yangtze River, the dam will supply an estimated 84 billion kilowatt-hours of hydroelectric power per year.

2002

A new order of insects—*Mantophasmatodea*—is found both preserved in 45 million-year-old amber and living in southern Africa.

Hubble Space Telescope

Minerals of the Earth's Crust

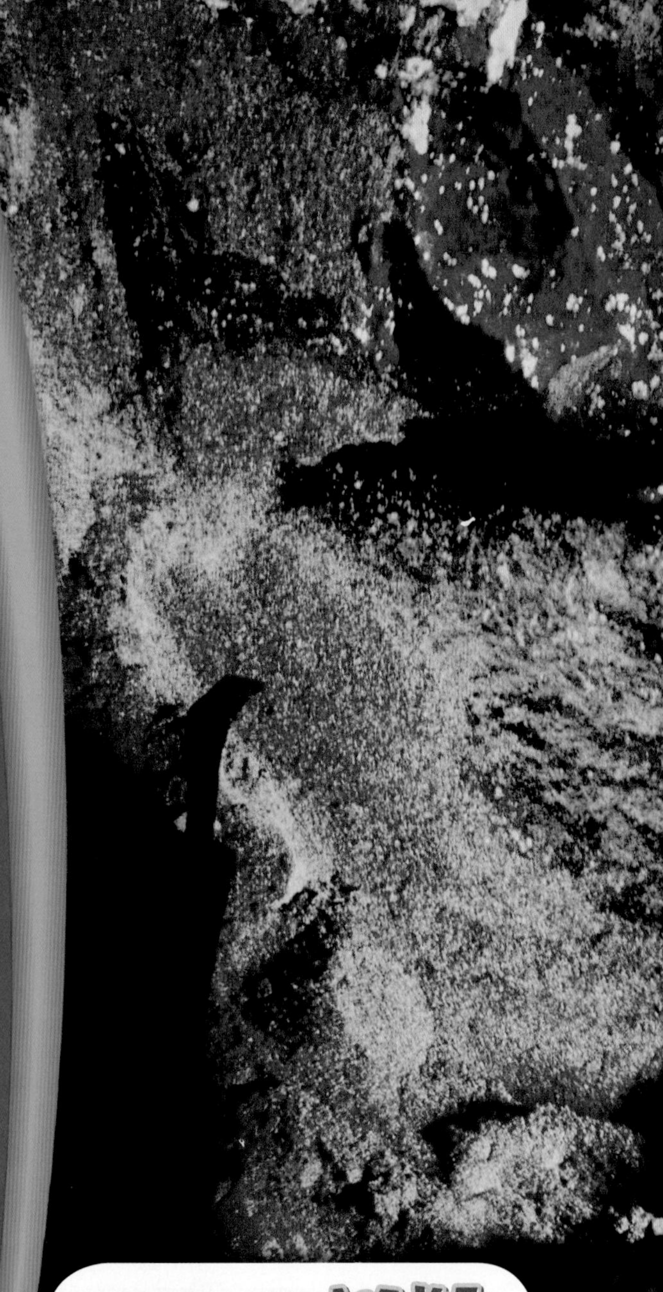

About the PHOTO

Fluorescence is the ability that some minerals have to glow under ultraviolet light. The beauty of mineral fluorescence is well represented at the Sterling Hill Mine in Franklin, New Jersey. In this picture taken at the mine, minerals in the rock glow as brightly as if they had been freshly painted by an artist.

PRE-READING ACTIVITY

Graphic Organizer

Concept Map Before you read the chapter, create the graphic organizer entitled "Concept Map" described in the **Study Skills** section of the Appendix. As you read the chapter, fill in the concept map with details about minerals.

START-UP ACTIVITY

What Is Your Classroom Made Of?

One of the properties of minerals is that minerals are made from nonliving material. Complete the following activity to see if you can determine whether items in your classroom are made from living or nonliving materials.

Procedure

1. On a **sheet of paper,** make two columns. Label one column "Materials made from living things." Label the second column "Materials made from nonliving things."
2. Look around your classroom. Choose a variety of items to put on your list. Some items that you might select are your clothing, your desk, books, notebook paper, pencils, the classroom windows, doors, walls, the ceiling, and the floor.
3. With a partner, discuss each item that you have chosen. Decide into which column each item should be placed. Write down the reason for your decision.

Analysis

1. Are most of the items that you chose made of living or nonliving materials?

SECTION 1

What Is a Mineral?

You may think that all minerals look like gems. But, in fact, most minerals look more like rocks. Does this mean that minerals are the same as rocks? Well, not really. So, what's the difference?

READING WARM-UP

Objectives

- Describe the structure of minerals.
- Describe the two major groups of minerals.

Terms to Learn

mineral
element
compound
crystal
silicate mineral
nonsilicate mineral

READING STRATEGY

Paired Summarizing Read this section silently. In pairs, take turns summarizing the material. Stop to discuss ideas that seem confusing.

For one thing, rocks are made of minerals, but minerals are not made of rocks. A **mineral** is a naturally formed, inorganic solid that has a definite crystalline structure.

Mineral Structure

By answering the four questions in **Figure 1,** you can tell whether an object is a mineral. If you cannot answer "yes" to all four questions, you don't have a mineral. Three of the four questions may be easy to answer. The question about crystalline structure may be more difficult. To understand what crystalline structure is, you need to know a little about the elements that make up a mineral. **Elements** are pure substances that cannot be broken down into simpler substances by ordinary chemical means. All minerals contain one or more of the 92 naturally occurring elements.

Is it nonliving material? A mineral is inorganic, meaning it isn't made of living things.

Is it a solid? Minerals can't be gases or liquids.

Does it have a crystalline structure? Minerals are crystals, which have a repeating inner structure that is often reflected in the shape of the crystal. Minerals generally have the same chemical composition throughout.

Is it formed in nature? Crystalline materials made by people aren't classified as minerals.

Figure 1 *The answers to these four questions will determine whether an object is a mineral.*

Atoms and Compounds

Each element is made of only one kind of atom. An *atom* is the smallest part of an element that has all the properties of that element. Like other substances, minerals are made up of atoms of one or more elements.

Most minerals are made of compounds of several different elements. A **compound** is a substance made of two or more elements that have been chemically joined, or bonded. Halite, NaCl, for example, is a compound of sodium, Na, and chlorine, Cl, as shown in **Figure 2.** A few minerals, such as gold and silver, are composed of only one element. A mineral that is composed of only one element is called a *native element.*

Figure 2 *When atoms of sodium (purple) and chlorine (green) join, they form a compound commonly known as rock salt, or the mineral halite.*

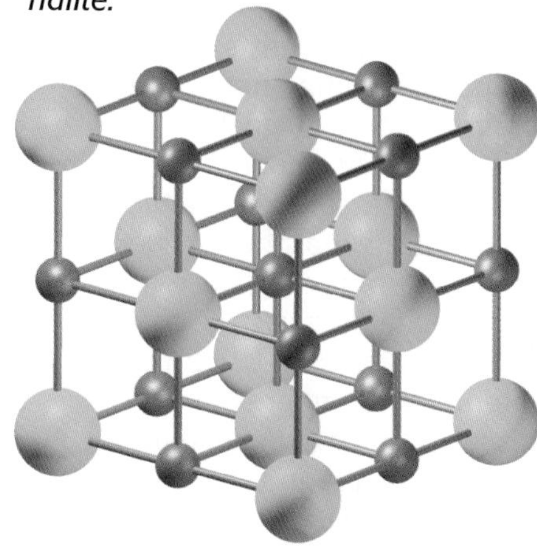

✓ Reading Check **How does a compound differ from an element?** (*See the Appendix for answers to Reading Checks.*)

Crystals

Solid, geometric forms of minerals produced by a repeating pattern of atoms that is present throughout the mineral are called **crystals.** A crystal's shape is determined by the arrangement of the atoms within the crystal. The arrangement of atoms in turn is determined by the kinds of atoms that make up the mineral. Each mineral has a definite crystalline structure. All minerals can be grouped into crystal classes according to the kinds of crystals they form. **Figure 3** shows how the atomic structure of gold gives rise to cubic crystals.

mineral a naturally formed, inorganic solid that has a definite crystalline structure

element a substance that cannot be separated or broken down into simpler substances by chemical means

compound a substance made up of atoms of two or more different elements joined by chemical bonds

crystal a solid whose atoms, ions, or molecules are arranged in a definite pattern

Figure 3 **Composition of the Mineral Gold**

The mineral gold is composed of gold atoms arranged in a crystalline structure.

The atomic structure of gold

The crystal structure of gold

Crystals of the mineral gold

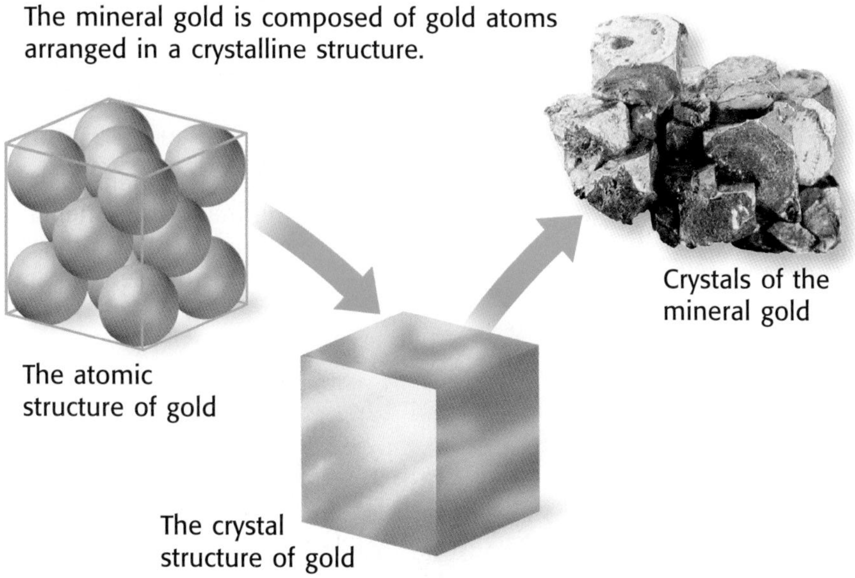

Two Groups of Minerals

The most common classification of minerals is based on chemical composition. Minerals are divided into two groups based on their chemical composition. These groups are the silicate minerals and the nonsilicate minerals.

Silicate Minerals

Silicon and oxygen are the two most common elements in the Earth's crust. Minerals that contain a combination of these two elements are called **silicate minerals.** Silicate minerals make up more than 90% of the Earth's crust. The rest of the Earth's crust is made up of nonsilicate minerals. Silicon and oxygen usually combine with other elements, such as aluminum, iron, magnesium, and potassium, to make up silicate minerals. Some of the more common silicate minerals are shown in **Figure 4.**

Nonsilicate Minerals

Minerals that do not contain a combination of the elements silicon and oxygen form a group called the **nonsilicate minerals.** Some of these minerals are made up of elements such as carbon, oxygen, fluorine, and sulfur. **Figure 5** on the following page shows the most important classes of nonsilicate minerals.

Reading Check **How do silicate minerals differ from nonsilicate minerals?**

CONNECTION TO Biology

WRITING SKILL **Magnetite** The mineral magnetite has a special property—it is magnetic. Scientists have found that some animals' brains contain magnetite. And scientists have shown that certain fish can sense magnetic fields because of the magnetite in the brains of these fish. The magnetite gives the fish a sense of direction. Using the Internet or another source, research other animals that have magnetite in their brains. Summarize your findings in a short essay.

silicate mineral a mineral that contains a combination of silicon, oxygen, and one or more metals

nonsilicate mineral a mineral that does not contain compounds of silicon and oxygen

Figure 4 **Common Silicate Minerals**

Quartz is the basic building block of many rocks.

Feldspar minerals are the main component of most rocks on the Earth's surface.

Mica minerals separate easily into sheets when they break. Biotite is one of several kinds of mica.

CRITICAL THINKING

17 **Concept Mapping** Use the following terms to create a concept map: *minerals, calcite, silicate minerals, gypsum, carbonates, nonsilicate minerals, quartz,* and *sulfates.*

18 **Making Inferences** Imagine that you are trying to determine the identity of a mineral. You decide to do a streak test. You rub the mineral across the streak plate, but the mineral does not leave a streak. Has your test failed? Explain your answer.

19 **Applying Concepts** Why would cleavage be important to gem cutters, who cut and shape gemstones?

20 **Applying Concepts** Imagine that you work at a jeweler's shop and someone brings in some gold nuggets for sale. You are not sure if the nuggets are real gold. Which identification tests would help you decide whether the nuggets are gold?

21 **Identifying Relationships** Suppose you are in a desert. You are walking across the floor of a dry lake, and you see crusts of cubic halite crystals. How do you suppose the halite crystals formed? Explain your answer.

INTERPRETING GRAPHICS

The table below shows the temperatures at which various minerals melt. Use the table below to answer the questions that follow.

Melting Points of Various Minerals

Mineral	Melting Point (°C)
Mercury	−39
Sulfur	+113
Halite	801
Silver	961
Gold	1,062
Copper	1,083
Pyrite	1,171
Fluorite	1,360
Quartz	1,710
Zircon	2,500

22 According to the table, what is the approximate difference in temperature between the melting points of the mineral that has the lowest melting point and the mineral that has the highest melting point?

23 Which of the minerals listed in the table do you think is a liquid at room temperature?

24 Pyrite is often called *fool's gold.* Using the information in the table, how could you determine if a mineral sample is pyrite or gold?

25 Convert the melting points of the minerals shown in the table from degrees Celsius to degrees Fahrenheit. Use the formula °F = (9/5 × °C) + 32.

Standardized Test Preparation

READING

Read each of the passages below. Then, answer the questions that follow each passage.

Passage 1 In North America, copper was mined at least 6,700 years ago by the ancestors of the Native Americans who live on Michigan's upper peninsula. Much of this mining took place on Isle Royale, an island in Lake Superior. These ancient people removed copper from the rock by using stone hammers and wedges. The rock was sometimes heated first to make breaking it up easier. Copper that was mined was used to make jewelry, tools, weapons, fish hooks, and other objects. These objects were often marked with designs. The Lake Superior copper was traded over long distances along ancient trade routes. Copper objects have been found in Ohio, Florida, the Southwest, and the Northwest.

1. In the passage, what does *ancient* mean?

- **A** young
- **B** future
- **C** modern
- **D** early

2. According to the passage, what did the ancient copper miners do?

- **F** They mined copper in Ohio, Florida, the Southwest, and the Northwest.
- **G** They mined copper by cooling the rock in which the copper was found.
- **H** They mined copper by using stone tools.
- **I** They mined copper for their use only.

3. Which of the following statements is a fact according to the passage?

- **A** Copper could be shaped into different objects.
- **B** Copper was unknown outside of Michigan's upper peninsula.
- **C** Copper could be mined easily from the rock in which it was found.
- **D** Copper could not be marked with designs.

Passage 2 Most mineral names end in *-ite*. The practice of so naming minerals dates back to the ancient Romans and Greeks, who added *-ites* and *-itis* to common words to indicate a color, a use, or the chemistry of a mineral. More recently, mineral names have been used to honor people, such as scientists, mineral collectors, and even rulers of countries. Other minerals have been named after the place where they were discovered. These place names include mines, quarries, hills, mountains, towns, regions, and even countries. Finally, some minerals have been named after gods in Greek, Roman, and Scandinavian mythology.

1. In the passage, what does *practice* mean?

- **A** skill
- **B** custom
- **C** profession
- **D** use

2. According to the passage, the ancient Greeks and Romans did not name minerals after what?

- **F** colors
- **G** chemical properties
- **H** people
- **I** uses

3. Which of the following statements is a fact according to the passage?

- **A** Minerals are sometimes named for the country in which they are discovered.
- **B** Minerals are never named after their collectors.
- **C** All mineral names end in *-ite*.
- **D** All of the known minerals were named by the Greeks and Romans.

INTERPRETING GRAPHICS

A sample of feldspar was analyzed to find out what it was made of. The graph below shows the results of the analysis. Use the graph below to answer the questions that follow.

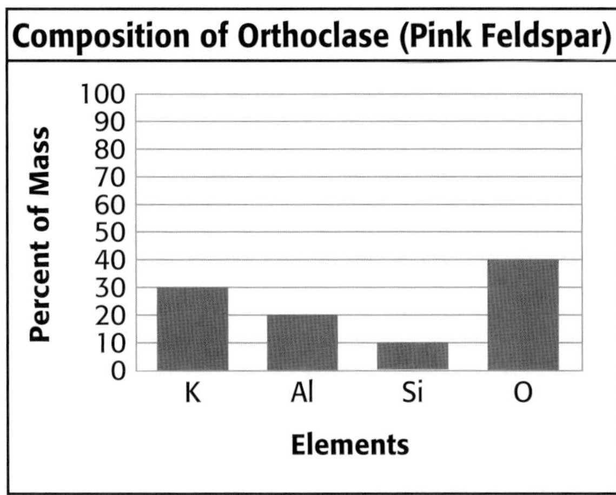

1. The sample consists of four elements: potassium, K, aluminum, Al, silicon, Si, and oxygen, O. Which element makes up the largest percentage of your sample?

A potassium
B aluminum
C silicon
D oxygen

2. Silicate minerals, such as feldspar, contain a combination of silicon and oxygen. What percentage of your sample is composed of silicon and oxygen combined?

F 30%
G 40%
H 50%
I 70%

3. If your sample has a mass of 10 g, how many grams of oxygen does it contain?

A 1 g
B 2 g
C 4 g
D 8 g

4. Your sample of orthoclase has a hardness of 6. Which of the following minerals will scratch your sample?

F gypsum
G corundum
H calcite
I apatite

MATH

Read each question below, and choose the best answer.

1. Gold classified as 24-karat is 100% gold. Gold classified as 18-karat is 18 parts gold and 6 parts another, similar metal. The gold is therefore 18/24, or 3/4, pure. What is the percentage of pure gold in 18-karat gold?

A 10%
B 25%
C 50%
D 75%

2. Gold's specific gravity is 19. Pyrite's specific gravity is 5. What is the difference in the specific gravities of gold and pyrite?

F 8 g/cm^3
G 10 g/cm^3
H 12 g/cm^3
I 14 g/cm^3

3. In a quartz crystal, there is one silicon atom for every two oxygen atoms. So, the ratio of silicon atoms to oxygen atoms is 1:2. If there were 8 million oxygen atoms in a sample of quartz, how many silicon atoms would there be in the sample?

A 2 million
B 4 million
C 8 million
D 16 million

Science in Action

Science Fiction

"The Metal Man" by Jack Williamson

In a dark, dusty corner of Tyburn College Museum stands a life-sized statue of a man. Except for its strange greenish color, the statue looks quite ordinary. But if you look closely, you will see the perfect detail of the hair and skin. On the statue's chest, you will also see a strange mark—a dark crimson shape with six sides. No one knows how the statue ended up in the dark corner. But most people in Tyburn believe that the metal man is, or once was, Professor Thomas Kelvin of Tyburn College's geology department. Read for yourself the strange story of Professor Kelvin and the Metal Man, which is in the *Holt Anthology of Science Fiction*.

Language Arts Activity

WRITING SKILL Read "The Metal Man" by Jack Williamson. Write a short essay explaining how the ideas in the story are related to what you are learning.

HOLT ANTHOLOGY OF
Science Fiction
HOLT, RINEHART AND WINSTON

Weird Science

Wieliczka Salt Mine

Imagine an underground city that is made entirely of salt. Within the city are churches, chapels, rooms of many kinds, and salt lakes. Sculptures of biblical scenes, saints, and famous historical figures carved from salt are found throughout the city. Even chandeliers of salt hang from the ceilings. Such a city is located 16 km southeast of Krakow, Poland, inside the Wieliczka (VEE uh LEETS kuh) Salt Mine. As the mine grew over the past 700 years, it turned into an elaborate underground city. Miners constructed chapels to patron saints so they could pray for a safe day in the mine. Miners also developed superstitions about the mine. So, images that were meant to bring good luck were carved in salt. In 1978, the mine was added to UNESCO's list of endangered world heritage sites. Many of the sculptures in the mine have begun to dissolve because of the humidity in the air. Efforts to save the treasures in the mine from further damage were begun in 1996.

Social Studies Activity

WRITING SKILL Research some aspect of the role of salt in human history. For example, subjects might include the Saharan and Tibetan salt trade or the use of salt as a form of money in ancient Poland. Report your findings in a one-page essay.

People in Science

Jamie Hill

The Emerald Man Jamie Hill was raised in the Brushy Mountains of North Carolina. While growing up, Hill gained firsthand knowledge of the fabulous green crystals that could be found in the mountains. These green crystals were emeralds. Emerald is the green variety of the silicate mineral beryl and is a valuable gemstone. Emerald crystals form in pockets, or openings, in rock known as *pegmatite*.

Since 1985, Hill has been searching for pockets containing emeralds in rock near the small town of Hiddenite, North Carolina. He has been amazingly successful. Hill has discovered some spectacular emerald crystals. The largest of these crystals weighs 858 carats and is on display at the North Carolina Museum of Natural Science. Estimates of the total value of the emeralds that Hill has discovered so far are well in the millions of dollars. Hill's discoveries have made him a celebrity, and he has appeared both on national TV and in magazines.

Math ACTIVITY

An emerald discovered by Jamie Hill in 1999 was cut into a 7.85-carat stone that sold for $64,000 per carat. What was the total value of the cut stone?

To learn more about these Science in Action topics, visit **go.hrw.com** and type in the keyword **HZ5MINF.**

Current Science

Check out Current Science® articles related to this chapter by visiting go.hrw.com. Just type in the keyword HZ5CS03.

Weathering and Soil Formation

About the PHOTO

Need a nose job, Mr. President? The carving of Thomas Jefferson that is part of the Mount Rushmore National Memorial is having its nose inspected by a National Parks worker. The process of weathering has caused cracks to form in the carving of President Jefferson. National Parks workers use a sealant to protect the memorial from moisture, which can cause further cracking.

PRE-READING ACTIVITY

FOLDNOTES **Key-Term Fold** Before you read the chapter, create the FoldNote entitled "Key-Term Fold" described in the **Study Skills** section of the Appendix. Write a key term from the chapter on each tab of the key-term fold. Under each tab, write the definition of the key term.

Air

The car shown in **Figure 8** is undergoing chemical weathering due to the air. The oxygen in the air is reacting with the iron in the car, causing the car to rust. Water speeds up the process. But the iron would rust even if no water were present. Scientists call this process oxidation.

Oxidation is a chemical reaction in which an element, such as iron, combines with oxygen to form an oxide. This common form of chemical weathering is what causes rust. Old cars, aluminum cans, and your bike can experience oxidation if left exposed to air and rain for long periods of time.

Reading Check What can cause oxidation?

Figure 8 *Rust is a result of chemical weathering.*

SECTION Review

Summary

- Ice wedging is a form of mechanical weathering in which water seeps into rock cracks and then freezes and expands.
- Wind, water, and gravity cause mechanical weathering by abrasion.
- Animals and plants cause mechanical weathering by turning the soil and breaking apart rocks.
- Water, acids, and air chemically weather rock by weakening the bonds between mineral grains of the rock.

Using Key Terms

1. In your own words, write a definition for each of the following terms: *weathering, mechanical weathering, abrasion, chemical weathering* and *acid precipitation.*

Understanding Key Ideas

2. Which of the following things cannot cause mechanical weathering?
   a. water
   b. acid
   c. wind
   d. animals
3. List three things that cause chemical weathering of rocks.
4. Describe three ways abrasion occurs in nature.
5. Describe the similarity in the ways tree roots and ice mechanically weather rock.
6. Describe five sources of chemical weathering.

Critical Thinking

7. **Making Inferences** Why does acid precipitation weather rocks faster than normal precipitation?
8. **Making Comparisons** Compare the weather processes that affect a rock on top of a mountain and a rock buried beneath the ground.

Math Skills

9. Substances that have a pH of less than 7 are acidic. For each pH unit lower, the acidity is ten times greater. For example, normal precipitation is slightly acidic at a 5.6 pH. If acid precipitation were measured at 4.6 pH, it would be 10 times more acidic than normal precipitation. How many times more acidic would precipitation at 3.6 pH be than normal precipitation?

SCILINKS.
NSTA
Developed and maintained by the National Science Teachers Association
For a variety of links related to this chapter, go to www.scilinks.org
Topic: Weathering
SciLinks code: HSM1648

SECTION 2

Rates of Weathering

Have you ever seen a cartoon in which a character falls off a cliff and lands on a ledge? Ledges exist in nature because the rock that the ledge is made of weathers more slowly than the surrounding rock.

READING WARM-UP

Objectives

- Explain how the composition of rock affects the rate of weathering.
- Describe how a rock's total surface area affects the rate at which the rock weathers.
- Describe how differences in elevation and climate affect the rate of weathering.

Terms to Learn

differential weathering

READING STRATEGY

Reading Organizer As you read this section, create an outline of the section. Use the headings from the section in your outline.

Weathering is a process that takes a long time. However, some rock will weather faster than other rock. The rate at which a rock weathers depends on climate, elevation, and the makeup of the rock.

Differential Weathering

Hard rocks, such as granite, weather more slowly than softer rocks, such as limestone. **Differential weathering** is a process by which softer, less weather resistant rocks wear away and leave harder, more weather resistant rocks behind.

Figure 1 shows a landform that has been shaped by differential weathering. Devils Tower was once a mass of molten rock deep inside an active volcano. When the molten rock cooled and hardened, it was protected from weathering by the outer rock of the volcano. After thousands of years of weathering, the soft outer parts of the volcano have worn away. The harder, more resistant rock is all that remains.

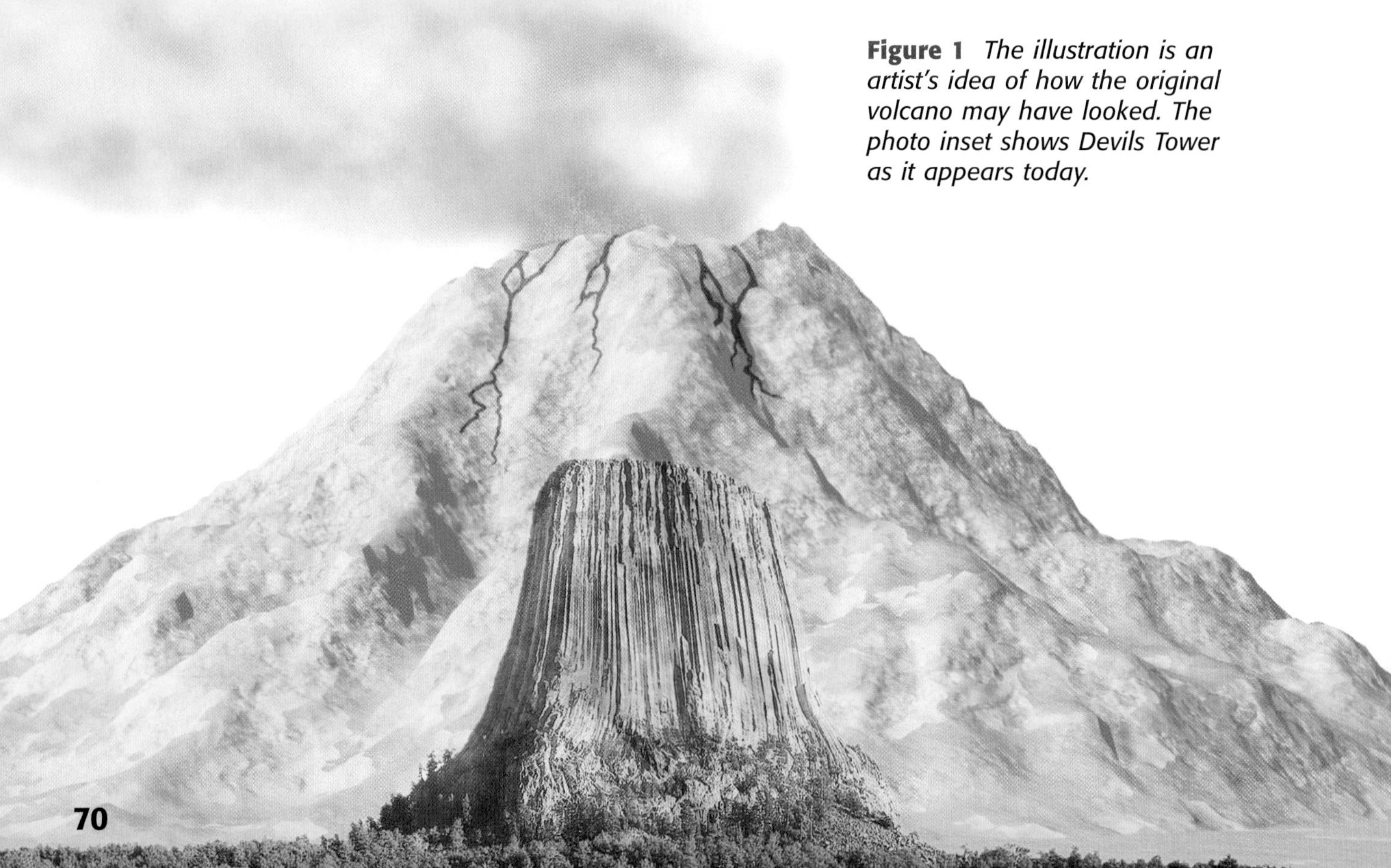

Figure 1 *The illustration is an artist's idea of how the original volcano may have looked. The photo inset shows Devils Tower as it appears today.*

The Shape of Rocks

Weathering takes place on the outer surface of rocks. Therefore, the more surface area that is exposed to weathering, the faster the rock will be worn down. A large rock has a large surface area. But a large rock also has a large volume. Because of the large rock's volume, the large rock will take a long time to wear down.

If a large rock is broken into smaller fragments, weathering of the rock happens much more quickly. The rate of weathering increases because a smaller rock has more surface area to volume than a larger rock has. So, more of a smaller rock is exposed to the weathering process. **Figure 2** shows this concept in detail.

differential weathering the process by which softer, less weather resistant rocks wear away and leave harder, more weather resistant rocks behind

Reading Check **How does an increase in surface area affect the rate of weathering?** *(See the Appendix for answers to Reading Checks.)*

Figure 2 **Total Surface Area to Volume**

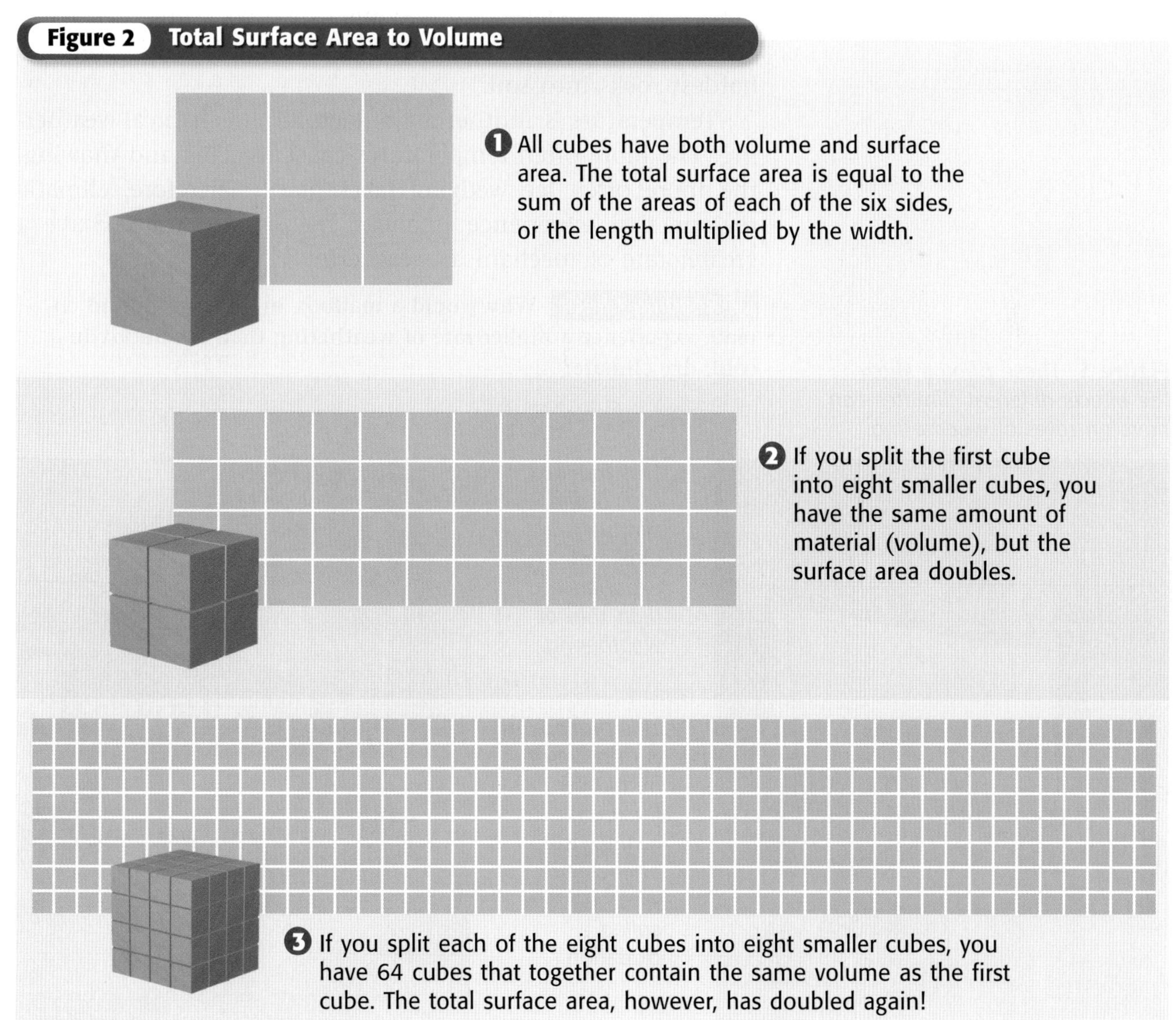

1 All cubes have both volume and surface area. The total surface area is equal to the sum of the areas of each of the six sides, or the length multiplied by the width.
2 If you split the first cube into eight smaller cubes, you have the same amount of material (volume), but the surface area doubles.
3 If you split each of the eight cubes into eight smaller cubes, you have 64 cubes that together contain the same volume as the first cube. The total surface area, however, has doubled again!

Ice Wedging

WRITING SKILL To understand ice wedging, try this activity at home with a parent. Fill a small, plastic water bottle with water. Plug the opening with a piece of putty. Place the bottle in the freezer overnight. Describe in your **science journal** what happened to the putty.

Weathering and Climate

The rate of weathering in an area is greatly affected by the climate of that area. *Climate* is the average weather condition in an area over a long period of time. For example, the two mailboxes shown in **Figure 3** are in two different climates. The mailbox on the left is in a dry climate. The mailbox on the right is in a warm, humid climate. As you can see, the mailbox in the warm, humid climate is rusty.

Temperature and Water

The rate of chemical weathering happens faster in warm, humid climates. The rusty mailbox has experienced a type of chemical weathering called oxidation. Oxidation, like other chemical reactions, happens at a faster rate when temperatures are higher and when water is present.

Water also increases the rate of mechanical weathering. The freezing of water that seeps into the cracks of rocks is the process of ice wedging. Ice wedging causes rocks to break apart. Over time, this form of weathering can break down even the hardest rocks into soil.

Temperature is another major factor in mechanical weathering. The more often temperatures cause freezing and thawing, the more often ice wedging takes place. Therefore, climatic regions that experience frequent freezes and thaws have a greater rate of mechanical weathering.

Reading Check **Why would a mailbox in a warm, humid climate experience a higher rate of weathering than a mailbox in a cold, dry climate?**

Figure 3 *These photos show the effects different climates can have on rates of weathering.*

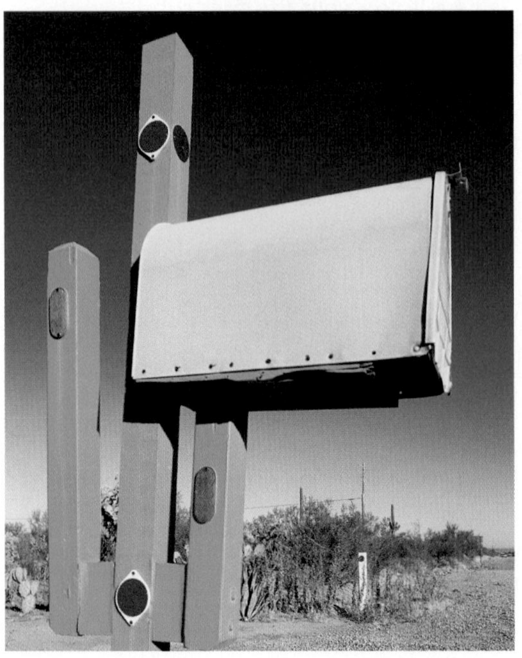

This mailbox is in a dry climate and does not experience a high rate of weathering.

This mailbox is in a warm, humid climate. It experiences a high rate of chemical weathering called oxidation.

Weathering and Elevation

Just like everything else, mountains are exposed to air and water. As a result, mountain ranges are weathered down. Weathering happens on mountains in the same way it does everywhere else. However, as shown in **Figure 4,** rocks at higher elevations, as on a mountain, are exposed to more wind, rain, and ice than the rocks at lower elevations are. This increase in wind, rain, and ice at higher elevations causes the peaks of mountains to weather faster.

Gravity affects weathering, too. The steepness of mountain slopes increases the effects of mechanical and chemical weathering. Steep slopes cause rainwater to quickly run off the sides of mountains. The rainwater carries the sediment down the mountain's slope. This continual removal of sediment exposes fresh rock surfaces to the effects of weathering. New rock surfaces are also exposed to weathering when gravity causes rocks to fall away from the sides of mountains. The increased surface area means weathering happens at a faster rate.

Reading Check **Why do mountaintops weather faster than rocks at sea level?**

Figure 4 *The ice, rain, and wind that these mountain peaks are exposed to cause them to weather at a fast rate.*

SECTION Review

Summary

- Hard rocks weather more slowly than softer rocks.
- The more surface area of a rock that is exposed to weathering, the faster the rock will be worn down.
- Chemical weathering occurs faster in warm, humid climates.
- Weathering occurs faster at high elevations because of an increase in ice, rain, and wind.

Using Key Terms

1. In your own words, write a definition for the term *differential weathering*.

Understanding Key Ideas

2. A rock will have a lower rate of weathering when the rock
   a. is in a humid climate.
   b. is a very hard rock, such as granite.
   c. is at a high elevation.
   d. has more surface area exposed to weathering.
3. How does surface area affect the rate of weathering?
4. How does climate affect the rate of weathering?
5. Why does the peak of a mountain weather faster than the rocks at the bottom of the mountain?

Math Skills

6. The surface area of an entire cube is 96 cm^2. If the length and width of each side are equal, what is the length of one side of the cube?

Critical Thinking

7. **Making Inferences** Does the rate of chemical weathering increase or stay the same when a rock becomes more mechanically weathered? Why?

SCILINKS.
NSTA
Developed and maintained by the National Science Teachers Association
For a variety of links related to this chapter, go to www.scilinks.org
Topic: Rates of Weathering
SciLinks code: HSM1269

SECTION 3

From Bedrock to Soil

Most plants need soil to grow. But what exactly is soil? Where does it come from?

READING WARM-UP

Objectives

- Describe the source of soil.
- Explain how the different properties of soil affect plant growth.
- Describe how various climates affect soil.

Terms to Learn

soil
parent rock
bedrock
soil texture
soil structure
humus
leaching

READING STRATEGY

Prediction Guide Before you read this section, write the title of each heading in this section. Next, under each heading, write what you think you will learn.

The Source of Soil

To a scientist, **soil** is a loose mixture of small mineral fragments, organic material, water, and air that can support the growth of vegetation. But not all soils are the same. Because soils are made from weathered rock fragments, the type of soil that forms depends on the type of rock that weathers. The rock formation that is the source of mineral fragments in the soil is called **parent rock.**

Bedrock is the layer of rock beneath soil. In this case, the bedrock is the parent rock because the soil above it formed from the bedrock below. Soil that remains above its parent rock is called *residual soil.*

Soil can be blown or washed away from its parent rock. This soil is called *transported soil.* **Figure 1** shows one way that soil is moved from one place to another. Both wind and the movement of glaciers are also responsible for transporting soil.

Reading Check **What is soil formed from?** (*See the Appendix for answers to Reading Checks.*)

soil a loose mixture of rock fragments, organic material, water, and air that can support the growth of vegetation

parent rock a rock formation that is the source of soil

bedrock the layer of rock beneath soil

Figure 1 *Transported soil may be moved long distances from its parent rock by rivers, such as this one.*

Figure 2 **Soil Texture**

The proportion of these different-sized particles in soil determine the soil's texture.

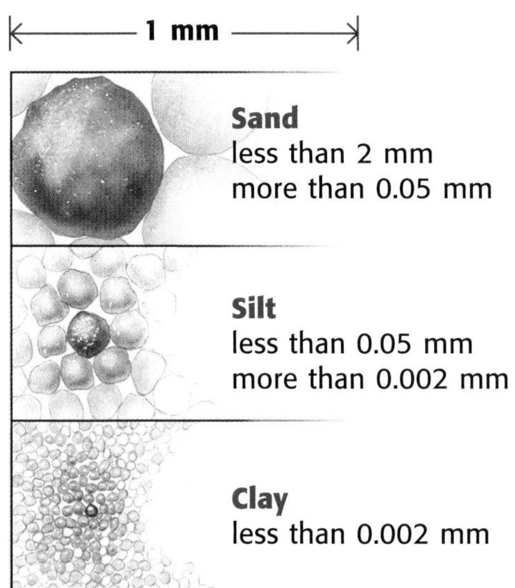

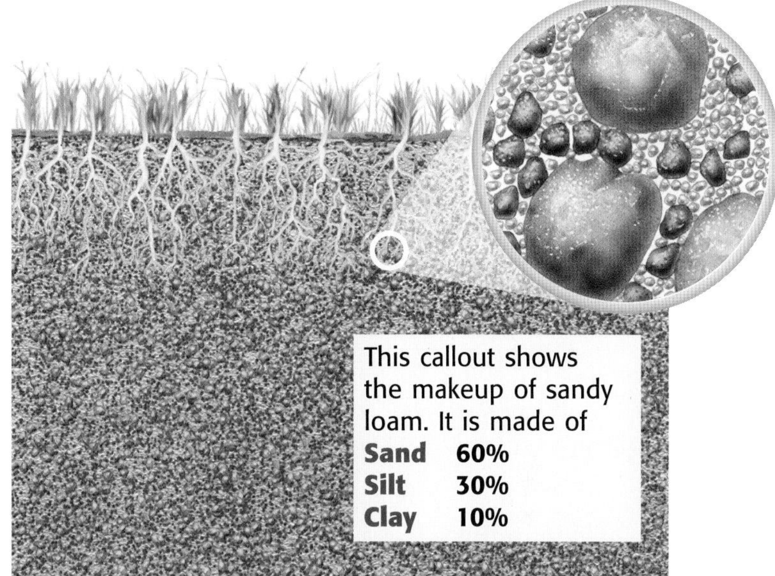

This callout shows the makeup of sandy loam. It is made of
Sand 60%
Silt 30%
Clay 10%

Soil Properties

Some soils are great for growing plants. Other soils can't support the growth of plants. To better understand soil, you will next learn about its properties, such as soil texture, soil structure, and soil fertility.

Soil Texture and Soil Structure

Soil is made of different-sized particles. These particles can be as large as 2 mm, such as sand. Other particles can be too small to see without a microscope. **Soil texture** is the soil quality that is based on the proportions of soil particles. **Figure 2** shows the soil texture for a one type of soil.

Soil texture affects the soil's consistency. Consistency describes a soil's ability to be worked and broken up for farming. For example, soil texture that has a large proportion of clay can be hard and difficult for farmers to break up.

Soil texture influences the *infiltration,* or ability of water to move through soil. Soil should allow water to get to the plants' roots without causing the soil to be completely saturated.

Water and air movement through soil is also influenced by soil structure. **Soil structure** is the arrangement of soil particles. Soil particles are not always evenly spread out. Often, one type of soil particle will clump in an area. A clump of one type of soil can either block water flow or help water flow, which affects soil moisture.

soil texture the soil quality that is based on the proportions of soil particles.

soil structure the arrangement of soil particles

humus the dark, organic material formed in soil from the decayed remains of plants and animals

leaching the removal of substances that can be dissolved from rock, ore, or layers of soil due to the passing of water

Soil Fertility

Nutrients in soil, such as iron, are necessary for plants to grow. Some soils are rich in nutrients. Other soils may not have many nutrients or are not able to supply the nutrients to the plants. A soil's ability to hold nutrients and to supply nutrients to a plant is described as *soil fertility*. Many nutrients in soil come from the parent rock. Other nutrients come from **humus,** which is the organic material formed in soil from the decayed remains of plants and animals. These remains are broken down into nutrients by decomposers, such as bacteria and fungi.

Soil Horizons

Because of the way soil forms, soil often ends up in a series of layers, with humus-rich soil on top, sediment below that, and bedrock on the bottom. Geologists call these layers *horizons*. The word *horizon* tells you that the layers are horizontal. **Figure 3** shows what these horizons can look like. You can see these layers in some road cuts.

The top layer of soil is often called the *topsoil*. Topsoil contains more humus than the layers below it. The humus is rich in the nutrients plants need to be healthy. This is why good topsoil is necessary for farming.

Figure 3 **Soil Horizons**

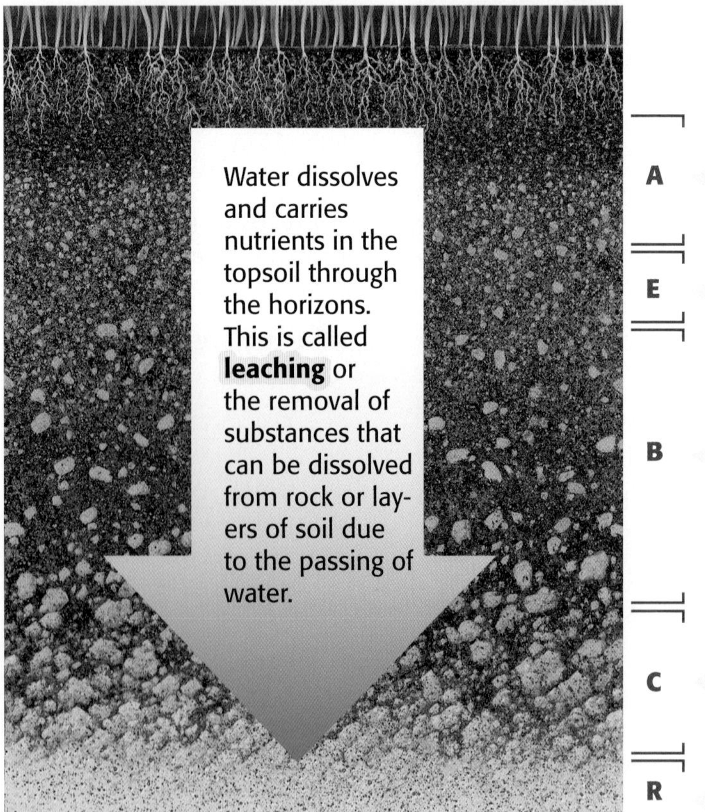

Water dissolves and carries nutrients in the topsoil through the horizons. This is called **leaching** or the removal of substances that can be dissolved from rock or layers of soil due to the passing of water.
A
E
B
C
R

A This horizon consists of the topsoil. Topsoil contains more humus than any other soil horizon. Soil in forests often has an O horizon. The O horizon is made up of litter from dead plants and animals.

E This horizon experiences intense leaching of nutrients.

B This horizon collects the dissolved substances and nutrients deposited from the upper horizons.

C This horizon is made of partially weathered bedrock.

R This horizon is made of bedrock that has little or no weathering.

Soil pH

Soils can be acidic or basic. The pH scale is used to measure how acidic or basic a soil is and ranges from 0 to 14. The midpoint, which is 7, is neutral. Soil that has a pH below 7 is acidic. Soil that has a pH above 7 is basic.

The pH of a soil influences how nutrients dissolve in the soil. For example, plants are unable to take up certain nutrients from soils that are basic, or that have a high pH. Soils that have a low pH can restrict other important nutrients from hungry plants. Because different plants need different nutrients, the right pH for a soil depends on the plants growing in it.

CONNECTION TO Social Studies

WRITING SKILL **Deforestation in Brazil** In Brazil, rain forests have been cut down at an alarmingly high rate, mostly by farmers. However, tropical rain forest topsoil is very thin and is not suitable for long-term farming. Research the long-term effects of deforestation on the farmers and indigenous people of Brazil. Then, write a one page report on your findings.

Soil and Climate

Soil types vary from place to place. One reason for this is the differences in climate. As you read on, you will see that climate can make a difference in the types of soils that develop around the world.

Tropical Rain Forest Climates

Take a look at **Figure 4.** In tropical rain forest climates, the air is very humid and the land receives a large amount of rain. Because of warm temperatures, crops can be grown year-round. The warm soil temperature also allows dead plants and animals to decay easily. This provides rich humus to the soil.

Because of the lush plant growth, you may think that tropical rain forest soils are the most nutrient-rich in the world. However, tropical rain forest soils are nutrient poor. The heavy rains in this climate leach precious nutrients from the topsoil into deeper layers of soil. The result is that tropical topsoil is very thin. Another reason tropical rain forest soil is nutrient poor is that the lush vegetation has a great demand for nutrients. The nutrients that aren't leached away are quickly taken up by plants and trees that live off the soil.

Reading Check **Why is the topsoil in tropical rain forests thin?**

Figure 4 *Lush tropical rain forests have surprisingly thin topsoil.*

Desert Climates

While tropical climates get a lot of rain, deserts get less than 25 cm a year. Leaching of nutrients is not a problem in desert soils. But the lack of rain causes many other problems, such as very low rates of chemical weathering and less ability to support plant and animal life. A low rate of weathering means soil is created at a slower rate.

Some water is available from groundwater. Groundwater can trickle in from surrounding areas and seep to the surface. But as soon as the water is close to the surface, it evaporates. So, any materials that were dissolved in the water are left behind in the soil. Without the water to dissolve the minerals, the plants are unable to take them up. Often, the chemicals left behind are various types of salts. These salts can sometimes become so concentrated that the soil becomes toxic, or poisonous, even to desert plants! Death Valley, shown in **Figure 5,** is a desert that has toxic levels of salt in the soil.

Figure 5 *The salty conditions of desert soils make it difficult for many plants to survive.*

Temperate Forest and Grassland Climates

Much of the continental United States has a temperate climate. An abundance of weathering occurs in temperate climates. Temperate areas get enough rain to cause a high level of chemical weathering, but not so much that the nutrients are leached out of the soil. Frequent changes in temperature lead to frost action. As a result, thick, fertile soils develop, as shown in **Figure 6.**

Temperate soils are some of the most-productive soils in the world. In fact, the midwestern part of the United States has earned the nickname "breadbasket" for the many crops the region's soil supports.

Reading Check **Which climate has the most-productive soil?**

For another activity related to this chapter, go to **go.hrw.com** and type in the keyword **HZ5WSFW.**

Figure 6 *The rich soils in areas that have a temperate climate support a vast farming industry.*

Arctic Climates

Arctic areas have so little precipitation that they are like cold deserts. In arctic climates, as in desert climates, chemical weathering occurs very slowly. So, soil formation also occurs slowly. Slow soil formation is why soil in arctic areas, as shown in **Figure 7,** is thin and unable to support many plants.

Arctic climates also have low soil temperatures. At low temperatures, decomposition of plants and animals happens more slowly or stops completely. Slow decomposition limits the amount of humus in the soil, which limits the nutrients available. These nutrients are necessary for plant growth.

Figure 7 *Arctic soils, such as the soil along Denali Highway, in Alaska, cannot support lush vegetation.*

SECTION Review

Summary

- Soil is formed from the weathering of bedrock.
- Soil texture affects how soil can be worked for farming and how well water passes through it.
- The ability of soil to provide nutrients so that plants can survive and grow is called *soil fertility*.
- The pH of a soil influences which nutrients plants can take up from the soil.
- Different climates have different types of soil, depending on the temperature and rainfall.

Using Key Terms

1. Use each of the following terms in a separate sentence: *soil, parent rock, bedrock, soil texture, soil structure, humus,* and *leaching.*

Understanding Key Ideas

2. Which of the following soil properties influences soil moisture?
   a. soil horizon
   b. soil fertility
   c. soil structure
   d. soil pH
3. Which of the following soil properties influences how nutrients can be dissolved in soil?
   a. soil texture
   b. soil fertility
   c. soil structure
   d. soil pH
4. When is parent rock the same as bedrock?
5. What is the difference between residual and transported soils?
6. Which climate has the most thick, fertile soil?
7. How does soil temperature influence arctic soil?

Math Skills

8. If a soil sample is 60% sand particles and has 30 million particles of soil, how many of those soil particles are sand?

Critical Thinking

9. **Identifying Relationships** In which type of climate would leaching be more common—tropical rain forest or desert?
10. **Making Comparisons** Although arctic climates are extremely different from desert climates, their soils may be somewhat similar. Explain why.

SCILINKS
NSTA
Developed and maintained by the National Science Teachers Association
For a variety of links related to this chapter, go to www.scilinks.org
Topic: Soil and Climate
SciLinks code: HSM1408

SECTION 4

Soil Conservation

Believe it or not, soil can be endangered, just like plants and animals. Because soil takes thousands of years to form, it is not easy to replace.

READING WARM-UP

Objectives

- Describe three important benefits that soil provides.
- Describe four methods of preventing soil damage and loss.

Terms to Learn

soil conservation
erosion

READING STRATEGY

Reading Organizer As you read this section, make a table comparing the four methods of preventing soil damage and loss.

If we do not take care of our soils, we can ruin them or even lose them. Soil is a resource that must be conserved. **Soil conservation** is a method to maintain the fertility of the soil by protecting the soil from erosion and nutrient loss.

soil conservation a method to maintain the fertility of the soil by protecting the soil from erosion and nutrient loss

The Importance of Soil

Soil provides minerals and other nutrients for plants. If the soil loses these nutrients, then plants will not be able to grow. Take a look at the plants shown in **Figure 1.** The plants on the right look unhealthy because they are not getting enough nutrients. There is enough soil to support the plant's roots, but the soil is not providing them with the food they need. The plants on the left are healthy because the soil they live in is rich in nutrients.

All animals get their energy from plants. The animals get their energy either by eating the plants or by eating animals that have eaten plants. So, if plants can't get their nutrients from the soil, animals can't get their nutrients from plants.

Reading Check **Why is soil important?** (*See the Appendix for answers to Reading Checks.*)

Housing

Soil also provides a place for animals to live. The region where a plant or animal lives is called its *habitat.* Earthworms, grubs, spiders, ants, moles, and prairie dogs all live in soil. If the soil disappears, so does the habitat for these animals.

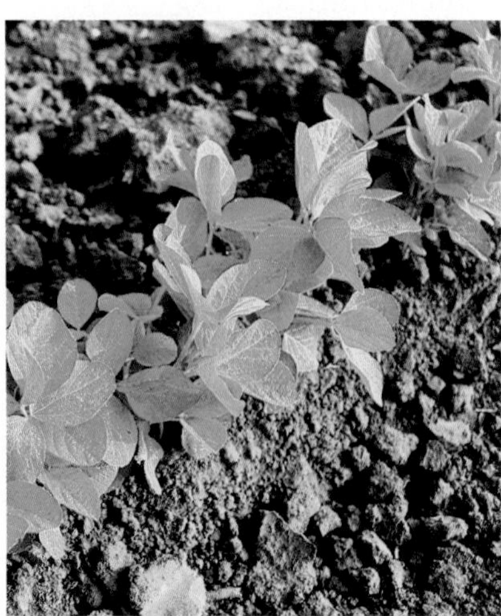

Figure 1 *Both of these photos show the same crop, but the soil in the photo on the right is poor in nutrients.*

Water Storage

Soil is also extremely important to plants for water storage. Without soil to hold water, plants would not get the moisture or the nutrients they need. Soil also keeps water from running off, flowing elsewhere, and possibly causing flooding.

Making Soil

Suppose it takes 500 years for 2 cm of new soil to form in a certain area. But the soil is eroding at a rate of 1 mm per year. Is the soil eroding faster than it can be replaced? Explain.

Soil Damage and Loss

What would happen if there were no soil? Soil loss is a serious problem around the world. Soil damage can lead to soil loss. Soil can be damaged from overuse by poor farming techniques or by overgrazing. Overused soil can lose its nutrients and become infertile. Plants can't grow in soil that is infertile. Without plants to hold and help cycle water, the area can become a desert. This process, formally known as *desertification,* is called *land degradation*. Without plants and moisture, the soil can be blown or washed away.

Soil Erosion

When soil is left unprotected, it can be exposed to erosion. **Erosion** is the process by which wind, water, or gravity transport soil and sediment from one location to another. **Figure 2** shows Providence Canyon, which was formed from the erosion of soil when trees were cut down to clear land for farming. Roots from plants and trees are like anchors to the soil. Roots keep topsoil from being eroded. Therefore, plants and trees protect the soil. By taking care of the vegetation, you also take care of the soil.

erosion the process by which wind, water, ice, or gravity transport soil and sediment from one location to another

Figure 2 *Providence Canyon has suffered soil erosion from the cutting of forests for farmland.*

Figure 3 Soil Conservation Techniques

Contour plowing helps prevent erosion from heavy rains.

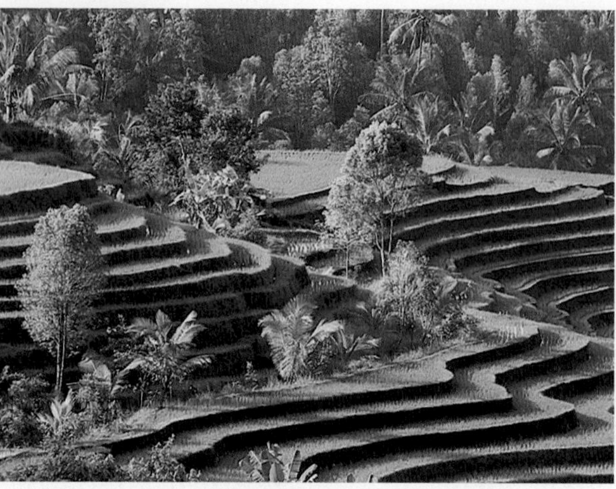

Terracing prevents erosion from heavy rains on steep hills.

No-till farming prevents erosion by providing cover that reduces water runoff.

Soybeans are a **cover crop** which restores nutrients to soil.

Contour Plowing and Terracing

If farmers plowed rows so that they ran up and down hills, what might happen during a heavy rain? The rows would act as river valleys and channel the rainwater down the hill, which would erode the soil. To prevent erosion in this way, a farmer could plow across the slope of the hills. This is called contour plowing. In *contour plowing,* the rows act as a series of dams instead of a series of rivers. **Figure 3** shows contour plowing and three other methods of soil conservation. If the hills are really steep, farmers can use *terracing*. Terracing changes one steep field into a series of smaller, flatter fields. *No-till farming,* which is the practice of leaving old stalks, provides cover from rain. The cover reduces water runoff and slows soil erosion.

Cover Crop and Crop Rotation

In the southern United States, during the early 1900s, the soil had become nutrient poor by the farming of only one crop, cotton. George Washington Carver, the scientist shown in **Figure 4,** urged farmers to plant soybeans and peanuts instead of cotton. Some plants, such as soybeans and peanuts, helped to restore important nutrients to the soil. These plants are called cover crops. *Cover crops* are crops that are planted between harvests to replace certain nutrients and prevent erosion. Cover crops prevent erosion by providing cover from wind and rain.

Another way to slow down nutrient depletion is through *crop rotation.* If the same crop is grown year after year in the same field, certain nutrients become depleted. To slow this process, a farmer can plant different crops. A different crop will use up less nutrients or different nutrients from the soil.

Figure 4 *George Washington Carver taught soil conservation techniques to farmers.*

Reading Check **What can soybeans and peanuts do for nutrient-poor soil?**

SECTION Review

Summary

- Soil is important for plants to grow, for animals to live in, and for water to be stored.
- Soil erosion and soil damage can be prevented by contour plowing, terracing, using cover crop, and practicing crop rotation.

Using Key Terms

1. In your own words, write a definition for each of the following terms: *soil conservation* and *erosion.*

Understanding Key Ideas

2. What are three important benefits that soil provides?

3. Practicing which of the following soil conservation techniques will replace nutrients in the soil?

- **a.** cover crop use
- **b.** no-till farming
- **c.** terracing
- **d.** contour plowing

4. How does crop rotation benefit soil?

5. List four methods of soil conservation, and describe how each helps prevent the loss of soil.

Math Skills

6. Suppose it takes 500 years to form 2 cm of new soil without erosion. If a farmer needs at least 35 cm of soil to plant a particular crop, how many years will the farmer need to wait before planting his or her crop?

Critical Thinking

7. Applying Concepts Why do land animals, even meat eaters, depend on soil to survive?

For a variety of links related to this chapter, go to www.scilinks.org

Topic: Soil Conservation
SciLinks code: HSM1409

Using Scientific Methods

Model-Making Lab

Rockin' Through Time

OBJECTIVES

Design a model to understand how abrasion breaks down rocks.

Evaluate the effects of abrasion.

MATERIALS

- bottle, plastic, wide-mouthed, with lid, 3 L
- graph paper or computer
- markers
- pieces of limestone, all about the same size (24)
- poster board
- tap water

SAFETY

Wind, water, and gravity constantly change rocks. As wind and water rush over the rocks, the rocks may be worn smooth. As rocks bump against one another, their shapes change. The form of mechanical weathering that occurs as rocks collide and scrape together is called *abrasion*. In this activity, you will shake some pieces of limestone to model the effects of abrasion.

Ask a Question

1. How does abrasion break down rocks? How can I use this information to identify rocks that have been abraded in nature?

Form a Hypothesis

2. Formulate a hypothesis that answers the questions above.

Test the Hypothesis

3. Copy the chart on the next page onto a piece of poster board. Allow enough space to place rocks in each square.
4. Lay three of the limestone pieces on the poster board in the area marked "0 shakes." Be careful not to bump the poster board after you have added the rocks.
5. Place the remaining 21 rocks in the 3 L bottle. Then, fill the bottle halfway with water.
6. Close the lid of the bottle securely. Shake the bottle vigorously 100 times.
7. Remove three rocks from the bottle, and place them on the poster board in the box that indicates the number of times the rocks have been shaken.
8. Repeat steps 6 and 7 six times until all of the rocks have been added to the board.

Analyze the Results

1. **Examining Data** Describe the surface of the rocks that you placed in the area marked "0 shakes." Are they smooth or rough?

2. **Describing Events** How did the shape of the rocks change as you performed this activity?

3. **Constructing Graphs** Using graph paper or a computer, construct a graph, table, or chart that describes how the shapes of the rocks changed as a result of the number of times they were shaken.

Rocks Table	
0 shakes	100 shakes
200 shakes	300 shakes
400 shakes	500 shakes
600 shakes	700 shakes

Draw Conclusions

4. **Drawing Conclusions** Why did the rocks change?

5. **Evaluating Results** How did the water change during the activity? Why did it change?

6. **Making Predictions** What would happen if you used a much harder rock, such as granite, for this experiment?

7. **Interpreting Information** How do the results of this experiment compare with what happens in a river?

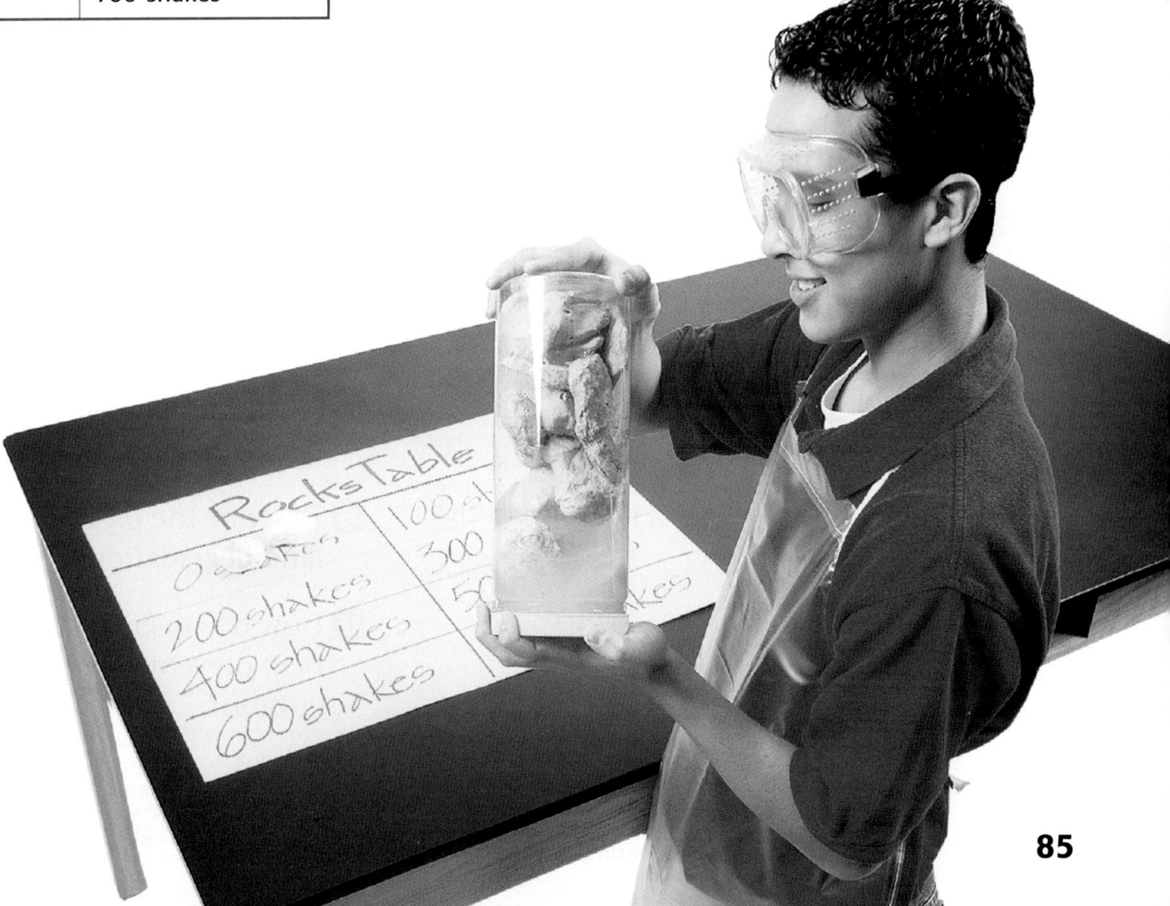

Chapter Review

USING KEY TERMS

1. In your own words, write a definition for each of the following terms: *abrasion* and *soil texture*.

2. Use each of the following terms in a separate sentence: *soil conservation* and *erosion*.

For each pair of terms, explain how the meanings of the terms differ.

3. *mechanical weathering* and *chemical weathering*

4. *soil* and *parent rock*

UNDERSTANDING KEY IDEAS

Multiple Choice

5. Which of the following processes is a possible effect of water?
   - **a.** mechanical weathering
   - **b.** chemical weathering
   - **c.** abrasion
   - **d.** All of the above

6. In which climate would you find the fastest rate of chemical weathering?
   - **a.** a warm, humid climate
   - **b.** a cold, humid climate
   - **c.** a cold, dry climate
   - **d.** a warm, dry climate

7. Which of the following properties does soil texture affect?
   - **a.** soil pH
   - **b.** soil temperature
   - **c.** soil consistency
   - **d.** None of the above

8. Which of the following properties describes a soil's ability to supply nutrients?
   - **a.** soil structure
   - **b.** infiltration
   - **c.** soil fertility
   - **d.** consistency

9. Soil is important because it provides
   - **a.** housing for animals.
   - **b.** nutrients for plants.
   - **c.** storage for water.
   - **d.** All of the above

10. Which of the following soil conservation techniques prevents erosion?
    - **a.** contour plowing
    - **b.** terracing
    - **c.** no-till farming
    - **d.** All of the above

Short Answer

11. Describe the two major types of weathering.

12. Why is Devils Tower higher than the surrounding area?

13. Why is soil in temperate forests thick and fertile?

14. What can happen to soil when soil conservation is not practiced?

15. Describe the process of land degradation.

16. How do cover crops help prevent soil erosion?

CRITICAL THINKING

17 **Concept Mapping** Use the following terms to create a concept map: *weathering, chemical weathering, mechanical weathering, abrasion, ice wedging, oxidation,* and *soil.*

18 **Analyzing Processes** Heat generally speeds up chemical reactions. But weathering, including chemical weathering, is usually slowest in hot, dry climates. Why?

19 **Making Inferences** Mechanical weathering, such as ice wedging, increases surface area by breaking larger rocks into smaller rocks. Draw conclusions about how mechanical weathering can affect the rate of chemical weathering.

20 **Evaluating Data** A scientist has a new theory. She believes that climates that receive heavy rains all year long have thin topsoil. Given what you have learned, decide if the scientist's theory is correct. Explain your answer.

21 **Analyzing Processes** What forms of mechanical and chemical weathering would be most common in the desert? Explain your answer.

22 **Applying Concepts** If you had to plant a crop on a steep hill, what soil conservation techniques would you use to prevent erosion?

23 **Making Comparisons** Compare the weathering processes in a warm, humid climate with those in a dry, cold climate.

INTERPRETING GRAPHICS

The graph below shows how the density of water changes when temperature changes. The denser a substance is, the less volume it occupies. In other words, as most substances get colder, they contract and become denser. But water is unlike most other substances. When water freezes, it expands and becomes less dense. Use the graph below to answer the questions that follow.

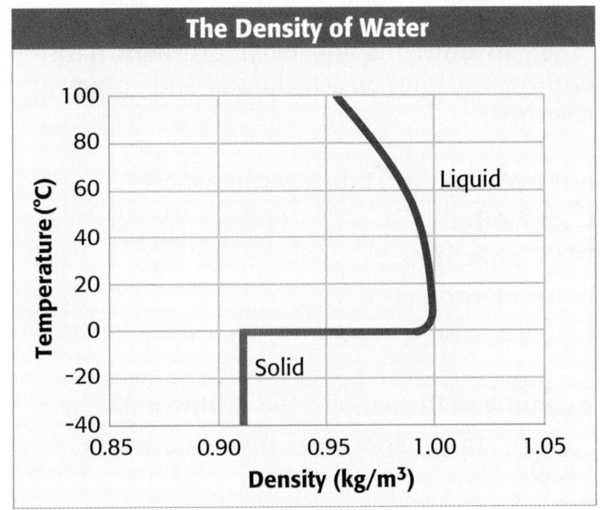

24 Which has the greater density: water at 40°C or water at –20°C?

25 How would the line in the graph look if water behaved like most other liquids?

26 Which substance would be a more effective agent of mechanical weathering: water or another liquid? Why?

Standardized Test Preparation

READING

Read each of the passages below. Then, answer the questions that follow each passage.

Passage 1 Earthworms are very important for forming soil. As they search for food by digging tunnels in the soil, they expose rocks and minerals to the effects of weathering. Over time, this process makes new soil. And as the worms dig tunnels, they mix the soil, which allows air and water and smaller organisms to move deeper into the soil. Worms have huge appetites. They eat organic matter and other materials in the soil. One earthworm can eat an amount equal to about half its body weight each day! Eating all of that food means that earthworms leave behind a lot of waste. Earthworm wastes, called *castings,* are very high in nutrients and make excellent natural fertilizer. Castings enrich the soil and enhance plant growth.

1. In the passage, what does *enhance* mean?

A to weaken
B to improve
C to smooth out
D to decrease

2. According to the passage, the earthworms

F eat organic matter and other materials in soil.
G do not have much of an appetite.
H love to eat castings.
I cannot digest organic matter in soil.

3. Which of the following statements is a fact according to the passage?

A Earthworms are not important for forming soil.
B Earthworms only eat organic matter in the soil.
C An earthworm can eat an amount that equals half its body weight each day.
D Earthworms eat little food but leave behind a lot of waste.

Passage 2 Worms are not the only living things that help create soil. Plants also play a part in the weathering process. As the roots of plants grow and seek out water and nutrients, they help break large rock fragments into smaller ones. Have you ever seen a plant growing in a crack in the sidewalk? As the plant grows, its roots spread into tiny cracks in the sidewalk. These roots apply pressure to the cracks, and over time, the cracks get bigger. As the plants make the cracks bigger, ice wedging can occur more readily. As the cracks expand, more water runs into them. When the water freezes, it expands and presses against the walls of the crack, which makes the crack even larger. Over time, the weathering caused by water, plants, and worms helps break down rock to form soil.

1. How do plants make it easier for ice wedging to occur?

A Plant roots block the cracks and don't allow water to enter.
B Plant roots provide moisture to cracks.
C Plant roots make the cracks larger, which allows more water to enter the cracks.
D Plants absorb excess water from cracks.

2. For ice wedging to occur,

F water in cracks must freeze.
G plant roots must widen cracks.
H acid is needed.
I water is not needed.

3. Which of the following statements is a fact according to the passage?

A Plant roots can strangle earthworms.
B Earthworms eat plant roots.
C Plant roots cannot crack sidewalks.
D Plant roots break large rock fragments into smaller ones.

INTERPRETING GRAPHICS

The graph below shows the average yearly rainfall in five locations. Use the graph below to answer the questions that follow.

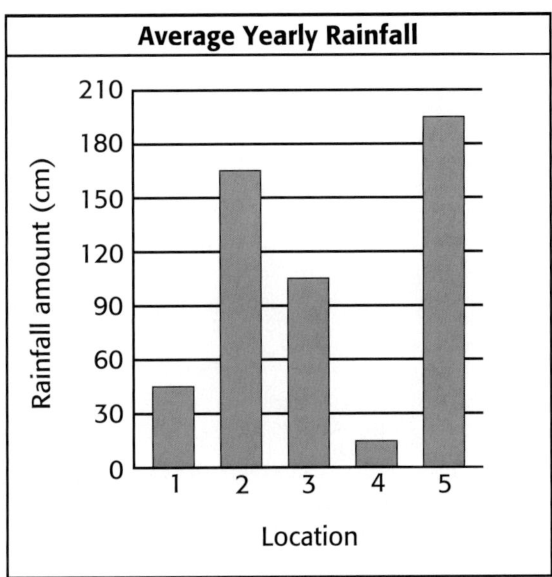

1. Which location has the **most** average yearly rainfall?

A 1
B 2
C 4
D 5

2. At which location would you expect to find the **most** chemical weathering?

F 1
G 3
H 4
I 5

3. At which location would you expect to find the **least** amount of chemical weathering?

A 2
B 3
C 4
D 5

MATH

Read each question below, and choose the best answer.

1. If an earthworm that weighs 1.5 g eats an amount equal to half its body weight in a day, how much does the earthworm eat in 1 week?

A 10.5 g
B 7 g
C 5.25 g
D 1.5 g

2. Calculate the surface area of a cube that measures 3 cm by 3 cm.

F 9 cm
G 9 cm^2
H 54 cm
I 54 cm^2

3. If a mountain peak weathers away 2 cm every 6 years, how many years will the mountain peak take to weather away 1 m?

A 8 years
B 12 years
C 180 years
D 300 years

4. The rock ledge that lies under a waterfall erodes about 3 cm each year. How much of the rock will erode over a period of 18 months?

F 4.5 cm
G 6 cm
H 21 cm
I 54 cm

5. A garden shop charges $0.30 for each ground-cover seedling. How many seedlings can you buy for $6.00?

A 5 seedlings
B 18 seedlings
C 20 seedlings
D 200 seedlings

Science in Action

Science, Technology, and Society

Flying Fertilizer

Would you believe that dust from storms in large deserts can be transported over the oceans to different continents? Dust from the Gobi Desert in China has traveled all the way to Hawaii! In many cases, the dust is a welcome guest. Iron in dust from the Sahara, a desert in Africa, fertilizes the canopies of South American rain forests. In fact, research has shown that the canopies of Central and South American rain forests get much of their nutrients from dust from the Sahara!

Social Studies ACTIVITY

Find pictures on the Internet or in magazines that show how people in rain forests live. Make a poster by using the pictures you find.

Scientific Discoveries

Strange Soil

Mysterious patterns of circles, polygons, and stripes were discovered in the soil in remote areas in Alaska and the Norwegian islands. At first, scientists were puzzled by these strange designs in remote areas. Then, the scientists discovered that these patterns were created by the area's weathering process, which includes cycles of freezing and thawing. When the soil freezes, the soil expands. When the soil thaws, the soil contracts. This process moves and sorts the particles of the soil into patterns.

Language Arts ACTIVITY

WRITING SKILL Write a creative short story describing what life would be like if you were a soil circle on one of these remote islands.

People in Science

J. David Bamberger

Habitat Restoration J. David Bamberger knows how important taking care of the environment is. Therefore, he has turned his ranch into the largest habitat restoration project in Texas. For Bamberger, restoring the habitat started with restoring the soil. One way Bamberger restored the soil was to manage the grazing of the grasslands and to make sure that grazing animals didn't expose the soil. Overgrazing causes soil erosion. When cattle clear the land of its grasses, the soil is exposed to wind and rain, which can wash the topsoil away.

Bamberger also cleared his land of most of the shrub, *juniper*. Juniper requires so much water per day that it leaves little water in the soil for the grasses and wildflowers. The change in the ranch since Bamberger first bought it in 1959 is most obvious at the fence-line border of his ranch. Beyond the fence is a small forest of junipers and little other vegetation. On Bamberger's side, the ranch is lush with grasses, wildflowers, trees, and shrubs.

Math ACTIVITY

Bamberger's ranch is 2,300 hectares. There are 0.405 hectares in 1 acre. How many acres is Bamberger's ranch?

To learn more about these Science in Action topics, visit go.hrw.com and type in the keyword **HZ5WSFF.**

Current Science

Check out Current Science® articles related to this chapter by visiting go.hrw.com. Just type in the keyword HZ5CS10.

The Flow of Fresh Water

About the PHOTO

You can hear the roar of Iguaçu (EE gwah SOO) Falls for miles. The Iguaçu River travels more than 500 km across Brazil before it tumbles off the edge of a volcanic plateau in a series of 275 individual waterfalls. Over the past 20,000 years, erosion has caused the falls to move 28 km upstream.

PRE-READING ACTIVITY

FOLDNOTES **Booklet** Before you read the chapter, create the FoldNote entitled "Booklet" described in the **Study Skills** section of the Appendix. Label each page of the booklet with a main idea from the chapter. As you read the chapter, write what you learn about each main idea on the appropriate page of the booklet.

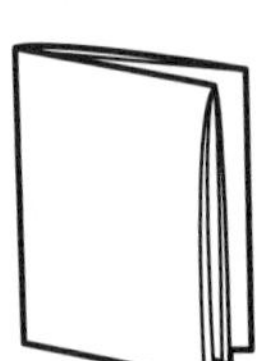

The Stages of a River

In the early 1900s, William Morris Davis developed a model for the stages of river development. According to his model, rivers evolve from a youthful stage to an old-age stage. He thought that all rivers erode in the same way and at the same rate.

Today, scientists support a different model that considers factors of stream development that differ from those considered in Davis's model. For example, because different materials erode at different rates, one river may develop more quickly than another river. Many factors, including climate, gradient, and load, influence the development of a river. Scientists no longer use Davis's model to explain river development, but they still use many of his terms to describe a river. These terms describe a river's general features, not a river's actual age.

CONNECTION TO Language Arts

Huckleberry Finn Mark Twain's famous book, *The Adventures of Huckleberry Finn,* describes the life of a boy who lived on the Mississippi River. Mark Twain's real name was Samuel Clemens. Do research to find out why Clemens chose to use the name Mark Twain and how the name relates to the Mississippi River.

Youthful Rivers

A youthful river, such as the one shown in **Figure 5,** erodes its channel deeper rather than wider. The river flows quickly because of its steep gradient. Its channel is narrow and straight. The river tumbles over rocks in rapids and waterfalls. Youthful rivers have very few tributaries.

▲ **Figure 5** *This youthful river is located in Yellowstone National Park in Wyoming. Rapids and falls are found where the river flows over hard, resistant rock.*

Mature Rivers

A mature river, as shown in **Figure 6,** erodes its channel wider rather than deeper. The gradient of a mature river is not as steep as that of a youthful river. Also, a mature river has fewer falls and rapids. A mature river is fed by many tributaries. Because of its good drainage, a mature river has more discharge than a youthful river.

Reading Check **What are the characteristics of a mature river?**

◀ **Figure 6** *A mature river, such as this one in the Amazon basin of Peru, curves back and forth. The bends in the river's channel are called* meanders.

Figure 7 *This old river is located in New Zealand.*

Old Rivers

An old river has a low gradient and little erosive energy. Instead of widening and deepening its banks, the river deposits rock and soil in and along its channel. Old rivers, such as the one in **Figure 7,** are characterized by wide, flat *flood plains*, or valleys, and many bends. Also, an old river has fewer tributaries than a mature river because the smaller tributaries have joined together.

Rejuvenated Rivers

Rejuvenated (ri JOO vuh NAYT ed) rivers are found where the land is raised by tectonic activity. When land rises, the river's gradient becomes steeper, and the river flows more quickly. The increased gradient of a rejuvenated river allows the river to cut more deeply into the valley floor. Steplike formations called *terraces* often form on both sides of a stream valley as a result of rejuvenation. Can you find the terraces in **Figure 8**?

Reading Check **How do rejuvenated rivers form?**

Figure 8 *This rejuvenated river is located in Canyonlands National Park in Utah.*

SECTION Review

- Rivers cause erosion by removing and transporting soil and rock from the riverbed.
- The water cycle is the movement of Earth's water from the ocean to the atmosphere to the land and back to the ocean.
- A river system is made up of a network of streams and rivers.
- A watershed is a region that collects runoff water that then becomes part of a river or a lake.
- A stream with a high gradient has more energy for eroding soil and rock.
- When a stream's discharge increases, its erosive energy also increases.
- A stream with a load of large particles has a higher rate of erosion than a stream with a dissolved load.
- A developing river can be described as youthful, mature, old, or rejuvenated.

Using Key Terms

1. Use each of the following terms in a separate sentence: *erosion, water cycle, tributary, watershed, divide, channel,* and *load.*

Understanding Key Ideas

2. Which of the following drains a watershed?
   a. a divide
   b. a drainage basin
   c. a tributary
   d. a water system
3. Describe how the Grand Canyon was formed.
4. Draw the water cycle. In your drawing, label *condensation, precipitation,* and *evaporation.*
5. What are three factors that affect the rate of stream erosion?
6. Which stage of river development is characterized by flat flood plains?

Critical Thinking

7. **Making Inferences** How does the water cycle help develop river systems?
8. **Making Comparisons** How do youthful rivers, mature rivers, and old rivers differ?

Interpreting Graphics

Use the pie graph below to answer the questions that follow.

Distribution of Water in the World

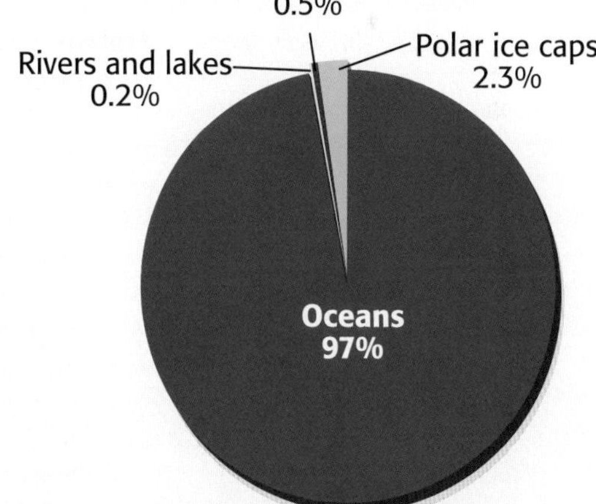

9. Where is most of the water in the world found?
10. In what form is the majority of the world's fresh water?

SCILINKS
NSTA
Developed and maintained by the National Science Teachers Association
For a variety of links related to this chapter, go to www.scilinks.org
Topic: Rivers and Streams
SciLinks code: HSM1316

SECTION 2

Stream and River Deposits

If your job were to carry millions of tons of soil across the United States, how would you do it? You might use a bulldozer or a dump truck, but it would still take you a long time. Did you know that rivers do this job every day?

READING WARM-UP

Objectives

- Describe the four different types of stream deposits.
- Describe how the deposition of sediment affects the land.

Terms to Learn

deposition
delta
alluvial fan
floodplain

READING STRATEGY

Prediction Guide Before reading this section, write the title of each heading in this section. Next, under each heading, write what you think you will learn.

Rivers erode and move enormous amounts of material, such as soil and rock. Acting as liquid conveyor belts, rivers often carry fertile soil to farmland and wetlands. Although erosion is a serious problem, rivers also renew soils and form new land. As you will see in this section, rivers create some of the most impressive landforms on Earth.

Deposition in Water

You have learned how flowing water erodes the Earth's surface. After rivers erode rock and soil, they drop, or *deposit,* their load downstream. **Deposition** is the process in which material is laid down or dropped. Rock and soil deposited by streams are called *sediment*. Rivers and streams deposit sediment where the speed of the water current decreases. **Figure 1** shows this type of deposition.

Figure 1 *This photo shows erosion and deposition at a bend, or meander, of a river in Alaska.*

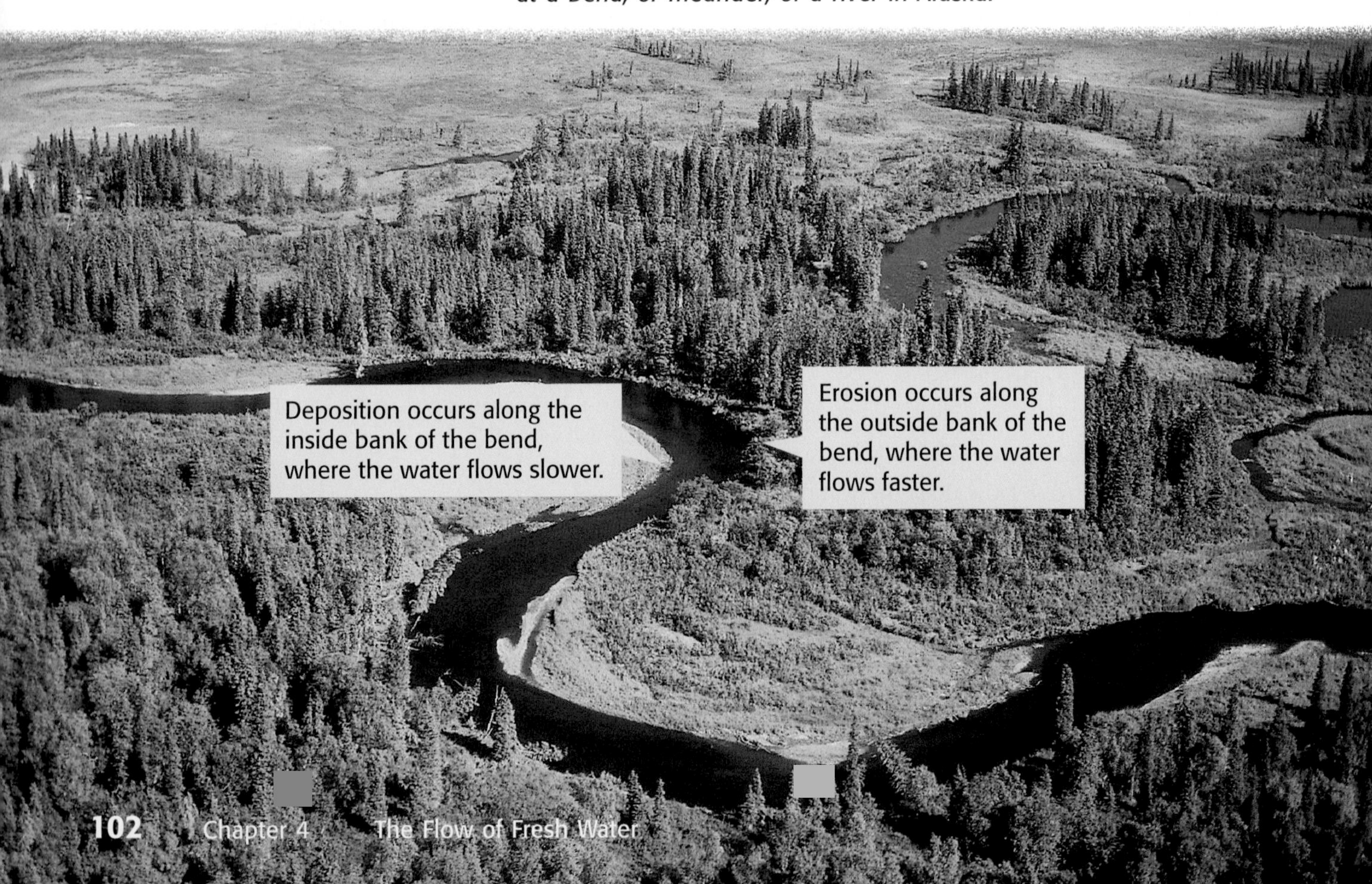

Deposition occurs along the inside bank of the bend, where the water flows slower.
Erosion occurs along the outside bank of the bend, where the water flows faster.

Placer Deposits

Heavy minerals are sometimes deposited at places in a river where the current slows down. This kind of sediment is called a *placer deposit* (PLAS uhr dee PAHZ it). Some placer deposits contain gold. During the California gold rush, which began in 1849, many miners panned for gold in the placer deposits of rivers, as shown in **Figure 2.**

Figure 2 *Miners rushed to California in the 1850s to find gold. They often found it in the bends of rivers in placer deposits.*

Delta

A river's current slows when a river empties into a large body of water, such as a lake or an ocean. As its current slows, a river often deposits its load in a fan-shaped pattern called a **delta.** In **Figure 3,** you can see an astronaut's view of the Nile Delta. A delta usually forms on a flat surface and is made mostly of mud. These mud deposits form new land and cause the coastline to grow. The world's deltas are home to a rich diversity of plant and animal life.

If you look back at the map of the Mississippi River watershed, you can see where the Mississippi Delta has formed. It has formed where the Mississippi River flows into the Gulf of Mexico. Each of the fine mud particles in the delta began its journey far upstream. Parts of Louisiana are made up of particles that were transported from places as far away as Montana, Minnesota, Ohio, and Illinois!

Reading Check **What are deltas made of?** (*See the Appendix for answers to Reading Checks.*)

deposition the process in which material is laid down

delta a fan-shaped mass of material deposited at the mouth of a stream

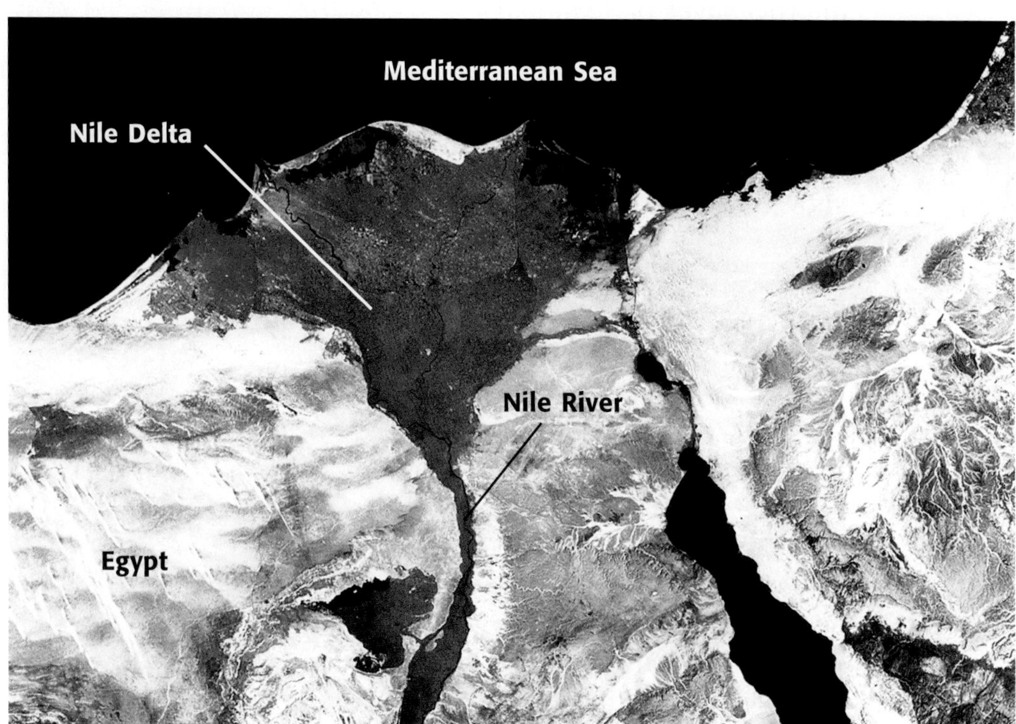

Figure 3 *As sediment is dropped at the mouth of the Nile River, in Egypt, a delta forms.*

Figure 4 *An alluvial fan, like this one at Death Valley in California, forms when an eroding stream changes rapidly into a depositing stream.*

Deposition on Land

alluvial fan a fan-shaped mass of material deposited by a stream when the slope of the land decreases sharply

floodplain an area along a river that forms from sediments deposited when the river overflows its banks

When a fast-moving mountain stream flows onto a flat plain, the stream slows down very quickly. As the stream slows down, it deposits sediment. The sediment forms an alluvial fan, such as the one shown in **Figure 4. Alluvial fans** are fan-shaped deposits that, unlike deltas, form on dry land.

Floodplains

During periods of high rainfall or rapid snow melt, a sudden increase in the volume of water flowing into a stream can cause the stream to overflow its banks. The area along a river that forms from sediment deposited when a river overflows its banks is called a **floodplain.** When a stream floods, a layer of sediment is deposited across the flood plain. Each flood adds another layer of sediment.

Flood plains are rich farming areas because periodic flooding brings new soil to the land. However, flooding can cause damage, too. When the Mississippi River flooded in 1993, farms were destroyed, and entire towns were evacuated. **Figure 5** shows an area north of St. Louis, Missouri, that was flooded.

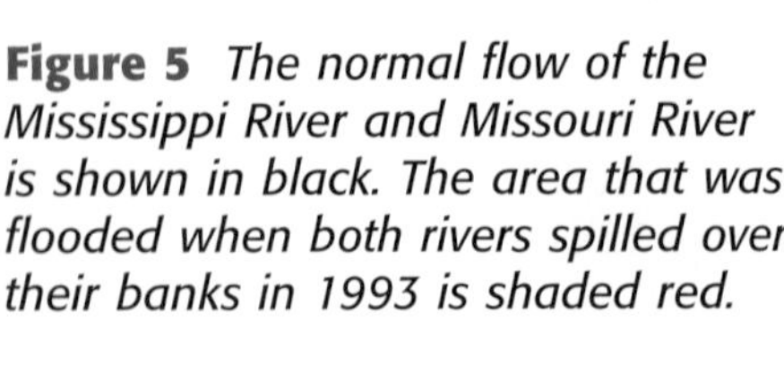

Figure 5 *The normal flow of the Mississippi River and Missouri River is shown in black. The area that was flooded when both rivers spilled over their banks in 1993 is shaded red.*

Flooding Dangers

The flooding of the Mississippi River in 1993 caused damage in nine states. But floods can damage more than property. Many people have lost their lives to powerful floods. As shown in **Figure 6,** flash flooding can take a driver by surprise. However, there are ways that floods can be controlled.

One type of barrier that can be built to help control flooding is called a *dam*. A dam is a barrier that can redirect the flow of water. A dam can prevent flooding in one area and create an artificial lake in another area. The water stored in the artificial lake can be used to irrigate farmland during droughts and provide drinking water to local towns and cities. The stored water can also be used to generate electricity.

Overflow from a river can also be controlled by a barrier called a *levee*. A levee is the buildup of sediment deposited along the channel of a river. This buildup helps keep the river inside its banks. People often use sandbags to build artificial levees to control water during serious flooding.

Figure 6 *Cars driven on flooded roads can easily be carried down to deeper, more dangerous water.*

Reading Check **List two ways that the flow of water can be controlled.**

SECTION Review

Summary

- Sediment forms several types of deposits.
- Sediments deposited where a river's current slows are called *placer deposits.*
- A delta is a fan-shaped deposit of sediment where a river meets a large body of water.
- Alluvial fans can form when a river deposits sediment on land.
- Flooding brings rich soil to farmland but can also lead to property damage and death.

Using Key Terms

1. In your own words, write a definition for each of the following terms: *deposition* and *flood plain.*

Understanding Key Ideas

2. Which of the following forms at places in a river where the current slows?
   a. a placer deposit
   b. a delta
   c. a flood plain
   d. a levee
3. Which of the following can help to prevent a flood?
   a. a placer deposit
   b. a delta
   c. a flood plain
   d. a levee
4. Where do alluvial fans form?
5. Explain why flood plains are both good and bad areas for farming.

Math Skills

6. A river flows at a speed of 8 km/h. If you floated on a raft in this river, how far would you have traveled after 5 h?

Critical Thinking

7. **Identifying Relationships** What factors increase the likelihood that sediment will be deposited?
8. **Making Comparisons** How are alluvial fans and deltas similar?

For a variety of links related to this chapter, go to www.scilinks.org

Topic: Stream Deposits
SciLinks code: HSM1458

SECTION 3

Water Underground

Imagine that instead of turning on a faucet to get a glass of water, you pour water from a chunk of solid rock! This idea may sound crazy, but millions of people get their water from within rock that is deep underground.

READING WARM-UP

Objectives

- Identify and describe the location of the water table.
- Describe an aquifer.
- Explain the difference between a spring and a well.
- Explain how caves and sinkholes form as a result of erosion and deposition.

Terms to Learn

water table, aquifer, porosity, permeability, recharge zone, artesian spring

READING STRATEGY

Discussion Read this section silently. Write down questions that you have about this section. Discuss your questions in a small group.

Although you can see some of Earth's water in streams and lakes, you cannot see the large amount of water that flows underground. The water located within the rocks below the Earth's surface is called *groundwater.* Groundwater not only is an important resource but also plays an important role in erosion and deposition.

The Location of Groundwater

Surface water seeps underground into the soil and rock. This underground area is divided into two zones. Rainwater passes through the upper zone, called the *zone of aeration.* Farther down, the water collects in an area called the *zone of saturation.* In this zone, the spaces between the rock particles are filled with water.

These two zones meet at a boundary known as the **water table,** shown in **Figure 1.** The water table rises during wet seasons and falls during dry seasons. In wet regions, the water table can be at or just beneath the soil's surface. In dry regions, such as deserts, the water table may be hundreds of meters beneath the ground.

water table the upper surface of underground water; the upper boundary of the zone of saturation

Reading Check Describe where the zone of aeration is located. (*See the Appendix for answers to Reading Checks.*)

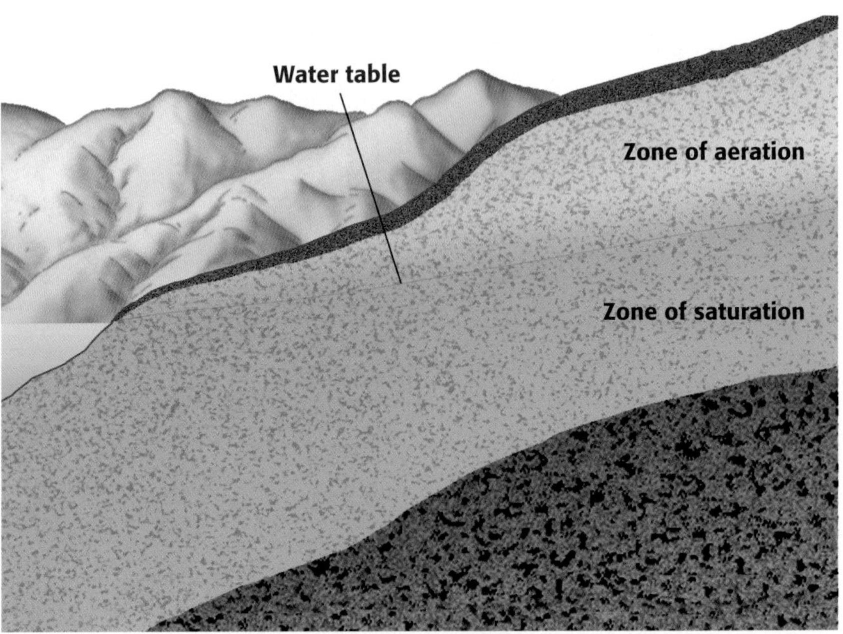

Figure 1 *The water table is the upper surface of the zone of saturation.*

Aquifers

A rock layer that stores groundwater and allows the flow of groundwater is called an **aquifer.** An aquifer can be described by its ability to hold water and its ability to allow water to pass freely through it.

aquifer a body of rock or sediment that stores groundwater and allows the flow of groundwater

porosity the percentage of the total volume of a rock or sediment that consists of open spaces

permeability the ability of a rock or sediment to let fluids pass through its open spaces, or pores

Porosity

The more open spaces, or pores, between particles in an aquifer, the more water the aquifer can hold. The percentage of open space between individual rock particles in a rock layer is called **porosity.**

Porosity is influenced by the differences in sizes of the particles in the rock layer. If a rock layer contains many particles of different sizes, it is likely that small particles will fill up the different-sized empty spaces between large particles. Therefore, a rock layer with particles of different sizes has a low percentage of open space between particles and has low porosity. On the other hand, a rock layer containing same-sized particles has high porosity. This rock layer has high porosity because smaller particles are not present to fill the empty space between particles. So, there is more open space between particles.

For another activity related to this chapter, go to **go.hrw.com** and type in the keyword **HZ5DEPW.**

Permeability

If the pores of a rock layer are connected, groundwater can flow through the rock layer. A rock's ability to let water pass through is called **permeability.** A rock that stops the flow of water is *impermeable.*

The larger the particles are, the more permeable the rock layer is. Because large particles have less surface area relative to their volume than small particles do, large particles cause less friction. *Friction* is a force that causes moving objects to slow down. Less friction allows water to flow more easily through the rock layer, as shown in **Figure 2.**

Figure 2 *Large particles, shown at left, have less total surface area—and so cause less friction—than small particles, shown at right, do.*

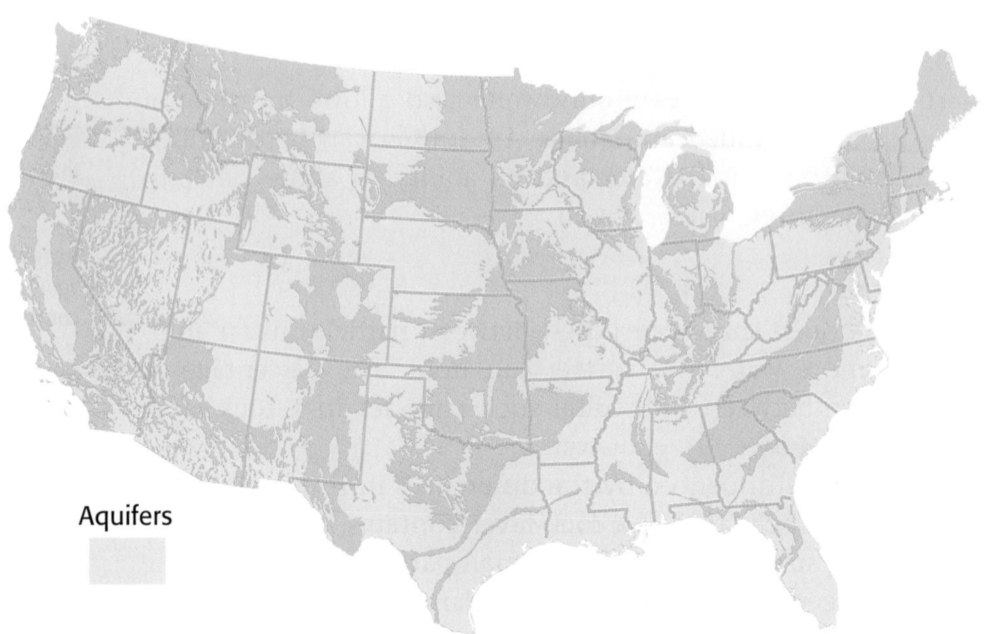

Figure 3 *This map shows aquifers in the United States (excluding Alaska and Hawaii).*

Aquifer Geology and Geography

recharge zone an area in which water travels downward to become part of an aquifer

The best aquifers usually form in permeable materials, such as sandstone, limestone, or layers of sand and gravel. Some aquifers cover large underground areas and are an important source of water for cities and agriculture. The map in **Figure 3** shows the location of the major aquifers in the United States.

Recharge Zones

Like rivers, aquifers depend on the water cycle to maintain a constant flow of water. The ground surface where water enters an aquifer is called the **recharge zone.** The size of the recharge zone depends on how permeable rock is at the surface. If the surface rock is permeable, water can seep down into the aquifer. If the aquifer is covered by an impermeable rock layer, water cannot reach the aquifer. Construction of buildings on top of the recharge zone can also limit the amount of water that enters an aquifer.

Reading Check **What factors affect the size of the recharge zone?**

Water Conservation

Did you know that water use in the United States has been reduced by 15% in the last 20 years? This decrease is due in part to the conservation efforts of people like you. Work with a parent to create a water budget for your household. Figure out how much water your family uses every day. Identify ways to reduce your water use, and then set a goal to limit your water use over the course of a week.

Springs and Wells

Groundwater movement is determined by the slope of the water table. Like surface water, groundwater tends to move downslope, toward lower elevations. If the water table reaches the Earth's surface, water will flow out from the ground and will form a *spring*. Springs are an important source of drinking water. In areas where the water table is higher than the Earth's surface, lakes will form.

Artesian Springs

A sloping layer of permeable rock sandwiched between two layers of impermeable rock is called an *artesian formation*. The permeable rock is an aquifer, and the top layer of impermeable rock is called a *cap rock,* as shown in **Figure 4.** Artesian formations are the source of water for artesian springs. An **artesian spring** is a spring whose water flows from a crack in the cap rock of the aquifer. Artesian springs are sometimes found in deserts, where they are often the only source of water.

Most springs have cool water. However, some springs have hot water. The water becomes hot when it flows deep in the Earth, because Earth's temperature increases with depth. The temperature of some hot springs can reach 50°C!

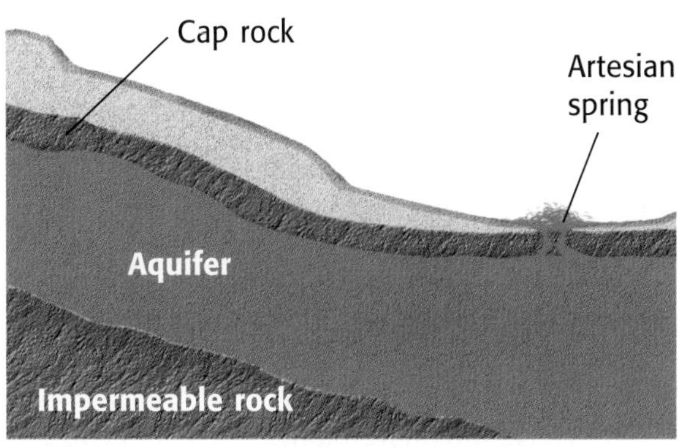

Figure 4 *Artesian springs form when water from an aquifer flows through cracks in the cap rock of an artesian formation.*

Wells

A human-made hole that is deeper than the level of the water table is called a *well*. If a well is not deep enough, as shown in **Figure 5,** it will dry up when the water table falls below the bottom of the well. Also, if an area has too many wells, groundwater can be removed too rapidly. If groundwater is removed too rapidly, the water table will drop, and all of the wells will run dry.

artesian spring a spring whose water flows from a crack in the cap rock over the aquifer

Reading Check How deep must a well be to reach water?

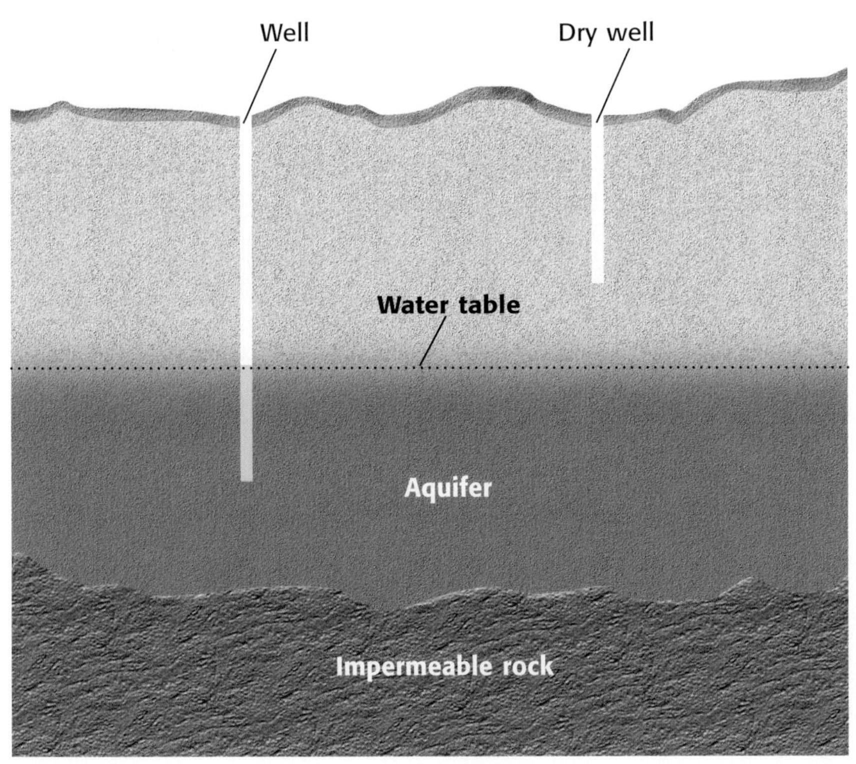

Figure 5 *A well must be drilled deep enough so that when the water table drops, the well still contains water.*

Underground Erosion and Deposition

As you have learned, rivers cause erosion when water removes and transports rock and soil from its banks. Groundwater can also cause erosion. However, groundwater causes erosion by dissolving rock. Some groundwater contains weak acids, such as carbonic acid, that dissolve the rock. Also, some types of rock, such as limestone, dissolve in groundwater more easily than other types do.

When underground erosion happens, caves can form. Most of the world's caves formed over thousands of years as groundwater dissolved the limestone of the cave sites. Some caves, such as the one shown in **Figure 6,** reach spectacular proportions.

CONNECTION TO Environmental Science

Bat Environmentalists
Most bat species live in caves. Bats are night-flying mammals that play an important role in the environment. Bats eat vast quantities of insects. Many bat species also pollinate plants and distribute seeds. Can you think of other animals that eat insects, pollinate plants, and distribute seeds? Create a poster that includes pictures of these other animals.

ACTIVITY

Cave Formations

Although caves are formed by erosion, they also show signs of deposition. Water that drips from a crack in a cave's ceiling leaves behind deposits of calcium carbonate. Sharp, icicle-shaped features that form on cave ceilings are known as *stalactites* (stuh LAK tiets). Water that falls to the cave's floor adds to cone-shaped features known as *stalagmites* (stuh LAG MIETS). If water drips long enough, the stalactites and stalagmites join to form a *dripstone column.*

Reading Check What process causes the formation of stalactites and stalagmites?

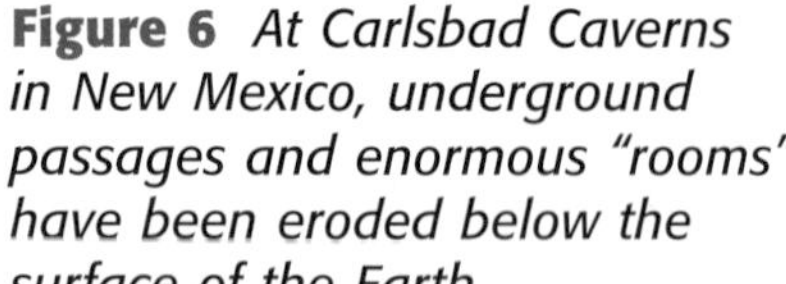

Figure 6 *At Carlsbad Caverns in New Mexico, underground passages and enormous "rooms" have been eroded below the surface of the Earth.*

5. Continue until you have observed steam rising off the water, the glass plate becoming foggy, and water dripping from the glass plate.

6. Carefully set the glass plate on a counter or other safe surface as directed by your teacher.

7. Turn off the hot plate, and allow the beaker to cool. Move the hot beaker with gloves or tongs if you are directed to do so by your teacher.

Analyze the Results

1. **Constructing Charts** Copy the illustration shown above. On your sketch, draw and label the water cycle as it happened in your model. Include arrows and labels for *evaporation, condensation,* and *precipitation*.

2. **Analyzing Results** Compare the water level in the beaker now with the water level at the beginning of the experiment. Was there a change? Explain why or why not.

Draw Conclusions

3. **Making Predictions** If you had used a scale or a balance to measure the mass of the water in the beaker before and after this activity, would the mass have changed? Explain.

4. **Analyzing Charts** How is your model similar to the Earth's water cycle? On your sketch of the illustration, label where the processes shown in the model reflect the Earth's water cycle.

5. **Drawing Conclusions** When you finished this experiment, the water in the beaker was still hot. What stores much of the energy in the Earth's water cycle?

Applying Your Data

As rainwater runs over the land, the water picks up minerals and salts. Do these minerals and salts evaporate, condense, and precipitate as part of the water cycle? Where do they go?

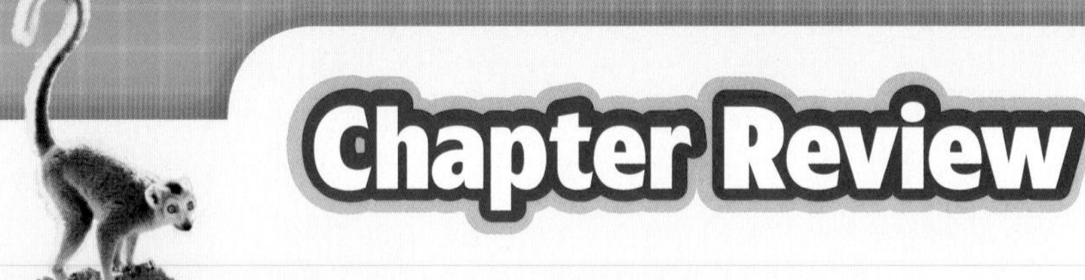

Chapter Review

USING KEY TERMS

The statements below are false. For each statement, replace the underlined term to make a true statement.

1. A stream that flows into a lake or into a larger stream is a <u>water cycle</u>.

2. The area along a river that forms from sediment deposited when the river overflows is a <u>delta</u>.

3. A rock's ability to let water pass through it is called <u>porosity</u>.

For each pair of terms, explain how the meanings of the terms differ.

4. *divide* and *watershed*

5. *artesian springs* and *wells*

6. *point-source pollution* and *nonpoint-source pollution*

UNDERSTANDING KEY IDEAS

Multiple Choice

7. Which of the following processes is not part of the water cycle?
   - **a.** evaporation
   - **b.** percolation
   - **c.** condensation
   - **d.** deposition

8. Which features are common in youthful river channels?
   - **a.** meanders
   - **b.** flood plains
   - **c.** rapids
   - **d.** sandbars

9. Which depositional feature is found at the coast?
   - **a.** delta
   - **b.** flood plain
   - **c.** alluvial fan
   - **d.** placer deposit

10. Caves are mainly a product of
    - **a.** erosion by rivers.
    - **b.** river deposition.
    - **c.** water pollution.
    - **d.** erosion by groundwater.

11. Which of the following is necessary for aquatic life to survive?
    - **a.** dissolved oxygen
    - **b.** nitrates
    - **c.** alkalinity
    - **d.** point-source pollution

12. During primary treatment at a sewage treatment plant,
    - **a.** water is sent to an aeration tank.
    - **b.** water is mixed with bacteria and oxygen.
    - **c.** dirty water is passed through a large screen.
    - **d.** water is sent to a settling tank where chlorine is added.

Short Answer

13. Identify and describe the location of the water table.

14. Explain how surface water enters an aquifer.

15. Why are caves usually found in limestone-rich regions?

CRITICAL THINKING

16 **Concept Mapping** Use the following terms to create a concept map: *zone of aeration, zone of saturation, water table, gravity, porosity,* and *permeability*.

17 **Identifying Relationships** What is water's role in erosion and deposition?

18 **Analyzing Processes** What are the features of a river channel that has a steep gradient?

19 **Analyzing Processes** Why is groundwater hard to clean?

20 **Evaluating Conclusions** How can water be considered both a renewable and a nonrenewable resource? Give an example of each case.

21 **Analyzing Processes** Does water vapor lose or gain energy during the process of condensation? Explain.

INTERPRETING GRAPHICS

The hydrograph below illustrates data collected on river flow during field investigations over a period of 1 year. The discharge readings are from the Yakima River, in Washington. Use the hydrograph below to answer the questions that follow.

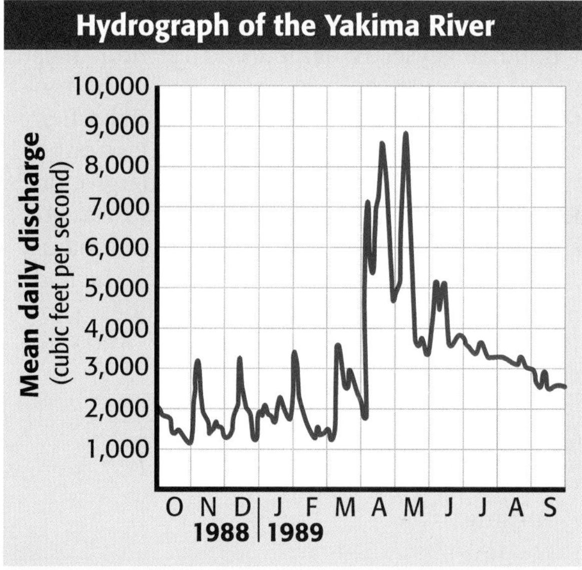

22 In which months is there the highest river discharge?

23 Why is there such a high river discharge during these months?

24 What might cause the peaks in river discharge between November and March?

Standardized Test Preparation

READING

Read each of the passages below. Then, answer the questions that follow each passage.

Passage 1 In parts of Yellowstone National Park, boiling water from deep in the ground blasts into the sky. These blasts of steam come from lakes of strange-colored boiling mud that gurgle and hiss. These features are called geysers. Yellowstone's most popular geyser is named Old Faithful. It is given this name because it erupts every 60 min to 70 min without fail. A geyser is formed when a narrow vent connects one or more underground chambers to Earth's surface. These underground chambers are heated by nearby molten rock. As underground water flows into the vent and chambers, it is heated above 100°C. This superheated water quickly turns to steam and explodes, projecting scalding water 60 m into the air. And Old Faithful erupts right on schedule!

1. In the passage, what does *scalding* mean?

- **A** muddy
- **B** burning
- **C** gurgling
- **D** steaming

2. According to the passage, what happens to underground water when geysers form?

- **F** It is heated by molten rock.
- **G** It is cycled to Earth's center.
- **H** It travels 60 m through vents.
- **I** It is poured into volcanoes.

3. Which of the following is a fact in the passage?

- **A** Old Faithful erupts every 60 min.
- **B** Old Faithful is located in Yellowstone National Park.
- **C** There are six geysers at Yellowstone National Park.
- **D** Molten rock explodes from geysers.

Passage 2 In the Mississippi Delta, long-legged birds step lightly through the marsh and hunt fish or frogs for breakfast. Hundreds of species of plants and animals start another day in this fragile ecosystem. This delta ecosystem is in danger of being destroyed. The threat comes from efforts to make the river more useful. Large portions of the river bottom were dredged to deepen the river for ship traffic. Underwater channels were built to control flooding. What no one realized was that sediments that once formed new land now passed through the channels and flowed out into the ocean. Those river sediments had once replaced the land that was lost every year to erosion. Without them, the river can't replace land lost to erosion. So, the Mississippi River Delta is shrinking. By 1995, more than half of the wetlands were already gone—swept out to sea by waves along the Louisiana coast.

1. In the passage, what does *dredged* mean?

- **A** moved to the side
- **B** circulated
- **C** cleaned
- **D** scooped up

2. Based on the passage, which of the following statements about the Mississippi River is true?

- **F** The river never floods.
- **G** The river is not wide enough for ships.
- **H** The river's delicate ecosystem is in danger.
- **I** The river is disappearing.

3. Which of the following is a fact in the passage?

- **A** By 1995, more than half of the Mississippi River was gone.
- **B** Underwater channels controlled flooding.
- **C** Channels help form new land.
- **D** Sediment cannot replace lost land.

INTERPRETING GRAPHICS

The chart below shows four wells drilled at different depths. Use the chart below to answer the questions that follow.

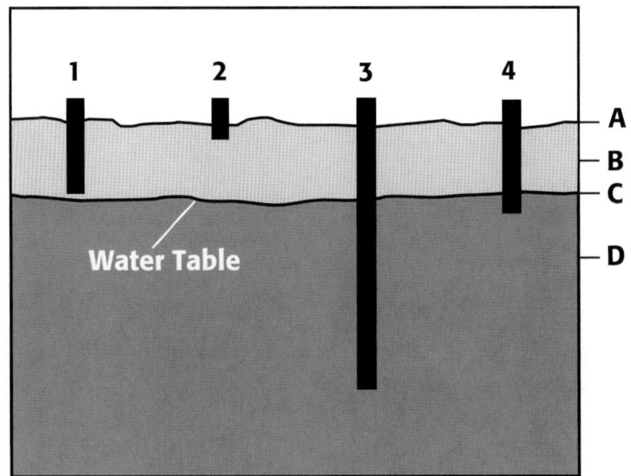

1. A well-drilling company offers the four types of wells shown in the chart. Which well is most likely to be a reliable source of groundwater?
   A 1
   B 2
   C 3
   D 4

2. If the area experienced heavy rains, toward which level would the water table move?
   F The water table would move toward level B.
   G The water table would move toward level D.
   H The water table would stay at level C.
   I The water table will be gone.

3. If the water table moves to level D, which wells will still be able to provide water?
   A all wells
   B wells 1 and 2
   C well 3
   D wells 3 and 4

4. Which well is most likely to be an unreliable source of groundwater?
   F 1
   G 2
   H 3
   I 4

MATH

Read each question below, and choose the best answer.

1. A river flows at a speed of 10 km/h. If a boat travels upstream at a speed of 15 km/h, how far will it travel in 3 h?
   A 10 km
   B 15 km
   C 20 km
   D 25 km

2. Water contamination is often measured in parts per million (ppm). If the concentration of a pollutant is 5 ppm, there are 5 parts of the pollutant in 1 million parts of water. If the concentration of gasoline is 3 ppm in 2,000,000 L of water, how many liters of gasoline are in the water?
   F 3 L
   G 6 L
   H 9 L
   I 10 L

3. One family uses 70 L of water a day for showering. If everyone in the family agreed to shorten his or her shower from 10 min to 5 min, how many liters of water would be saved each day?
   A 5 L
   B 10 L
   C 35 L
   D 70 L

4. A family uses 800 L of water per day. Of those 800 L, 200 L are used for flushing the toilet. Calculate the percentage of water that the family uses to flush the toilet.
   F 25%
   G 30%
   H 50%
   I 60%

5. A river flows at a speed of 8 km/h. If you floated on a raft in this river, how far will you have traveled after 5 h?
   A 5 km
   B 16 km
   C 40 km
   D 80 km

Science in Action

Weird Science

Secret Lake

Would you believe there is a freshwater lake more than 3 km below an Antarctic glacier near the South Pole? It is surprising that Lake Vostok can remain in a liquid state at a place where the temperature can fall below –50°C. Scientists believe that the intense pressure from the overlying ice heats the lake and keeps it from freezing. Geothermal energy, which is the energy within the surface of the Earth, also contributes to warmer temperatures. The other unique thing about Lake Vostok is the discovery of living microbes under the glacier that covers the lake!

Language Arts ACTIVITY

Look up the word *geothermal* in the dictionary. What is the meaning of the roots *geo-* and *-thermal*? Find other words in the dictionary that begin with the root *geo-*.

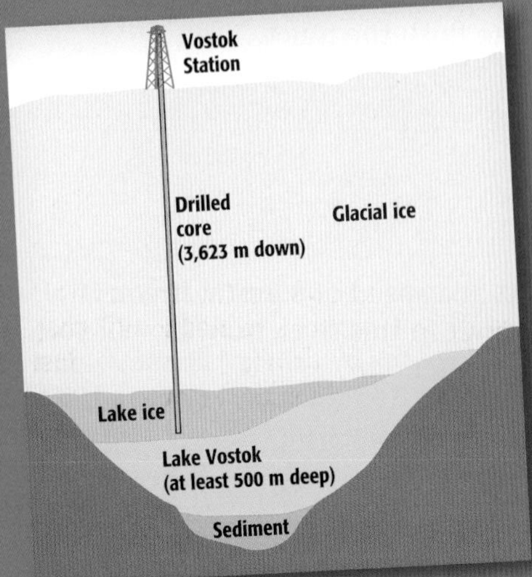

Scientific Discoveries

Sunken Forests

Imagine having your own little secret forest. In Ankarana National Park, in Madagascar, there are plenty of them. Within the limestone mountain of the park, caves have formed from the twisting path of the flowing groundwater. In many places in the caves, the roof has collapsed to form a sinkhole. The light that now shines through the collapsed roof of the cave has allowed miniature sunken forests to grow. Each sunken forest has unique characteristics. Some have crocodiles. Others have blind cavefish. You can even find some species that can't be found anywhere else in the world!

Social Studies ACTIVITY

Find out how Madagascar's geography contributes to the biodiversity of the island nation. Make a map of the island that highlights some of the unique forms of life found there.

People in Science

Rita Colwell

A Water Filter for All Did you ever drink a glass of water through a piece of cloth? Dr. Rita Colwell, director of the National Science Foundation, has found that filtering drinking water through a cloth can actually decrease the number of disease-causing bacteria in the water. This discovery is very important for the people of Bangladesh, where deadly outbreaks of cholera are frequent. People are usually infected by the cholera bacteria by drinking contaminated water. Colwell knew that filtering the water would remove the bacteria. The water would then be safe to drink. Unfortunately, filters were too expensive for most of the people to buy. Colwell tried filtering the water with a sari. A sari is a long piece of colorful cloth that many women in Bangladesh wear as skirtlike cloth. Filtering the water with the sari cloth did the trick. The amount of cholera bacteria in the water was reduced. Fewer people contracted cholera, and many lives were saved!

Math ACTIVITY

With the cloth water-filter method, there was a 48% reduction in the occurrence of cholera. If there were 125 people out of 100,000 who contracted cholera before the cloth-filter method was used, how many people per 100,000 contracted cholera after using the cloth-filter method?

To learn more about these Science in Action topics, visit **go.hrw.com** and type in the keyword **HZ5DEPF.**

Current Science

Check out Current Science® articles related to this chapter by visiting go.hrw.com. Just type in the keyword HZ5CS11.

5

The Ocean

About the PHOTO

No, this isn't a traffic jam or the result of careless navigation. Hurricane Hugo is to blame for this major boat pile up. When Hurricane Hugo hit South Carolina's coast in 1989, the hurricane's strong winds created large ocean waves. These ocean waves carried these boats right onto the shore.

PRE-READING ACTIVITY

Graphic Organizer

Concept Map Before you read the chapter, create the graphic organizer entitled "Concept Map" described in the **Study Skills** section of the Appendix. As you read the chapter, fill in the concept map with details about each type of ocean water movement.

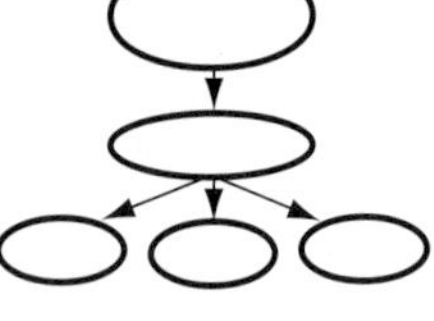

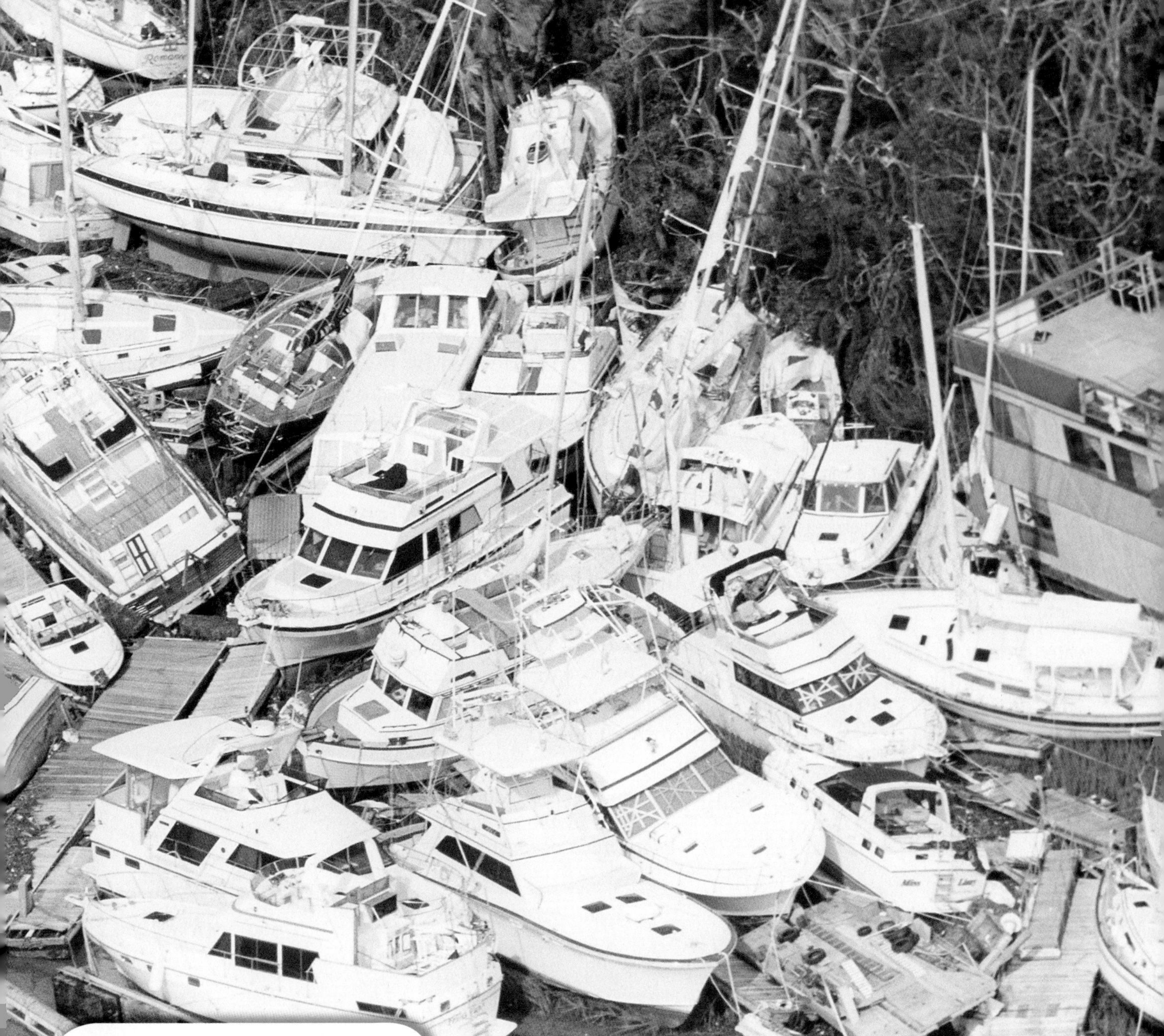

START-UP ACTIVITY

When Whirls Collide

Some ocean currents flow in a clockwise direction, while other ocean currents flow in a counterclockwise direction. Sometimes these currents collide. In this activity, you and your lab partner will demonstrate how two currents flowing in opposite directions affect one another.

Procedure

1. Fill a large **tub** with **water** 5 cm deep.
2. Add **10 drops of red food coloring** to the water at one end of the tub.
3. Add **10 drops of blue food coloring** to the water at the other end of the tub.
4. Using a **pencil,** quickly stir the water at one end of the tub in a clockwise direction while your partner stirs the water at the other end in a counterclockwise direction. Stir both ends for 5 s.
5. Draw what you see happening in the tub immediately after you stop stirring. (Both ends should be swirling.)

Analysis

1. How did the blue water and the red water interact?
2. How does this activity relate to how ocean currents interact?

SECTION 1

Earth's Oceans

What makes Earth so different from Mars? What does Earth have that Mercury doesn't?

Earth stands out from the other planets in our solar system primarily for one reason—71% of the Earth's surface is covered with water. Most of Earth's water is found in the global ocean. The global ocean is divided by the continents into four main oceans. The divisions of the global ocean are shown in **Figure 1.** The ocean is a unique body of water that plays many parts in regulating Earth's environment.

READING WARM-UP

Objectives

- List the major divisions of the global ocean.
- Describe the history of Earth's oceans.
- Identify the properties of ocean water.
- Describe the interactions between the ocean and the atmosphere.

Terms to Learn

salinity
water cycle

READING STRATEGY

Discussion Read this section silently. Write down questions that you have about this section. Discuss your questions in a small group.

Divisions of the Global Ocean

The largest ocean is the *Pacific Ocean*. It flows between Asia and the Americas. The volume of the *Atlantic Ocean*, the second-largest ocean, is about half the volume of the Pacific. The *Indian Ocean* is the third-largest ocean. The *Arctic Ocean* is the smallest ocean. This ocean is unique because much of its surface is covered by ice. Therefore, the Arctic Ocean has not been fully explored.

Figure 1 *The global ocean is divided by the continents into four main oceans.*

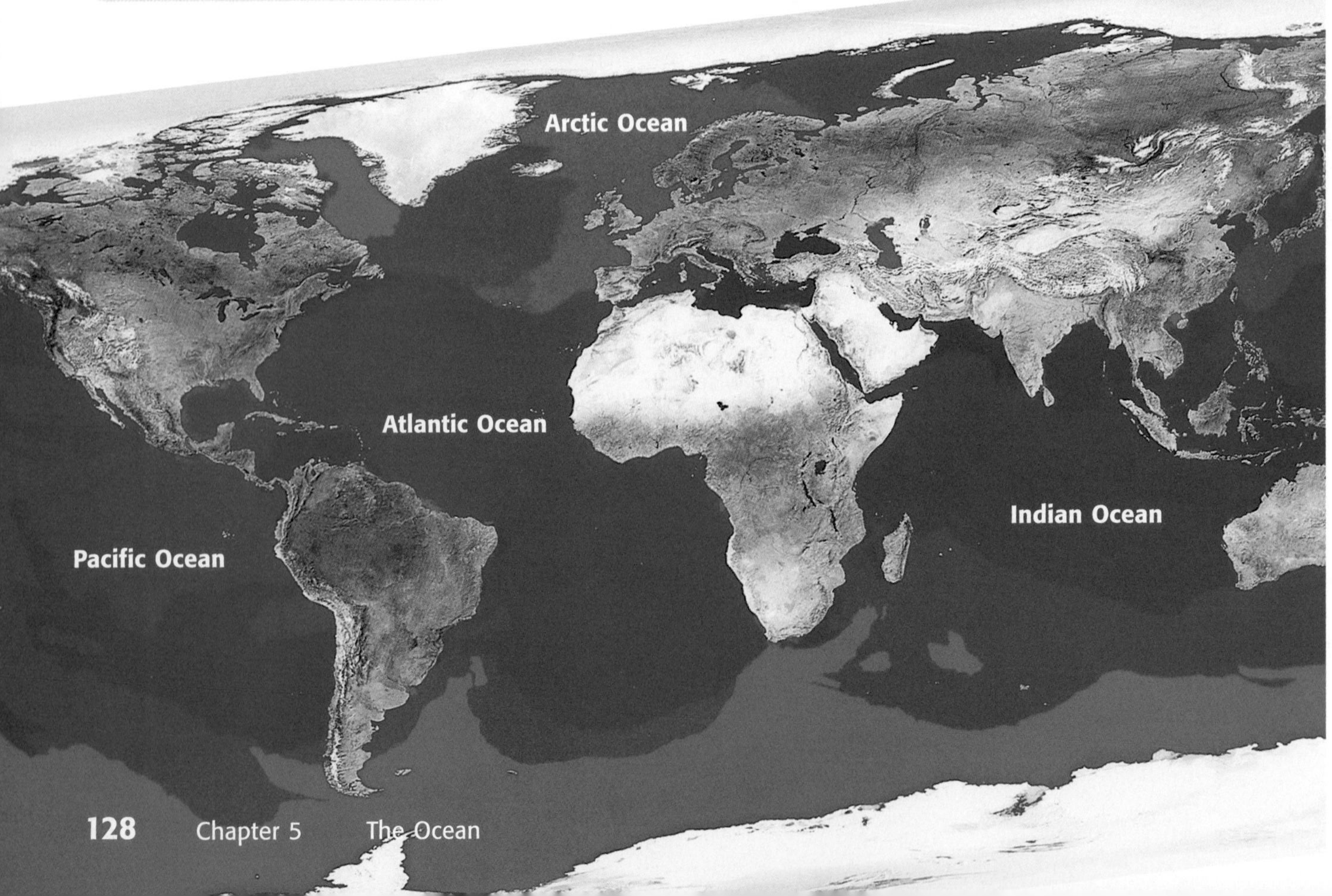

The Ocean and the Water Cycle

If you could sit on the moon and look down at Earth, what would you see? You would notice that Earth's surface is made up of three basic components—water, land, and clouds (air). All three are part of a process called the water cycle, as shown in **Figure 7.** The **water cycle** is the continuous movement of water from the ocean to the atmosphere to the land and back to the ocean. The ocean is an important part of the water cycle because nearly all of Earth's water is in the ocean.

water cycle the continuous movement of water from the ocean to the atmosphere to the land and back to the ocean

Figure 7 **The Water Cycle**

Condensation As water vapor rises into the atmosphere, it cools and interacts with dust particles. Eventually, the water vapor turns to liquid water. This change from a gas to a liquid is called *condensation.*

Evaporation The sun heats liquid water, causing it to rise into the atmosphere as water vapor. This physical change from a liquid to a gas is called *evaporation.* Water evaporates directly from oceans, lakes, rivers, falling rain, plants, animals, and other sources.

Precipitation When water droplets become heavy enough, they fall back to Earth's surface as precipitation. *Precipitation* is solid or liquid water that falls to Earth. Most precipitation falls directly back into the ocean.

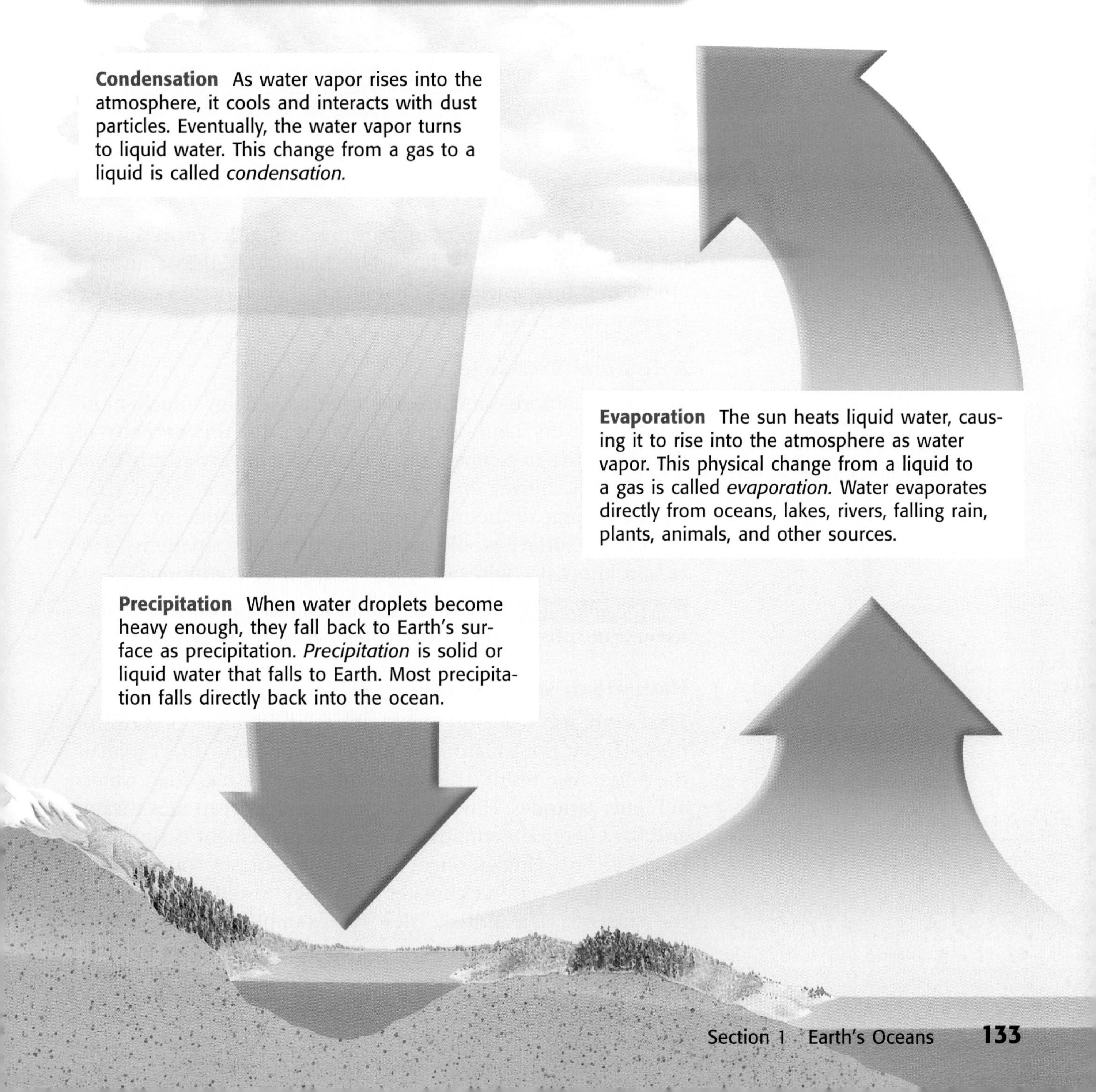

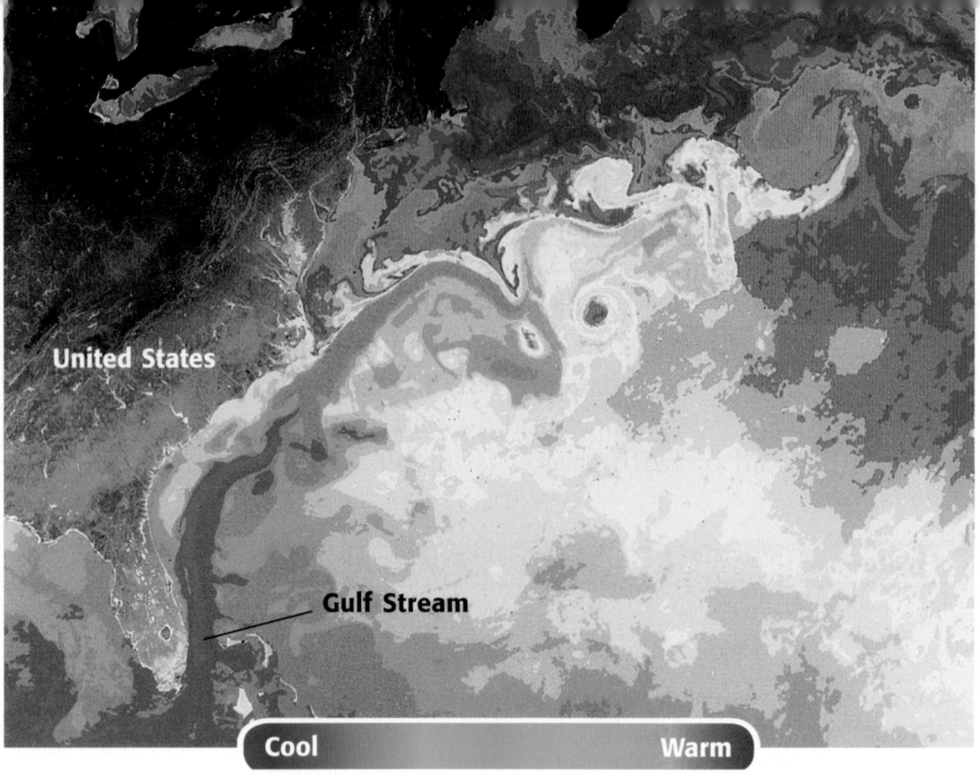

Figure 8 *This infrared satellite image shows the Gulf Stream moving warm water from lower latitudes to higher latitudes.*

A Global Thermostat

The ocean plays an important part in keeping the Earth suitable for life. Perhaps the most important function of the ocean is to absorb and hold energy from sunlight. This function regulates temperatures in the atmosphere.

A Thermal Exchange

The ocean absorbs and releases thermal energy much more slowly than dry land does. If it were not for this property of the ocean, the air temperature on Earth could vary greatly from above 100°C during the day to below –100°C at night. This rapid exchange of thermal energy between the atmosphere and the Earth's surface would cause violent weather patterns. Life as you know it could not exist under these conditions.

Reading Check **How would the air temperature on land be different if the ocean did not release thermal energy so slowly?**

Have Heat, Will Travel

The ocean also regulates temperatures at different locations of the Earth. At the equator, the sun's rays are more direct than at the poles. As a result, the waters there are warmer than waters at higher latitudes. However, currents in the ocean move water and the energy it contains. Part of this movement is shown in **Figure 8.** This circulation of warm water causes some coastal lands to have warmer climates than they would have without the currents. The British Isles, for example, have a warmer climate than most regions at the same latitude. This warmer climate is due to the warm water of the Gulf Stream.

SECTION

Review

Summary

- The global ocean is divided by the continents into four main oceans: Pacific Ocean, Atlantic Ocean, Indian Ocean, and Arctic Ocean.
- The four oceans as we know them today formed within the last 300 million years.
- Salts have been added to the ocean for billions of years. Salinity is a measure of the amount of dissolved salts in a given weight or mass of liquid.
- The three temperature zones of ocean water are the surface zone, the thermocline, and the deep zone.
- The water cycle is the continuous movement of water from the ocean to the atmosphere to the land and back to the ocean. The ocean plays the largest role in the water cycle.
- The ocean stabilizes Earth's weather conditions by absorbing and holding thermal energy.

Using Key Terms

1. In your own words, write a definition for each of the following terms: *salinity* and *water cycle*.

Understanding Key Ideas

2. The top layer of ocean water that extends to 300 m below sea level is called the
   a. deep zone.
   b. surface zone.
   c. Gulf Stream.
   d. thermocline.
3. Name the major divisions of the global ocean.
4. Explain how Earth's first oceans formed.
5. Why is the ocean an important part of the water cycle?
6. Between which two steps of the water cycle does the ocean fit?

Critical Thinking

7. **Making Inferences** Describe how the ocean plays a role in stabilizing Earth's weather conditions.
8. **Identifying Relationships** List one factor that affects salinity in the ocean and one factor that affects ocean temperatures. Explain how each factor affects salinity or temperature.

Interpreting Graphics

Use the image below to answer the questions that follow.

9. At which stage would solid or liquid water fall to the Earth?
10. At which stage would the sun's energy cause liquid to rise into the atmosphere as water vapor?

SCILINKS.
NSTA
Developed and maintained by the National Science Teachers Association
For a variety of links related to this chapter, go to www.scilinks.org
Topic: Exploring Earth's Oceans
SciLinks code: HSM0557

SECTION 2

Currents

Imagine that you are stranded on a desert island. You stuff a distress message into a bottle and throw it into the ocean. Is there any way to predict where your bottle may land?

READING WARM-UP

Objectives

- Describe surface currents.
- List the three factors that control surface currents.
- Describe deep currents.
- Identify the three factors that form deep currents.

Terms to Learn

ocean current
surface current
Coriolis effect
deep current

READING STRATEGY

Reading Organizer As you read this section, create an outline of the section. Use the headings from the section in your outline.

Actually, there is a way to predict where the bottle will end up. Ocean water contains streamlike movements of water called **ocean currents.** Currents are influenced by a number of factors, including weather, the Earth's rotation, and the position of the continents. With knowledge of ocean currents, people are able to predict where objects in the open ocean will be carried.

ocean current a movement of ocean water that follows a regular pattern

One Way to Explore Currents

In the 1940s, a Norwegian explorer named Thor Heyerdahl tried to answer questions about human migration across the ocean. Heyerdahl theorized that the inhabitants of Polynesia originally sailed from Peru on rafts powered only by the wind and ocean currents. In 1947, Heyerdahl and a crew of five people set sail from Peru on a raft, which is shown in **Figure 1.**

On the 97th day of their expedition, Heyerdahl and his crew landed on an island in Polynesia. Currents had carried the raft westward more than 6,000 km across the South Pacific. This landing supported Heyerdahl's theory that ocean currents carried the ancient Peruvians across the Pacific to Polynesia.

Reading Check **What was Heyerdahl's theory, and how did he prove it?** (*See the Appendix for answers to Reading Checks.*)

Figure 1 *The handcrafted Kon-Tiki was made mainly from materials that would have been available to ancient Peruvians.*

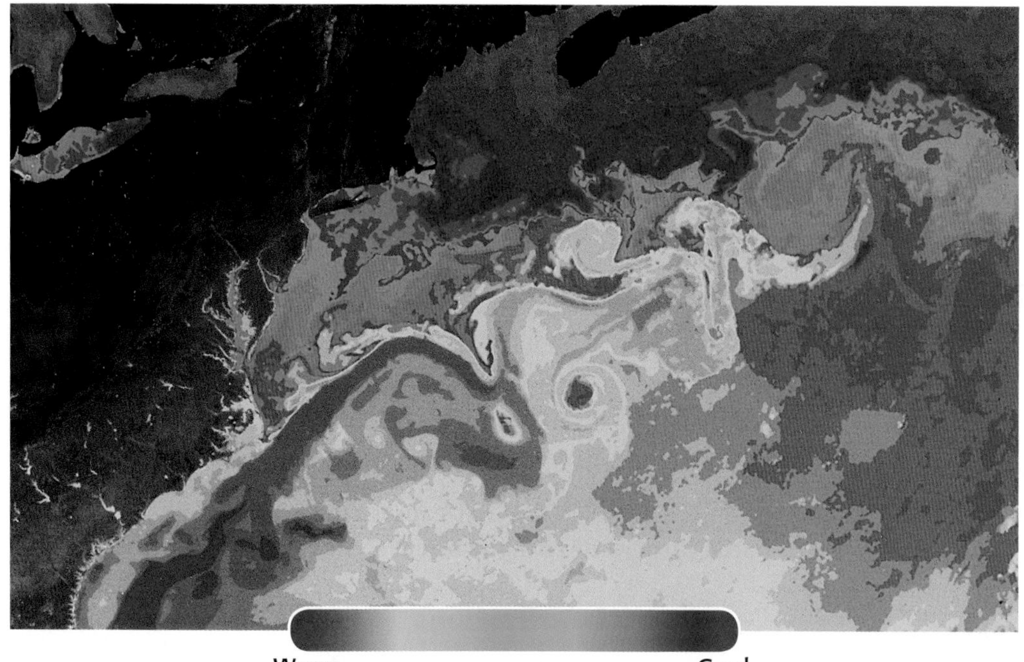

Figure 2 *This infrared satellite image shows the Gulf Stream current moving warm water from lower latitudes to higher latitudes.*

Surface Currents

Horizontal, streamlike movements of water that occur at or near the surface of the ocean are called **surface currents.** Surface currents can reach depths of several hundred meters and lengths of several thousand kilometers and can travel across oceans. The Gulf Stream, shown in **Figure 2,** is one of the longest surface currents—it transports 25 times more water than all the rivers in the world.

Surface currents are controlled by three factors: global winds, the Coriolis effect, and continental deflections. These three factors keep surface currents flowing in distinct patterns around the Earth.

surface current a horizontal movement of ocean water that is caused by wind and that occurs at or near the ocean's surface

Global Winds

Have you ever blown gently on a cup of hot chocolate? You may have noticed ripples moving across the surface, as in **Figure 3.** These ripples are caused by a tiny surface current created by your breath. In much the same way that you create ripples, winds that blow across the Earth's surface create surface currents in the ocean.

Different winds cause currents to flow in different directions. Near the equator, the winds blow ocean water east to west, but closer to the poles, ocean water is blown west to east. Merchant ships often use these currents to travel more quickly back and forth across the oceans.

Figure 3 *Winds form surface currents in the ocean, much like blowing on a cup of hot chocolate forms ripples.*

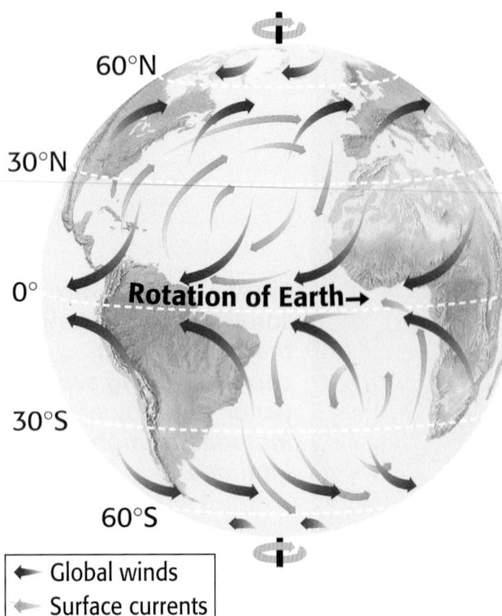

Figure 4 *The rotation of the Earth causes surface currents (yellow arrows) and global winds (purple arrows) to curve as they move across the Earth's surface.*

The Coriolis Effect

The Earth's rotation causes wind and surface currents to move in curved paths rather than in straight lines. The apparent curving of moving objects from a straight path due to the Earth's rotation is called the **Coriolis effect.** To understand the Coriolis effect, imagine trying to roll a ball straight across a turning merry-go-round. Because the merry-go-round is spinning, the path of the ball will curve before it reaches the other side. **Figure 4** shows how the Coriolis effect causes surface currents in the Northern Hemisphere to turn clockwise, and surface currents in the Southern Hemisphere to turn counterclockwise.

Reading Check **What causes currents to move in curved paths instead of straight lines?**

Coriolis effect the apparent curving of the path of a moving object from an otherwise straight path due to the Earth's rotation

Continental Deflections

If the Earth's surface were covered only with water, surface currents would travel freely across the globe in a very uniform pattern. However, you know that water does not cover the entire surface of the Earth. Continents rise above sea level over roughly one-third of the Earth's surface. When surface currents meet continents, the currents *deflect,* or change direction. Notice in **Figure 5** how the Brazil Current deflects southward as it meets the east coast of South America.

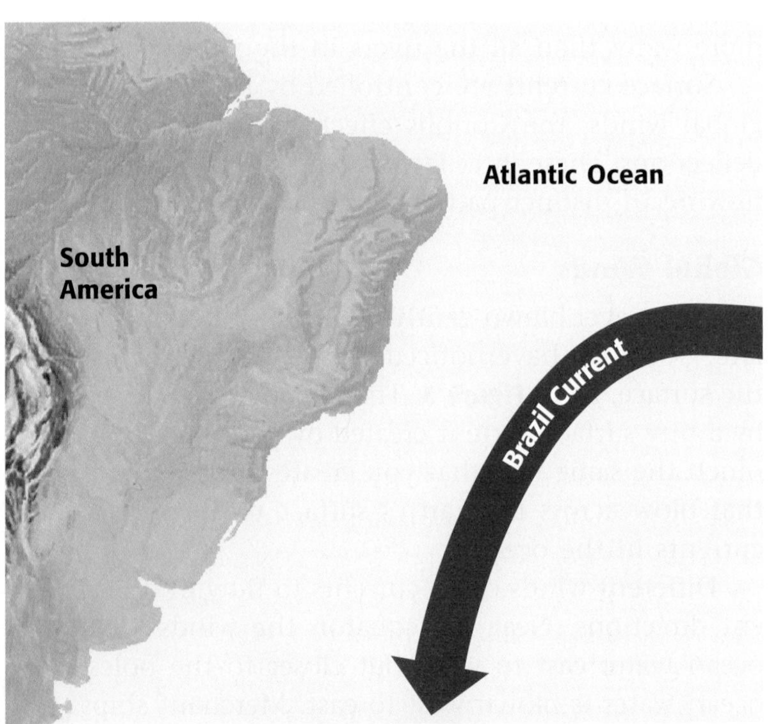

Figure 5 *If South America were not in the way, the Brazil Current would probably flow farther west.*

SCHOOL to HOME

Coriolis Effect in Your Sink?

WRITING SKILL Some people think the Coriolis effect can be seen in sinks. Does water draining from sinks turns clockwise in the Northern Hemisphere and counterclockwise in the Southern Hemisphere? Research this question at the library, on the Internet, and in your sink at home with a parent. Write what you learn in your **science journal.**

ACTIVITY

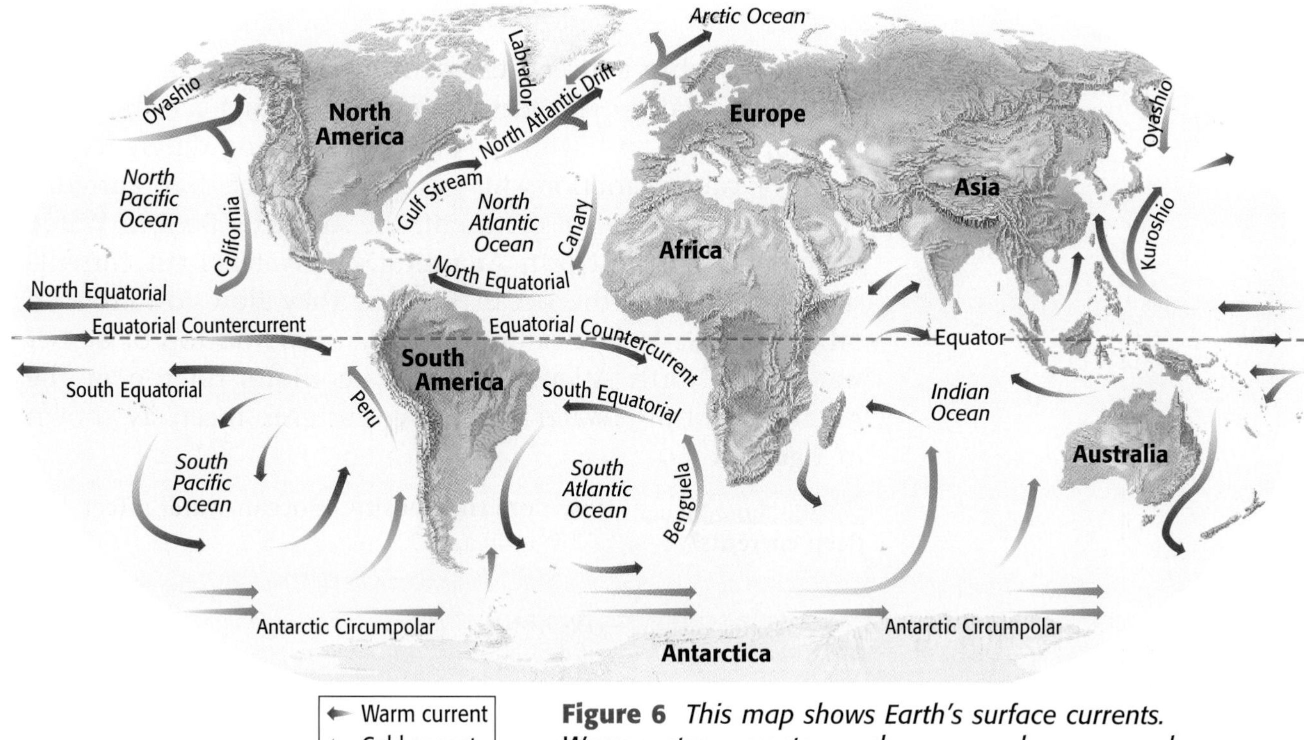

Figure 6 *This map shows Earth's surface currents. Warm-water currents are shown as red arrows, and cold-water currents are shown as blue arrows.*

Taking Temperatures

All three factors—global winds, the Coriolis effect, and continental deflections—work together to form a pattern of surface currents on Earth. But currents are also affected by the temperature of the water in which they form. Warm-water currents begin near the equator and carry warm water to other parts of the ocean. Cold-water currents begin closer to the poles and carry cool water to other parts of the ocean. As you can see on the map in **Figure 6,** all the oceans are connected and both warm-water and cold-water currents travel from one ocean to another.

Reading Check **What three factors form a pattern of surface currents on Earth?**

deep current a streamlike movement of ocean water far below the surface

Deep Currents

Streamlike movements of ocean water located far below the surface are called **deep currents.** Unlike surface currents, deep currents are not directly controlled by wind. Instead, deep currents form in parts of the ocean where water density increases. *Density* is the amount of matter in a given space, or volume. The density of ocean water is affected by temperature and *salinity*—a measure of the amount of dissolved salts or solids in a liquid. Both decreasing the temperature of ocean water and increasing the water's salinity increase the water's density.

CONNECTION TO Physics

Convection Currents While winds are often responsible for ocean currents, the sun is the initial energy source of the winds and currents. Because the sun heats the Earth more in some places than in others, convection currents are formed. These currents transfer thermal energy. Which ocean currents do you think carry more thermal energy, currents located near the equator or currents located near the poles?

Formation and Movement of Deep Currents

The relationship between the density of ocean water and the formation of deep currents is shown in **Figure 7.** Differences in temperature and salinity—and the resulting differences in density—cause variations in the movement of deep currents. For example, the deepest current, the Antarctic Bottom Water, is denser than the North Atlantic Deep Water. Both currents spread out across the ocean floor as they flow toward each other. Because less-dense water always flows on top of denser water, the North Atlantic Deep Water flows on top of the Antarctic Bottom Water when the currents meet, as shown in **Figure 8.**

Reading Check **How does the density of ocean water affect deep currents?**

Figure 7 How Deep Currents Form

Decreasing Temperature In Earth's polar regions, cold air chills the water molecules at the ocean's surface, which causes the molecules to slow down and move closer together. This reaction causes the water's volume to decrease. Thus, the water becomes denser. The dense water sinks and eventually travels toward the equator as a deep current along the ocean floor.

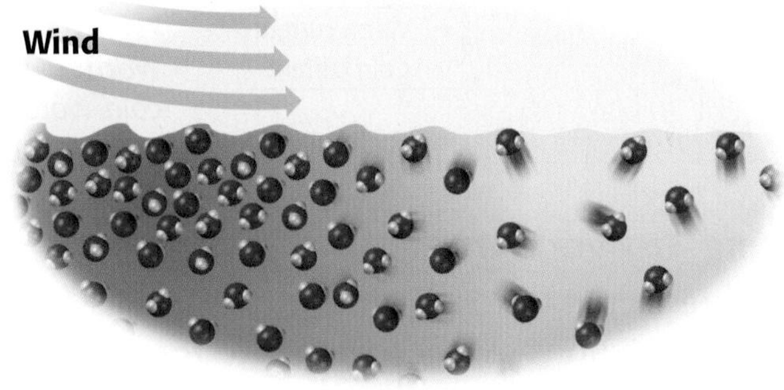

Increasing Salinity Through Freezing If the ocean water freezes at the surface, ice will float on top of the water because ice is less dense than liquid water. The dissolved solids are squeezed out of the ice and enter the liquid water below the ice. This process increases the salinity of the water. As a result of the increased salinity, the water's density increases.

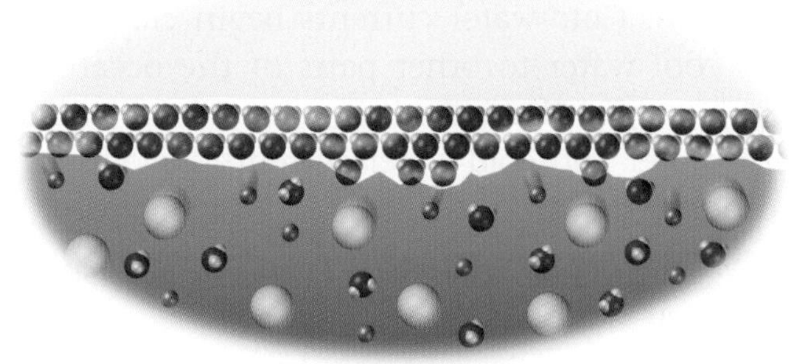

Increasing Salinity Through Evaporation Another way salinity increases is through evaporation of surface water, which removes water but leaves solids behind. This process is especially common in warm climates. Increasing salinity through freezing or evaporation causes water to become denser, to sink to the ocean floor, and to form a deep current.

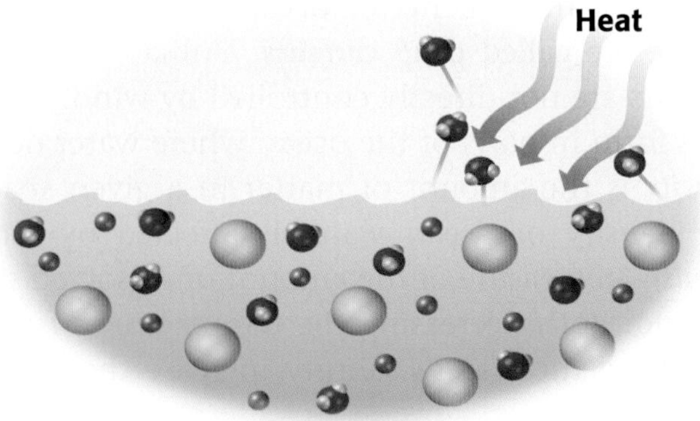

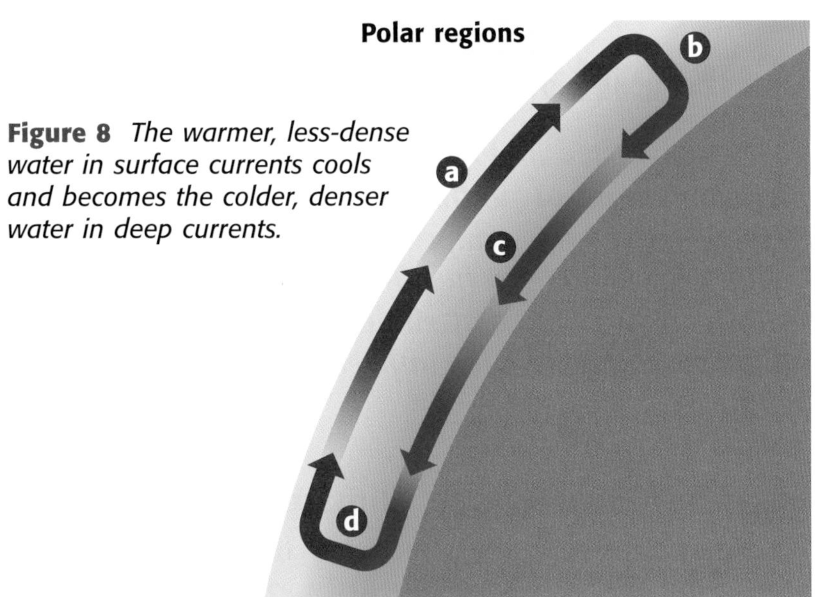
Polar regions
a
b
c
d

Figure 8 *The warmer, less-dense water in surface currents cools and becomes the colder, denser water in deep currents.*

a Surface currents carry the warmer, less-dense water from other ocean regions to polar regions.

b Warm water from surface currents replaces colder, denser water that sinks to the ocean floor.

c Deep currents carry colder, denser water along the ocean floor from polar regions to other ocean regions.

d Water from deep currents rises to replace water leaving surface currents.

SECTION Review

Summary

- Surface currents are streamlike movements of water at or near the surface of the ocean.
- Surface currents are controlled by three factors: global winds, the Coriolis effect, and continental deflections.
- Deep currents are streamlike movements of ocean water located far below the surface.
- Deep currents form where the density of ocean water increases. Water density depends on temperature and salinity.

Using Key Terms

The statements below are false. For each statement, replace the underlined word to make a true statement.

1. <u>Deep currents</u> are directly controlled by wind.
2. An increase in density in parts of the ocean can cause <u>surface currents</u> to form.

Understanding Key Ideas

3. Surface currents
   a. are formed by wind.
   b. are streamlike movements of water.
   c. can travel across entire oceans.
   d. All of the above
4. List three factors that control surface currents.
5. How does a continent affect the movement of a surface current?
6. Explain how temperature and salinity affect the formation of deep currents.

Math Skills

7. The Gulf Stream flows along the North Carolina coast at 90 million cubic meters per second and at 40 million cubic meters per second when it turns eastward. How much faster is the Gulf Stream flowing along the coast than when it turns eastward?

Critical Thinking

8. **Evaluating Conclusions** If there were no land on Earth's surface, what would the pattern of surface currents look like? Explain your answer.
9. **Making Comparisons** Compare the factors that contribute to the formation of surface currents and deep currents.

SCILINKS®
NSTA
Developed and maintained by the National Science Teachers Association
For a variety of links related to this chapter, go to www.scilinks.org
Topic: Ocean Currents
SciLinks code: HSM1061

SECTION 3

Currents and Climate

The Scilly Isles in England are located as far north as Newfoundland in northeast Canada. But the Scilly Isles experience warm temperatures almost all year long, while Newfoundland has long winters of frost and snow. How can two places at similar latitudes have completely different climates? This difference in climate is caused by surface currents.

READING WARM-UP

Objectives

- Explain how currents affect climate.
- Describe the effects of El Niño.
- Explain how scientists study and predict the pattern of El Niño.

Terms to Learn

upwelling
El Niño
La Niña

READING STRATEGY

Paired Summarizing Read this section silently. In pairs, take turns summarizing the material. Stop to discuss ideas that seem confusing.

Surface Currents and Climate

Surface currents greatly affect the climate in many parts of the world. Some surface currents warm or cool coastal areas year-round. Other surface currents sometimes change their circulation pattern. Changes in circulation patterns cause changes in atmosphere that affect the climate in many parts of the world.

Warm-Water Currents and Climate

Although surface currents are generally much warmer than deep currents, the temperatures of surface currents do vary. Surface currents are classified as warm-water currents or cold-water currents. Warm-water currents create warmer climates in coastal areas that would otherwise be much cooler. **Figure 1** shows how the Gulf Stream carries warm water from the Tropics to the North Atlantic Ocean. The Gulf Stream flows to the British Isles and creates a relatively mild climate for land at such high latitude. The Gulf Stream is the same current that makes the climate of the Scilly Isles very different from the climate of Newfoundland.

Figure 1 How Warm-Water Currents Affect Climate

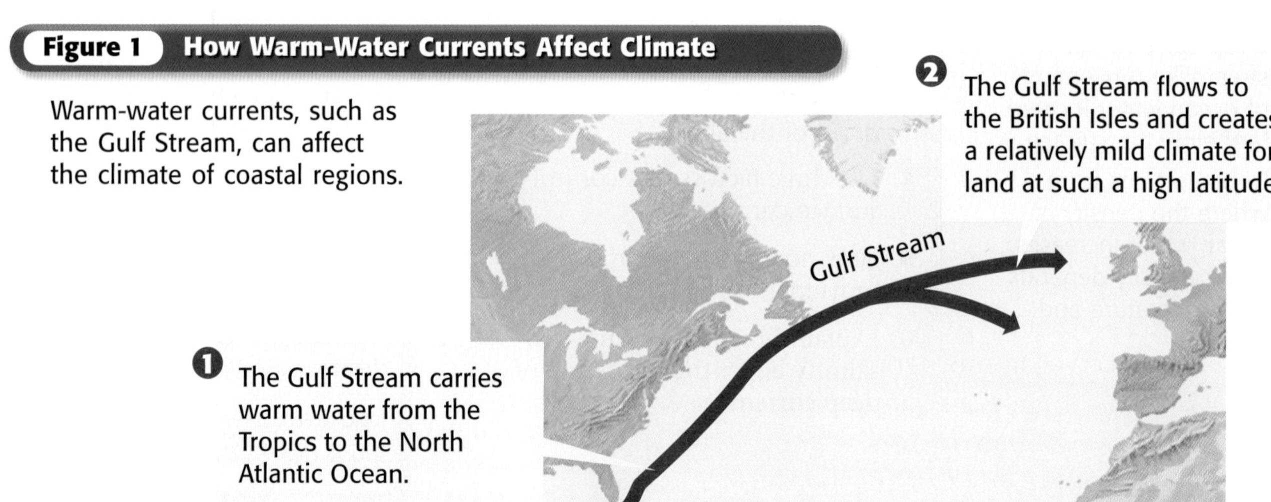
Gulf Stream
1 The Gulf Stream carries warm water from the Tropics to the North Atlantic Ocean.
2 The Gulf Stream flows to the British Isles and creates a relatively mild climate for land at such a high latitude.

Warm-water currents, such as the Gulf Stream, can affect the climate of coastal regions.

Figure 2 How Cold-Water Currents Affect Climate

Cold-water currents, such as the California Current, can affect the climate of coastal regions.

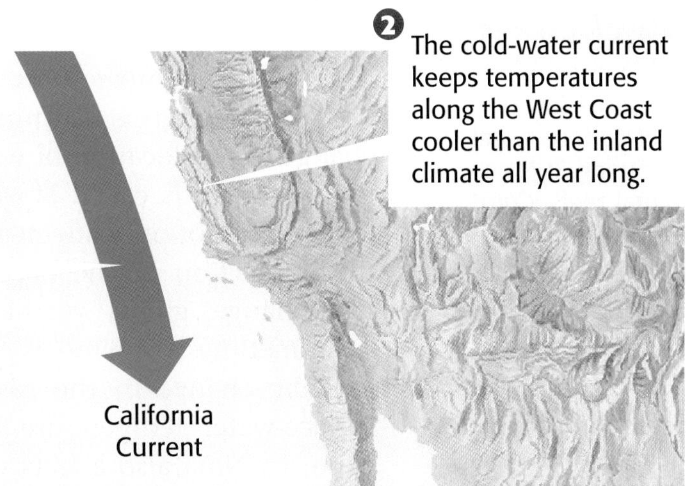

1 Cold water from the northern Pacific Ocean is carried south to Mexico by the California Current.
2 The cold-water current keeps temperatures along the West Coast cooler than the inland climate all year long.
California Current

Cold-Water Currents and Climate

Cold-water currents also affect the climate of the land near where they flow. **Figure 2** shows how the California Current carries cold water from the North Pacific Ocean southward to Mexico. The cold-water California Current keeps the climate along the West Coast cooler than the inland climate year-round.

upwelling the movement of deep, cold, and nutrient-rich water to the surface

Reading Check How do cold-water currents affect coastal regions?

Upwelling

When local wind patterns blow along the northwest coast of South America, they cause local surface currents to move away from the shore. This warm water is then replaced by deep, cold water. This movement causes upwelling to occur in the eastern Pacific. **Upwelling** is a process in which cold, nutrient-rich water from the deep ocean rises to the surface and replaces warm surface water, as shown in **Figure 3.** The nutrients from the deep ocean are made up of elements and chemicals, such as iron and nitrate. When these chemicals are brought to the sunny surface, they help tiny plants grow through the process of photosynthesis.

The process of upwelling is extremely important to organisms. The nutrients that are brought to the surface of the ocean support the growth of phytoplankton and zooplankton. These tiny plants and animals support other organisms such as fish and seabirds.

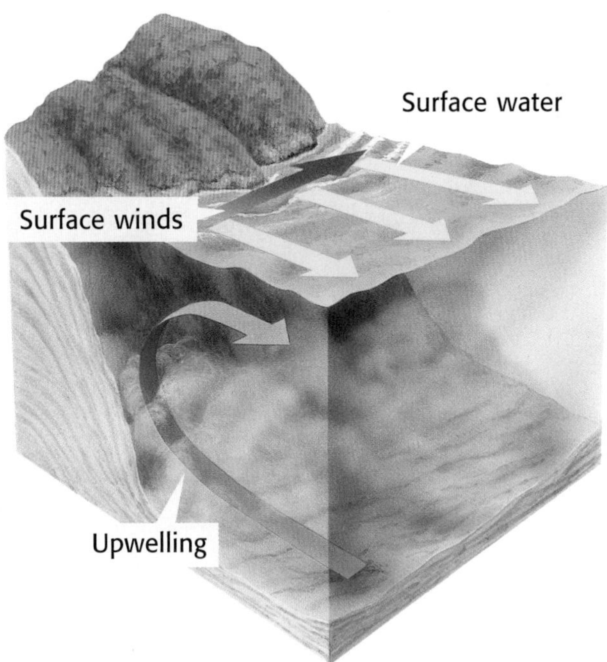

Surface water
Surface winds
Upwelling

Figure 3 *Upwelling causes cold, nutrient-rich water from the deep ocean to rise to the surface.*

El Niño

CONNECTION TO Environmental Science

El Niño and Coral Reefs
The increase of surface water temperatures during El Niño can destroy coral reefs. *Coral reefs* are fragile limestone ridges built by tiny coral animals. An increase in surface water temperature and exposure to the sun (due to a decrease in sea level) can cause corals to become bleached and die. Coral reefs support a diverse community of marine life. Create a world map that shows the locations of the coral reefs.

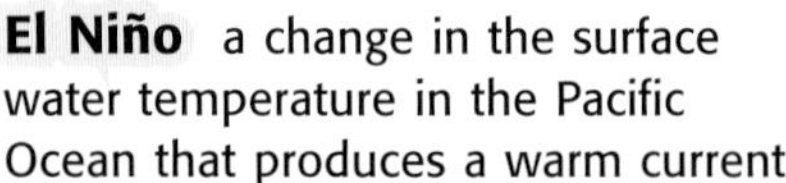

El Niño a change in the surface water temperature in the Pacific Ocean that produces a warm current

La Niña a change in the eastern Pacific Ocean in which the surface water temperature becomes unusually cool

Every 2 to 12 years, the South Pacific trade winds move less warm water to the western Pacific than they usually do. Thus, surface-water temperatures along the coast of South America rise. Gradually, this warming spreads westward. This periodic change in the location of warm and cool surface waters in the Pacific Ocean is called **El Niño.** El Niño can last for a year or longer and not only affects the surface waters but also changes the interaction of the ocean and the atmosphere, which in turn changes global weather patterns.

Sometimes, El Niño is followed by La Niña. **La Niña** is a periodic change in the eastern Pacific Ocean in which the surface-water temperature becomes unusually cool. Like El Niño, La Niña also affects weather patterns.

Effects of El Niño

El Niño alters weather patterns enough to cause disasters. These disasters include flash floods and mudslides in areas of the world that usually receive little rain, such as the southern half of the United States and Peru. **Figure 4** shows homes in Southern California destroyed by a mudslide caused by El Niño. While some regions flood, regions that usually get a lot of rain may experience *droughts,* an unusually long period during which rainfall is below average. During El Niño, severe droughts can occur in Indonesia and Australia. Periods of severe drought can lead to crop failure.

During El Niño, the upwelling of nutrient-rich water does not occur off the coast of South America, which affects the organisms that depend on the nutrients for food.

Figure 4 *This damage in Southern California was the result of excessive rain caused by El Niño in 1997.*

Studying and Predicting El Niño

Because El Niño occurs every 2 to 12 years, studying and predicting it can be difficult. However, it is important for scientists to learn as much as possible about El Niño because of its effects on organisms and land.

One way scientists collect data to predict an El Niño is through a network of buoys operated by the National Oceanic and Atmospheric Administration (NOAA). The buoys, some of which are anchored to the ocean floor, are located along the Earth's equator. The buoys record data about surface temperature, air temperature, currents, and winds. The buoys transmit some of the data on a daily basis to NOAA through a satellite in space.

When the buoys report that the South Pacific trade winds are not as strong as they usually are or that the surface temperatures of the tropical oceans have risen, scientists can predict that an El Niño is likely to occur.

Reading Check **Why is it important to study El Niño? Describe one way scientists study El Niño.**

For another activity related to this chapter, go to **go.hrw.com** and type in the keyword **HZ5H20W.**

SECTION Review

Summary

- Surface currents affect the climate of the land near which they flow.
- Warm-water currents bring warmer climates to coastal regions.
- Cold-water currents bring cooler climates to coastal regions.
- During El Niño, warm and cool surface waters change locations.
- El Niño can cause floods, mudslides, and drought.

Using Key Terms

1. Use each of the following terms in a separate sentence: *upwelling, El Niño,* and *La Niña.*

Understanding Key Ideas

2. The Gulf Stream carries warm water to the North Atlantic Ocean, which contributes to
- **a.** a harsh winter in the British Isles.
- **b.** a cold-water surface current that flows to the British Isles.
- **c.** a mild climate for the British Isles.
- **d.** a warm-water surface current that flows along the coast of California.

3. Why might the climate in Scotland be relatively mild even though the country is located at a high latitude?

4. Name two disasters caused by El Niño.

Math Skills

5. A fisher usually catches 540 kg of anchovies off the coast of Peru. During El Niño, the fisher caught 85% less fish. How many kilograms of fish did the fisher catch during El Niño?

Critical Thinking

6. Applying Concepts Many marine organisms depend on upwelling to bring nutrients to the surface. How might El Niño affect a fisher's way of life?

For a variety of links related to this chapter, go to www.scilinks.org

Topic: El Niño
SciLinks code: HSM0468

SECTION 4

Waves

Have you ever seen a surfer riding waves? Did you ever wonder where the waves come from? And why are some waves big, while others are small?

READING WARM-UP

Objectives

- Identify the parts of a wave.
- Explain how the parts of a wave relate to wave movement.
- Describe how ocean waves form and move.
- Classify types of waves.

Terms to Learn

undertow
longshore current
whitecap
swell
tsunami
storm surge

READING STRATEGY

Prediction Guide Before reading this section, write the title of each heading in this section. Next, write what you think you will learn under each heading.

We all know what ocean waves look like. Even if you've never been to the seashore, you've most likely seen waves on TV. But how do waves form and move? Waves are affected by a number of different factors. They can be formed by something as simple as wind or by something as violent as an earthquake. Ocean waves can travel through water slowly or incredibly quickly. Read on to discover the many forces that affect the formation and movement of ocean waves.

Anatomy of a Wave

Waves are made up of two main parts—crests and troughs. A *crest* is the highest point of a wave. A *trough* is the lowest point of a wave. Imagine a roller coaster designed with many rises and dips. The top of a rise on a roller-coaster track is similar to the crest of a wave, and the bottom of a dip in the track resembles the trough of a wave. The distance between two adjacent wave crests or wave troughs is a *wavelength*. The vertical distance between the crest and trough of a wave is called the *wave height*. **Figure 1** shows the parts of a wave.

✓ Reading Check **What is the lowest point of a wave called?** (*See the Appendix for answers to Reading Checks.*)

Figure 1 Parts of a Wave

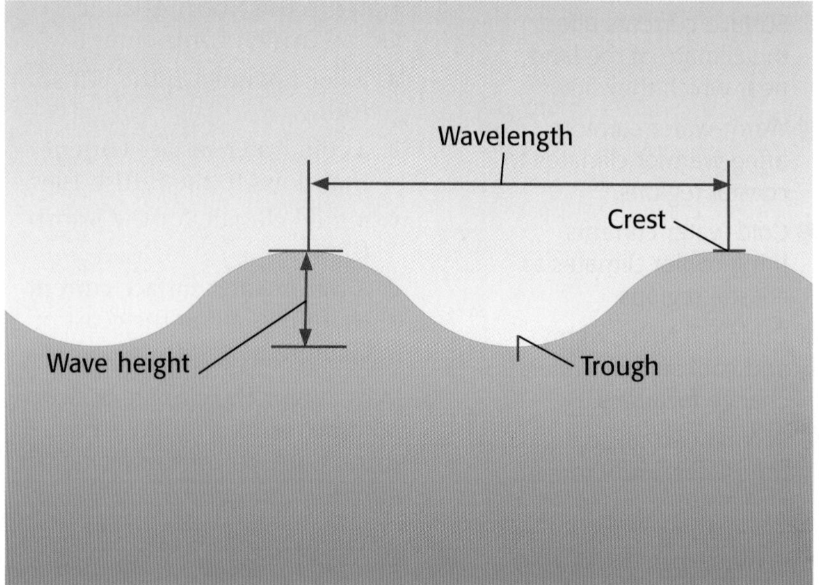

Wave Formation and Movement

If you have watched ocean waves before, you may have noticed that water appears to move across the ocean's surface. However, this movement is only an illusion. Most waves form as wind blows across the water's surface and transfers energy to the water. As the energy moves through the water, so do the waves. But the water itself stays behind, rising and falling in circular movements. Notice in **Figure 2** that the floating bottle remains in the same spot as the waves travel from left to right. This circular motion gets smaller as the water depth increases, because wave energy decreases as the water depth increases. Wave energy reaches only a certain depth. Below that depth, the water is not affected by wave energy.

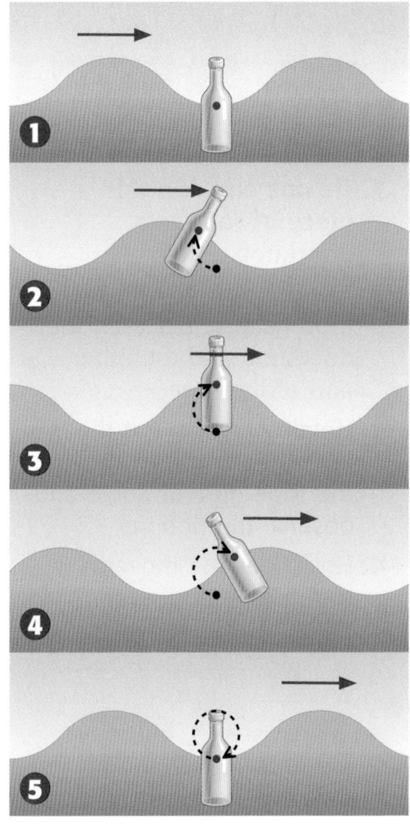

Figure 2 *Like the bottle in this figure, water remains in the same place as waves travel through it.*

Specifics of Wave Movement

Waves not only come in different sizes but also travel at different speeds. To calculate wave speed, scientists must know the wavelength and the wave period. *Wave period* is the time between the passage of two wave crests (or troughs) at a fixed point, as shown in **Figure 3.** Dividing wavelength by wave period gives you wave speed, as shown below.

$$\frac{\text{wavelength (m)}}{\text{wave period (s)}} = \text{wave speed (m/s)}$$

For any given wavelength, an increase in the wave period will decrease the wave speed and a decrease in the wave period will increase the wave speed.

Figure 3 Determining Wave Period

Direction of wave movement

Wave A

1 Notice that the waves are moving from left to right.

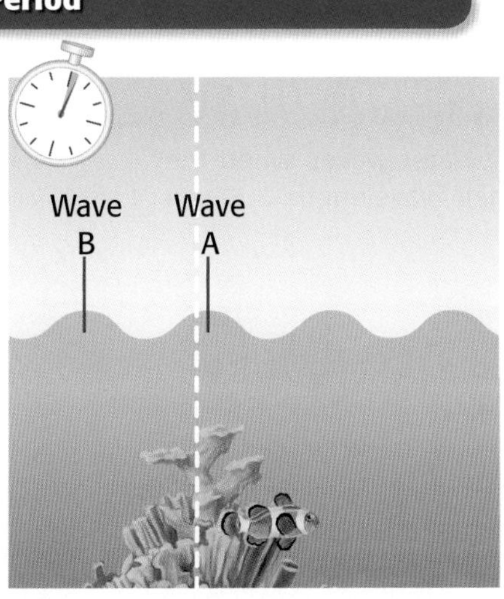

2 The clock begins running as Wave A passes the reef's peak.

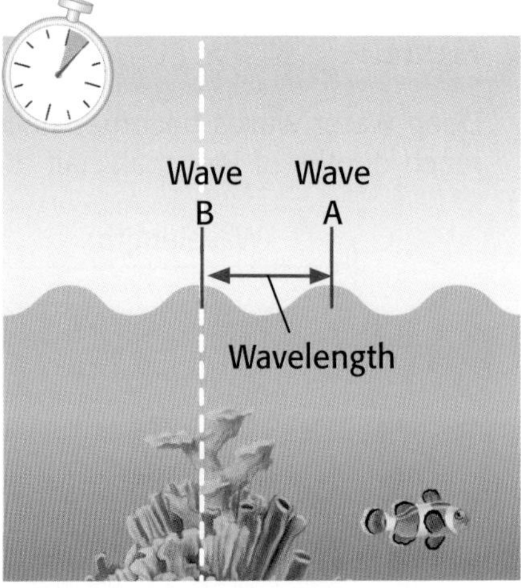

3 The clock stops as Wave B passes the reef's peak. The time shown on the clock (5 s) represents the wave period.

Doing the Wave

1. Tie one end of a **thin piece of rope** to a **doorknob**.
2. Tie a **ribbon** around the rope halfway between the doorknob and the other end of the rope.
3. Holding the rope at the untied end, quickly move the rope up and down and observe the ribbon.
4. How does the movement of the rope and ribbon relate to the movement of water and deep-water waves?
5. Repeat step 3, but move the rope higher and lower this time.
6. How does this affect the waves in the rope?

Types of Waves

As you learned earlier in this section, wind forms most ocean waves. Waves can also form by other mechanisms. Underwater earthquakes and landslides as well as impacts by cosmic bodies can form different types of waves. Most waves move in one way regardless of how they are formed. Depending on their size and the angle at which they hit the shore, waves can generate a variety of near-shore events, some of which can be dangerous to humans.

Deep-Water Waves and Shallow-Water Waves

Have you ever wondered why waves increase in height as they approach the shore? The answer has to do with the depth of the water. *Deep-water waves* are waves that move in water deeper than one-half their wavelength. When the waves reach water shallower than one-half their wavelength, they begin to interact with the ocean floor. These waves are called *shallow-water waves.* **Figure 4** shows how deep-water waves become shallow-water waves as they move toward the shore.

As deep-water waves become shallow-water waves, the water particles slow down and build up. This change forces more water between wave crests and increases wave height. Gravity eventually pulls the high wave crests down, which causes them to crash into the ocean floor as *breakers*. The area where waves first begin to tumble downward, or break, is called the *breaker zone.* Waves continue to break as they move from the breaker zone to the shore. The area between the breaker zone and the shore is called the *surf.*

Reading Check **How do deep-water waves become shallow-water waves?**

Figure 4 **Deep-Water and Shallow-Water Waves**

Deep-water waves become shallow-water waves when they reach depths of less than half of their wavelength.

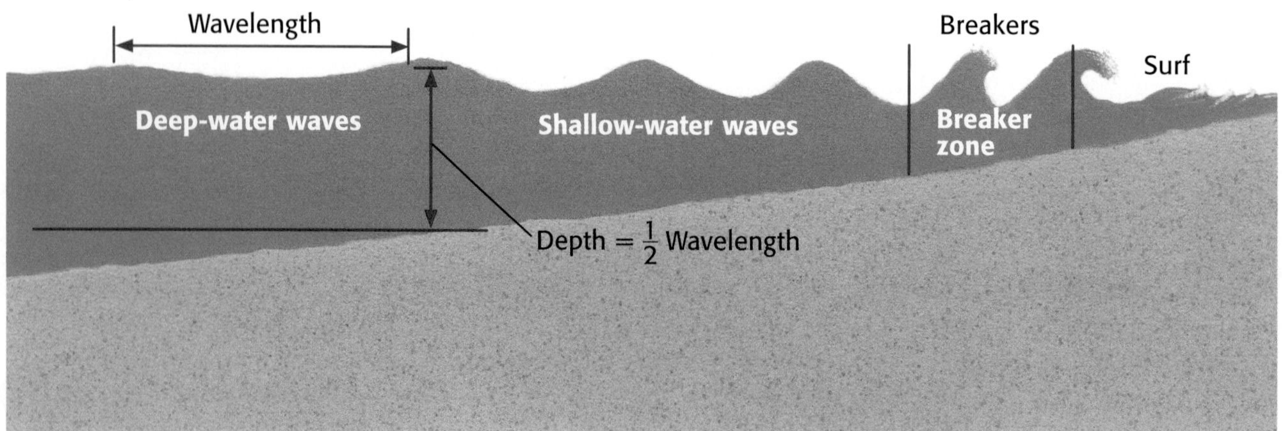

Figure 5 **Formation of an Undertow**

Head-on waves create an undertow.

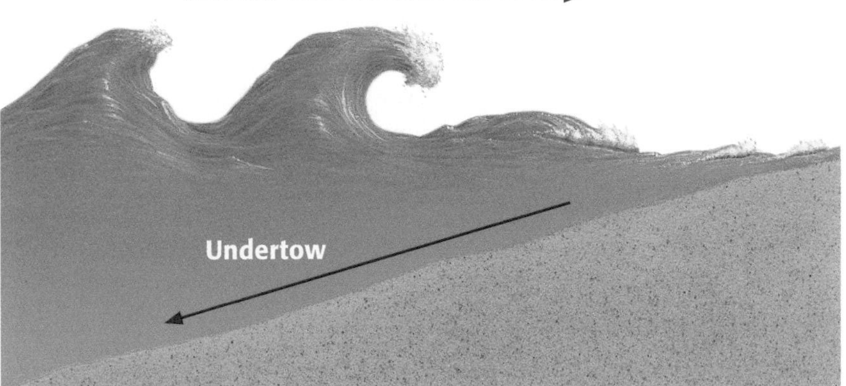

Shore Currents

When waves crash on the beach head-on, the water they moved through flows back to the ocean underneath new incoming waves. This movement of water, which carries sand, rock particles, and plankton away from the shore, is called an **undertow. Figure 5** illustrates the back-and-forth movement of water at the shore.

undertow a subsurface current that is near shore and that pulls objects out to sea

longshore current a water current that travels near and parallel to the shoreline

Longshore Currents

When waves hit the shore at an angle, they cause water to move along the shore in a current called a **longshore current,** which is shown in **Figure 6.** Longshore currents transport most of the sediment in beach environments. This movement of sand and other sediment both tears down and builds up the coastline. Unfortunately, longshore currents also carry and spread trash and other types of ocean pollution along the shore.

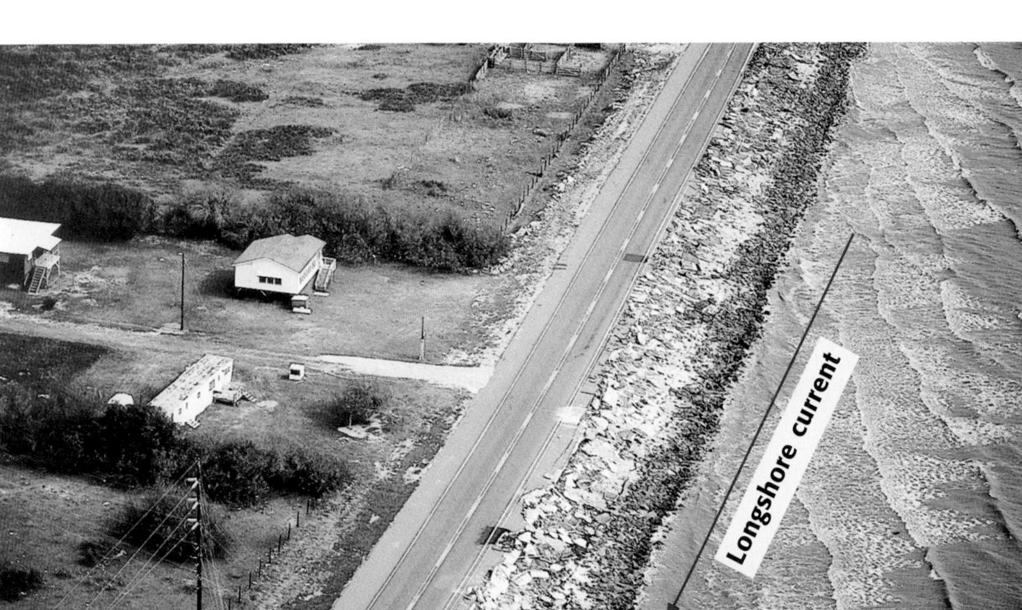

Figure 6 *Longshore currents form where waves approach beaches at an angle.*

Figure 7 *Whitecaps (left) break in the open ocean, while swells, (right), roll gently in the open ocean.*

Open-Ocean Waves

Sometimes waves called *whitecaps* form in the open ocean. **Whitecaps** are white, foaming waves with very steep crests that break in the open ocean before the waves get close to the shore. These waves usually form during stormy weather, and they are usually short-lived. Winds that are far away from the shore form waves called *swells*. **Swells** are rolling waves that move steadily across the ocean. Swells have longer wavelengths than whitecaps and can travel for thousands of kilometers. **Figure 7** shows how whitecaps and swells differ.

whitecap the bubbles in the crest of a breaking wave

swell one of a group of long ocean waves that have steadily traveled a great distance from their point of generation

tsunami a giant ocean wave that forms after a volcanic eruption, submarine earthquake, or landslide

Tsunamis

Professional surfers often travel to Hawaii to catch some of the highest waves in the world. But even the best surfers would not be able to handle a tsunami. **Tsunamis** are waves that form when a large volume of ocean water is suddenly moved up or down. This movement can be caused by underwater earthquakes, volcanic eruptions, landslides, underwater explosions, or the impact of a meteorite or comet. The majority of tsunamis occur in the Pacific Ocean because of the large number of earthquakes in that region. **Figure 8** shows how an earthquake can generate a tsunami.

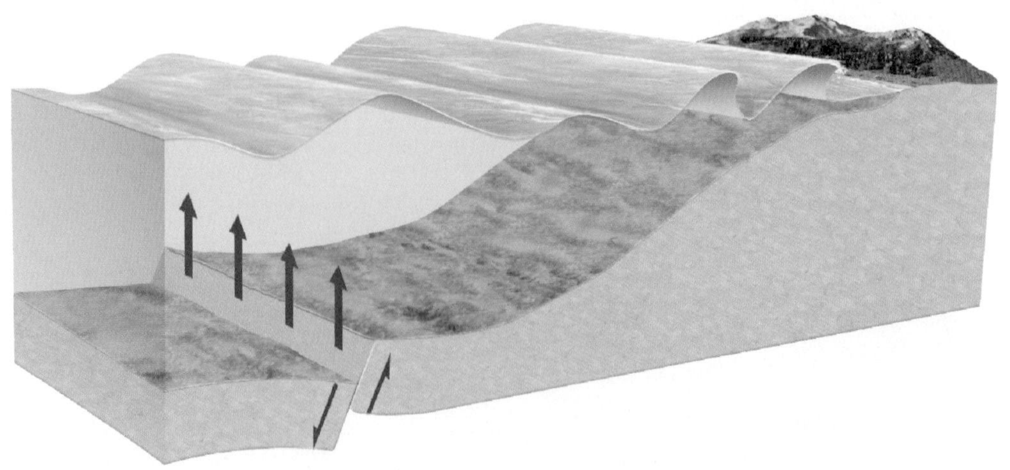

Figure 8 *An upward shift in the ocean floor creates an earthquake. The energy released by the earthquake pushes a large volume of water upward, which creates a series of tsunamis.*

Storm Surges

A local rise in sea level near the shore that is caused by strong winds from a storm, such as a hurricane, is called a **storm surge.** Winds form a storm surge by blowing water into a big pile under the storm. As the storm moves onto shore, so does the giant mass of water beneath it. Storm surges often disappear as quickly as they form, which makes them difficult to study. Storm surges contain a lot of energy and can reach about 8 m in height. Their size and power often make them the most destructive part of hurricanes.

storm surge a local rise in sea level near the shore that is caused by strong winds from a storm, such as those from a hurricane

Reading Check **What is a storm surge? Why are storm surges difficult to study?**

SECTION Review

Summary

- Waves are made up of two main parts—crests and troughs.
- Waves are usually created by the transfer of the wind's energy across the surface of the ocean.
- Waves travel through water near the water's surface, while the water itself rises and falls in circular movements.
- Wind-generated waves are classified as deep-water or shallow-water waves.
- When waves hit the shore at a certain angle, they can create either an undertow or a longshore current.
- Tsunamis are dangerous waves that can be very destructive to coastal communities.

Using Key Terms

For each pair of terms, explain how the meanings of the terms differ.

1. *whitecap* and *swell*
2. *undertow* and *longshore current*
3. *tsunami* and *storm surge*

Understanding Key Ideas

4. Longshore currents transport sediment
   a. to the open ocean.
   b. along the shore.
   c. only during low tide.
   d. only during high tide.
5. Where do deep-water waves become shallow-water waves?
6. Explain how water moves as waves travel through it.
7. Name five events that can cause a tsunami.
8. Describe the two parts of a wave.

Math Skills

9. If a barrier island that is 1 km wide and 10 km long loses 1.5 m of its width per year to erosion by a longshore current, how long will the island take to lose one-fourth of its width?

Critical Thinking

10. **Analyzing Processes** How would you explain a bottle moving across the water in the same direction that the waves are traveling? Make a drawing of the bottle's movement.
11. **Analyzing Processes** Describe the motion of a wave as it approaches the shore.
12. **Applying Concepts** Explain how energy plays a role in the creation of ocean waves.
13. **Making Comparisons** How does the formation of an undertow differ from the formation of a longshore current? How is sand on the beach affected by each?

SCILINKS.
NSTA
Developed and maintained by the National Science Teachers Association
For a variety of links related to this chapter, go to www.scilinks.org
Topic: Ocean Waves
SciLinks code: HSM1066

SECTION 5

Tides

If you stand at some ocean shores long enough, you will see the edge of the ocean shrink away from you. Wait longer, and you will see it return to its original place on the shore. Would you believe the moon causes this movement?

READING WARM-UP

Objectives

- Explain tides and their relationship with the Earth, sun, and moon.
- Describe four different types of tides.
- Analyze the relationship between tides and coastal land.

Terms to Learn

tide
tidal range
spring tide
neap tide

READING STRATEGY

Discussion Read this section silently. Write down questions that you have about this section. Discuss your questions in a small group.

You have learned how winds and earthquakes can move ocean water. But less obvious forces move ocean water in regular patterns called tides. **Tides** are daily changes in the level of ocean water. Tides are influenced by the sun and the moon, as shown in **Figure 1,** and they occur in a variety of cycles.

tide the periodic rise and fall of the water level in the oceans and other large bodies of water

The Lure of the Moon

The phases of the moon and their relationship to the tides were first discovered more than 2,000 years ago by a Greek explorer named *Pytheas*. But Pytheas and other early investigators could not explain the relationship. A scientific explanation was not given until 1687, when Sir Isaac Newton's theories on the principle of gravitation were published.

The gravity of the moon pulls on every particle of the Earth. But the pull on liquids is much more noticeable than on solids, because liquids move more easily. Even the liquid in an open soft drink is slightly pulled by the moon's gravity.

Reading Check How does the moon affect Earth's particles? (*See the Appendix for answers to Reading Checks.*)

High Tide and Low Tide

How often tides occur and the difference in tidal levels depend on the position of the moon as it revolves around the Earth. The moon's pull is strongest on the part of the Earth directly facing the moon.

Figure 1 *Although gravitational forces from both the sun and moon continuously pull on the Earth, the moon's gravity is the dominant force on Earth's tides.*

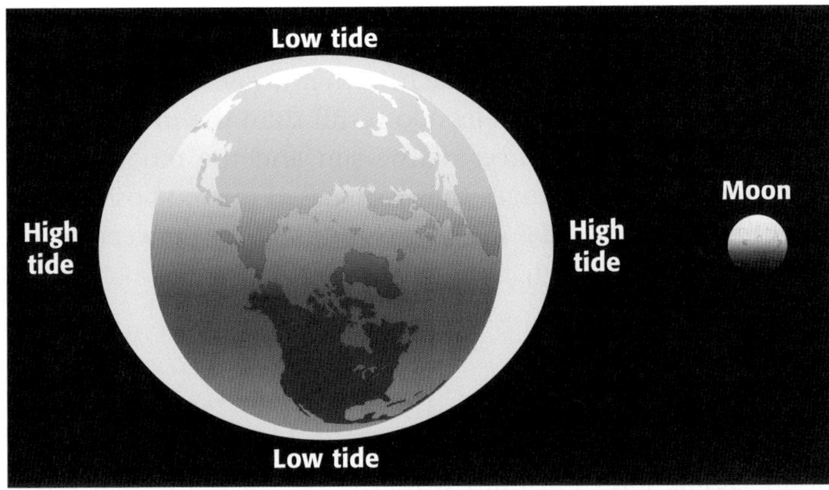

Figure 2 *High tide occurs on the part of Earth that is closest to the moon. At the same time, high tide also occurs on the opposite side of Earth.*

Battle of the Bulge

When part of the ocean is directly facing the moon, the water there bulges toward the moon. At the same time, water on the opposite side of the Earth bulges because of the rotation of the Earth and the motion of the moon around the Earth. These bulges are called *high tides*. Notice in **Figure 2** how the position of the moon causes the water to bulge. Also notice that when high tides occur, water is drawn away from the area between the high tides, which causes *low tides* to form.

CONNECTION TO Language Arts

WRITING SKILL **Mont-St-Michel Is Sometimes an Island?** Mont-St-Michel is located off the coast of France. Mont-St-Michel experiences extreme tides. The tides are so extreme that during high tide, it is an island and during low tide, it is connected to the mainland. Research the history behind Mont-St-Michel and then write a short story describing what it would be like to live there for a day. Be sure to include a description of Mont-St-Michel at high tide and at low tide.

Timing the Tides

The rotation of the Earth and the moon's revolution around the Earth determine when tides occur. If the Earth rotated at the same speed that the moon revolves around the Earth, the tides would not alternate between high and low. But the moon revolves around the Earth much more slowly than the Earth rotates. As **Figure 3** shows, a spot on Earth that is facing the moon takes 24 h and 50 m to rotate and face the moon again.

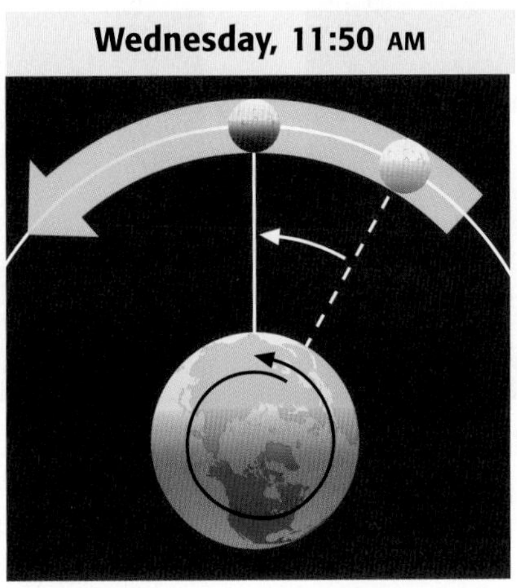

Figure 3 *Tides occur at different locations on Earth because the Earth rotates more quickly than the moon revolves around the Earth.*

Tidal Variations

The sun also affects tides. The sun is much larger than the moon, but the sun is also much farther away. As a result, the sun's influence on tides is less powerful than the moon's influence. The combined forces of the sun and the moon on the Earth result in tidal ranges that vary based on the positions of all three bodies. A **tidal range** is the difference between levels of ocean water at high tide and low tide.

tidal range the difference in levels of ocean water at high tide and low tide

spring tide a tide of increased range that occurs two times a month, at the new and full moons

neap tide a tide of minimum range that occurs during the first and third quarters of the moon

Reading Check What is a tidal range?

Spring Tides

When the sun, Earth, and moon are aligned, spring tides occur. **Spring tides** are tides with the largest daily tidal range and occur during the new and full moons, or every 14 days. The first time spring tides occur is when the moon is between the sun and Earth. The second time spring tides occur is when the moon and the sun are on opposite sides of the Earth. **Figure 4** shows the positions of the sun, Earth, and moon during spring tides.

Neap Tides

When the sun, Earth, and moon form a 90° angle, neap tides occur. **Neap tides** are tides with the smallest daily tidal range and occur during the first and third quarters of the moon. Neap tides occur halfway between the occurrence of spring tides. When neap tides occur, the gravitational forces on the Earth by the sun and moon work against each other. **Figure 4** shows the positions of the sun, Earth, and moon during neap tides.

Figure 4 Spring Tides and Neap Tides

Spring Tides During spring tides, the gravitational forces of the sun and moon pull on the Earth either from the same direction (left) or from opposite directions (right).

Neap Tides During neap tides, the sun and moon are at right angles with respect to the Earth. This arrangement lessens their gravitational effect on the Earth.

Figure 5 *It's a good thing the people on this beach (left) knew when high tide occurred (right). These photos show the Bay of Fundy, in New Brunswick, Canada. The Bay of Fundy has the greatest tidal range on Earth.*

Tides and Topography

After a tidal range has been measured, the times that tides occur can be accurately predicted. This information can be useful for people who live near or visit the coast, as shown in **Figure 5.** In some coastal areas that have narrow inlets, movements of water called tidal bores occur. A *tidal bore* is a body of water that rushes up through a narrow bay, estuary, or river channel during the rise of high tide and causes a very sudden tidal rise. Tidal bores occur in coastal areas of China, the British Isles, France, and Canada.

SECTION Review

Summary

- Tides are caused by the gravitational forces of the moon and sun on the Earth.
- The moon's gravity is the main force behind the tides.
- The positions of the sun and moon relative to the position of the Earth cause tidal ranges.
- The four different types of tides are: high tides, low tides, spring tides, and neap tides.

Using Key Terms

1. In your own words, write a definition for each of the following terms: *spring tides* and *neap tides*.

Understanding Key Ideas

2. Tides are at their highest during
   a. spring tide.
   b. neap tide.
   c. a tidal bore.
   d. the daytime.
3. Which tides have minimum tidal range? Which tides have maximum tidal range?
4. What causes tidal ranges?

Math Skills

5. If it takes 24 h and 50 min for a spot on Earth that is facing the moon to rotate to face the moon again, how many minutes does it take?

Critical Thinking

6. **Applying Concepts** How many days pass between the minimum and the maximum of the tidal range in any given area? Explain your answer.
7. **Analyzing Processes** Explain how the position of the moon relates to the occurrence of high tides and low tides.

SCILINKS®
NSTA
Developed and maintained by the National Science Teachers Association
For a variety of links related to this chapter, go to www.scilinks.org
Topic: Tides
SciLinks code: HSM1525

Using Scientific Methods

Skills Practice Lab

OBJECTIVES

Demonstrate the effects of temperature and salinity on the density of water.

Describe why some parts of the ocean turn over, while others do not.

MATERIALS

- beakers, 400 mL (5)
- blue and red food coloring
- bucket of ice
- gloves, heat-resistant
- hot plate
- plastic wrap, 4 pieces, approximately 30 cm × 20 cm
- salt
- spoon
- tap water
- watch or clock

SAFETY

Up from the Depths

Every year, the water in certain parts of the ocean "turns over." That is, the water at the bottom rises to the top and the water at the top falls to the bottom. This yearly change brings fresh nutrients from the bottom of the ocean to the fish living near the surface. However, the water in some parts of the ocean never turns over. By completing this activity, you will find out why not.

Keep in mind that some parts of the ocean are warmer at the bottom, and some are warmer at the top. And sometimes the saltiest water is at the bottom and sometimes not. As you complete this activity, you will investigate how these factors help determine whether the water will turn over.

Ask a Question

1. Why do some parts of the ocean turn over and not others?

Form a Hypothesis

2. Write a hypothesis that is a possible answer to the question above. Explain your reasoning.

Test the Hypothesis

3. Label the beakers 1 through 5. Fill beakers 1 through 4 with tap water.
4. Add a drop of blue food coloring to the water in beakers 1 and 2, and stir with the spoon.
5. Place beaker 1 in the bucket of ice for 10 min.
6. Add a drop of red food coloring to the water in beakers 3 and 4, and stir with the spoon.
7. Set beaker 3 on a hot plate turned to a low setting for 10 min.
8. Add one spoonful of salt to the water in beaker 4, and stir with the spoon.

9. While beaker 1 is cooling and beaker 3 is heating, copy the observations table below on a sheet of paper.

Observations Table	
Mixture of water	**Observations**
Warm water placed above cold water	
Cold water placed above warm water	DO NOT WRITE IN BOOK
Salty water placed above fresh water	
Fresh water placed above salty water	

10. Pour half of the water in beaker 1 into beaker 5. Return beaker 1 to the bucket of ice.

11. Tuck a sheet of plastic wrap into beaker 5 so that the plastic rests on the surface of the water and lines the upper half of the beaker.

12. Put on your gloves. Slowly pour half of the water in beaker 3 into the plastic-lined upper half of beaker 5 to form two layers of water. Return beaker 3 to the hot plate, and remove your gloves.

13. Very carefully, pull on one edge of the plastic wrap and remove it so that the warm, red water rests on the cold, blue water.
Caution: The plastic wrap may be warm.

14. Wait about 5 minutes, and then observe the layers in beaker 5. Did one layer remain on top of the other? Was there any mixing or turning over? Record your observations in your observations table.

15. Empty beaker 5, and rinse it with clean tap water.

16. Repeat the procedure used in steps 10–15. This time, pour warm, red water from beaker 3 on the bottom and cold, blue water from beaker 1 on top. (Use gloves when pouring warm water.)

17. Again, repeat the procedure used in steps 10–15. This time, pour blue tap water from beaker 2 on the bottom and red, salty water from beaker 4 on top.

18. Repeat the procedure used in steps 10–15 a third time. This time, pour red, salty water from beaker 4 on the bottom and blue tap water from beaker 2 on top.

Analyze the Results

1. **Analyzing Data** Compare the results of all four trials. Explain why the water turned over in some of the trials but not in all of them.

Draw Conclusions

2. **Evaluating Results** What is the effect of temperature and salinity on the density of water?

3. **Drawing Conclusions** What makes the temperature of ocean water decrease? What could make the salinity of ocean water increase?

4. **Drawing Conclusions** What reasons can you give to explain why some parts of the ocean do not turn over in the spring while some do?

Applying Your Data

Suggest a method for setting up a model that tests the combined effects of temperature and salinity on the density of water. Consider using more than two water samples and dyes.

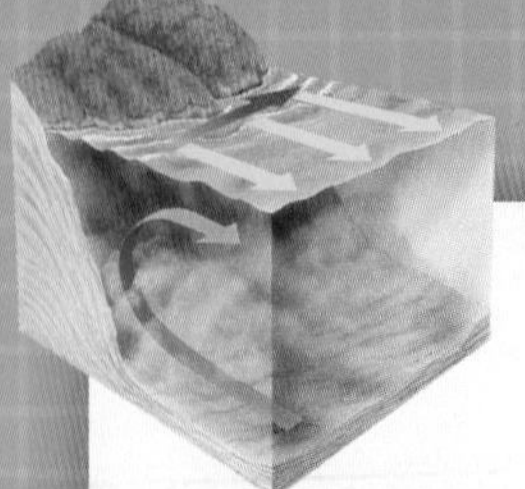

Chapter Review

USING KEY TERMS

For each pair of terms, explain how the meanings of the terms differ.

1. *surface current* and *deep current*
2. *El Niño* and *La Niña*
3. *spring tide* and *neap tide*
4. *tide* and *tidal range*

UNDERSTANDING KEY IDEAS

Multiple Choice

5. Deep currents form when
   - **a.** cold air decreases water density.
   - **b.** warm air increases water density.
   - **c.** the ocean surface freezes and solids from the water underneath are removed.
   - **d.** salinity increases.

6. When waves come near the shore,
   - **a.** they speed up.
   - **b.** they maintain their speed.
   - **c.** their wavelength increases.
   - **d.** their wave height increases.

7. The largest ocean is the
   - **a.** Indian Ocean.
   - **b.** Pacific Ocean.
   - **c.** Atlantic Ocean.
   - **d.** Arctic Ocean.

8. Tidal range is greatest during
   - **a.** spring tide.
   - **b.** neap tide.
   - **c.** a tidal bore.
   - **d.** the daytime.

9. Tides alternate between high and low because the moon revolves around the Earth
   - **a.** at the same speed the Earth rotates.
   - **b.** at a much faster speed than the Earth rotates.
   - **c.** at a much slower speed than the Earth rotates.
   - **d.** at different speeds.

10. El Niño can cause
    - **a.** droughts to occur in Indonesia and Australia.
    - **b.** upwelling to occur off the coast of South America.
    - **c.** earthquakes.
    - **d.** droughts to occur in the southern half of the United States.

Short Answer

11. Explain the relationship between upwelling and El Niño.
12. Describe the two parts of a wave. Describe how these two parts relate to wavelength and wave height.
13. Compare the relative positions of the Earth, moon, and sun during the spring and neap tides.
14. Explain how climate and water movement can affect salinity.
15. Describe how warm-water currents affect the climate in the British Isles.
16. Describe the factors that form deep currents.
17. Describe the parts of the water cycle.

CRITICAL THINKING

18 **Concept Mapping** Use the following terms to create a concept map: *wind, deep currents, sun's gravity, types of ocean-water movement, surface currents, tides, increasing water density, waves,* and *moon's gravity.*

19 **Identifying Relationships** Why are tides more noticeable in Earth's oceans than on its land?

20 **Expressing Opinions** Explain why it's important to study El Niño and La Niña.

21 **Applying Concepts** Suppose you and a friend are planning a fishing trip to the ocean. Your friend tells you that the fish bite more in his secret fishing spot during low tide. If low tide occurred at the spot at 7 a.m. today and you are going to fish there in 1 week, at what time will low tide occur in that spot?

22 **Identifying Relationships** Describe how global winds, the Coriolis Effect, and continental deflections form a pattern of surface currents on Earth.

INTERPRETING GRAPHICS

The diagram below shows some of Earth's major surface currents that flow in the Western Hemisphere. Use the diagram to answer the questions that follow.

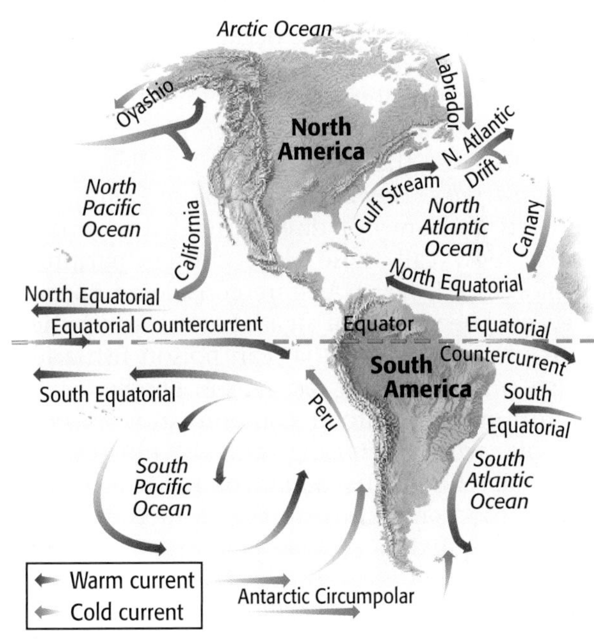

23 List two warm-water currents and two cold-water currents.

24 How do you think the Labrador Current affects the climate of Canada and Greenland?

Standardized Test Preparation

READING

Read each of the passages below. Then, answer the questions that follow each passage.

Passage 1 When certain algae grow rapidly, they clump together on the ocean's surface in an algal bloom that changes the color of the water. Because these algal blooms often turn the water red or reddish brown and tidal conditions were believed to cause the blooms, people called these blooms *red tides*. However, algal blooms are not always red and are not directly related to tides. Scientists now call these algae clusters harmful algal blooms (HABs). HABs are considered harmful because the species of algae that makes up the blooms produces toxins that can poison fish and shellfish, which in turn can poison people.

Unfortunately, seafood contamination is not noticeable without testing and is not easily eliminated. The toxins don't change the flavor of the seafood, and cooking the seafood doesn't eliminate the toxins.

1. Why did scientists start calling red tides *HABs*?

- **A** The name *HABs* is easier to remember.
- **B** The name *red tides* was not accurate in describing the phenomenon.
- **C** The algal blooms are actually green.
- **D** The term *red tides* did not reflect the danger of the blooms.

2. How can a person tell if seafood has been contaminated by HABs?

- **F** Contaminated seafood has a reddish color.
- **G** HABs change the flavor of the seafood.
- **H** Seafood contaminated by HABs has a strange smell.
- **I** Unfortunately, there is no easy way to tell.

Passage 2 Tsunamis are the most destructive waves in the ocean. Most tsunamis are caused by earthquakes on the ocean floor, but some can be caused by volcanic eruptions and underwater landslides. Tsunamis are sometimes called *tidal waves,* which is misleading because tsunamis have no connection with tides.

Tsunamis commonly have a wave period of about 15 min and a wave speed of about 725 km/h, which is about as fast as a jet airliner. By the time a tsunami reaches the shore, its height may be 30 to 40 m.

In 1960, a tsunami was triggered by an earthquake off the coast of South America. The tsunami was so powerful that it crossed the Pacific Ocean and hit the city of Hilo, on the coast of Hawaii, approximately 10,000 km away. The same tsunami then continued on to strike Japan.

1. The word *misleading* was used in this passage to describe the use of the term *tidal waves* because

- **A** tsunamis are related to tides.
- **B** tsunamis can cause extensive damage to shores.
- **C** tsunamis are related to earthquakes.
- **D** tsunamis are not related to tides.

2. Which of the following statements is a fact from the passage?

- **F** All tsunamis are caused by earthquakes.
- **G** A tsunami can travel as fast as a jet airliner.
- **H** The tsunami of 1960 caused destruction only in Japan.
- **I** Tsunamis are caused by surface currents.

INTERPRETING GRAPHICS

The diagram below shows the possible positions of the moon relative to the Earth and sun during different tidal ranges. Use the diagram below to answer the questions that follow.

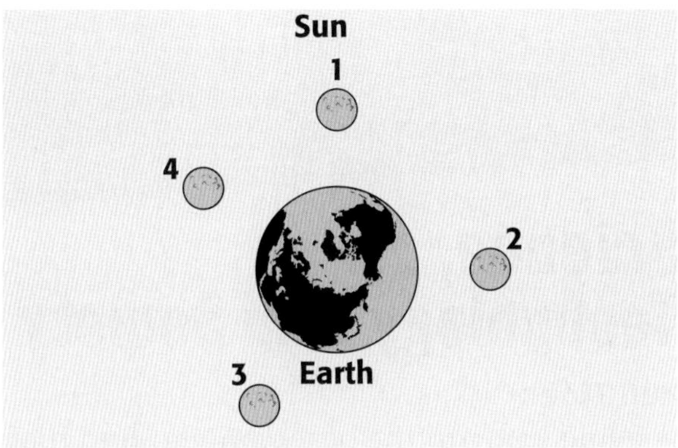

1. At which position would the moon be during a neap tide?
   A 1
   B 2
   C 3
   D 4

2. At which position would the moon be during a spring tide?
   F 1
   G 2
   H 3
   I 4

3. The tidal range would be greater when the moon is at position 3 than when the moon is at position 4 because
   A position 4 forms a 90° angle with the sun and the Earth.
   B position 3 is very near a neap-tide position.
   C position 3 is very near a spring-tide position.
   D position 4 is very near a spring-tide position.

MATH

Read each question below, and choose the best answer.

1. If a wave has a speed of 3 m/s and a wavelength of 12 m, what is its period? Use the following equation to answer the question above:

$$\frac{\text{wavelength (m)}}{\text{wave period (s)}} = \text{wave speed (m/s)}$$

   A 36 s
   B 4 m
   C 24 s
   D 4 s

2. Antarctic Bottom Water takes 750 years to move from the Antarctic coast to the equator. If the distance between the equator and the Antarctic coast is about 10,000 km, approximately how many kilometers does the bottom water move each year?
   F 13 km
   G 200 km
   H 75 km
   I 1 km

3. A boat is traveling north at 20 km/h against a current that is moving south at 12 km/h. What is the overall speed and direction of the boat?
   A 8 km/h north
   B 8 km/h south
   C 32 km/h north
   D 32 km/h south

4. Imagine that you are in a rowboat on the open ocean. You count 2 waves traveling right under your boat in 10 seconds. You estimate the wavelength to be 3 m. What is the wave speed?
   F 0.6 m/s
   G 6.0 m/s
   H 0.3 m/s
   I 3.0 m/s

Science in Action

Weird Science

Using Toy Ducks to Track Ocean Currents

Accidents can sometimes lead to scientific discovery. For example, on January 10, 1992, 29,000 plastic tub toys spilled overboard when a container ship traveling northwest of Hawaii ran into a storm. In November of that year, those toys began washing up on Alaskan beaches. When oceanographers heard about this, they placed advertisements in newspapers along the Alaskan coast asking people who found the toys to call them. Altogether, hundreds of toys were recovered. Using recovery dates and locations and computer models, oceanographers were able to re-create the toys' drift and figure out which currents carried the toys. As for the remaining toys, currents may carry them to a number of different destinations. Some may travel through the Arctic Ocean and eventually reach Europe!

Math ACTIVITY

Between January 10, 1992, and November 16, 1992, some of the toys were carried approximately 3,220 km from the cargo-spill site to the coast of Alaska. Calculate the average distance traveled by these toys per day. (Hint: The year 1992 was a leap year.)

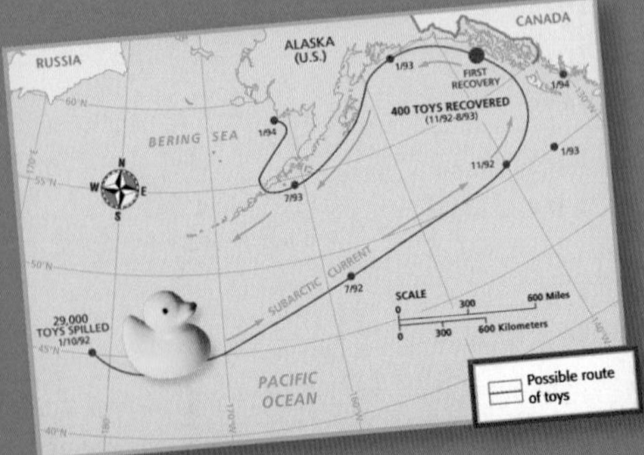

Science, Technology, and Society

Red Tides

Imagine going to the beach only to find that the ocean water has turned red and that a lot of fish are floating belly up. What could cause such damage to the ocean? It may surprise you to find that the answer is single-celled algae. When certain algae grow rapidly, they clump together on the ocean's surface in what are known as algal blooms. These algal blooms have been commonly called *red tides* because the blooms often turn the water red or reddish-brown. The term scientists use for these sudden explosions in algae growth is *harmful algal blooms* (HABs). The blooms are harmful because certain species of algae produce toxins that can poison fish, shellfish, and people who eat poisoned fish or shellfish. Toxic blooms can be carried hundreds of miles on ocean currents. HABs can ride into an area on an ocean current and cause fish to die and people who eat the poisoned fish or shellfish to become ill.

Social Studies ACTIVITY

Some scientists think that factors related to human activities, such as agricultural runoff into the ocean, are causing more HABs than occurred in the past. Other scientists disagree. Find out more about this issue, and have a class debate about the roles humans play in creating HABs.

Careers

Cristina Castro

Marine Biologist Have you ever imagined watching whales for a living? Cristina Castro does. Castro works as a marine biologist with the Pacific Whale Foundation in Ecuador. She is studying the migratory patterns of a whale species known as the *humpback whale*. Each year, the humpback whale migrates from feeding grounds in the Antarctic to the warm waters off Ecuador, where the whales breed. Her studies take place largely in the Machalilla National Park. The park is a two-mile stretch of beach that is protected by the government of Ecuador.

In her research, Cristina Castro focuses on the connection between El Niño events and the number of humpback whales in the waters off Ecuador. Castro believes that during an El Niño event, the waters off Ecuador are too hot for the whales. When the whales get hot, they have a difficult time cooling off because they have a thick coat of blubber that provides insulation. So, Castro believes that the whales stay in colder waters during an El Niño event.

Language Arts ACTIVITY

WRITING SKILL Research the humpback whale's migratory route from Antarctica to Ecuador. Write a short story in which you tell of the migration from the point of view of a young whale.

To learn more about these Science in Action topics, visit go.hrw.com and type in the keyword **HZ5H2OF.**

Current Science

Check out Current Science® articles related to this chapter by visiting go.hrw.com. Just type in the keyword HZ5CS14.

The Atmosphere

About the PHOTO

Imagine climbing a mountain and taking only one out of three breaths! As altitude increases, the density of the atmosphere decreases. At the heights shown in this picture, the atmosphere is so thin that it contains only 30% of the amount of oxygen found in the atmosphere at sea level. So, most mountaineers carry part of their atmosphere with them—in the form of oxygen tanks.

PRE-READING ACTIVITY

FOLDNOTES **Booklet** Before you read the chapter, create the FoldNote entitled "Booklet" described in the **Study Skills** section of the Appendix. Label each page of the booklet with a main idea from the chapter. As you read the chapter, write what you learn about each main idea on the appropriate page of the booklet.

START-UP ACTIVITY

Does Air Have Mass?

In this activity, you will compare an inflated balloon with a deflated balloon to find out if air has mass.

Procedure

1. In a **notebook,** answer the following questions: Does air have mass? Will an inflated balloon weigh more than a deflated balloon?
2. Inflate **two large balloons,** and tie the balloons closed. Attach each balloon to opposite ends of a **meterstick** using identical **pushpins.** Balance the meterstick on a **pencil** held by a volunteer. Check that the meterstick is perfectly balanced.
3. Predict what will happen when you pop one balloon. Record your predictions.
4. Put on **safety goggles,** and carefully pop one of the balloons with a **pushpin.**
5. Record your observations.

Analysis

1. Explain your observations. Was your prediction correct?
2. Based on your results, does air have mass? If air has mass, is the atmosphere affected by Earth's gravity? Explain your answers.

SECTION 1

Characteristics of the Atmosphere

If you were lost in the desert, you could survive for a few days without food and water. But you wouldn't last more than five minutes without the atmosphere.

READING WARM-UP

Objectives

- Describe the composition of Earth's atmosphere.
- Explain why air pressure changes with altitude.
- Explain how air temperature changes with atmospheric composition.
- Describe the layers of the atmosphere.

Terms to Learn

atmosphere, air pressure, troposphere, stratosphere, mesosphere, thermosphere

READING STRATEGY

Mnemonics As you read this section, create a mnemonic device to help you remember the layers of the Earth's atmosphere.

The **atmosphere** is a mixture of gases that surrounds Earth. In addition to containing the oxygen you need to breathe, the atmosphere protects you from the sun's damaging rays. The atmosphere is always changing. Every breath you take, every tree that is planted, and every vehicle you ride in affects the atmosphere's composition.

The Composition of the Atmosphere

As you can see in **Figure 1,** the atmosphere is made up mostly of nitrogen gas. The oxygen you breathe makes up a little more than 20% of the atmosphere. In addition to containing nitrogen and oxygen, the atmosphere contains small particles, such as dust, volcanic ash, sea salt, dirt, and smoke. The next time you turn off the lights at night, shine a flashlight, and you will see some of these tiny particles floating in the air.

Water is also found in the atmosphere. Liquid water (water droplets) and solid water (snow and ice crystals) are found in clouds. But most water in the atmosphere exists as an invisible gas called *water vapor.* When atmospheric conditions change, water vapor can change into solid or liquid water, and rain or snow might fall from the sky.

Reading Check **Describe the three physical states of water in the atmosphere.** (*See the Appendix for answers to Reading Checks.*)

Figure 1 **Composition of the Atmosphere**

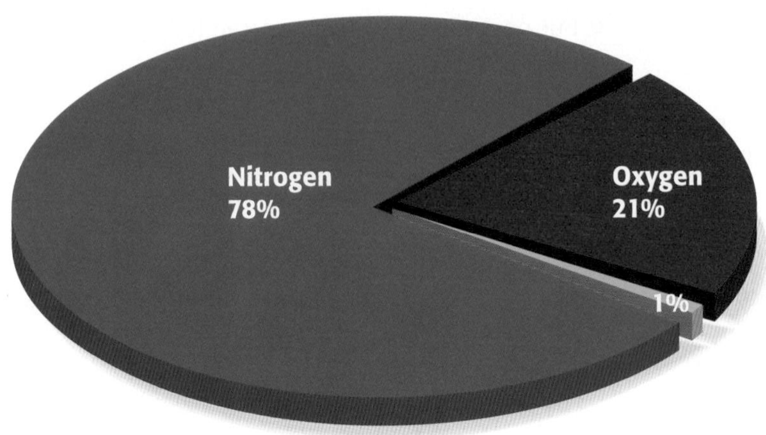

Nitrogen, the most common atmospheric gas, is released when dead plants and dead animals break down and when volcanoes erupt.

Oxygen, the second most common atmospheric gas, is made by phytoplankton and plants.

The **remaining 1%** of the atmosphere is made up of argon, carbon dioxide, water vapor, and other gases.

Atmospheric Pressure and Temperature

What would carrying a column of air that is 700 km high feel like? You may be surprised to learn that you carry this load every day. While air is not very heavy, its weight adds up. At sea level, a square inch of surface area is under almost 15 lb of air. Carrying that much air on such a small surface area is like carrying a large bowling ball on the tip of your finger!

As Altitude Increases, Air Pressure Decreases

The atmosphere is held around the Earth by gravity. Gravity pulls gas molecules in the atmosphere toward the Earth's surface, causing air pressure. **Air pressure** is the measure of the force with which air molecules push on a surface. Air pressure is strongest at the Earth's surface because more air is above you. As you move farther away from the Earth's surface, fewer gas molecules are above you. So, as altitude (distance from sea level) increases, air pressure decreases. Think of air pressure as a human pyramid, as shown in **Figure 2.** The people at the bottom of the pyramid can feel all the weight and pressure of the people on top. Air pressure works in a similar way.

Atmospheric Composition Affects Air Temperature

Air temperature also changes as altitude increases. The temperature differences result mainly from the way solar energy is absorbed as it moves through the atmosphere. Some parts of the atmosphere are warmer because they contain a high percentage of gases that absorb solar energy. Other parts of the atmosphere contain less of these gases and are cooler.

CONNECTION TO Physics

Air-Pressure Experiment
Does air pressure push only downward? Try this experiment to find out. Fill a plastic cup to the brim with water. Firmly hold a piece of cardboard over the mouth of the cup. Quickly invert the glass over a sink, and observe what happens. How do the effects of air pressure explain your observations?

atmosphere a mixture of gases that surrounds a planet or moon

air pressure the measure of the force with which air molecules push on a surface

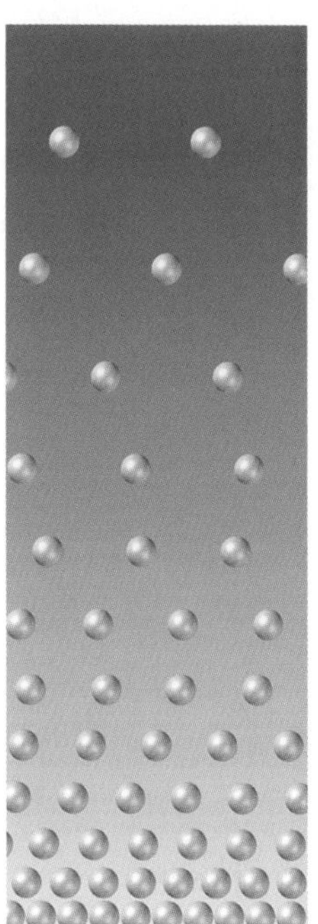

Figure 2 *As in a human pyramid, air pressure increases closer to the Earth's surface.*

Layers of the Atmosphere

Based on temperature changes, the Earth's atmosphere is divided into four layers, as shown in **Figure 3.** These layers are the *troposphere, stratosphere, mesosphere,* and *thermosphere.* Although these words might sound complicated, the name of each layer gives you clues about its features.

For example, *-sphere* means "ball," which suggests that each layer of the atmosphere surrounds the Earth like a hollow ball. *Tropo-* means "turning" or "change," and the troposphere is the layer where gases turn and mix. *Strato-* means "layer," and the stratosphere is the sphere where gases are layered and do not mix very much. *Meso-* means "middle," and the mesosphere is the middle layer. Finally, *thermo-* means "heat," and the thermosphere is the sphere where temperatures are highest.

Reading Check **What does the name of each atmospheric layer mean?**

Modeling the Atmosphere
In teams, use a metric ruler to create an illustrated scale model of the atmosphere similar to the one shown on this page. Assume that the atmosphere is about 700 km high. If you reduced the height of the atmosphere by a factor of 100,000, your scale model would be 7 m long, and the troposphere would be 16 cm long. Think of a creative way to display your model. You could use sidewalk chalk, stakes and string, poster board, or other materials approved by your teacher. Do some research to add interesting information about each layer.

ACTIVITY

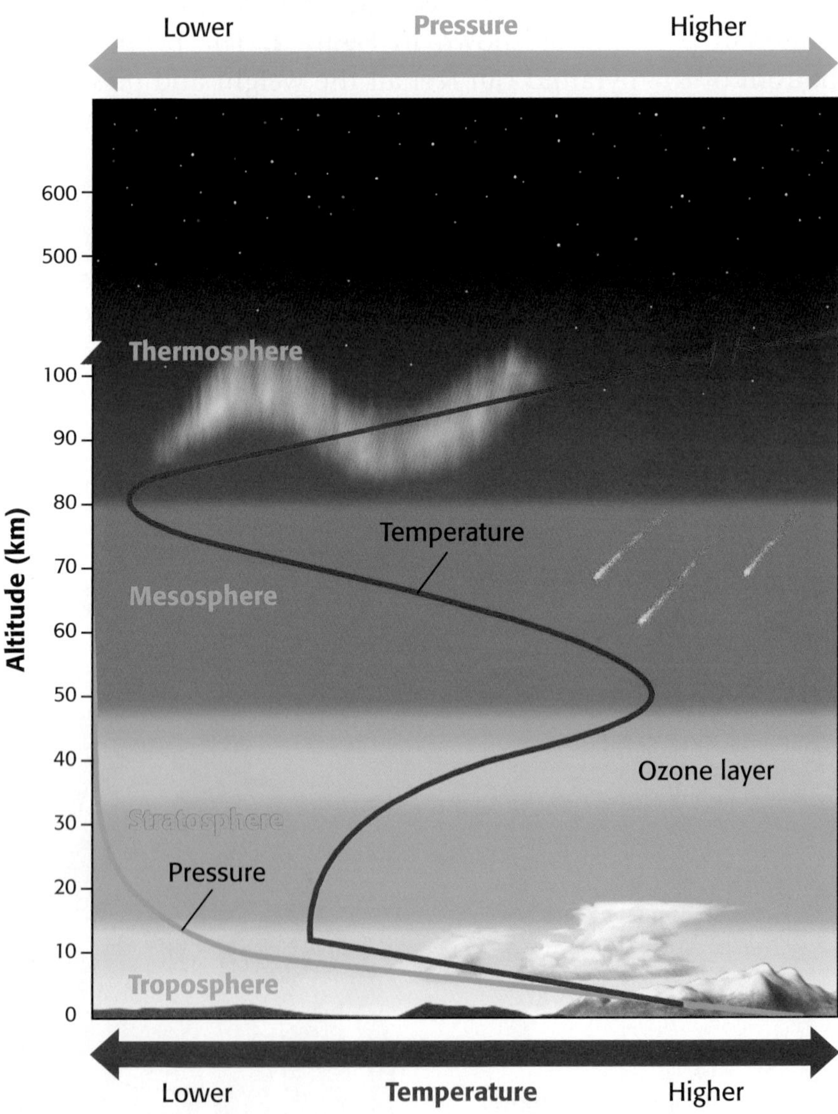

Figure 3 *The layers of the atmosphere are defined by changes in temperature.*

The Troposphere: The Layer in Which We Live

The lowest layer of the atmosphere, which lies next to the Earth's surface, is called the **troposphere.** The troposphere is also the densest atmospheric layer. It contains almost 90% of the atmosphere's total mass! Almost all of the Earth's carbon dioxide, water vapor, clouds, air pollution, weather, and life-forms are in the troposphere. As shown in **Figure 4,** temperatures vary greatly in the troposphere. Differences in air temperature and density cause gases in the troposphere to mix continuously.

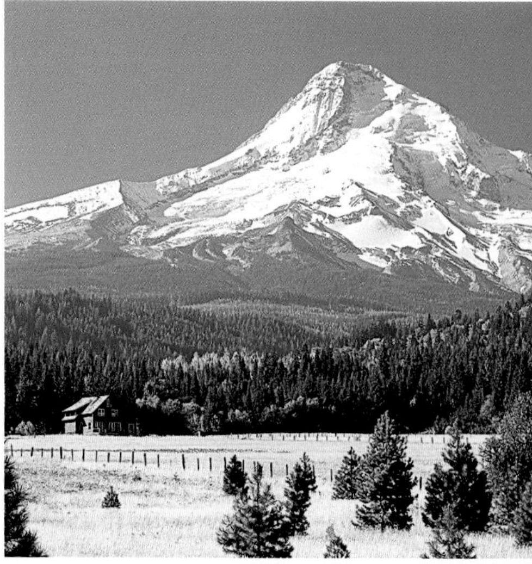

Figure 4 *As altitude increases in the troposphere, temperature decreases. Snow remains all year on this mountaintop.*

The Stratosphere: Home of the Ozone Layer

The atmospheric layer above the troposphere is called the **stratosphere. Figure 5** shows the boundary between the stratosphere and the troposphere. Gases in the stratosphere are layered and do not mix as much as gases in the troposphere. The air is also very thin in the stratosphere and contains little moisture. The lower stratosphere is extremely cold. Its temperature averages –60°C. But temperature rises as altitude increases in the stratosphere. This rise happens because ozone in the stratosphere absorbs ultraviolet radiation from the sun, which warms the air. Almost all of the ozone in the stratosphere is contained in the ozone layer. The *ozone layer* protects life on Earth by absorbing harmful ultraviolet radiation.

The Mesosphere: The Middle Layer

Above the stratosphere is the mesosphere. The **mesosphere** is the middle layer of the atmosphere. It is also the coldest layer. As in the troposphere, the temperature decreases as altitude increases in the mesosphere. Temperatures can be as low as –93°C at the top of the mesosphere.

troposphere the lowest layer of the atmosphere, in which temperature decreases at a constant rate as altitude increases

stratosphere the layer of the atmosphere that is above the troposphere and in which temperature increases as altitude increases

mesosphere the layer of the atmosphere between the stratosphere and the thermosphere and in which temperature decreases as altitude increases

Figure 5 *This photograph of Earth's atmosphere was taken from space. The troposphere is the yellow layer; the stratosphere is the white layer.*

The Thermosphere: The Edge of the Atmosphere

thermosphere the uppermost layer of the atmosphere, in which temperature increases as altitude increases

The uppermost atmospheric layer is called the **thermosphere.** In the thermosphere, temperature again increases with altitude. Atoms of nitrogen and oxygen absorb high-energy solar radiation and release thermal energy, which causes temperatures in the thermosphere to be 1,000°C or higher.

When you think of an area that has high temperatures, you probably think of a place that is very hot. Although the thermosphere has very high temperatures, it does not feel hot. Temperature is different from heat. Temperature is a measure of the average energy of particles in motion. The high temperature of the thermosphere means that particles in that layer are moving very fast. Heat, however, is the transfer of thermal energy between objects of different temperatures. Particles must touch one another to transfer thermal energy. The space between particles in the thermosphere is so great that particles do not transfer much energy. In other words, the density of the thermosphere is so low that particles do not often collide and transfer energy. **Figure 6** shows how air density affects the heating of the troposphere and the thermosphere.

Reading Check **Why doesn't the thermosphere feel hot?**

Figure 6 **Temperature in the Troposphere and the Thermosphere**

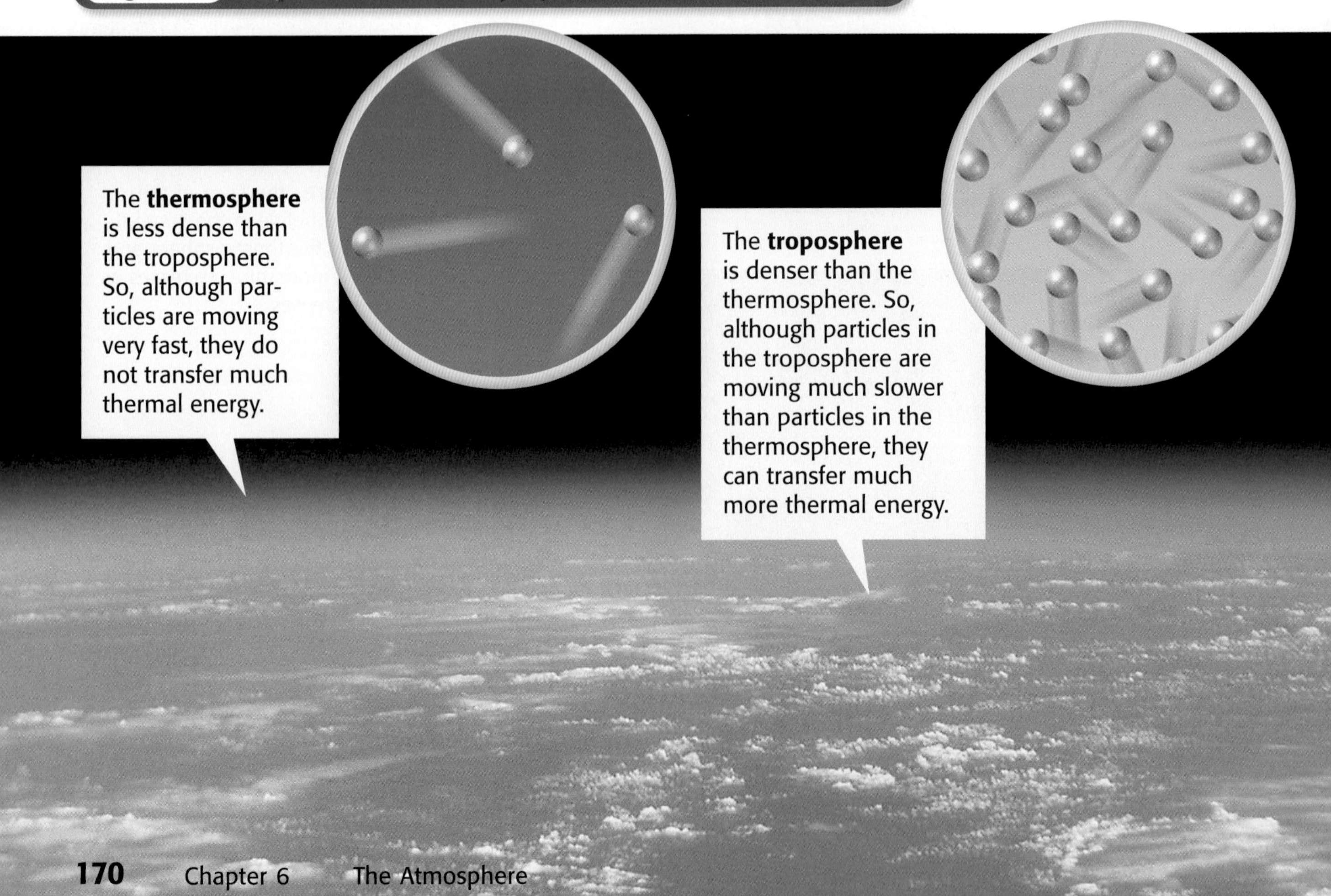

The **thermosphere** is less dense than the troposphere. So, although particles are moving very fast, they do not transfer much thermal energy.
The **troposphere** is denser than the thermosphere. So, although particles in the troposphere are moving much slower than particles in the thermosphere, they can transfer much more thermal energy.

INTERPRETING GRAPHICS

Use the illustration below to answer the questions that follow.

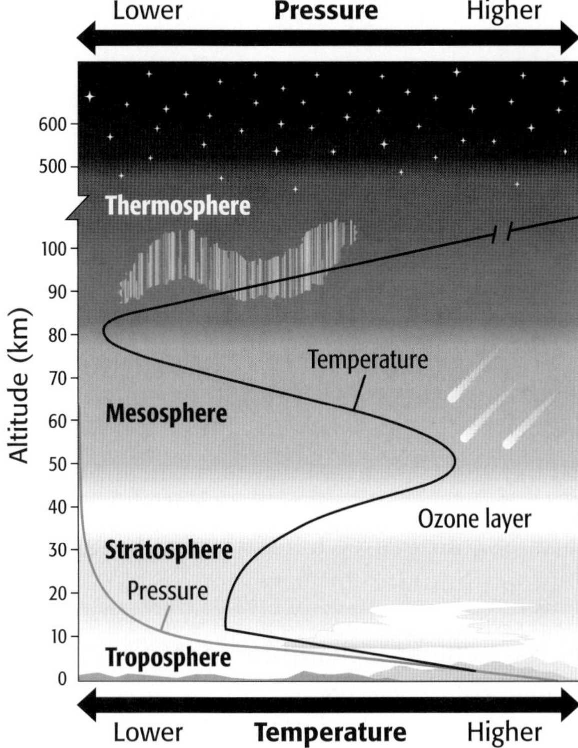

1. Which of the following statements describes how temperature changes in the mesosphere?

A Temperature increases as altitude increases.
B Temperature decreases as altitude increases.
C Temperature decreases as pressure increases.
D Temperature does not change as pressure increases.

2. In which layers does temperature decrease as pressure decreases?

F the troposphere and the mesosphere
G the troposphere and the stratosphere
H the ozone layer and the troposphere
I the ozone layer and the thermosphere

3. A research balloon took measurements at 23 km, 35 km, 52 km, 73 km, 86 km, 92 km, 101 km, and 110 km. Which measurements were taken in the mesosphere?

A measurements at 23 km and 35 km
B measurements at 52 km and 73 km
C measurements at 86 km and 92 km
D measurements at 101 km and 110 km

MATH

Read each question below, and choose the best answer.

1. An airplane is flying at a speed of 500 km/h when it encounters a jet stream moving in the same direction at 150 km/h. If the plane flies with the jet stream, how much farther will the plane travel in 1.5 h?

A 950 km
B 525 km
C 225 km
D 150 km

2. Today's wind speed was measured at 18 km/h. What was the wind speed in meters per hour?

F 1.8 m/h
G 180 m/h
H 1,800 m/h
I 18,000 m/h

3. Rockport received 24.1 cm of rain on Monday, 12.5 cm of rain on Tuesday, and 5.8 cm of rain on Thursday. The rest of the week, it did not rain. How much rain did Rockport receive during the week?

A 18.3 cm
B 36.6 cm
C 42.4 cm
D 45.7 cm

4. A weather station recorded the following temperatures during a 5 h period: 15°C, 18°C, 13°C, 15°C, and 20°C. What was the average temperature during this period?

F 14.2°C
G 15.2°C
H 16.2°C
I 20.2°C

5. The temperature in Waterford, Virginia, increased 1.3°C every hour for 5 h. If the temperature in the morning was –4°C, what was the temperature 4 h later?

A 2.5°C
B 2.3°C
C 1.3°C
D 1.2°C

Science in Action

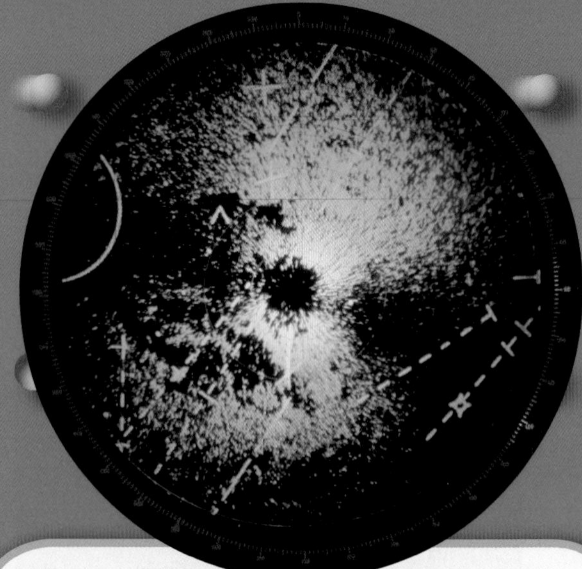

Science, Technology, and Society

The HyperSoar Jet

Imagine traveling from Chicago to Tokyo in 72 minutes. If the HyperSoar jet becomes a reality, you may be able to travel to the other side of the world in less time than it takes to watch a movie! To accomplish this amazing feat, the jet would "skip" across the upper stratosphere. To begin skipping, the jet would climb above the stratosphere, turn off its engines, and glide for about 60 km. Then, gravity would pull the jet down to where the air is denser. The denser air would cause the jet to soar upward. In this way, the jet would skip across a layer of dense air until it was ready to land. Each 2-minute skip would cover about 450 km, and the HyperSoar would be able to fly at Mach 10—a speed of 3 km/s!

Math ACTIVITY

A trip on the HyperSoar from Chicago to Tokyo would require about 18 "skips." Each skip is 450 km. If the trip is 10,123 km, how many kilometers will the jet travel when it is not skipping?

Weird Science

Radar Zoology

"For tonight's forecast, expect a light shower of mayflies. A wave of warblers will approach from the south. Tomorrow will be cloudy, and a band of free-tailed bats will move to the south in the early evening." Such a forecast may not make the evening news, but it is a familiar scenario for radar zoologists. Radar zoologists use a type of radar called *NEXRAD* to track migrating birds, bands of bats, and swarms of insects. NEXRAD tracks animals in the atmosphere in the same way that it tracks storms. The system sends out a microwave signal. If the signal hits an object, some of the energy reflects back to a receiver. NEXRAD has been especially useful to scientists who study bird migration. Birds tend to migrate at night, when the atmosphere is more stable, so until now, nighttime bird migration has been difficult to observe. NEXRAD has also helped identify important bird migration routes and critical stopovers. For example, scientists have discovered that many birds migrate over the Gulf of Mexico instead of around it.

Social Studies ACTIVITY

Geography plays an important role in bird migration. Many birds ride the "thermals" produced by mountain ranges. Find out what thermals are, and create a map of bird migration routes over North America.

Careers

Ellen Paneok

Bush Pilot For Ellen Paneok, understanding weather patterns is a matter of life and death. As a bush pilot, she flies mail, supplies, and people to remote villages in Alaska that can be reached only by plane. Bad weather is one of the most serious challenges Paneok faces. "It's beautiful up here," she says, "but it can also be harsh." One dangerous situation is landing a plane in mountainous regions. "On top of a mountain you can't tell which way the wind is blowing," Paneok says. In this case, she flies in a rectangular pattern to determine the wind direction. Landing a plane on the frozen Arctic Ocean is also dangerous. In white-out conditions, the horizon can't be seen because the sky and the ground are the same color. "It's like flying in a milk bottle full of milk," Paneok says. In these conditions, she fills black plastic garbage bags and drops them from the plane to help guide her landing.

Paneok had to overcome many challenges to become a pilot. As a child, she lived in seven foster homes before being placed in an all-girls' home at the age of 14. In the girls' home, she read a magazine about careers in aviation and decided then and there that she wanted to become a pilot. At first, she faced a lot of opposition from people telling her that she wouldn't be able to become a pilot. Now, she encourages young people to pursue their goals. "If you decide you want to go for it, go for it. There may be obstacles in your way, but you've just got to find a way to go over them, get around them, or dig under them," she says.

Ellen Paneok is shown at right with two of her Inupiat passengers.

Language Arts ACTIVITY

Beryl Markham lived an exciting life as a bush pilot delivering mail and supplies to remote areas of Africa. Read about her life or the life of Bessie Coleman, one of the most famous African American women in the history of flying.

To learn more about these Science in Action topics, visit **go.hrw.com** and type in the keyword **HZ5ATMF.**

Current Science

Check out Current Science® articles related to this chapter by visiting go.hrw.com. Just type in the keyword HZ5CS15.

7

Climate and Weather

About the PHOTO

Flamingos in the bathroom? This may look like someone's idea of a practical joke, but in fact, it's a practical idea! These flamingos reside at the Miami-Metro Zoo in Florida. They were put in the bathroom for protection against the incredibly dangerous winds of Hurricane Floyd in September of 1999.

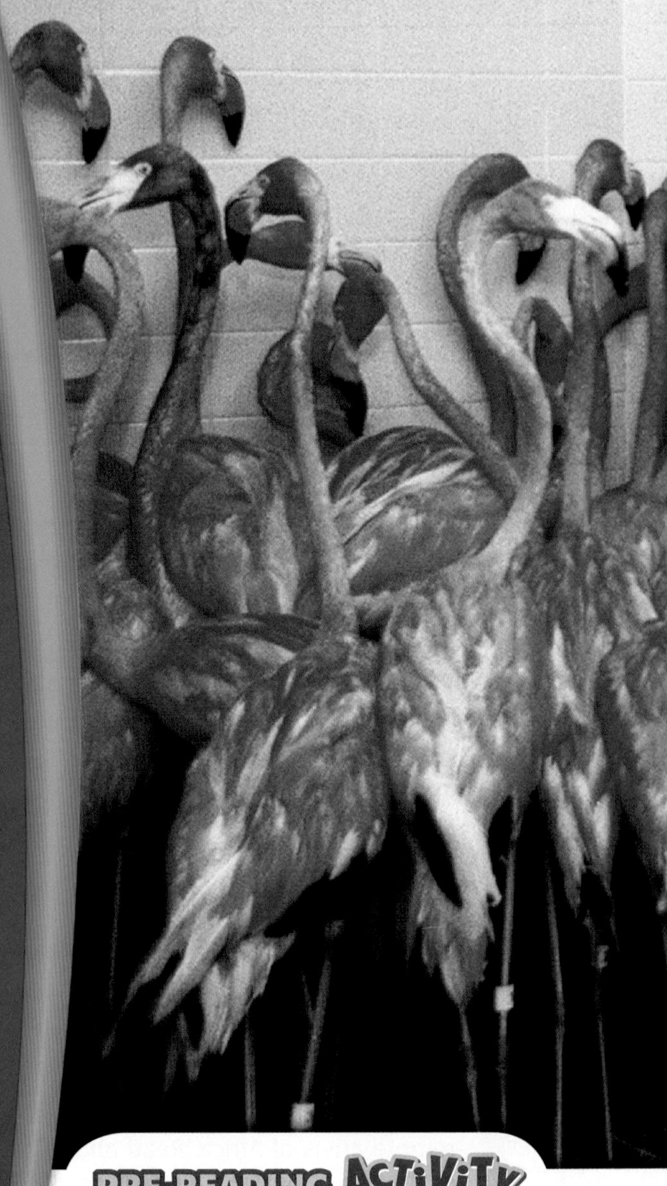

PRE-READING ACTIVITY

FOLDNOTES **Layered Book** Before you read the chapter, create the FoldNote entitled "Layered Book" described in the **Study Skills** section of the Appendix. Label the tabs of the layered book with "Climate," "Water in the air," "Air masses and fronts," "Severe weather," and "Forecasting the weather." As you read the chapter, write information you learn about each category under the appropriate tab.

START-UP ACTIVITY

Meeting of the Masses

In this activity, you will model what happens when two air masses that have different temperature characteristics meet.

Procedure

1. Pour **500 mL of water** into a **beaker.** Pour **500 mL of cooking oil** into a **second beaker.** The water represents a dense cold air mass. The cooking oil represents a less dense warm air mass.
2. Predict what would happen to the two liquids if you tried to mix them.
3. Pour the contents of both beakers into a **clear, plastic, rectangular container** at the same time from opposite ends of the container.
4. Observe the interaction of the oil and water.

Analysis

1. What happens when the liquids meet?
2. Does the prediction that you made in step 2 of the Procedure match your results?
3. Using your results, hypothesize what would happen if a cold air mass met a warm air mass.

SECTION 1

What Is Climate?

READING WARM-UP

Objectives

- Explain the difference between weather and climate.
- Identify five factors that determine climates.
- Identify the three climate zones of the world.

Terms to Learn

weather
climate
latitude
prevailing winds
elevation
surface current
biome

READING STRATEGY

Discussion Read this section silently. Write down questions that you have about this section. Discuss your questions in a small group.

Suppose you receive a call from a friend who is coming to visit you tomorrow. To decide what clothing to bring, he asks about the current weather in your area.

You step outside to see if rain clouds are in the sky and to check the temperature. But what would you do if your friend asked you about the climate in your area? What is the difference between weather and climate?

Climate Vs. Weather

The main difference between weather and climate is the length of time over which both are measured. **Weather** is the condition of the atmosphere at a particular time. Weather conditions vary from day to day and include temperature, humidity, precipitation, wind, and visibility. **Climate,** on the other hand, is the average weather condition in an area over a long period of time. Climate is mostly determined by two factors—temperature and precipitation. Different parts of the world can have different climates, as shown in **Figure 1.** But why are climates so different? The answer is complicated. It includes factors in addition to temperature and precipitation, such as latitude, wind patterns, mountains, large bodies of water, and ocean currents.

Reading Check How is climate different from weather? (*See the Appendix for answers to Reading Checks.*)

Figure 1 *How does the climate in northern Africa differ from the climate where you live?*

Latitude

Think of the last time you looked at a globe. Do you recall the thin, horizontal lines that circle the globe? Those lines are called lines of latitude. **Latitude** is the distance north or south, measured in degrees, from the equator. In general, the temperature of an area depends on its latitude. The higher the latitude is, the colder the climate tends to be. One of the coldest places on Earth, the North Pole, is 90° north of the equator. However, the equator, at latitude 0°, is usually hot.

As shown in **Figure 2,** if you were to take a trip to different latitudes in the United States, you would experience different climates. For example, the climate in Washington, D.C., which is at a higher latitude, is different from the climate in Texas.

Solar Energy and Latitude

Solar energy, which is energy from the sun, heats the Earth. The amount of direct solar energy a particular area receives is determined by latitude. **Figure 3** shows how the curve of the Earth affects the amount of direct solar energy at different latitudes. Notice that the sun's rays hit the equator directly, at almost a 90° angle. At this angle, a small area of the Earth's surface receives more direct solar energy than at a lesser angle. As a result, that area has high temperatures. However, the sun's rays strike the poles at a lesser angle than they do the equator. At this angle, the same amount of direct solar energy that hits the area at the equator is spread over a larger area at the poles. The result is lower temperatures at the poles.

Figure 2 *Winter in south Texas (top) is different from winter in Washington D.C. (bottom).*

weather the short-term state of the atmosphere, including temperature, humidity, precipitation, wind, and visibility

climate the average weather condition in an area over a long period of time

latitude the distance north or south from the equator; expressed in degrees

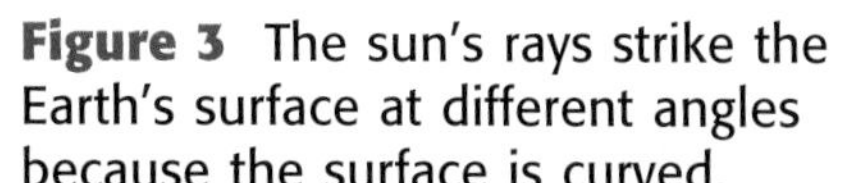

Figure 3 The sun's rays strike the Earth's surface at different angles because the surface is curved.

Seasons and Latitude

In most places in the United States, the year consists of four seasons. But there are places in the world that do not have such seasonal changes. For example, areas near the equator have approximately the same temperatures and same amount of daylight year-round. Seasons happen because the Earth is tilted on its axis at a 23.5° angle. This tilt affects how much solar energy an area receives as Earth moves around the sun. **Figure 4** shows how latitude and the tilt of the Earth determine the seasons and the length of the day in a particular area.

Reading Check **Why is there less seasonal change near the equator?**

Figure 4 **The Seasons**

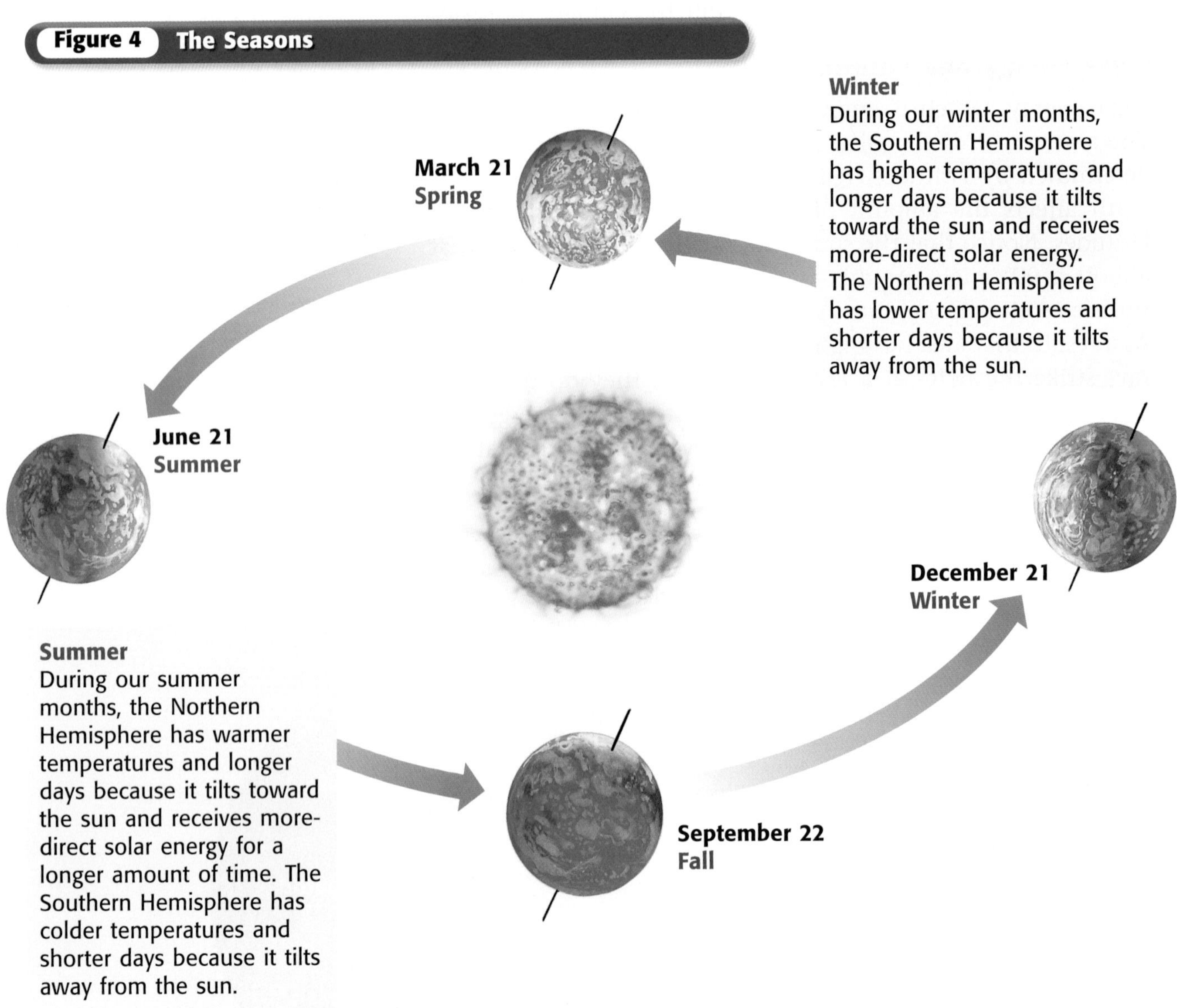

Winter
During our winter months, the Southern Hemisphere has higher temperatures and longer days because it tilts toward the sun and receives more-direct solar energy. The Northern Hemisphere has lower temperatures and shorter days because it tilts away from the sun.

Summer
During our summer months, the Northern Hemisphere has warmer temperatures and longer days because it tilts toward the sun and receives more-direct solar energy for a longer amount of time. The Southern Hemisphere has colder temperatures and shorter days because it tilts away from the sun.

Careers

Cristy Mitchell

Meteorologist Predicting floods, observing a tornado develop inside a storm, watching the growth of a hurricane, and issuing flood warnings are all in a day's work for Cristy Mitchell. As a meteorologist for the National Weather Service, Mitchell spends each working day observing the powerful forces of nature. When asked what made her job interesting, Mitchell replied, "There's nothing like the adrenaline rush you get when you see a tornado coming!"

Perhaps the most familiar field of meteorology is weather forecasting. However, meteorology is also used in air-pollution control, weather control, agricultural planning, and even criminal and civil investigations. Meteorologists also study trends in Earth's climate.

Meteorologists such as Mitchell use high-tech tools—computers and satellites—to collect data. By analyzing such data, Mitchell is able to forecast the weather.

Social Studies ACTIVITY

An almanac is a type of calendar that contains various information, including weather forecasts and astronomical data, for every day of the year. Many people used almanacs before meteorologists started to forecast the weather on TV. Use an almanac from the library to find out what the weather was on the day that you were born.

To learn more about these Science in Action topics, visit **go.hrw.com** and type in the keyword **HZ5WEAF.**

Current Science

Check out Current Science® articles related to this chapter by visiting go.hrw.com. Just type in the keyword HZ5CS16.

Studying Space

About the PHOTO

This time-exposure photograph was taken at an observatory located high in the mountains of Chile. As the night passed, the photograph recorded the stars as they circled the southern celestial pole. Just as Earth's rotation causes the sun to appear to move across the sky during the day, Earth's rotation also causes the stars to appear to move across the night sky.

PRE-READING ACTIVITY

FOLDNOTES

Four-Corner Fold

Before you read the chapter, create the FoldNote entitled "Four-Corner Fold" described in the **Study Skills** section of the Appendix. Label the flaps of the four-corner fold with "Astronomy," "Telescopes," "Mapping the Stars," and "Artificial Satellites." As you read the chapter, write information you learn about each category under the appropriate flap.

People in Science

Neil deGrasse Tyson

Star Writer When Neil deGrasse Tyson was nine years old, he visited a planetarium for the first time. Tyson was so affected by the experience he decided at that moment to dedicate his life to studying the universe. Tyson began studying the stars through a telescope on the roof of his apartment building. This interest led Tyson to attend the Bronx High School of Science, where he studied astronomy and physics. Tyson's passion for astronomy continued when he was a student at Harvard. However, Tyson soon realized that he wanted to share his love of astronomy with the public. So, today Tyson is America's best-known astrophysicist. When something really exciting happens in the universe, such as the discovery of evidence of water on Mars, Tyson is often asked to explain the discovery to the public. He has been interviewed hundreds of times on TV programs and has written several books. Tyson also writes a monthly column in the magazine *Natural History*. But writing and appearing on TV isn't even his day job! Tyson is the director of the Hayden Planetarium in New York—the same planetarium that ignited his interest in astronomy when he was nine years old!

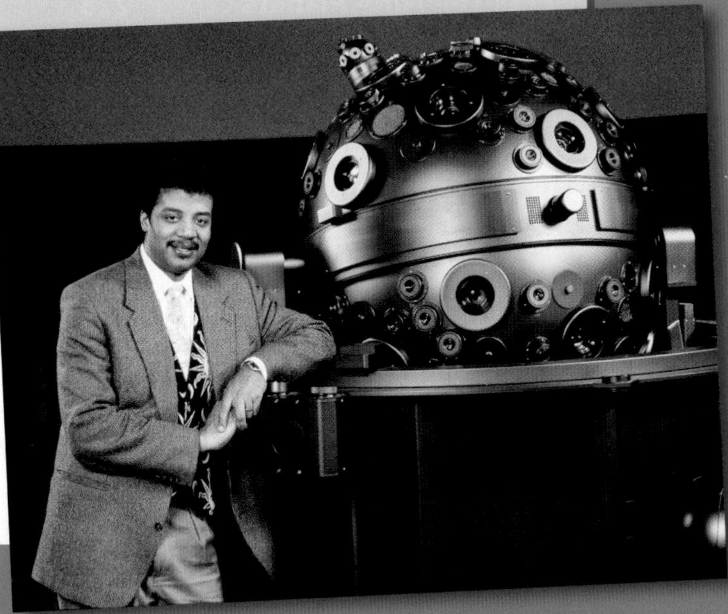

Language Arts ACTIVITY

WRITING SKILL Be a star writer! Visit a planetarium or find a Web site that offers a virtual tour of the universe. Write a magazine-style article about the experience.

To learn more about these Science in Action topics, visit **go.hrw.com** and type in the keyword **HZ5OBSF.**

Current Science

Check out Current Science® articles related to this chapter by visiting go.hrw.com. Just type in the keyword HZ5CS18.

A Family of Planets

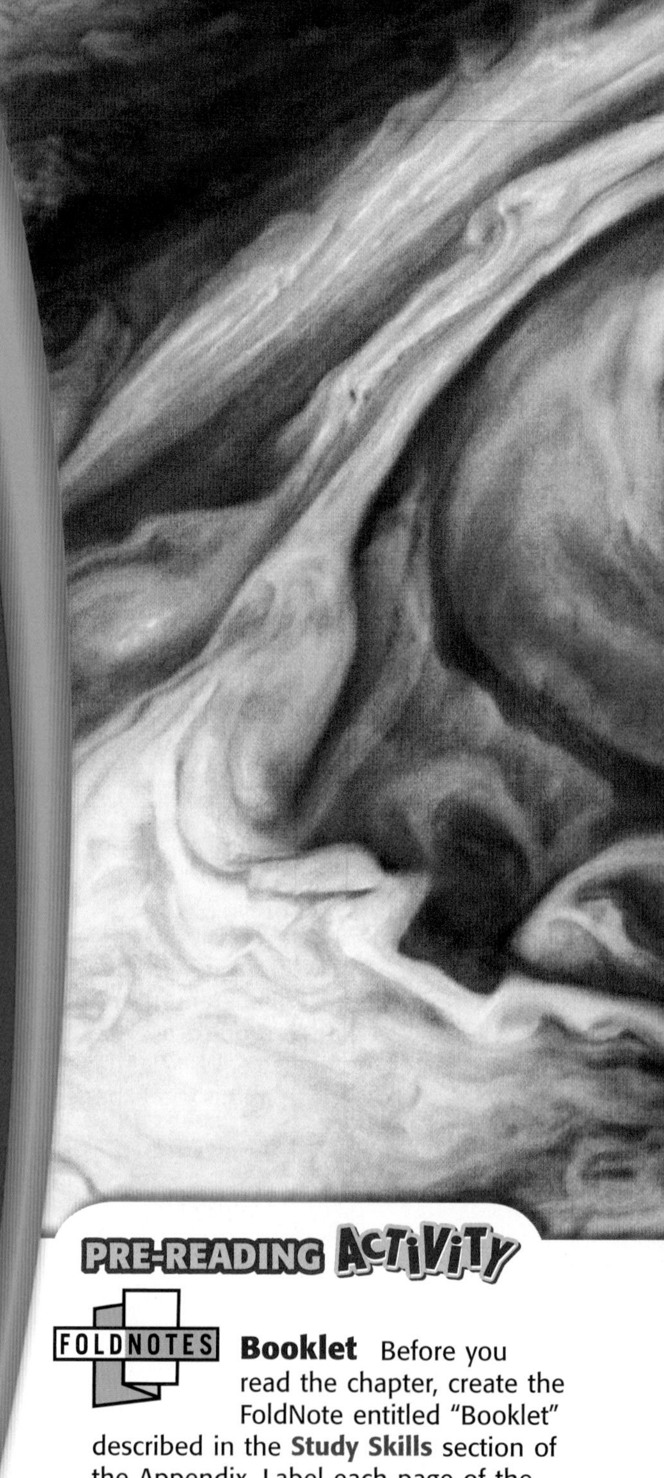

About the PHOTO

These rich swirls of color may remind you of a painting you might see in an art museum. But this photograph is of the planet Jupiter. The red swirl, called the Great Red Spot, is actually a hurricane-like storm system that is 3 times the diameter of Earth!

PRE-READING ACTIVITY

FOLDNOTES **Booklet** Before you read the chapter, create the FoldNote entitled "Booklet" described in the **Study Skills** section of the Appendix. Label each page of the booklet with a name of a planet in our solar system. As you read the chapter, write what you learn about each planet on the appropriate page of the booklet.

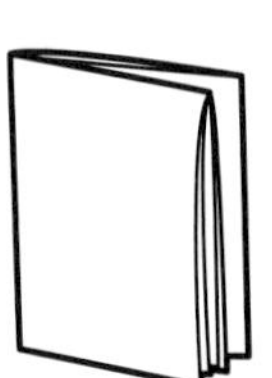

START-UP ACTIVITY

Measuring Space

Do the following activity to get a better idea of your solar neighborhood.

Procedure

1. Use a **meterstick** and some **chalk** to draw a line 2 m long on a **chalkboard.** Draw a large dot at one end of the line. This dot represents the sun.
2. Draw smaller dots on the line to represent the relative distances of each of the planets from the sun, based on information in the table.

Analysis

1. What do you notice about how the planets are spaced?

Planet	Distance from sun	
	Millions of km	Scaled to cm
Mercury	57.9	2
Venus	108.2	4
Earth	149.6	5
Mars	227.9	8
Jupiter	778.4	26
Saturn	1,424.0	48
Uranus	2,827.0	97
Neptune	4,499.0	151
Pluto	5,943.0	200

SECTION 1

The Nine Planets

Did you know that planets, when viewed from Earth, look like stars to the naked eye? Ancient astronomers were intrigued by these "stars" which seemed to wander in the sky.

READING WARM-UP

Objectives

- List the planets in the order in which they orbit the sun.
- Explain how scientists measure distances in space.
- Describe how the planets in our solar system were discovered.
- Describe three ways in which the inner planets and outer planets differ.

Terms to Learn

astronomical unit

READING STRATEGY

Paired Summarizing Read this section silently. In pairs, take turns summarizing the material. Stop to discuss ideas that seem confusing.

Ancient astronomers named these "stars" planets, which means "wanderers" in Greek. These astronomers knew planets were physical bodies and could predict their motions. But scientists did not begin to explore these worlds until the 17th century, when Galileo used the telescope to study planets and stars. Now, scientists have completed more than 150 successful missions to moons, planets, comets, and asteroids in our cosmic neighborhood.

Our Solar System

Our *solar system,* shown in **Figure 1,** includes the sun, the planets, and many smaller objects. In some cases, these bodies may be organized into smaller systems of their own. For example, the Saturn system is made of the planet Saturn and the several moons that orbit Saturn. In this way, our solar system is a combination of many smaller systems.

Figure 1 *These images show the relative diameters of the planets and the sun.*

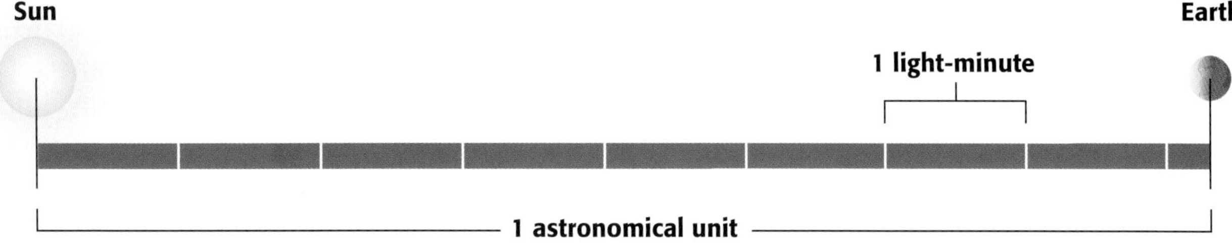

Figure 2 *One astronomical unit equals about 8.3 light-minutes.*

Measuring Interplanetary Distances

One way that scientists measure distances in space is by using the astronomical unit. One **astronomical unit** (AU) is the average distance between the sun and Earth, or approximately 150,000,000 km. Another way to measure distances in space is by using the speed of light. Light travels at about 300,000 km/s in space. This means that in 1 s, light travels 300,000 km.

In 1 min, light travels nearly 18,000,000 km. This distance is also called a *light-minute.* Look at **Figure 2.** Light from the sun takes 8.3 min to reach Earth. So, the distance from Earth to the sun, or 1 AU, is 8.3 light-minutes. Distances in the solar system can be measured in light-minutes and light-hours.

astronomical unit the average distance between the Earth and the sun; approximately 150 million kilometers (symbol, AU)

Reading Check How far does light travel in 1 s? (*See the Appendix for answers to Reading Checks.*)

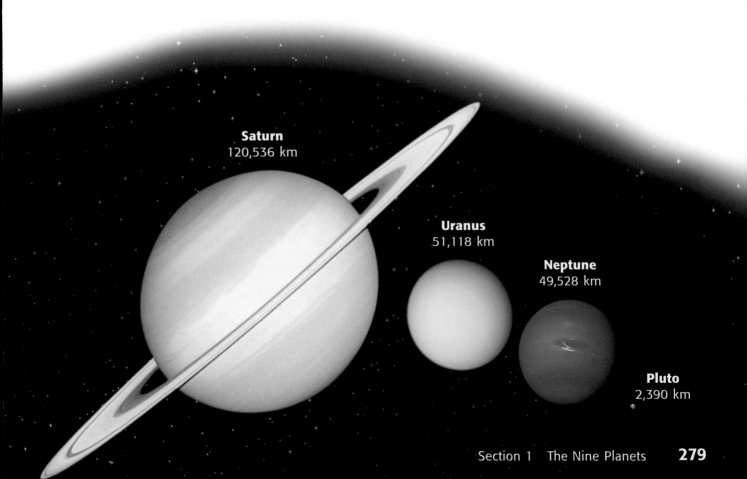

Saturn
120,536 km

Uranus
51,118 km

Neptune
49,528 km

Pluto
2,390 km

The Discovery of the Solar System

For another activity related to this chapter, go to **go.hrw.com** and type in the keyword **HZ5FAMW.**

Up until the 17th century, the universe was thought to have only eight bodies. These bodies included the planets Earth, Mercury, Venus, Mars, Jupiter, and Saturn, the sun, and the Earth's moon. These bodies are the only ones that can be seen from Earth without using a telescope.

After the telescope was invented in the 17th century, however, more discoveries were made. By the end of the 17th century, nine more large bodies were discovered. These bodies were moons of Jupiter and Saturn.

By the 18th century, the planet Uranus, along with two of its moons and two more of Saturn's moons, was discovered. In the 19th century, Neptune, as well as moons of several other planets, was discovered. Finally, in the 20th century, the ninth planet, Pluto, was discovered.

The Inner and Outer Solar Systems

The solar system is divided into two main parts: the inner solar system and the outer solar system. The inner solar system contains the four planets that are closest to the sun. The outer solar system contains the planets that are farthest from the sun.

The Inner Planets

The planets of the inner solar system, shown in **Figure 3,** are more closely spaced than the planets of the outer solar system. The inner planets are also known as the *terrestrial planets* because their surfaces are dense and rocky. However, each of the inner planets is unique.

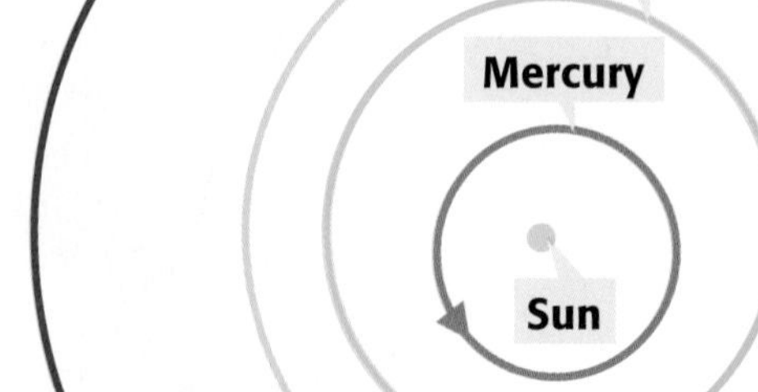

Figure 3 *The inner planets are the planets that are closest to the sun.*

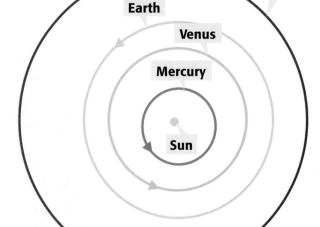

The Outer Planets

The planets of the outer solar system include Jupiter, Saturn, Uranus, Neptune, and Pluto. The outer planets are very different from the inner planets, as you will soon find out.

Unlike the inner planets, the outer planets, except for Pluto, are large and are composed mostly of gases. Because of this, Jupiter, Saturn, Uranus, and Neptune are known as gas giants. The atmospheres of these planets blend smoothly into the denser layers of their interiors. The icy planet Pluto is the only planet of the outer solar system that is small, dense, and rocky. You can see a diagram of the outer solar system in **Figure 4.**

Reading Check **Which planets are in the outer solar system?**

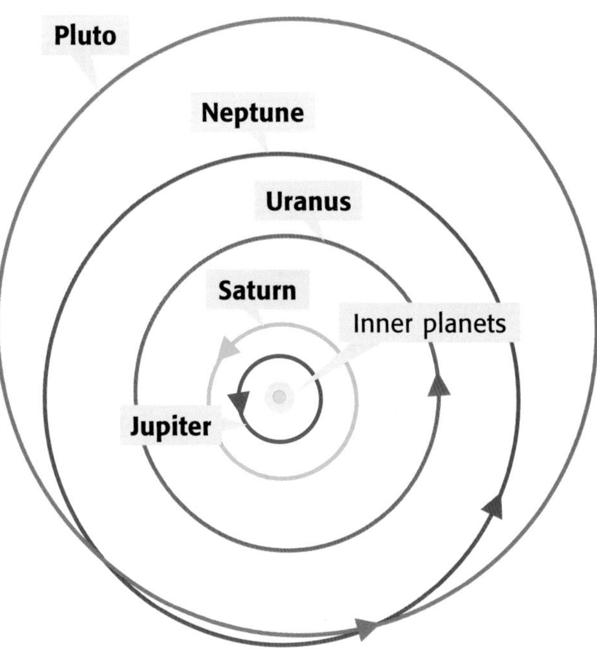

Figure 4 The planets of the outer solar system are the farthest from the sun.

SECTION Review

Summary

- In the order in which they orbit the sun, the nine planets are Mercury, Venus, Earth, Mars, Jupiter, Saturn, Uranus, Neptune, and Pluto.
- Two ways in which scientists measure distances in space are to use astronomical units and to use light-years.
- The inner planets are spaced more closely together, are smaller, and are rockier than the outer planets.

Using Key Terms

1. In your own words, write a definition for the term *astronomical unit.*

Understanding Key Ideas

2. When was the planet Uranus discovered?
   a. before the 17th century
   b. in the 18th century
   c. in the 19th century
   d. in the 20th century
3. The invention of what instrument helped early scientists discover more bodies in the solar system?
4. Which of the nine planets are included in the outer solar system?
5. Describe how the inner planets are different from the outer planets.

Math Skills

6. If Venus is 6.0 light-minutes from the sun, what is Venus's distance from the sun in astronomical units?

Critical Thinking

7. **Analyzing Methods** The distance between Earth and the sun is measured in light-minutes, but the distance between Pluto and the sun is measured in light-hours. Explain why.

SECTION 2

The Inner Planets

In the inner solar system, you will find one of the hottest places in our solar system as well as the only planet known to support life.

READING WARM-UP

Objectives

- Explain the difference between a planet's period of rotation and period of revolution.
- Describe the difference between prograde and retrograde rotation.
- Describe the individual characteristics of Mercury, Venus, Earth, and Mars.
- Identify the characteristics that make Earth suitable for life.

Terms to Learn

terrestrial planet
prograde rotation
retrograde rotation

READING STRATEGY

Reading Organizer As you read this section, create an outline of the section. Use the headings from the section in your outline.

The inner planets are also called **terrestrial planets** because, like Earth, they are very dense and rocky. The inner planets are smaller, denser, and rockier than the outer planets. In this section, you will learn more about the individual characteristics of Mercury, Venus, Earth, and Mars.

terrestrial planet one of the highly dense planets nearest to the sun; Mercury, Venus, Mars, and Earth

Mercury: Closest to the Sun

If you visited the planet Mercury, shown in **Figure 1,** you would find a very strange world. For one thing, on Mercury you would weigh only 38% of what you weigh on Earth. The weight you have on Earth is due to surface gravity, which is less on less massive planets. Also, because of Mercury's slow rotation, a day on Mercury is almost 59 Earth days long! The amount of time that an object takes to rotate once is called its *period of rotation.* So, Mercury's period of rotation is almost 59 Earth days long.

A Year on Mercury

Another curious thing about Mercury is that its year is only 88 Earth days long. As you know, a *year* is the time that a planet takes to go around the sun once. The motion of a body orbiting another body in space is called *revolution.* The time an object takes to revolve around the sun once is called its *period of revolution.* Every 88 Earth days, or 1.5 Mercurian days, Mercury revolves once around the sun.

Figure 1 *This image of Mercury was taken by the* Mariner 10 *spacecraft on March 24, 1974, from a distance of 5,380,000 km.*

Mercury Statistics	
Distance from sun	3.2 light-minutes
Period of rotation	58 days, 19 h
Period of revolution	88 days
Diameter	4,879 km
Density	5.43 g/cm^3
Surface temperature	−173°C to 427°C
Surface gravity	38% of Earth's

Venus Statistics	
Distance from sun Period of rotation Period of revolution	6.0 light-minutes 243 days, 16 h (R)* 224 days, 17 h
Diameter Density Surface temperature Surface gravity	12,104 km 5.24 g/cm^3 464°C 91% of Earth's

*R = retrograde rotation

Figure 2 *This image of Venus was taken by* Mariner 10 *on February 5, 1974. The uppermost layer of clouds contains sulfuric acid.*

Venus: Earth's Twin?

Look at **Figure 2.** In many ways, Venus is more like Earth than any other planet. Venus is only slightly smaller, less massive, and less dense than Earth. But in other ways, Venus is very different from Earth. On Venus, the sun rises in the west and sets in the east. The reason is that Venus and Earth rotate in opposite directions. Earth is said to have **prograde rotation** because it appears to spin in a *counterclockwise* direction when it is viewed from above its North Pole. If a planet spins in a *clockwise* direction, the planet is said to have **retrograde rotation.**

prograde rotation the counterclockwise spin of a planet or moon as seen from above the planet's North Pole; rotation in the same direction as the sun's rotation

retrograde rotation the clockwise spin of a planet or moon as seen from above the planet's North Pole

The Atmosphere of Venus

Of the terrestrial planets, Venus has the densest atmosphere. Venus's atmosphere has 90 times the pressure of Earth's atmosphere! The air on Venus is mostly carbon dioxide, but the air is also made of some of the most destructive acids known. The carbon dioxide traps thermal energy from sunlight in a process called the *greenhouse effect.* The greenhouse effect causes Venus's surface temperature to be very high. At 464°C, Venus has the hottest surface of any planet in the solar system.

Mapping Venus's Surface

Between 1990 and 1992, the *Magellan* spacecraft mapped the surface of Venus by using radar waves. The radar waves traveled through the clouds and bounced off the planet's surface. Data gathered from the radar waves showed that Venus, like Earth, has volcanoes.

Reading Check **What technology was used to map the surface of Venus?** (*See the Appendix for answers to Reading Checks.*)

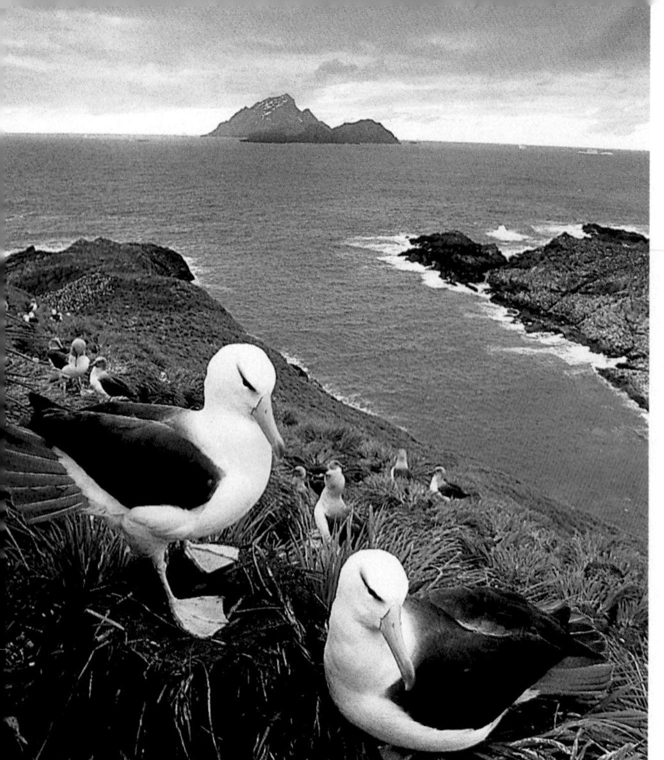

Figure 3 *Earth is the only planet known to support life.*

Earth: An Oasis in Space

Living things, such as the plants and birds in **Figure 3,** can live on Earth. And as far as scientists know, Earth is the only planet that can support life. Earth is mostly rock. But nearly three-fourths of Earth's surface is covered by a thin layer of water. The entire planet is covered by a thin blanket of air. Water and the gases in air help support life. Why do the conditions for life exist on Earth, but not on nearby planets?

Water on Earth

Earth formed at just the right distance from the sun. Earth is warm enough to keep most of its water from freezing. But unlike Venus, Earth is cool enough to keep its water from boiling away. Liquid water is a vital part of the chemical processes that living things depend on for survival.

The Earth from Space

The picture of Earth shown in **Figure 4** was taken from space. You might think that the only goal of space exploration is to make discoveries beyond Earth. But the National Aeronautics and Space Administration (NASA) has a program to study Earth by using satellites in the same way that scientists study other planets. This program is called the Earth Science Enterprise. Its goal is to study the Earth as a global system that is made of smaller systems. These smaller systems include the atmosphere, land, ice, the oceans, and life. The program will also help us understand how humans affect the global environment. By studying Earth from space, scientists hope to understand how different parts of the global system interact.

Reading Check **What is the Earth Science Enterprise?**

Earth Statistics	
Distance from sun	8.3 light-minutes
Period of rotation	23 h, 56 min
Period of revolution	365 days, 6 h
Diameter	12,756 km
Density	5.52 g/cm^3
Surface temperature	−13°C to 37°C
Surface gravity	100% of Earth's

Figure 4 *This image of Earth was taken on December 7, 1972, by the crew of the* Apollo 17 *spacecraft while on their way to the moon.*

Mars Statistics	
Distance from sun Period of rotation Period of revolution	12.7 light-minutes 24 h, 40 min 1 year, 322 days
Diameter Density Surface temperature Surface gravity	6,794 km 3.93 g/cm^3 −123°C to 37°C 38% of Earth's

Figure 5 *This Viking orbiter image shows the eastern hemisphere of Mars. The large circular feature in the center is the impact crater Schiaparelli, which has a diameter of 450 km.*

Mars: Our Intriguing Neighbor

Mars, shown in **Figure 5,** is perhaps the most studied planet in the solar system other than Earth. Much of our knowledge of Mars has come from information gathered by spacecraft. *Viking 1* and *Viking 2* landed on Mars in 1976, and *Mars Pathfinder* landed on Mars in 1997.

The Atmosphere of Mars

Because of its thinner atmosphere and greater distance from the sun, Mars is a cold planet. Midsummer temperatures recorded by the *Mars Pathfinder* range from –13°C to –77°C. Martian air is so thin that the air pressure on the surface of Mars is about the same as it is 30 km above Earth's surface. This distance is about 3 times higher than most planes fly! The air pressure is so low that any liquid water would quickly boil away. The only water found on the surface of Mars is in the form of ice.

Water on Mars

Even though liquid water cannot exist on Mars's surface today, there is strong evidence that it existed there in the past. **Figure 6** shows an area on Mars with features that might have resulted from deposition of sediment in a lake. This finding means that in the past Mars might have been a warmer place and had a thicker atmosphere.

Figure 6 *The origin of the features shown in this image is unknown. The features might have resulted from deposition of sediment in a lake.*

CONNECTION TO Physics

WRITING SKILL **Boiling Point on Mars** At sea level on Earth's surface, water boils at 100°C. But if you try to boil water on top of a high mountain, you will find that the boiling point is lower than 100°C. Do some research to find out why. Then, in your own words, explain why liquid water cannot exist on Mars, based on what you learned.

Where Is the Water Now?

Mars has two polar icecaps made of both frozen water and frozen carbon dioxide. But the polar icecaps do not have enough water to create a thick atmosphere or rivers. Looking closely at the walls of some Martian craters, scientists have found that the debris around the craters looks as if it were made by the flow of mud rather than by dry soil. In this case, where might some of the "lost" Martian water have gone? Many scientists think that it is frozen beneath the Martian soil.

Martian Volcanoes

Mars has a rich volcanic history. Unlike Earth, where volcanoes exist in many places, Mars has only two large volcanic systems. The largest, the Tharsis region, stretches 8,000 km across the planet. The largest mountain in the solar system, Olympus Mons, is an extinct shield volcano similar to Mauna Kea on the island of Hawaii. Mars not only is smaller and cooler than Earth but also has a slightly different chemical makeup. This makeup may have kept the Martian crust from moving around as Earth's crust does. As a result, the volcanoes kept building up in the same spots on Mars. Images and data sent back by probes such as the *Sojourner* rover, shown in **Figure 7,** are helping to explain Mars's mysterious past.

Reading Check **What characteristics of Mars may explain why Mars has only two large volcanic systems?**

Figure 7 *The* Sojourner *rover, part of the Mars Pathfinder mission, is shown here creeping up to a rock named Yogi to measure its composition. The solar panel on the rover's back collected the solar energy used to power the rover's motor.*

A True Planet?

Because Pluto is so small and is so unusual, some scientists think that it should not be classified as a planet. In fact, some scientists agree that Pluto could be considered a large asteroid or comet—large enough to have its own satellite. However, because Pluto was historically classified as a planet, it most likely will remain so.

Pluto is the only planet that has not been visited by a NASA mission. However, plans are underway to visit Pluto and Charon in 2006. During this mission, scientists hope to learn more about this unusual planet and map the surface of both Pluto and Charon.

Surviving Space

WRITING SKILL Imagine it is the year 2150 and you are flying a spacecraft to Pluto. Suddenly, your systems fail, giving you only one chance to land safely. You can't head back to Earth. With a parent, write a paragraph explaining which planet you would choose to land on.

ACTIVITY

SECTION Review

Summary

- Jupiter is the largest planet in our solar system. Energy from the interior of Jupiter is transferred to its exterior.
- Saturn is the second-largest planet and, in some ways, is still forming as a planet.
- Uranus's axis of rotation is tilted by almost 90°.
- Neptune has a faint ring, and its atmosphere contains belts of clouds.
- Pluto is the smallest planet, and its moon, Charon, is more than half its size.

Using Key Terms

1. In your own words, write a definition for the term *gas giant.*

Understanding Key Ideas

2. The many colors of Jupiter's atmosphere are probably caused by _____ in the atmosphere.
   - **a.** clouds of water
   - **b.** methane
   - **c.** ammonia
   - **d.** organic compounds
3. Why do scientists claim that Saturn, in a way, is still forming?
4. Why does Uranus have a blue green color?
5. What is unusual about Pluto's moon, Charon?
6. What is the Great Red Spot?
7. Explain why Jupiter radiates more energy into space than it receives from the sun.
8. How do the gas giants differ from the terrestrial planets?
9. What is so unusual about Uranus's axis of rotation?

Math Skills

10. Pluto is 5.5 light-hours from the sun. How far is Pluto from the sun in astronomical units? (Hint: 1 AU = 8.3 light-minutes)
11. If Jupiter is 43.3 light-minutes from the sun and Neptune is 4.2 light-hours from the sun, how far from Jupiter is Neptune?

Critical Thinking

12. **Evaluating Data** What conclusions can your draw about the properties of a planet just by knowing how far it is from the sun?
13. **Applying Concepts** Why isn't the word *surface* included in the statistics for the gas giants?

For a variety of links related to this chapter, go to www.scilinks.org

Topic: The Outer Planets
SciLinks code: HSM1091

SECTION 4

Moons

If you could, which moon would you visit? With volcanoes, craters, and possible underground oceans, the moons in our solar system would be interesting places to visit.

READING WARM-UP

Objectives

- Describe the current theory of the origin of Earth's moon.
- Explain what causes the phases of Earth's moon.
- Describe the difference between a solar eclipse and a lunar eclipse.
- Describe the individual characteristics of the moons of other planets.

Terms to Learn

satellite
phase
eclipse

READING STRATEGY

Reading Organizer As you read this section, make a table comparing solar eclipses and lunar eclipses.

Natural or artificial bodies that revolve around larger bodies such as planets are called **satellites.** Except for Mercury and Venus, all of the planets have natural satellites called *moons.*

Luna: The Moon of Earth

Scientists have learned a lot from studying Earth's moon, which is also called *Luna*. The lunar rocks brought back during the Apollo missions were found to be about 4.6 billion years old. Because these rocks have hardly changed since they formed, scientists know the solar system itself is about 4.6 billion years old.

The Surface of the Moon

As you can see in **Figure 1,** the moon's history is written on its face. The surfaces of bodies that have no atmospheres preserve a record of almost all of the impacts that the bodies have had. Because scientists now know the age of the moon, they can count the number of impact craters to find the rate of cratering since the birth of our solar system. By knowing the rate of cratering, scientists are able to use the number of craters on any body to estimate how old the body's surface is. That way, scientists don't need to bring back rock samples.

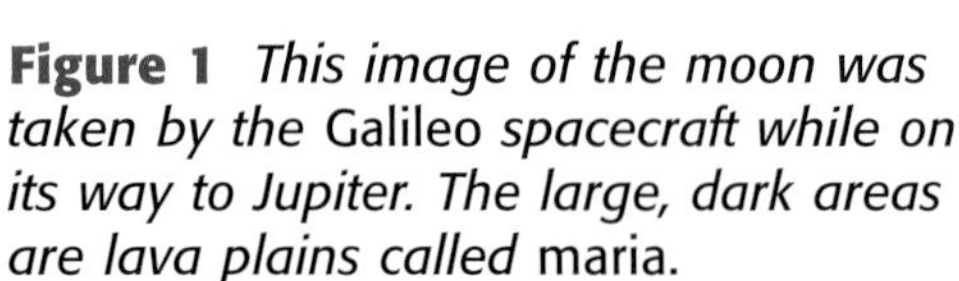

Figure 1 *This image of the moon was taken by the* Galileo *spacecraft while on its way to Jupiter. The large, dark areas are lava plains called* maria.

Moon Statistics	
Period of rotation	27 days, 9 hours
Period of revolution	27 days, 7 hours
Diameter	3,475 km
Density	3.34 g/cm^3
Surface temperature	−170 to 134°C
Surface gravity	16% of Earth's

Lunar Origins

Before scientists had rock samples from the moon, there were three popular explanations for the moon's formation: (1) The moon was a separate body captured by Earth's gravity, (2) the moon formed at the same time and from the same materials as the Earth, and (3) the newly formed Earth was spinning so fast that a piece flew off and became the moon.

When rock samples of the moon were brought back from the Apollo mission, the mystery was solved. Scientists found that the composition of the moon was similar to that of Earth's mantle. This evidence from the lunar rock samples supported the third explanation for the moon's formation.

The current theory is that a large, Mars-sized object collided with Earth while the Earth was still forming, as shown in **Figure 2.** The collision was so violent that part of the Earth's mantle was blasted into orbit around Earth to form the moon.

satellite a natural or artificial body that revolves around a planet

Reading Check **What is the current explanation for the formation of the moon?** (*See the Appendix for answers to Reading Checks.*)

Figure 2 Formation of the Moon

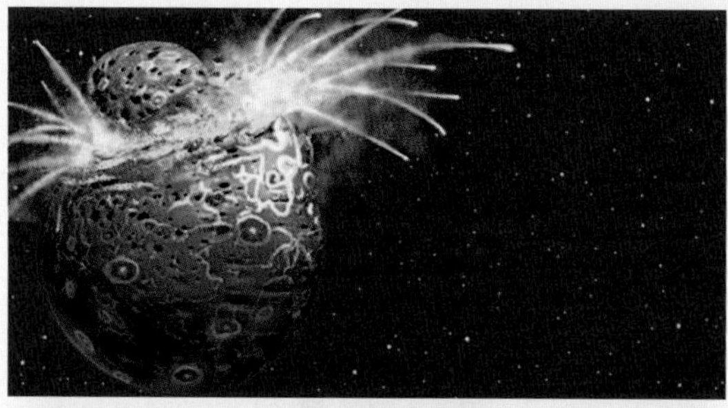

1 Impact
About 4.6 billion years ago, when Earth was still mostly molten, a large body collided with Earth. Scientists reason that the object must have been large enough to blast part of Earth's mantle into space, because the composition of the moon is similar to that of Earth's mantle.

2 Ejection
The resulting debris began to revolve around the Earth within a few hours of the impact. This debris consisted of mantle material from Earth and from the impacting body as well as part of the iron core of the impacting body.

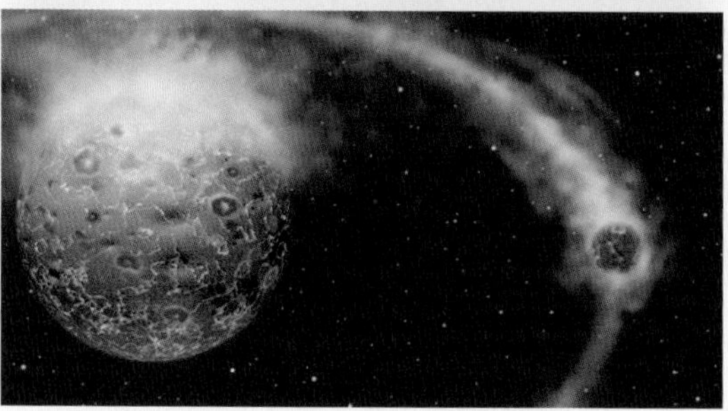

3 Formation
Soon after the giant impact, the clumps of material ejected into orbit around Earth began to join together to form the moon. Much later, as the moon cooled, additional impacts created deep basins and fractured the moon's surface. Lunar lava flowed from those cracks and flooded the basins to form the lunar maria that we see today.

Phases of the Moon

From Earth, one of the most noticeable aspects of the moon is its continually changing appearance. Within a month, the moon's Earthward face changes from a fully lit circle to a thin crescent and then back to a circle. These different appearances of the moon result from its changing position relative to Earth and the sun. As the moon revolves around Earth, the amount of sunlight on the side of the moon that faces Earth changes. The different appearances of the moon due to its changing position are called **phases.** The phases of the moon are shown in **Figure 3.**

phase the change in the sunlit area of one celestial body as seen from another celestial body

Waxing and Waning

When the moon is *waxing,* the sunlit fraction that we can see from Earth is getting larger. When the moon is *waning,* the sunlit fraction is getting smaller. Notice in **Figure 3** that even as the phases of the moon change, the total amount of sunlight that the moon gets remains the same. Half the moon is always in sunlight, just as half the Earth is always in sunlight. But because the moon's period of rotation is the same as its period of revolution, on Earth you always see the same side of the moon. If you lived on the far side of the moon, you would see the sun for half of each lunar day, but you would never see the Earth!

Figure 3 *The positions of the moon, sun, and Earth determine which phase the moon is in. The photo insets show how the moon looks from Earth at each phase.*

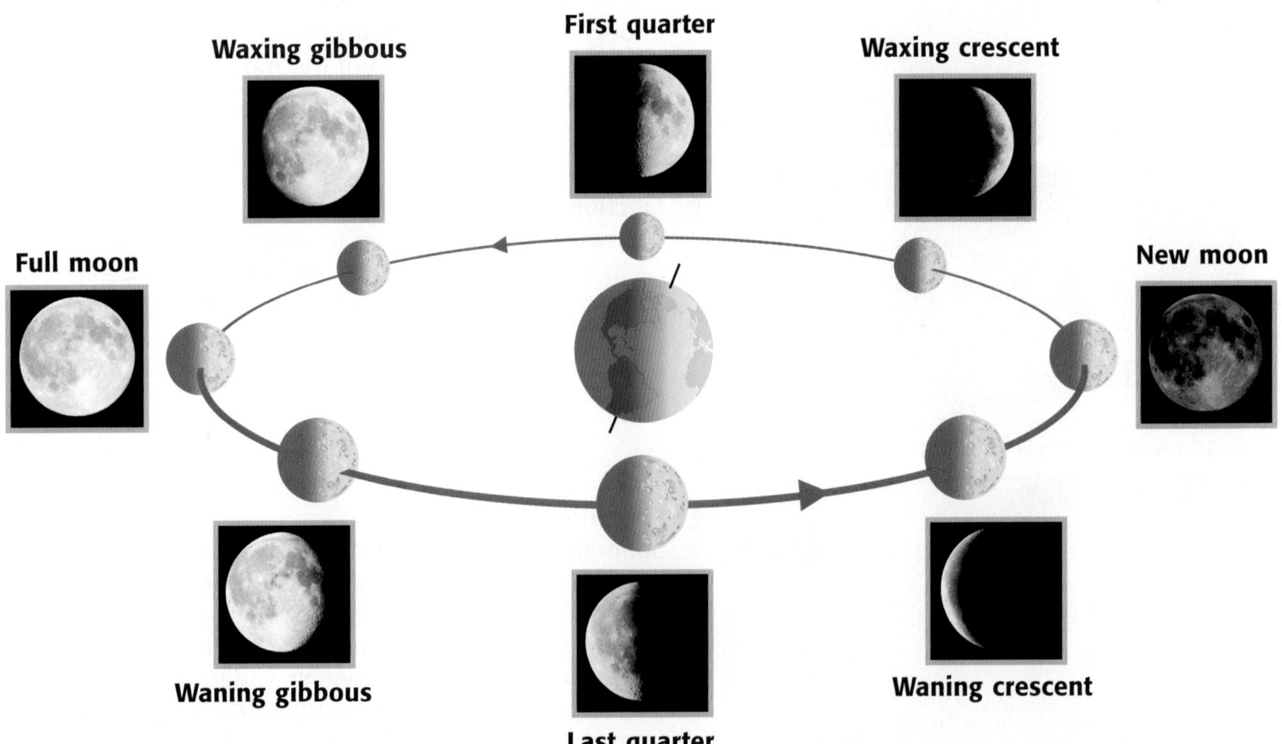

NEVER look directly at the sun! You can permanently damage your eyes.

Figure 4 *On the left is a diagram of the positions of the Earth and the moon during a solar eclipse. On the right is a picture of the sun's outer atmosphere, or* corona, *which is visible only when the entire disk of the sun is blocked by the moon.*

Eclipses

When the shadow of one celestial body falls on another, an **eclipse** occurs. A *solar eclipse* happens when the moon comes between Earth and the sun and the shadow of the moon falls on part of Earth. A *lunar eclipse* happens when Earth comes between the sun and the moon and the shadow of Earth falls on the moon.

Solar Eclipses

Because the moon's orbit is elliptical, the distance between the moon and the Earth changes. During an *annular eclipse*, the moon is farther from the Earth. The disk of the moon does not completely cover the disk of the sun. A thin ring of the sun shows around the moon's outer edge. When the moon is closer to the Earth, the moon appears to be the same size as the sun. During a *total solar eclipse*, the disk of the moon completely covers the disk of the sun, as shown in **Figure 4.**

eclipse an event in which the shadow of one celestial body falls on another

Reading Check **Describe what happens during a solar eclipse.**

Clever Insight

1. Cut out a circle of **heavy, white paper.** This circle will represent Earth.
2. Find **two spherical objects** and **several other objects** of different shapes.
3. Hold up each object in front of a **lamp** (which represents the sun) so that the object's shadow falls on the white paper circle.
4. Rotate your objects in all directions, and record the shapes of the shadows that the objects make.
5. Which objects always cast a curved shadow?

Figure 5 *On the left, you can see that the moon can have a reddish color during a lunar eclipse. On the right, you can see the positions of Earth and the moon during a lunar eclipse.*

Lunar Eclipses

As shown in **Figure 5,** the view during a lunar eclipse is spectacular. Earth's atmosphere acts like a lens and bends some of the sunlight into the Earth's shadow. When sunlight hits the particles in the atmosphere, blue light is filtered out. As a result, most of the remaining light that lights the moon is red.

The Tilted Orbit of the Moon

You may be wondering why you don't see solar and lunar eclipses every month. The reason is that the moon's orbit around Earth is tilted—by about 5°—relative to the orbit of Earth around the sun. This tilt is enough to place the moon out of Earth's shadow for most full moons and Earth out of the moon's shadow for most new moons.

Reading Check **Explain why you don't see solar and lunar eclipses every month.**

The Moons of Other Planets

The moons of the other planets range in size from very small to as large as terrestrial planets. All of the gas giants have multiple moons, and scientists are still discovering new moons. Some moons have very elongated, or elliptical, orbits, and some moons even orbit their planet backward! Many of the very small moons may be captured asteroids. As scientists are learning from recent space missions, moons may be some of the most bizarre and interesting places in the solar system!

The Moons of Mars

Mars's two moons, Phobos and Deimos, are small, oddly shaped satellites. Both moons are very dark. Their surface materials are much like those of some asteroids—large, rocky bodies in space. Scientists think that these two moons are asteroids caught by Mars's gravity.

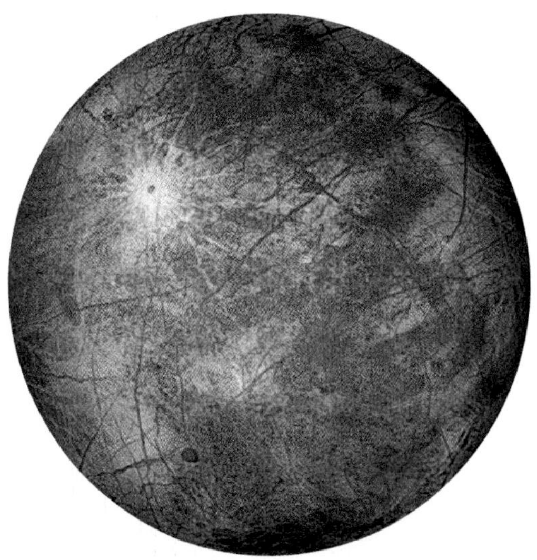

Figure 6 *Europa, Jupiter's fourth largest moon, might have liquid water beneath the moon's icy surface.*

The Moons of Jupiter

Jupiter has dozens of moons. The four largest moons—Ganymede, Callisto, Io, and Europa—were discovered in 1610 by Galileo. They are known as the *Galilean satellites*. The largest moon, Ganymede, is even larger than the planet Mercury! Many of the smaller moons probably are captured asteroids.

The Galilean satellite closest to Jupiter is Io, a truly bizarre world. Io is caught in a gravitational tug of war between Jupiter and Io's nearest neighbor, the moon Europa. This constant tugging stretches Io a little and causes it to heat up. As a result, Io is the most volcanically active body in the solar system!

Recent pictures of the moon Europa, shown in **Figure 6,** support the idea that liquid water may lie beneath the moon's icy surface. This idea makes many scientists wonder if life could have evolved in the underground oceans of Europa.

The Moons of Saturn

Like Jupiter, Saturn has dozens of moons. Most of these moons are small bodies that are made mostly of frozen water but contain some rocky material. The largest satellite, Titan, was discovered in 1655 by Christiaan Huygens. In 1980, the *Voyager 1* spacecraft flew past Titan and discovered a hazy orange atmosphere, as shown in **Figure 7.** Earth's early atmosphere may have been much like Titan's is now. In 1997, NASA launched the *Cassini* spacecraft to study Saturn and its moons, including Titan. By studying Titan, scientists hope to learn more about how life began on Earth.

Reading Check **How can scientists learn more about how life began on Earth by studying Titan?**

Figure 7 *Titan is Saturn's largest moon.*

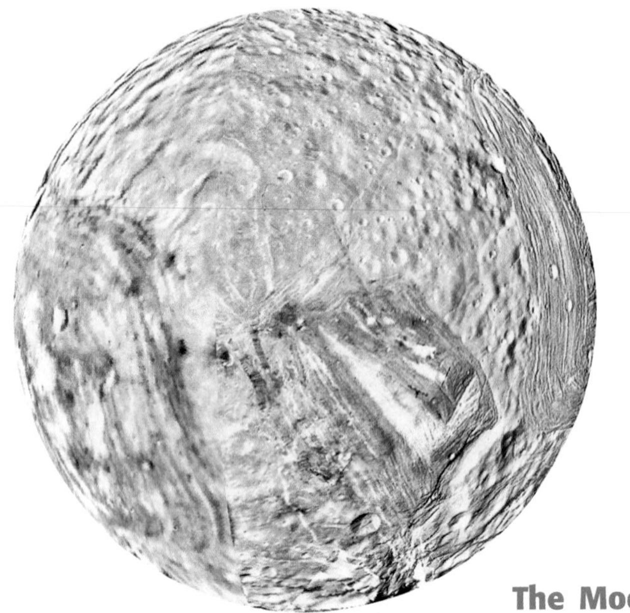

Figure 8 *This* Voyager 2 *image shows Miranda, the most unusual moon of Uranus. Its patchwork terrain indicates that it has had a violent history.*

The Moons of Uranus

Uranus has several moons. Like the moons of Saturn, Uranus's largest moons are made of ice and rock and are heavily cratered. The small moon Miranda, shown in **Figure 8,** has some of the strangest features in the solar system. Miranda's surface has smooth, cratered plains as well as regions that have grooves and cliffs. Scientists think that Miranda may have been hit and broken apart in the past. Gravity pulled the pieces together again, leaving a patchwork surface.

The Moons of Neptune

Neptune has several known moons, only one of which is large. This large moon, Triton, is shown in **Figure 9.** It revolves around the planet in a *retrograde,* or "backward," orbit. This orbit suggests that Triton may have been captured by Neptune's gravity. Triton has a very thin atmosphere made mostly of nitrogen gas. Triton's surface is mostly frozen nitrogen and methane. *Voyager 2* images reveal that Triton is geologically active. "Ice volcanoes," or geysers, eject nitrogen gas high into the atmosphere. The other moons of Neptune are small, rocky worlds much like the smaller moons of Saturn and Jupiter.

The Moon of Pluto

Pluto's only known moon, Charon, was discovered in 1978. Charon's period of revolution is the same as Pluto's period of rotation—about 6.4 days. So, one side of Pluto always faces Charon. In other words, if you stood on the surface of Pluto, Charon would always occupy the same place in the sky. Charon's orbit around Pluto is tilted relative to Pluto's orbit around the sun. As a result, Pluto, as seen from Earth, is sometimes eclipsed by Charon. But don't hold your breath; this eclipse happens only once every 120 years!

Reading Check **How often is Pluto eclipsed by Charon?**

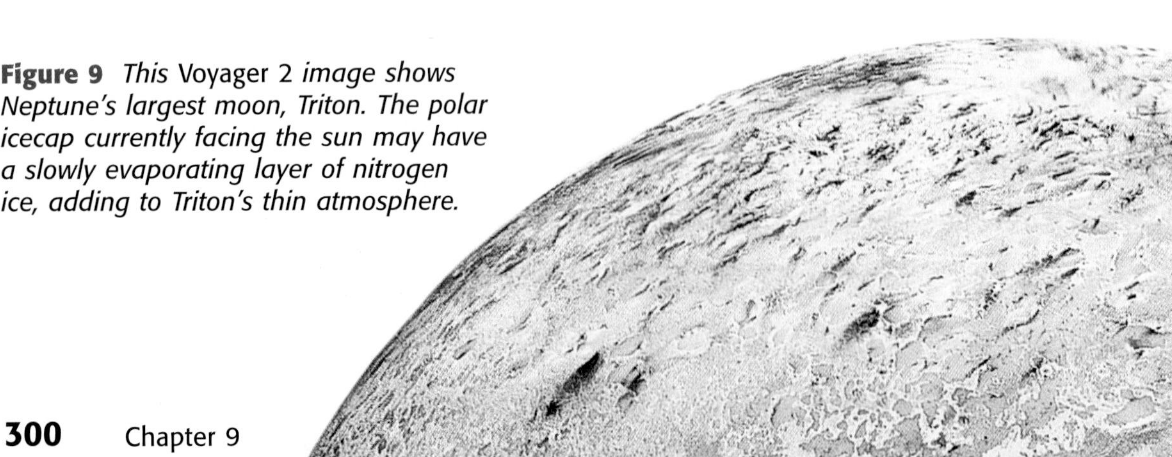

Figure 9 *This* Voyager 2 *image shows Neptune's largest moon, Triton. The polar icecap currently facing the sun may have a slowly evaporating layer of nitrogen ice, adding to Triton's thin atmosphere.*

SECTION
Review

Summary

- Scientists reason that the moon formed from the debris that was created after a large body collided with Earth.
- As the moon revolves around Earth, the amount of sunlight on the side of the moon changes. Because the amount of sunlight on the side of the moon changes, the moon's appearance from Earth changes. These changes in appearance are the phases of the moon.
- A solar eclipse happens when the shadow of the moon falls on Earth.
- A lunar eclipse happens when the shadow of Earth falls on the moon.
- Mars has 2 moons: Phobos and Deimos.
- Jupiter has dozens of moons. Ganymede, Io, Callisto, and Europa are the largest.
- Saturn has dozens of moons. Titan is the largest.
- Uranus has several moons.
- Neptune has several moons. Triton is the largest.
- Pluto has 1 known moon, Charon.

Using Key Terms

Complete each of the following sentences by choosing the correct term from the word bank.

satellite   eclipse

1. A(n) _____, or a body that revolves around a larger body, can be either artificial or natural.
2. A(n) _____ occurs when the shadow of one body in space falls on another body.

Understanding Key Ideas

3. Which of the following is a Galilean satellite?
   a. Phobos
   b. Deimos
   c. Ganymede
   d. Charon
4. Describe the current theory for the origin of Earth's moon.
5. What is the difference between a solar eclipse and a lunar eclipse?
6. What causes the phases of Earth's moon?

Critical Thinking

7. **Analyzing Methods** How can astronomers use the age of a lunar rock to estimate the age of the surface of a planet such as Mercury?
8. **Identifying Relationships** Charon stays in the same place in Pluto's sky, but the moon moves across Earth's sky. What causes this difference?

Interpreting Graphics

Use the diagram below to answer the questions that follow.

9. What type of eclipse is shown in the diagram?
10. Describe what is happening in the diagram.
11. Make a sketch of the type of eclipse that is not shown in the diagram.

SCILINKS.
NSTA
Developed and maintained by the National Science Teachers Association
For a variety of links related to this chapter, go to www.scilinks.org
Topic: Moons of Other Planets
SciLinks code: HSM0993

SECTION 5

Small Bodies in the Solar System

READING WARM-UP

Objectives

- Explain why comets, asteroids, and meteoroids are important to the study of the formation of the solar system.
- Describe the similarities of and differences between asteroids and meteoroids.
- Explain how cosmic impacts may affect life on Earth.

Terms to Learn

comet
asteroid
asteroid belt
meteoroid
meteorite
meteor

READING STRATEGY

Discussion Read this section silently. Write down questions that you have about this section. Discuss your questions in a small group.

Imagine you are traveling in a spacecraft to explore the edge of our solar system. You see several small bodies, as well as the planets and their satellites, moving through space.

The solar system contains not only planets and moons but other small bodies, including comets, asteroids, and meteoroids. Scientists study these objects to learn about the composition of the solar system.

Comets

A small body of ice, rock, and cosmic dust loosely packed together is called a **comet**. Some scientists refer to comets as "dirty snowballs" because of their composition. Comets formed in the cold, outer solar system. Nothing much has happened to comets since the birth of the solar system 4.6 billion years ago. Comets are probably left over from the time when the planets formed. As a result, each comet is a sample of the early solar system. Scientists want to learn more about comets to piece together the history of our solar system.

Comet Tails

When a comet passes close enough to the sun, solar radiation heats the ice so that the comet gives off gas and dust in the form of a long tail, as shown in **Figure 1.** Sometimes, a comet has two tails—an *ion tail* and a *dust tail*. The ion tail is made of electrically charged particles called *ions*. The solid center of a comet is called its *nucleus*. Comet nuclei can range in size from less than half a kilometer to more than 100 km in diameter.

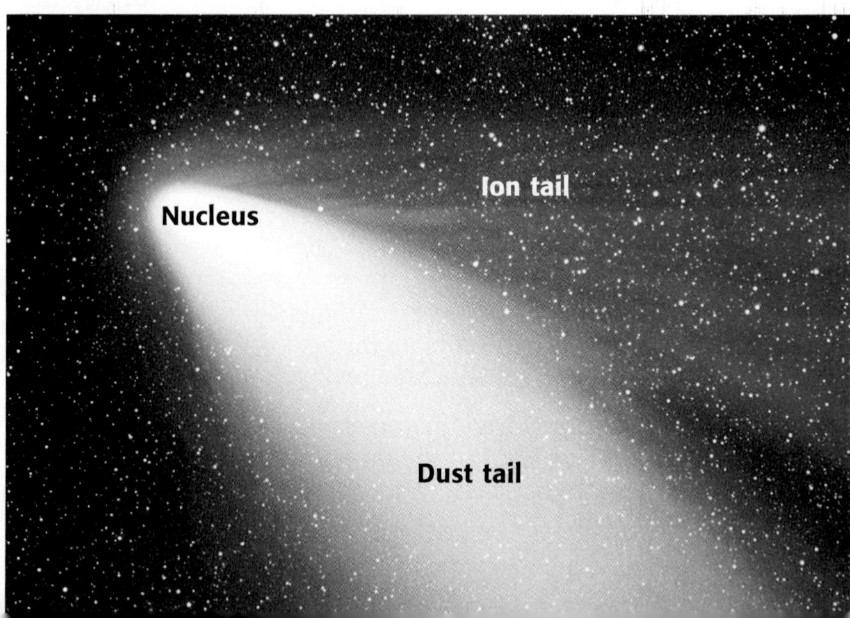

Figure 1 *This image shows the physical features of a comet when it is close to the sun. The nucleus of a comet is hidden by brightly lit gases and dust.*

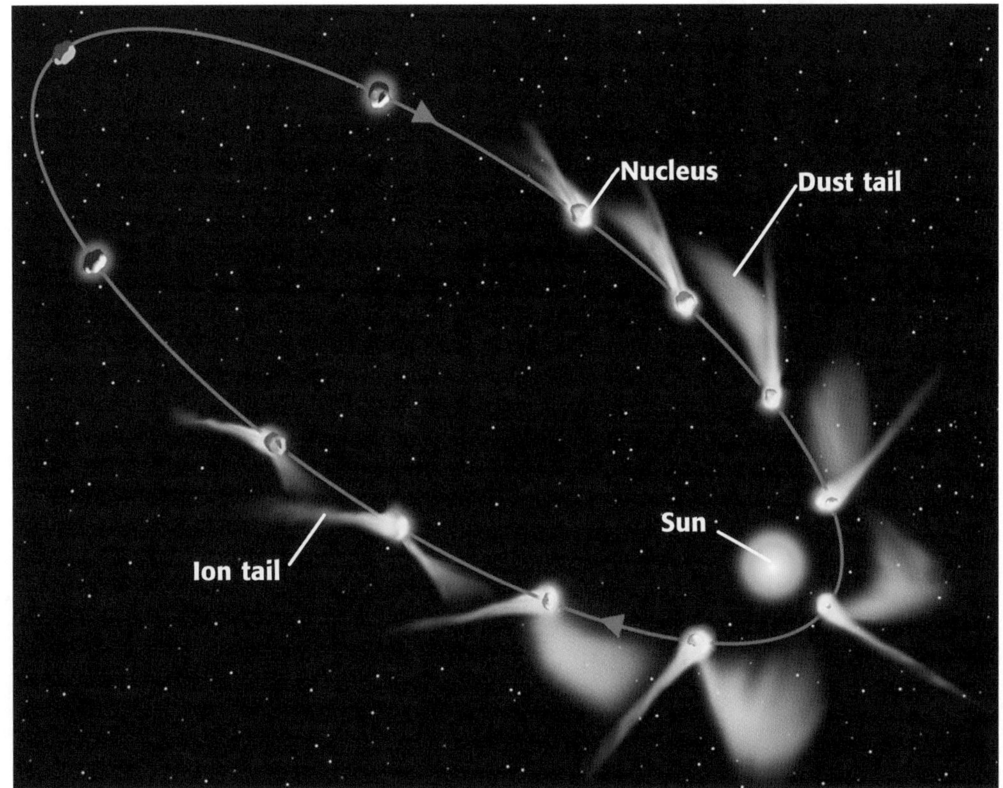

Figure 2 *Comets have very elongated orbits. When a comet gets close to the sun, the comet can develop one or two tails.*

Comet Orbits

The orbits of all bodies that move around the sun are ellipses. *Ellipses* are circles that are somewhat stretched out of shape. The orbits of most planets are close to perfect circles, but the orbits of comets are very elongated.

Notice in **Figure 2** that a comet's ion tail always points away from the sun. The reason is that the ion tail is blown away from the sun by *solar wind*, which is also made of ions. The dust tail tends to follow the comet's orbit around the sun. Dust tails do not always point away from the sun. When a comet is close to the sun, its tail can extend millions of kilometers through space!

comet a small body of ice, rock, and cosmic dust that follows an elliptical orbit around the sun and that gives off gas and dust in the form of a tail as it passes close to the sun

Comet Origins

Where do comets come from? Many scientists think that comets come from the Oort (AWRT) cloud, a spherical region that surrounds the solar system. When the gravity of a passing planet or star disturbs part of this cloud, comets can be pulled toward the sun. Another recently discovered region where comets exist is the Kuiper (KIE puhr) belt, which is the region outside the orbit of Neptune.

Reading Check **From which two regions do comets come?** *(See the Appendix for answers to Reading Checks.)*

CONNECTION TO Language Arts

WRITING SKILL **Interplanetary Journalist** In 1994, the world watched in awe as parts of the comet Shoemaker-Levy 9 collided with Jupiter, which caused enormous explosions. Imagine you were an interplanetary journalist who traveled through space to observe the comet during this time. Write an article describing your adventure.

asteroid a small, rocky object that orbits the sun, usually in a band between the orbits of Mars and Jupiter

asteroid belt the region of the solar system that is between the orbits of Mars and Jupiter and in which most asteroids orbit

Asteroids

Small, rocky bodies that revolve around the sun are called **asteroids.** They range in size from a few meters to more than 900 km in diameter. Asteroids have irregular shapes, although some of the larger ones are spherical. Most asteroids orbit the sun in the asteroid belt. The **asteroid belt** is a wide region between the orbits of Mars and Jupiter. Like comets, asteroids are thought to be material left over from the formation of the solar system.

Types of Asteroids

The composition of asteroids varies depending on where they are located within the asteroid belt. In the outermost region of the asteroid belt, asteroids have dark reddish brown to black surfaces. This coloring may indicate that the asteroids are rich in organic material. Asteroids that have dark gray surfaces are rich in carbon. In the innermost part of the asteroid belt are light gray asteroids that have either a stony or metallic composition. **Figure 3** shows three asteroids: Hektor, Ceres, and Vesta.

Figure 3 The Asteroid Belt

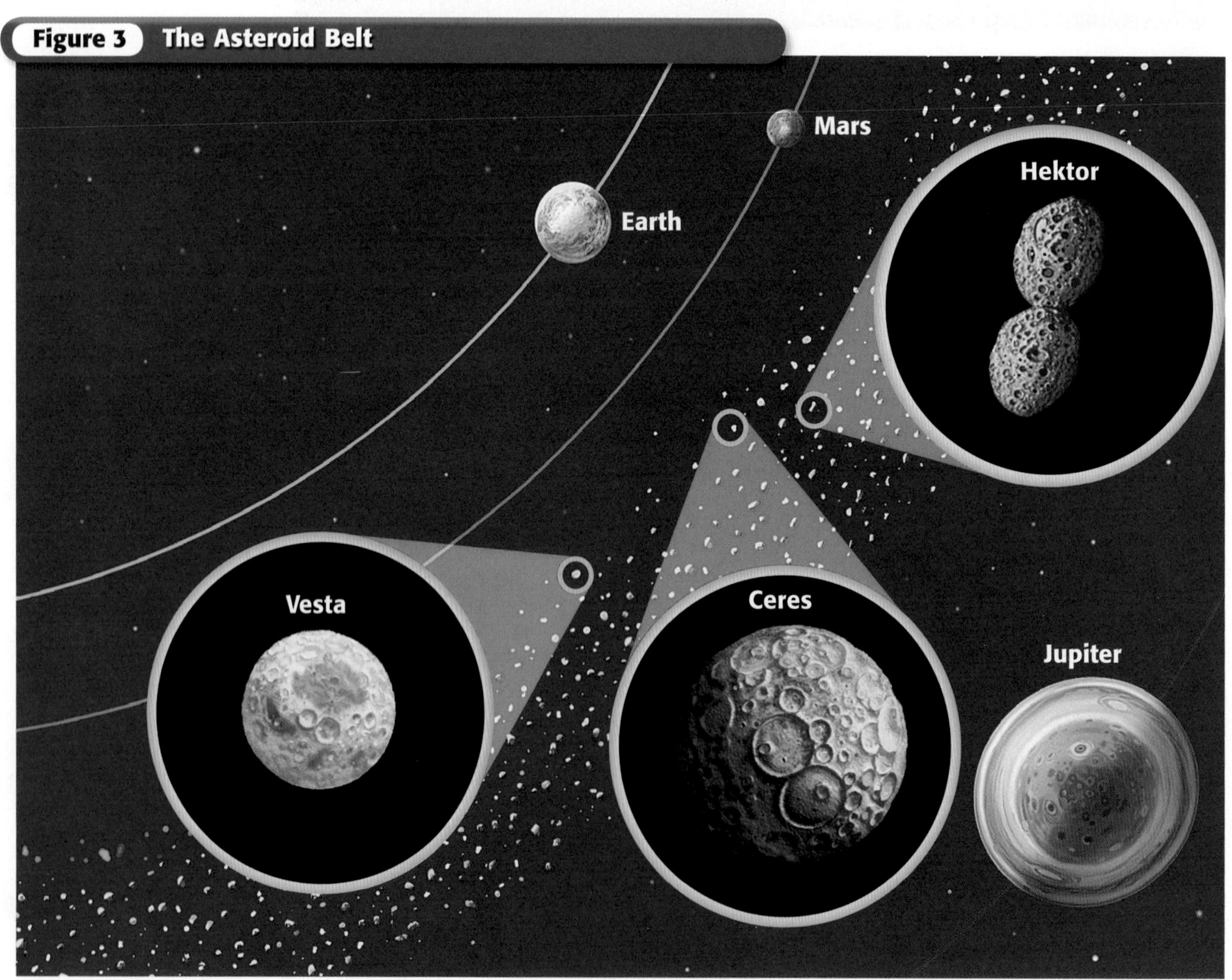

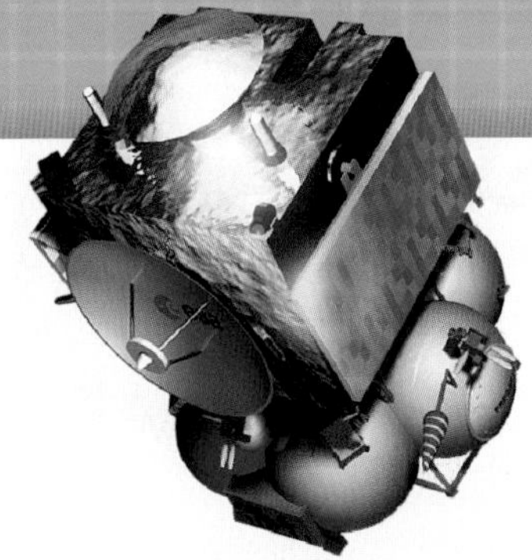

17 Explain the difference between prograde rotation and retrograde rotation.

18 Which characteristics of Earth make it suitable for life?

19 Describe the current theory for the origin of Earth's moon.

20 What causes the phases of the moon?

CRITICAL THINKING

21 **Concept Mapping** Use the following terms to create a concept map: *solar system, terrestrial planets, gas giants, moons, comets, asteroids,* and *meteoroids.*

22 **Applying Concepts** Even though we haven't yet retrieved any rock samples from Mercury's surface for radiometric dating, scientists know that the surface of Mercury is much older than that of Earth. How do scientists know this?

23 **Making Inferences** Where in the solar system might scientists search for life, and why?

24 **Analyzing Ideas** Is the far side of the moon always dark? Explain your answer.

25 **Predicting Consequences** If scientists could somehow bring Europa as close to the sun as the Earth is, 1 AU, how do you think Europa would be affected?

26 **Identifying Relationships** How did variations in the orbit of Uranus help scientists discover Neptune?

INTERPRETING GRAPHICS

The graph below shows density versus mass for Earth, Uranus, and Neptune. Mass is given in Earth masses—the mass of Earth is equal to 1 Earth mass. The relative volumes for the planets are shown by the size of each circle. Use the graph below to answer the questions that follow.

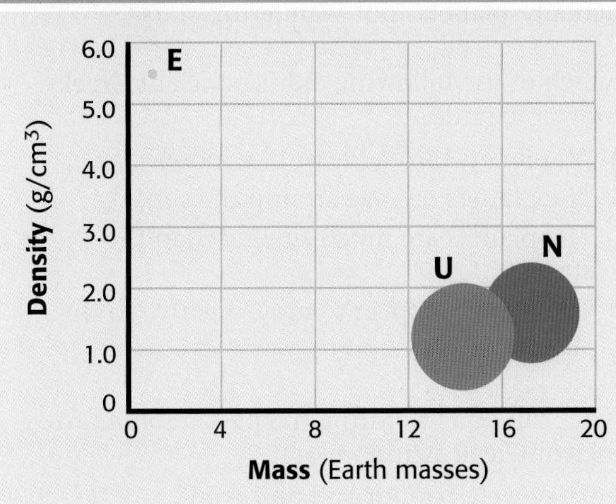

27 Which planet is denser, Uranus or Neptune? How can you tell?

28 You can see that although Earth has the smallest mass, it has the highest density of the three planets. How can Earth be the densest of the three when Uranus and Neptune have so much more mass than Earth does?

Standardized Test Preparation

READING

Read each of the passages below. Then, answer the questions that follow each passage.

Passage 1 Imagine that it is 200 BCE and you are an apprentice to a Greek astronomer. After years of observing the sky, the astronomer knows all of the constellations as well as the back of his hand. He shows you how the stars all move together—the whole sky spins slowly as the night goes on. He also shows you that among the thousands of stars in the sky, some of the brighter ones slowly change their position relative to the other stars. He names these stars *planetai*, the Greek word for "wanderers." Building on the observations of the ancient Greeks, we now know that the *planetai* are actually planets, not wandering stars.

1. Which of the following did the ancient Greeks know to be true?

A All planets have at least one moon.
B The planets revolve around the sun.
C The planets are much smaller than the stars.
D The planets appear to move relative to the stars.

2. What can you infer from the passage about the ancient Greek astronomers?

F They were patient and observant.
G They knew much more about astronomy than we do.
H They spent all their time counting stars.
I They invented astrology.

3. What does the word *planetai* mean in Greek?

A planets
B wanderers
C stars
D moons

Passage 2 To explain the source of short-period comets (comets that have a relatively short orbit), the Dutch-American astronomer Gerard Kuiper proposed in 1949 that a belt of icy bodies must lie beyond the orbits of Pluto and Neptune. Kuiper argued that comets were icy <u>planetesimals</u> that formed from the condensation that happened during the formation of our galaxy. Because the icy bodies are so far from any large planet's gravitational field (30 to 100 AU), they can remain on the fringe of the solar system. Some theorists speculate that the large moons Triton and Charon were once members of the Kuiper belt before they were captured by Neptune and Pluto. These moons and short-period comets have similar physical and chemical properties.

1. According to the passage, why can icy bodies remain at the edge of the solar system?

A The icy bodies are so small that they naturally float to the edge of the solar system.
B The icy bodies have weak gravitational fields and therefore do not orbit individual planets.
C The icy bodies are short-period comets, which can reside only at the edge of the solar system.
D The icy bodies are so far away from any large planet's gravitational field that they can remain at the edge of the solar system.

2. According to the passage, which of the following best describes the meaning of the word *planetesimal*?

F a small object that existed during the early development of the solar system
G an extremely tiny object in space
H a particle that was once part of a planet
I an extremely large satellite that was the result of a collision of two objects

INTERPRETING GRAPHICS

Use the diagrams below to answer the questions that follow.

Planet A 115 craters/km²

Planet B 75 craters/km²

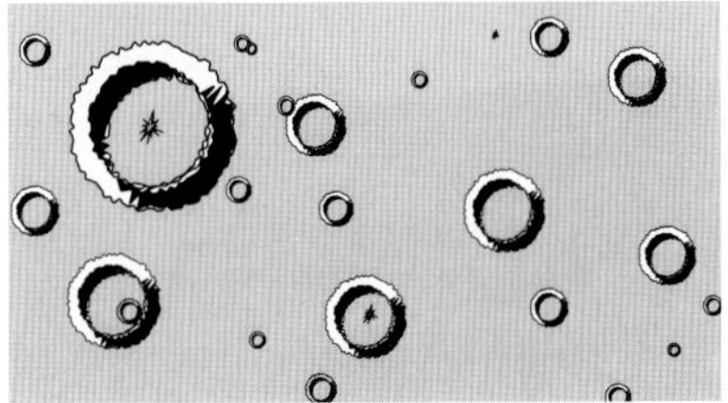

Planet C 121 craters/km²

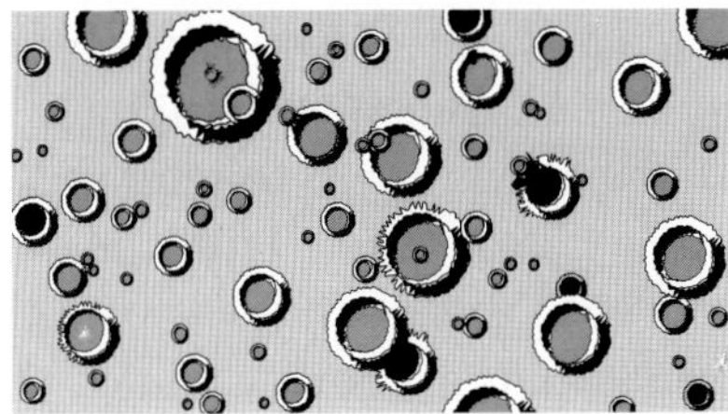

Planet D 97 craters/km²

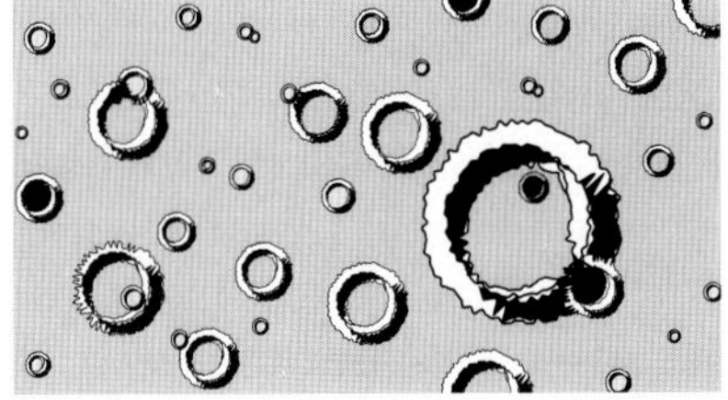

1. According to the information above, which planet has the oldest surface?

A planet A
B planet B
C planet C
D planet D

2. How many more craters per square kilometer are there on planet C than on planet B?

F 46 craters per square kilometer
G 24 craters per square kilometer
H 22 craters per square kilometer
I 6 craters per square kilometer

MATH

Read each question below, and choose the best answer.

1. Venus's surface gravity is 91% of Earth's. If an object weighs 12 N on Earth, how much would it weigh on Venus?

A 53 N
B 13 N
C 11 N
D 8 N

2. Earth's overall density is 5.52 g/cm^3, while Saturn's density is 0.69 g/cm^3. How many times denser is Earth than Saturn?

F 8 times
G 9 times
H 11 times
I 12 times

3. If Earth's history spans 4.6 billion years and the Phanerozoic eon was 543 million years, what percentage of Earth's history does the Phanerozoic eon represent?

A about 6%
B about 12%
C about 18%
D about 24%

4. The diameter of Venus is 12,104 km. The diameter of Mars is 6,794 km. What is the difference between the diameter of Venus and the diameter of Mars?

F 5,400 km
G 5,310 km
H 4,890 km
I 890 km

Science in Action

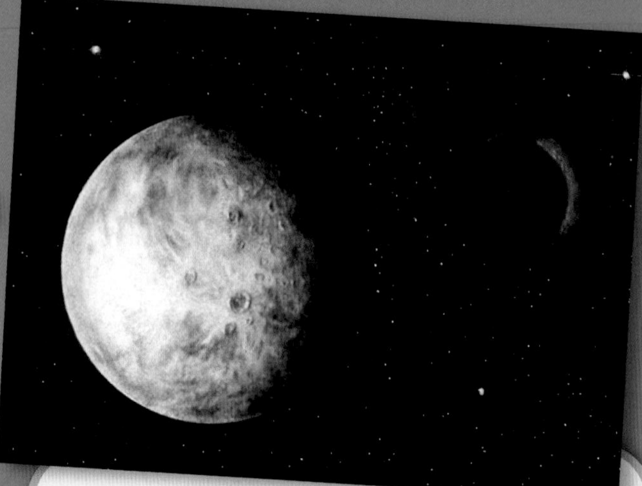

Science Fiction

"The Mad Moon" by Stanley Weinbaum

The third largest moon of Jupiter, called Io, can be a hard place to live. Grant Calthorpe is finding this out the hard way. Although living comfortably is possible in the small cities at the polar regions of Io, Grant has to spend most of his time in the moon's hot and humid jungles. Grant treks into the jungles of Io to gather ferva leaves so that they can be converted into useful medications for humans. During Grant's quest, he encounters loonies and slinkers, and he has to avoid blancha, a kind of tropical fever that causes hallucinations, weakness, and vicious headaches. Without proper medication a person with blancha can go mad or even die. In "The Mad Moon," you'll discover a dozen adventures with Grant Calthorpe as he struggles to stay alive—and sane.

Language Arts ACTIVITY

WRITING SKILL Read "The Mad Moon" by Stanley Weinbaum. Write a short story describing the adventures that you would have on Io if you were chosen as Grant Calthorpe's assistant.

HOLT ANTHOLOGY OF
Science Fiction
HOLT, RINEHART AND WINSTON

Scientific Debate

Is Pluto a Planet?

Is it possible that Pluto isn't a planet? Some scientists think so! Since 1930, Pluto has been included as one of the nine planets in our solar system. But observations in the 1990s led many astronomers to refer to Pluto as an object, not a planet. Other astronomers disagree with this change. Astronomers that refer to Pluto as an object do not think that it fits well with the other outer planets. Unlike the other outer planets, which are large and gaseous, Pluto is small and made of rock and ice. Pluto also has a very elliptical orbit that is unlike its neighboring planets. Astronomers that think Pluto is a planet point out that Pluto, like all other planets, has its own atmosphere and its own moon, called Charon. These and other factors have fueled a debate as to whether Pluto should be classified as a planet.

Math ACTIVITY

How many more kilometers is Earth's diameter compared to Pluto's diameter if Earth's diameter is 12,756 km and Pluto's diameter is 2,390 km?

Careers

Adriana C. Ocampo

Planetary Geologist Sixty-five million years ago, in what is now Mexico, a giant meteor at least six miles wide struck Earth. The meteor made a hole nine miles deep and over 100 miles wide. The meteor sent billions of tons of dust into Earth's atmosphere. This dust formed thick clouds. After forming, these clouds may have left the planet in total darkness for six months, and the temperature near freezing for ten years. Some scientists think that this meteor crash and its effect on the Earth's climate led to the extinction of the dinosaurs. Adriana Ocampo studies the site in Mexico made by the crater known as the Chicxulub (cheeks OO loob) impact crater. Ocampo is a planetary geologist and has been interested in space exploration since she was young. Ocampo's specialty is studying "impact craters." "Impact craters are formed when an asteroid or a comet collides with the Earth or any other terrestrial planet," explains Ocampo. Ocampo visits crater sites around the world to collect data. She also uses computers to create models of how the impact affected the planet. Ocampo has worked for NASA and has helped plan space exploration missions to Mars, Jupiter, Saturn, and Mercury. Ocampo currently works for the European Space Agency (ESA) and is part of the team getting ready to launch the next spacecraft that will go to Mars.

Social Studies ACTIVITY

Research information about impact craters. Find the different locations around the world where impact craters have been found. Make a world map that highlights these locations.

The circle on the map shows the site in Mexico made by the Chicxulub impact crater.

To learn more about these Science in Action topics, visit go.hrw.com and type in the keyword **HZ5FAMF.**

Current Science

Check out Current Science® articles related to this chapter by visiting go.hrw.com. Just type in the keyword HZ5CS21.

TIMELINE

Physical Science

In this unit, you will explore a basic question that people have been pondering for centuries: What is the nature of matter? You will learn how to define the word *matter* and the ways to describe matter and the changes it goes through. You will also learn how to classify different arrangements of matter as elements, compounds, or mixtures. In addition, you will learn about energy and the energy of waves. This timeline shows some of the events and discoveries that have occurred throughout history as scientists have sought to understand the nature of matter.

1661

Robert Boyle, a chemist in England, determines that elements are substances that cannot be broken down into anything simpler by chemical processes.

1712

Thomas Newcomen invents the first practical steam engine.

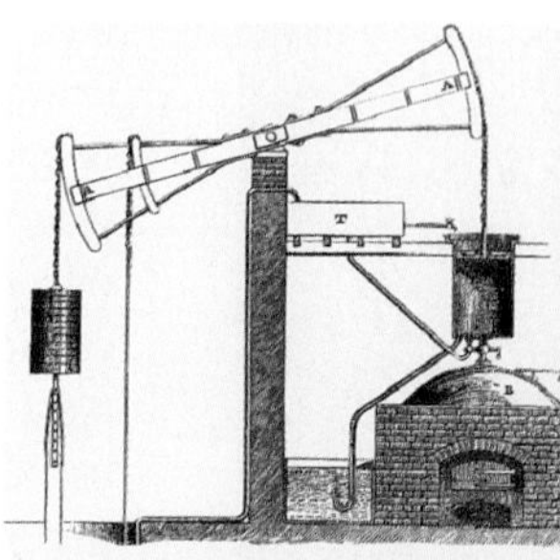

1937

The *Hindenburg* explodes while docking in Lakehurst, New Jersey. To make it lighter than air, the airship was filled with flammable hydrogen gas.

1971

The first commercially available "pocket" calculator is introduced. It has a mass of nearly 1 kg and a price of about $400, hardly the kind of pocket calculator that exists today.

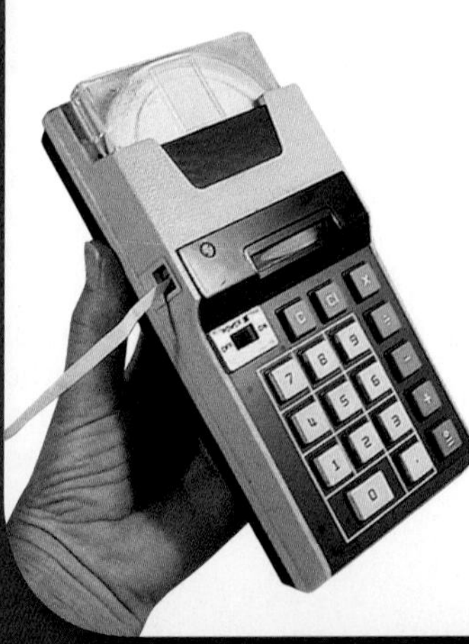

1766

English chemist Henry Cavendish discovers and describes the properties of a highly flammable substance now known as hydrogen gas.

1800

Current from an electric battery is used to separate water into the elements hydrogen and oxygen for the first time.

1920

American women win the right to vote with the ratification of the 19th Amendment to the Constitution.

1950

Silly Putty® is sold in a toy store for the first time. The soft, gooey substance quickly becomes popular because of its strange properties, including the ability to "pick up" the print from a newspaper page.

1957

The space age begins when the Soviet Union launches *Sputnik I*, the first artificial satellite to circle the Earth.

1989

An oil tanker strikes a reef in Prince William Sound, Alaska, and spills nearly 11 million gallons of oil. The floating oil injures or kills thousands of marine mammals and seabirds and damages the Alaskan coastline.

2000

The World's Fair, an international exhibition featuring exhibits and participants from around the world, is held in Hanover, Germany. The theme is "Humankind, Nature, and Technology."

2003

Sally Ride, the first American woman in space, is inducted into the Astronaut Hall of Fame.

10

The Properties of Matter

About the PHOTO

This giant ice dragon began as a 1,700 kg block of ice! Making the blocks of ice takes six weeks. Then, the ice blocks are stored at –30°C until the sculpting begins. The artist has to work at –10°C to keep the ice from melting. An ice sculptor has to be familiar with the many properties of water, including its melting point.

PRE-READING ACTIVITY

FOLDNOTES **Booklet** Before you read the chapter, create the FoldNote entitled "Booklet" described in the **Study Skills** section of the Appendix. Label each page of the booklet with a main idea from the chapter. As you read the chapter, write what you learn about each main idea on the appropriate page of the booklet.

Mass: The Measure of Inertia

Mass is a measure of inertia. An object that has a large mass is harder to get moving and harder to stop than an object that has less mass. The reason is that the object with the large mass has greater inertia. For example, imagine that you are going to push a grocery cart that has only one potato in it. Pushing the cart is easy because the mass and inertia are small. But suppose the grocery cart is stacked with potatoes, as in **Figure 7.** Now the total mass—and the inertia—of the cart full of potatoes is much greater. It will be harder to get the cart moving. And once the cart is moving, stopping the cart will be harder.

Figure 7 *Because of inertia, moving a cart full of potatoes is more difficult than moving a cart that is empty.*

SECTION Review

Summary

- Two properties of matter are volume and mass.
- Volume is the amount of space taken up by an object.
- The SI unit of volume is the liter (L).
- Mass is the amount of matter in an object.
- The SI unit of mass is the kilogram (kg).
- Weight is a measure of the gravitational force on an object, usually in relation to the Earth.
- Inertia is the tendency of an object to resist being moved or, if the object is moving, to resist a change in speed or direction. The more massive an object is, the greater its inertia.

Using Key Terms

1. Use the following terms in the same sentence: *volume* and *meniscus.*
2. In your own words, write a definition for each of the following terms: *mass, weight,* and *inertia.*

Understanding Key Ideas

3. Which of the following is matter?
   a. dust **b.** the moon **c.** strand of hair **d.** All of the above
4. A graduated cylinder is used to measure
   a. volume. **b.** weight. **c.** mass. **d.** inertia.
5. The volume of a solid is measured in
   a. liters.
   b. grams.
   c. cubic centimeters.
   d. All of the above
6. Mass is measured in
   a. liters. **b.** centimeters. **c.** newtons. **d.** kilograms.
7. Explain the relationship between mass and inertia.

Math Skills

8. A nugget of gold is placed in a graduated cylinder that contains 80 mL of water. The water level rises to 225 mL after the nugget is added to the cylinder. What is the volume of the gold nugget?
9. One newton equals about 100 g on Earth. How many newtons would a football weigh if it had a mass of 400 g?

Critical Thinking

10. **Identifying Relationships** Do objects with large masses always have large weights? Explain.
11. **Applying Concepts** Would an elephant weigh more or less on the moon than it would weigh on Earth? Explain your answer.

SCILINKS
NSTA
Developed and maintained by the National Science Teachers Association
For a variety of links related to this chapter, go to www.scilinks.org
Topic: What Is Matter?
SciLinks code: HSM1662

SECTION 2

Physical Properties

Have you ever played the game 20 Questions? The goal of this game is to figure out what object another person is thinking of by asking 20 yes/no questions or less.

READING WARM-UP

Objectives

- Identify six examples of physical properties of matter.
- Describe how density is used to identify substances.
- List six examples of physical changes.
- Explain what happens to matter during a physical change.

Terms to Learn

physical property
density
physical change

READING STRATEGY

Mnemonics As you read this section, create a mnemonic device to help you remember examples of physical properties.

If you can't figure out the object's identity after asking 20 questions, you may not be asking the right kinds of questions. What kinds of questions should you ask? You may want to ask questions about the physical properties of the object. Knowing the properties of an object can help you find out what it is.

Physical Properties

The questions in **Figure 1** help someone gather information about color, odor, mass, and volume. Each piece of information is a physical property of matter. A **physical property** of matter can be observed or measured without changing the matter's identity. For example, you don't have to change an apple's identity to see its color or to measure its volume.

Other physical properties, such as magnetism, the ability to conduct electric current, strength, and flexibility, can help someone identify how to use a substance. For example, think of a scooter with an electric motor. The magnetism produced by the motor is used to convert energy stored in a battery into energy that will turn the wheels.

Reading Check **List four physical properties.** (*See the Appendix for answers to Reading Checks.*)

Could I hold it in my hand? Yes.
Does it have an odor? Yes.
Is it safe to eat? Yes.
Is it orange? No.
Is it yellow? No.
Is it red? Yes.
Is it an apple? Yes!

Figure 1 *Asking questions about the physical properties of an object can help you identify it.*

Figure 2 **Examples of Physical Properties**

Thermal conductivity (KAHN duhk TIV uh tee) is the rate at which a substance transfers heat. Plastic foam is a poor conductor.

State is the physical form in which a substance exists, such as a solid, liquid, or gas. Ice is water in the solid state.

Density is the mass per unit volume of a substance. Lead is very dense, so it makes a good sinker for a fishing line.

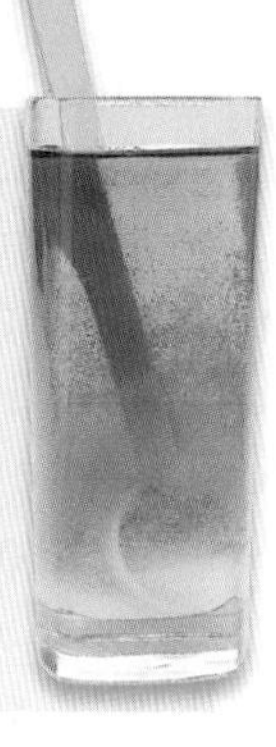

Solubility (SAHL yoo BIL uh tee) is the ability of a substance to dissolve in another substance. Flavored drink mix dissolves in water.

Ductility (duhk TIL uh tee) is the ability of a substance to be pulled into a wire. Copper is often used to make wiring because it is ductile.

Malleability (MAL ee uh BIL uh tee) is the ability of a substance to be rolled or pounded into thin sheets. Aluminum can be rolled into sheets to make foil.

Identifying Matter

You use physical properties every day. For example, physical properties help you determine if your socks are clean (odor), if your books will fit into your backpack (volume), or if your shirt matches your pants (color). **Figure 2** gives more examples of physical properties.

physical property a characteristic of a substance that does not involve a chemical change, such as density, color, or hardness

density the ratio of the mass of a substance to the volume of the substance

Density

Density is a physical property that describes the relationship between mass and volume. **Density** is the amount of matter in a given space, or volume. A golf ball and a table-tennis ball, such as those in **Figure 3**, have similar volumes. But a golf ball has more mass than a table-tennis ball does. So, the golf ball has a greater density.

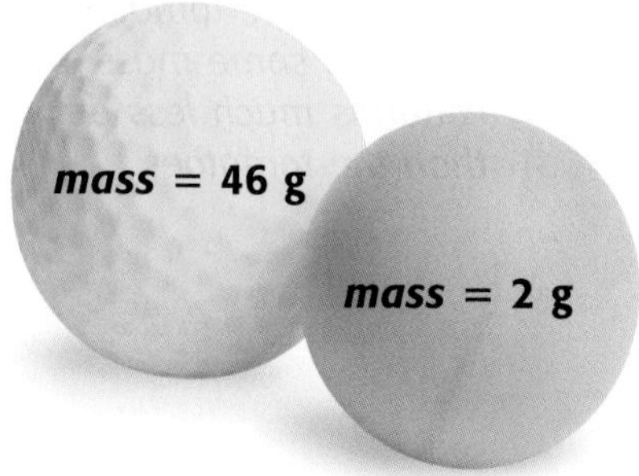

Figure 3 *A golf ball is denser than a table-tennis ball because the golf ball contains more matter in a similar volume.*

Liquid Layers

Figure 4 *This graduated cylinder contains six liquids. From top to bottom, they are corn oil, water, shampoo, dish detergent, antifreeze, and maple syrup.*

What do you think causes the liquid in **Figure 4** to look the way it does? Is it trick photography? No, it is differences in density! There are equal volumes of six liquids in the graduated cylinder. But because equal volumes of different substances usually have different masses, each liquid has a different density. If the liquids are carefully poured into the cylinder, they can form six layers because of the differences in density. The densest layer is on the bottom. The least dense layer is on top. The order of the layers shows the order of increasing density. Yellow is the least dense, followed by the colorless layer, red, blue, green, and brown (the densest).

Density of Solids

Which would you rather carry around all day: a kilogram of lead or a kilogram of feathers? At first, you might say feathers. But both the feathers and the lead have the same mass, just as the cotton balls and the tomatoes have the same mass, as shown in **Figure 5.** So, the lead would be less awkward to carry around than the feathers would. The feathers are much less dense than the lead. So, it takes a lot of feathers to equal the same mass of lead.

Knowing the density of a substance can also tell you if the substance will float or sink in water. If the density of an object is less than the density of water, the object will float. Likewise, a solid object whose density is greater than the density of water will sink when the object is placed in water.

Reading Check **What will happen to an object placed in water if the object's density is less than water's density?**

Figure 5 *The cotton balls and the tomatoes have the same mass. But cotton is much less dense than the tomatoes.*

Solving for Density

To find an object's density (D), first measure its mass (m) and volume (V). Then, use the equation below.

$$D = \frac{m}{V}$$

Units for density consist of a mass unit divided by a volume unit. Some units for density are g/cm^3, g/mL, kg/m^3, and kg/L. Remember that the volume of a solid is often given in cubic centimeters or cubic meters. So, the density of a solid should be given in units of g/cm^3 or kg/m^3.

Using Density to Identify Substances

Density is a useful physical property for identifying substances. Each substance has a density that differs from the densities of other substances. And the density of a substance is always the same at a given temperature and pressure. Look at **Table 1** to compare the densities of several common substances.

Table 1* Densities of Common Substances

Substance	Density* (g/cm^3)	Substance	Density* (g/cm^3)
Helium (gas)	0.00001663	Zinc (solid)	7.13
Oxygen (gas)	0.001331	Silver (solid)	10.50
Water (liquid)	1.00	Lead (solid)	11.35
Pyrite (solid)	5.02	Mercury (liquid)	13.55

*at 20°C and 1.0 atm

Liquid Density

1. Using a **balance**, measure the mass of a **graduated cylinder**.
2. Put **10 mL of water** in the cylinder and measure the mass of the cylinder and water.
3. Determine the mass of the water by subtracting the mass of the cylinder from the total mass.
4. Repeat steps 2 and 3 using **10 mL of vegetable oil.**
5. Use a calculator to find the densities of each of the liquids.
6. Compare the results. How do the masses relate to the densities of equal volumes of the two liquids?

Calculating Density What is the density of an object whose mass is 25 g and whose volume is 10 cm^3?

Step 1: Write the equation for density.

$$D = \frac{m}{V}$$

Step 2: Replace m and V with the measurements given in the problem, and solve.

$$D = \frac{25 \text{ g}}{10 \text{ cm}^3} = 2.5 \text{ g/cm}^3$$

The equation for density can also be rearranged to find mass and volume, as shown.

$m = D \times V$ (Rearrange by multiplying by V.)

$V = \frac{m}{D}$ (Rearrange by dividing by D.)

Now It's Your Turn

1. Find the density of a substance that has a mass of 45 kg and a volume of 43 m^3. (Hint: Make sure your answer's units are units of density.)
2. Suppose you have a lead ball whose mass is 454 g. What is the ball's volume? (Hint: Use **Table 1** above.)
3. What is the mass of a 15 mL sample of mercury?
4. Compare the masses of 10 cm^3 each of lead and silver.

Figure 6 Examples of Physical Changes

Changing from a solid to a liquid is a physical change. All changes of state are physical changes.

This aluminum can has gone through the physical change of being crushed. The properties of the can are the same.

Physical Changes Do Not Form New Substances

physical change a change of matter from one form to another without a change in chemical properties

A **physical change** is a change that affects one or more physical properties of a substance. Imagine that a piece of silver is pounded and molded into a heart-shaped pendant. This change is a physical one because only the shape of the silver has changed. The piece of silver is still silver. Its properties are the same. **Figure 6** shows more examples of physical changes.

Reading Check **What is a physical change?**

Examples of Physical Changes

Freezing water to make ice cubes and sanding a piece of wood are examples of physical changes. These changes do not change the identities of the substances. Ice is still water. And sawdust is still wood. Another interesting physical change takes place when certain substances dissolve in other substances. For example, when you dissolve sugar in water, the sugar seems to disappear. But if you heat the mixture, the water evaporates. Then, you will see that the sugar is still there. The sugar went through a physical change when it dissolved.

CONNECTION TO Geology

WRITING SKILL **Erosion** Erosion of soil is a physical change. Soil erodes when wind and water move soil from one place to another. Research the history of the Grand Canyon. Write a one-page report about how erosion formed the Grand Canyon.

Matter and Physical Changes

Physical changes do not change the identity of the matter involved. A stick of butter can be melted and poured over a bowl of popcorn, as shown in **Figure 7.** Although the shape of the butter has changed, the butter is still butter, so a physical change has occurred. In the same way, if you make a figure from a lump of clay, you change the clay's shape and cause a physical change. But the identity of the clay does not change. The properties of the figure are the same as those of the lump of clay.

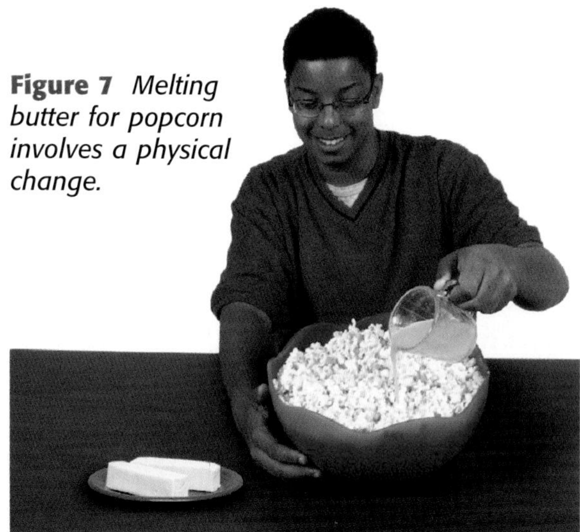

Figure 7 *Melting butter for popcorn involves a physical change.*

SECTION Review

Summary

- Physical properties of matter can be observed without changing the identity of the matter.
- Examples of physical properties are conductivity, state, malleability, ductility, solubility, and density.
- Density is the amount of matter in a given space.
- Density is used to identify substances because the density of a substance is always the same at a given pressure and temperature.
- When a substance undergoes a physical change, its identity stays the same.
- Examples of physical changes are freezing, cutting, bending, dissolving, and melting.

Using Key Terms

1. Use each of the following terms in a separate sentence: *physical property* and *physical change*.

Understanding Key Ideas

2. The units of density for a rectangular piece of wood are
   a. grams per milliliter.
   b. cubic centimeters.
   c. kilograms per liter.
   d. grams per cubic centimeter.
3. Explain why a golf ball is heavier than a table-tennis ball even though the balls are the same size.
4. Describe what happens to a substance when it goes through a physical change.
5. Identify six examples of physical properties.
6. List six physical changes that matter can go through.

Math Skills

7. What is the density of an object that has a mass of 350 g and a volume of 95 cm^3? Would this object float in water? Explain.
8. The density of an object is 5 g/cm^3, and the volume of the object is 10 cm^3. What is the mass of the object?

Critical Thinking

9. **Applying Concepts** How can you determine that a coin is not pure silver if you know the mass and volume of the coin?
10. **Identifying Relationships** What physical property do the following substances have in common: water, oil, mercury, and alcohol?
11. **Analyzing Processes** Explain how you would find the density of an unknown liquid if you have all of the laboratory equipment that you need.

For a variety of links related to this chapter, go to www.scilinks.org

Topic: Describing Matter; Physical Changes
SciLinks code: HSM0391; HSM1142

SECTION 3

Chemical Properties

How would you describe a piece of wood before and after it is burned? Has it changed color? Does it have the same texture? The original piece of wood changed, and physical properties alone can't describe what happened to it.

READING WARM-UP

Objectives

- Describe two examples of chemical properties.
- Explain what happens during a chemical change.
- Distinguish between physical and chemical changes.

Terms to Learn

chemical property
chemical change

READING STRATEGY

Reading Organizer As you read this section, create an outline of the section. Use the headings from the section in your outline.

Chemical Properties

Physical properties are not the only properties that describe matter. **Chemical properties** describe matter based on its ability to change into new matter that has different properties. For example, when wood is burned, ash and smoke are created. These new substances have very different properties than the original piece of wood had. Wood has the chemical property of flammability. *Flammability* is the ability of a substance to burn. Ash and smoke cannot burn, so they have the chemical property of nonflammability.

chemical property a property of matter that describes a substance's ability to participate in chemical reactions

Another chemical property is reactivity. *Reactivity* is the ability of two or more substances to combine and form one or more new substances. The photo of the old car in **Figure 1** illustrates reactivity and nonreactivity.

Reading Check **What does the term *reactivity* mean?** *(See the Appendix for answers to Reading Checks.)*

Figure 1 Reactivity with Oxygen

The iron used in this old car has the chemical property of **reactivity with oxygen.** When iron is exposed to oxygen, it rusts.

The bumper on this car still looks new because it is coated with chromium. Chromium has the chemical property of **nonreactivity with oxygen.**

Figure 2 **Physical Versus Chemical Properties**

Physical property

Shape Bending an iron nail will change its shape.

Chemical property

Reactivity with Oxygen An iron nail can react with oxygen in the air to form iron oxide, or rust.

State Rubbing alcohol is a clear liquid at room temperature.

Flammability Rubbing alcohol is able to burn easily.

Comparing Physical and Chemical Properties

How do you tell a physical property from a chemical property? You can observe physical properties without changing the identity of the substance. For example, you can find the density and hardness of wood without changing anything about the wood.

Chemical properties, however, aren't as easy to observe. For example, you can see that wood is flammable only while it is burning. And you can observe that gold is nonflammable only when it won't burn. But a substance always has chemical properties. A piece of wood is flammable even when it's not burning. **Figure 2** shows examples of physical and chemical properties.

Characteristic Properties

The properties that are most useful in identifying a substance are *characteristic properties*. These properties are always the same no matter what size the sample is. Characteristic properties can be physical properties, such as density and solubility, as well as chemical properties, such as flammability and reactivity. Scientists rely on characteristic properties to identify and classify substances.

CONNECTION TO Social Studies

WRITING SKILL **The Right Stuff** When choosing materials to use in manufacturing, you must make sure their properties are suitable for their uses. For example, false teeth can be made from acrylic plastic, porcelain, or gold. According to legend, George Washington wore false teeth made of wood. Do research and find what Washington's false teeth were really made of. In your **science journal,** write a paragraph about what you have learned. Include information about the advantages of the materials used in modern false teeth.

Changing Change

1. Place a folded **paper towel** in a small **pie plate.**
2. Pour **vinegar** into the pie plate until the entire paper towel is damp.
3. Place three shiny **pennies** on top of the paper towel.
4. Put the pie plate in a safe place. Wait 24 hours.
5. Describe and explain the change that took place.

Chemical Changes and New Substances

A **chemical change** happens when one or more substances are changed into new substances that have new and different properties. Chemical changes and chemical properties are not the same. Chemical properties of a substance describe which chemical changes will occur and which chemical changes will not occur. But chemical changes are the process by which substances actually change into new substances. You can learn about the chemical properties of a substance by looking at the chemical changes that take place.

You see chemical changes more often than you may think. For example, a chemical reaction happens every time a battery is used. Chemicals failing to react results in a dead battery. Chemical changes also take place within your body when the food you eat is digested. **Figure 3** describes other examples of chemical changes.

Reading Check **How does a chemical change differ from a chemical property?**

Figure 3 Examples of Chemical Changes

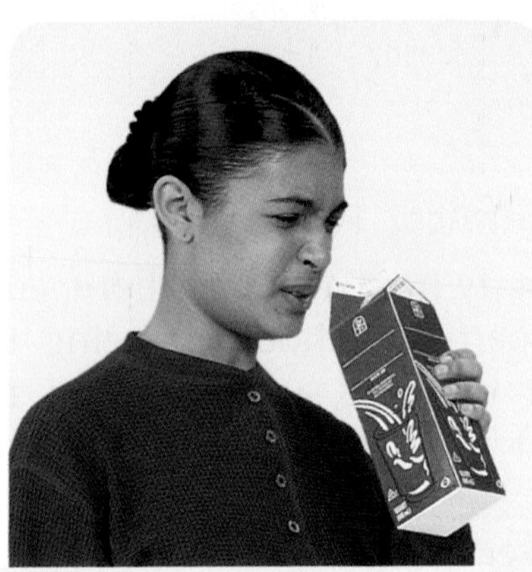

Soured milk smells bad because bacteria have formed new substances in the milk.

Effervescent tablets bubble when the citric acid and baking soda in them react in water.

The **hot gas** formed when hydrogen and oxygen join to make water helps blast the space shuttle into orbit.

The **Statue of Liberty** is made of orange-brown copper but it looks green from the metal's interaction with moist air. New copper compounds formed and these chemical changes made the statue turn green over time.

Figure 4 *Each of the original ingredients has different physical and chemical properties than the final product, the cake, does!*

What Happens During a Chemical Change?

A fun way to see what happens during chemical changes is to bake a cake. You combine eggs, flour, sugar, and other ingredients, as shown in **Figure 4.** When you bake the batter, you end up with something completely different. The heat of the oven and the interaction of the ingredients cause a chemical change. The result is a cake that has properties that differ from the properties of the ingredients.

chemical change a change that occurs when one or more substances change into entirely new substances with different properties

Signs of Chemical Changes

Look back at **Figure 3.** In each picture, at least one sign indicates a chemical change. Other signs that indicate a chemical change include a change in color or odor, production of heat, fizzing and foaming, and sound or light being given off.

In the cake example, you would smell the cake as it baked. You would also see the batter rise and begin to brown. When you cut the finished cake, you would see the air pockets made by gas bubbles that formed in the batter. These signs show that chemical changes have happened.

For another activity related to this chapter, go to **go.hrw.com** and type in keyword **HP5MATW.**

Matter and Chemical Changes

Chemical changes change the identity of the matter involved. So, most of the chemical changes that occur in your daily life, such as a cake baking, would be hard to reverse. Imagine trying to unbake a cake. However, some chemical changes can be reversed by more chemical changes. For example, the water formed in the space shuttle's rockets could be split into hydrogen and oxygen by using an electric current.

Figure 5 Physical and Chemical Changes

Change in Texture Grinding baking soda into a fine, powdery substance is a physical change.

Reactivity with Vinegar Gas bubbles are produced when vinegar is poured into baking soda.

CONNECTION TO Environmental Science

Acid Rain When fossil fuels are burned, a chemical change takes place. Sulfur from fossil fuels and oxygen from the air combine to produce sulfur dioxide, a gas. When sulfur dioxide enters the atmosphere, it undergoes another chemical change by interacting with water and oxygen. Research this chemical reaction. Make a poster describing the reaction and showing how the final product affects the environment.

ACTIVITY

Physical Versus Chemical Changes

The most important question to ask when trying to decide if a physical or chemical change has happened is, Did the composition change? The *composition* of an object is the type of matter that makes up the object and the way that the matter is arranged in the object. **Figure 5** shows both a physical and a chemical change.

A Change in Composition

Physical changes do not change the composition of a substance. For example, water is made of two hydrogen atoms and one oxygen atom. Whether water is a solid, liquid, or gas, its composition is the same. But chemical changes do alter the composition of a substance. For example, through a process called *electrolysis,* water is broken down into hydrogen and oxygen gases. The composition of water has changed, so you know that a chemical change has taken place.

Physical or Chemical Change?

1. Watch as your teacher places a burning **wooden stick** into a **test tube.** Record your observations.
2. Place a mixture of **powdered sulfur** and **iron filings** on a **sheet of paper.** Place a **bar magnet** underneath the paper, and try to separate the iron from the sulfur.
3. Drop an **effervescent tablet** into a **beaker of water.** Record your observations.
4. Identify whether each change is a physical change or a chemical change. Explain your answers.

Reversing Changes

Can physical and chemical changes be reversed? Many physical changes are easily reversed. They do not change the composition of a substance. For example, if an ice cube melts, you could freeze the liquid water to make another ice cube. But composition does change in a chemical change. So, most chemical changes are not easily reversed. Look at **Figure 6.** The chemical changes that happen when a firework explodes would be almost impossible to reverse, even if you collected all of the materials made in the chemical changes.

Figure 6 *This display of fireworks represents many chemical changes happening at the same time.*

SECTION Review

Summary

- Chemical properties describe a substance based on its ability to change into a new substance that has different properties.
- Chemical properties can be observed only when a chemical change might happen.
- Examples of chemical properties are flammability and reactivity.
- New substances form as a result of a chemical change.
- Unlike a chemical change, a physical change does not alter the identity of a substance.

Using Key Terms

1. In your own words, write a definition for each of the following terms: *chemical property* and *chemical change*.

Understanding Key Ideas

2. Rusting is an example of a
   - **a.** physical property.
   - **b.** physical change.
   - **c.** chemical property.
   - **d.** chemical change.
3. Which of the following is a characteristic property?
   - **a.** density
   - **b.** chemical reactivity
   - **c.** solubility in water
   - **d.** All of the above
4. Write two examples of chemical properties and explain what they are.
5. The Statue of Liberty was originally a copper color. After being exposed to the air, she turned a greenish color. What kind of change happened? Explain your answer.
6. Explain how to tell the difference between a physical and a chemical property.

Math Skills

7. The temperature of an acid solution is 25°C. A strip of magnesium is added, and the temperature rises 2°C each minute for the first 3 min. After another 5 min, the temperature has risen two more degrees. What is the final temperature?

Critical Thinking

8. **Making Comparisons** Describe the difference between physical and chemical changes in terms of what happens to the matter involved in each kind of change.
9. **Applying Concepts** Identify two physical properties and two chemical properties of a bag of microwave popcorn before popping and after.

SCILINKS®
NSTA
Developed and maintained by the National Science Teachers Association
For a variety of links related to this chapter, go to www.scilinks.org
Topic: Chemical Changes
SciLinks code: HSM0266

Skills Practice Lab

White Before Your Eyes

OBJECTIVES

Describe the physical properties of four substances.

Identify physical and chemical changes.

Classify four substances by their chemical properties.

MATERIALS

- baking powder
- baking soda
- carton, egg, plastic-foam
- cornstarch
- eyedroppers (3)
- iodine solution
- spatulas (4)
- stirring rod
- sugar
- vinegar
- water

SAFETY

You have learned how to describe matter based on its physical and chemical properties. You have also learned some signs that can help you determine whether a change in matter is a physical change or a chemical change. In this lab, you'll use what you have learned to describe four substances based on their properties and the changes that they undergo.

Procedure

1. Copy Table 1 and Table 2 shown on the next page. Be sure to leave plenty of room in each box to write down your observations.
2. Using a spatula, place a small amount of baking powder into three cups of your egg carton. Use just enough baking powder to cover the bottom of each cup. Record your observations about the baking powder's appearance, such as color and texture, in the "Unmixed" column of Table 1.

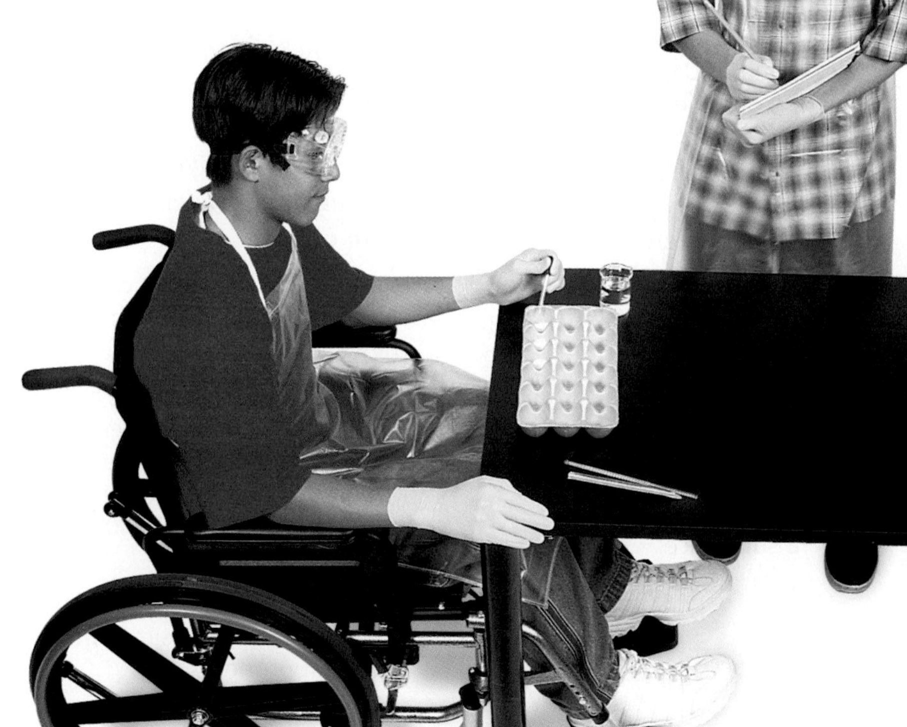

3. Use an eyedropper to add 60 drops of water to the baking powder in the first cup. Stir with the stirring rod. Record your observations in Table 1 in the column labeled "Mixed with water." Clean your stirring rod.

4. Use a clean dropper to add 20 drops of vinegar to the second cup of baking powder. Stir. Record your observations in Table 1 in the column labeled "Mixed with vinegar." Clean your stirring rod.

5. Use a clean dropper to add five drops of iodine solution to the third cup of baking powder. Stir. Record your observations in Table 1 in the column labeled "Mixed with iodine solution." Clean your stirring rod. **Caution:** Be careful when using iodine. Iodine will stain your skin and clothes.

6. Repeat steps 2–5 for each of the other substances (baking soda, cornstarch, and sugar). Use a clean spatula for each substance.

Analyze the Results

1. **Examining Data** What physical properties do all four substances share?

2. **Analyzing Data** In Table 2, write the type of change—physical or chemical—that you observed for each substance. State the property that the change demonstrates.

Draw Conclusions

3. **Evaluating Results** Classify the four substances by the chemical property of reactivity. For example, which substances are reactive with vinegar (acid)?

Table 1 Observations

Substance	Unmixed	Mixed with water	Mixed with vinegar	Mixed with iodine solution
Baking powder				
Baking soda				
Cornstarch				
Sugar				

Table 2 Changes and Properties

	Mixed with water		Mixed with vinegar		Mixed with iodine solution	
Substance	Change	Property	Change	Property	Change	Property
Baking powder						
Baking soda						
Cornstarch						
Sugar						

Chapter Review

USING KEY TERMS

1. Use each of the following terms in a separate sentence: *physical property, chemical property, physical change,* and *chemical change.*

For each pair of terms, explain how the meanings of the terms differ.

2. *mass* and *weight*
3. *inertia* and *mass*
4. *volume* and *density*

UNDERSTANDING KEY IDEAS

Multiple Choice

5. Which of the following properties is NOT a chemical property?
   - **a.** reactivity with oxygen
   - **b.** malleability
   - **c.** flammability
   - **d.** reactivity with acid
6. The volume of a liquid can be expressed in all of the following units EXCEPT
   - **a.** grams.
   - **b.** liters.
   - **c.** milliliters.
   - **d.** cubic centimeters.
7. The SI unit for the mass of a substance is the
   - **a.** gram.
   - **b.** liter.
   - **c.** milliliter.
   - **d.** kilogram.
8. The best way to measure the volume of an irregularly shaped solid is to
   - **a.** use a ruler to measure the length of each side of the object.
   - **b.** weigh the solid on a balance.
   - **c.** use the water displacement method.
   - **d.** use a spring scale.
9. Which of the following statements about weight is true?
   - **a.** Weight is a measure of the gravitational force on an object.
   - **b.** Weight varies depending on where the object is located in relation to the Earth.
   - **c.** Weight is measured by using a spring scale.
   - **d.** All of the above
10. Which of the following statements does NOT describe a physical property of a piece of chalk?
    - **a.** Chalk is a solid.
    - **b.** Chalk can be broken into pieces.
    - **c.** Chalk is white.
    - **d.** Chalk will bubble in vinegar.
11. Which of the following statements about density is true?
    - **a.** Density is measured in grams.
    - **b.** Density is mass per unit volume.
    - **c.** Density is measured in milliliters.
    - **d.** Density is a chemical property.

Short Answer

12. In one or two sentences, explain how the process of measuring the volume of a liquid differs from the process of measuring the volume of a solid.

13 What is the formula for calculating density?

14 List three characteristic properties of matter.

Math Skills

15 What is the volume of a book that has a width of 10 cm, a length that is 2 times the width, and a height that is half the width? Remember to express your answer in cubic units.

16 A jar contains 30 mL of glycerin (whose mass is 37.8 g) and 60 mL of corn syrup (whose mass is 82.8 g). Which liquid is on top? Show your work, and explain your answer.

CRITICAL THINKING

17 **Concept Mapping** Use the following terms to create a concept map: *matter, mass, inertia, volume, milliliters, cubic centimeters, weight,* and *gravity.*

18 **Applying Concepts** Develop a set of questions that would be useful when identifying an unknown substance. The substance may be a liquid, a gas, or a solid.

19 **Analyzing Processes** You are making breakfast for your friend Filbert. When you take the scrambled eggs to the table, he asks, "Would you please poach these eggs instead?" What scientific reason do you give Filbert for not changing his eggs?

20 **Identifying Relationships** You look out your bedroom window and see your new neighbor moving in. Your neighbor bends over to pick up a small cardboard box, but he cannot lift it. What can you conclude about the item(s) in the box? Use the terms *mass* and *inertia* to explain how you came to your conclusion.

21 **Analyzing Ideas** You may sometimes hear on the radio or on TV that astronauts are weightless in space. Explain why this statement is not true.

INTERPRETING GRAPHICS

Use the photograph below to answer the questions that follow.

22 List three physical properties of this aluminum can.

23 When this can was crushed, did it undergo a physical change or a chemical change?

24 How does the density of the metal in the crushed can compare with the density of the metal before the can was crushed?

25 Can you tell what the chemical properties of the can are by looking at the picture? Explain your answer.

Standardized Test Preparation

READING

Read each of the passages below. Then, answer the questions that follow each passage.

Passage 1 Astronomers were studying the motions of galaxies in space when they noticed something odd. They thought that the large gravitational force, which causes the galaxies to rotate rapidly, was due to a large amount of mass in the galaxies. Then, they discovered that the mass of the galaxies was not great enough to explain this large gravitational force. So, what was causing the additional gravitational force? One theory is that the universe contains matter that we cannot see with our eyes or our telescopes. Astronomers call this invisible matter dark matter.

1. According to this passage, what did astronomers originally think caused the rotation of the galaxies?

- **A** a lack of inertia
- **B** a large gravitational force
- **C** a small amount of mass in the galaxies
- **D** a small gravitational force

2. Why do you think astronomers use the term *dark matter*?

- **F** Dark matter refers to dark objects.
- **G** Dark matter refers to matter that we can't see.
- **H** You need a telescope to see dark matter.
- **I** All large objects are dark.

3. Which statement is the best summary of the passage?

- **A** The enormous amount of mass in the galaxies explains why the galaxies rotate.
- **B** Dark matter may be responsible for the gravitational force that causes the rotation of galaxies.
- **C** Invisible matter is called dark matter.
- **D** Galaxies rotate as they move through the universe.

Passage 2 Blimps and dirigibles are types of airships. An airship consists of an engine, a large balloon that contains gas, and a gondola that carries passengers and crew. Airships float in air because the gases that the airships contain are less dense than air. In the early 1900s, airships were commonly used for travel, including transatlantic flights. Airships were less frequently used after the 1937 explosion and crash of the *Hindenburg* in New Jersey. The *Hindenburg* was filled with flammable hydrogen gas instead of helium gas, which is nonflammable.

1. In this passage, what does *flammable* mean?

- **A** able to burn
- **B** able to float
- **C** able to sink
- **D** not able to burn

2. Which of the following statements is true according to the passage?

- **F** Hydrogen gas is nonflammable.
- **G** Airships float because they contain gases that are less dense than air.
- **H** Helium gas was used in the *Hindenburg*.
- **I** The gondola contains gas.

3. Which of the following statements about airships is true?

- **A** Airships are still a major mode of transportation.
- **B** Airships now contain nonflammable, hydrogen gas.
- **C** Airships consist of an engine, a gondola, and a large balloon.
- **D** Airships traveled only in the United States.

INTERPRETING GRAPHICS

The table below shows the properties of different substances. Use the table below to answer the questions that follow.

Properties of Some Substances*		
Substance	**State**	**Density (g/cm^3)**
Helium	Gas	0.0001663
Pyrite	Solid	5.02
Mercury	Liquid	13.55
Gold	Solid	19.32

* at room temperature and pressure

1. What could you use to tell pyrite (fool's gold) and gold apart?

A volume
B density
C mass
D state

2. What do you think would happen if you placed a nugget of pyrite into a beaker of mercury?

F The pyrite would sink.
G The pyrite would dissolve.
H The mercury and the pyrite would react.
I The pyrite would float.

3. If a nugget of pyrite and a nugget of gold each have a mass of 50 g, what can you conclude about the volume of each nugget?

A The volume of pyrite is greater than the volume of gold.
B The volume of pyrite is less than the volume of gold.
C The volumes of the substances are equal.
D There is not enough information to determine the answer.

4. Which substance has the **lowest** density?

F helium
G pyrite
H mercury
I gold

MATH

Read each question below, and choose the best answer.

1. Imagine that you have discovered a new element, and you want to find its density. It has a mass of 78.8 g and a volume of 8 cm^3. To find the density of the element, you must divide the element's mass by its volume. What is the density of the element?

A 0.102 g/cm^3
B 0.98 g/cm^3
C 9.85 g/cm^3
D 630.4 g/cm^3

2. Many soft drinks come in bottles that contain about 590 mL. If the density of a soft drink is 1.05 g/mL, what is the mass of the drink?

F 0.0018 g
G 498.2 g
H 561.9 g
I 619.5 g

3. If you have 150 g of pure gold and the density of gold is 19.32 g/cm^3, what is the volume of your gold nugget?

A 2,898 cm^3
B 7.76 cm^3
C 0.98 cm^3
D 0.13 cm^3

4. Three objects have a mass of 16 g each. But their volumes differ. Object A, a liquid, has a volume of 1.2 mL. Object B, a solid, has a volume of 3.2 cm^3. Object C, another solid, has a volume of 1.9 cm^3. Which object is the least dense?

F object A
G object B
H object C
I There is not enough information to determine the answer.

Science in Action

Scientific Debate

Paper or Plastic?

What do you choose at the grocery store: paper or plastic bags? Plastic bags are waterproof and take up less space. You can use them to line waste cans and to pack lunches. Some places will recycle plastic bags. But making 1 ton of plastic bags uses 11 barrels of oil, which can't be replaced, and produces polluting chemicals. On the other hand, making 1 ton of paper bags destroys 13 to 17 trees, which take years to replace. Paper bags, too, can be reused for lining waste cans and wrapping packages. Recycling paper pollutes less than recycling plastic does. What is the answer? Maybe we should reuse both!

Language Arts ACTIVITY

WRITING SKILL There are advantages and disadvantages of each kind of bag. Write a one-page essay defending your position on this subject. Support your opinion with facts.

Scientific Discoveries

What is Matter Made Of?

Early philosophers thought that most materials were made up of combinations of just a few basic things—earth, water, air, and fire. However, since the late 1700s, scientists have understood that all substances are made of atoms or combinations of atoms. Later, it was discovered that atoms are made of protons, neutrons, and electrons. Now we know that there are even smaller particles of matter called subatomic particles. Scientists are still working out the details of what the basic kinds of matter are on the smallest scale and of how they combine. These subatomic particle are called *elementary particles* and have no size or structure. One example of elementary particles are quarks, which make up protons and neutrons. So far, more than 300 elementary particles have been identified.

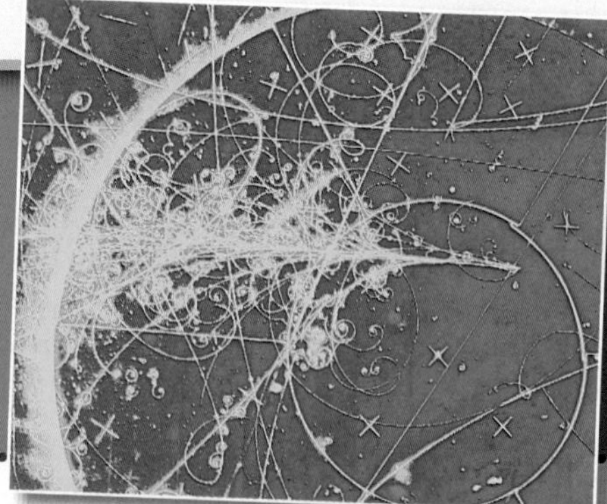

Social Studies ACTIVITY

Do some research on the history of scientific knowledge about matter. Make a poster that shows a timeline of events leading up to the discovery of the neutron in 1932.

Careers

Mimi So

Gemologist and Jewelry Designer A typical day for gemologist and jewelry designer Mimi So involves deciding what materials to work with. When she chooses a gemstone for a piece of jewelry, she must consider the size, hardness, color, grade, and cut of the stone. When choosing a metal to use as a setting for a stone, she must look at the hardness, melting point, color, and malleability of the metal. She needs to choose a metal that not only looks good with a particular stone but also has physical properties that will work with that stone. For example, Mimi So says emeralds are soft and fragile. A platinum setting would be too hard and could damage the emerald. So, emeralds are usually set in a softer metal, such as 18-karat gold.

The chemical properties of stones must also be considered. Heating can burn or discolor some gemstones. Mimi So says, "If you are using pearls in a design that requires heating the metal, the pearl is not a stone, so you cannot heat the pearl, because it would destroy the pearl."

Math Activity

Pure gold is 24-karat (24K). Gold that contains 18 parts gold and 6 parts other metals is 18-karat gold. The percentage of gold in 18K gold is found by dividing the amount of gold by the total amount of the material and then multiplying by 100%. For example, (18 parts gold)/(24 parts total) equals $0.75 \times 100\% = 75\%$ gold. Find the percentage of gold in 10K and 14K gold.

To learn more about these Science in Action topics, visit go.hrw.com and type in the keyword **HT5D6MTIF.**

Current Science

Check out Current Science® articles related to this chapter by visiting go.hrw.com. Just type in the keyword HP5CS02.

11

Elements, Compounds, and Mixtures

About the PHOTO

Within these liquid-filled glass lamps, colored globs slowly rise and fall. But what are these liquids, and what keeps them from mixing together? The liquid inside these lamps is a mixture. This mixture is composed of four compounds, which include mineral oil, wax, water, and alcohol. The water and alcohol mix, but they remain separated from the globs of wax and oil.

PRE-READING ACTIVITY

FOLDNOTES **Key-Term Fold** Before you read the chapter, create the FoldNote entitled "Key-Term Fold" described in the **Study Skills** section of the Appendix. Write a key term from the chapter on each tab of the key-term fold. Under each tab, write the definition of the key term.

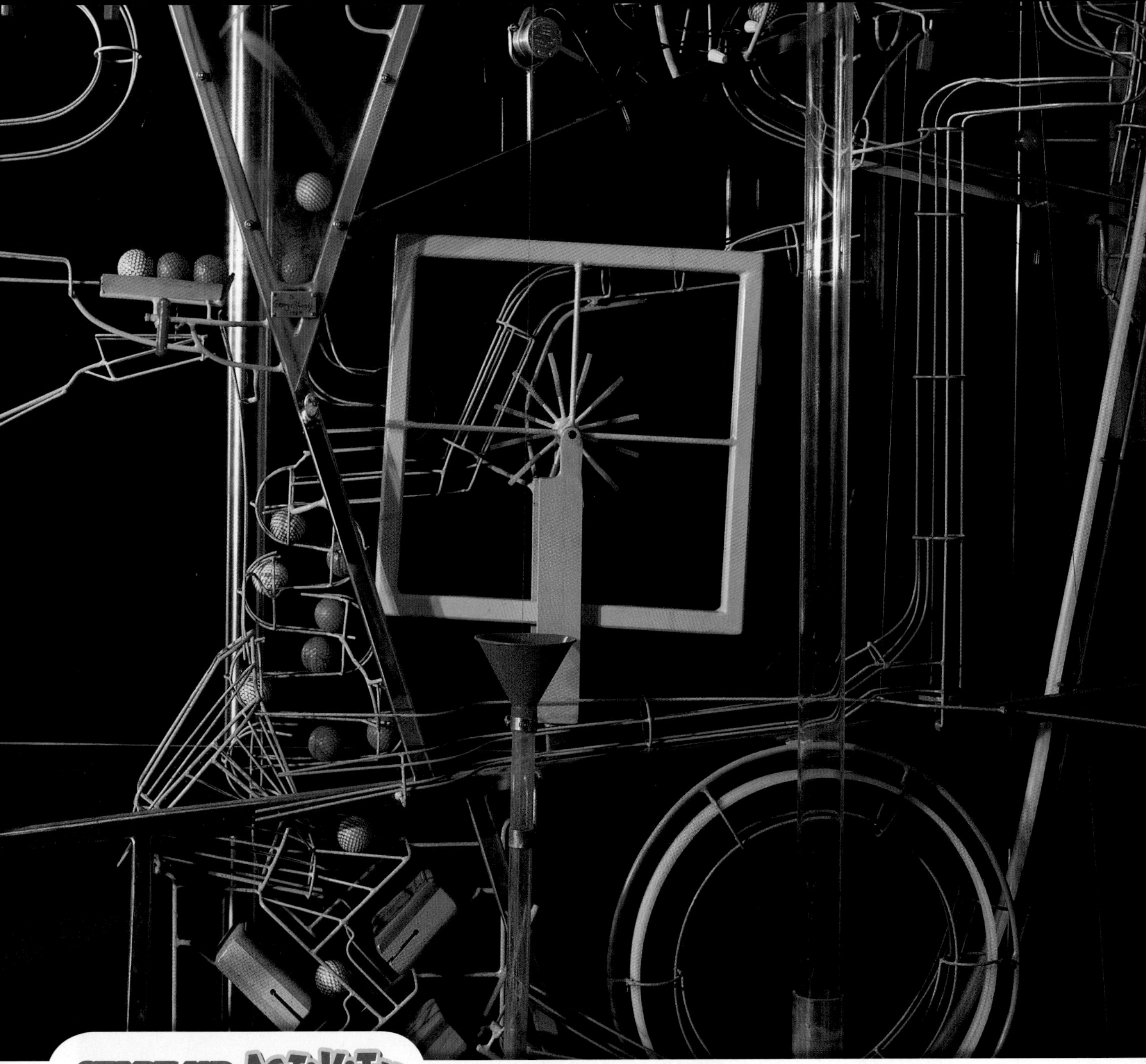

START-UP ACTIVITY

Energy Swings!

In this activity, you'll observe a moving pendulum to learn about energy.

Procedure

1. Make a pendulum by tying a **50 cm long string** around the hook of a **100 g hooked mass.**
2. Hold the string with one hand. Pull the mass slightly to the side, and let go of the mass without pushing it. Watch it swing at least 10 times.
3. Record your observations. Note how fast and how high the pendulum swings.
4. Repeat step 2, but pull the mass farther to the side.
5. Record your observations. Note how fast and how high the pendulum swings.

Analysis

1. Does the pendulum have energy? Explain your answer.
2. What causes the pendulum to move?
3. Do you think the pendulum had energy before you let go of the mass? Explain your answer.

SECTION 1

What Is Energy?

It's match point. The crowd is silent. The tennis player tosses the ball into the air and then slams it with her racket. The ball flies toward her opponent, who swings her racket at the ball. THWOOSH!! The ball goes into the net, causing it to shake. Game, set, and match!!

The tennis player needs energy to slam the ball with her racket. The ball also must have energy in order to cause the net to shake. Energy is around you all of the time. But what, exactly, is energy?

READING WARM-UP

Objectives

- Explain the relationship between energy and work.
- Compare kinetic and potential energy.
- Describe the different forms of energy.

Terms to Learn

energy
kinetic energy
potential energy
mechanical energy

READING STRATEGY

Discussion Read this section silently. Write down questions that you have about this section. Discuss your questions in a small group.

Energy and Work: Working Together

In science, **energy** is the ability to do work. Work is done when a force causes an object to move in the direction of the force. How do energy and work help you play tennis? The tennis player in **Figure 1** does work on her racket by exerting a force on it. The racket does work on the ball, and the ball does work on the net. When one object does work on another, energy is transferred from the first object to the second object. This energy allows the second object to do work. So, work is a transfer of energy. Like work, energy is expressed in units of joules (J).

Reading Check What is energy? (*See the Appendix for answers to Reading Checks.*)

energy the capacity to do work

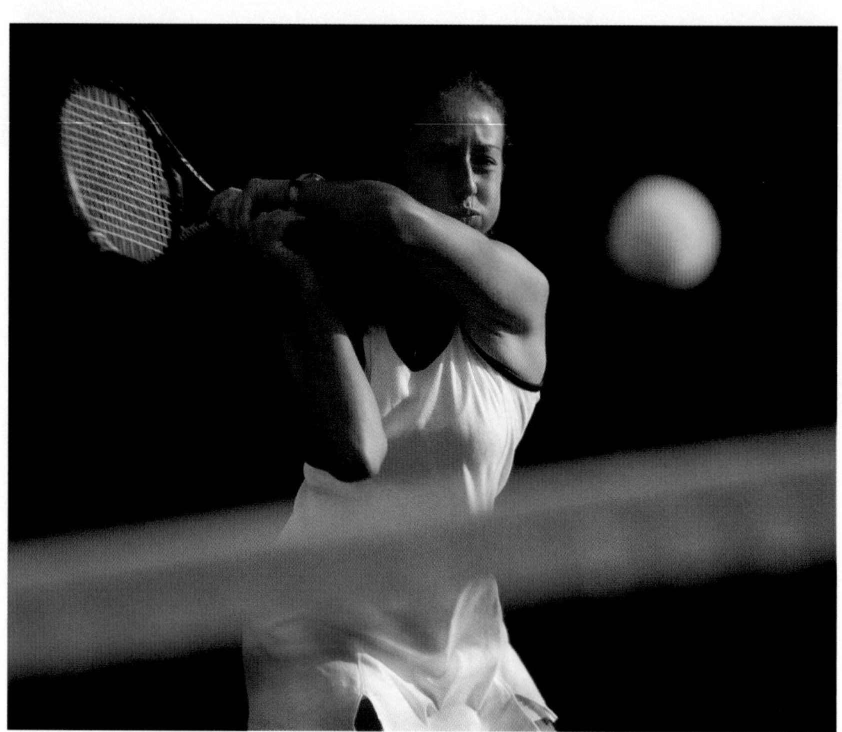

Figure 1 *The tennis player does work and transfers energy to the racket. With this energy, the racket can then do work on the ball.*

Kinetic Energy

In tennis, energy is transferred from the racket to the ball. As it flies over the net, the ball has kinetic (ki NET ik) energy. **Kinetic energy** is the energy of motion. All moving objects have kinetic energy. Like all forms of energy, kinetic energy can be used to do work. For example, kinetic energy allows a hammer to do work on a nail, as shown in **Figure 2.**

kinetic energy the energy of an object that is due to the object's motion

Kinetic Energy Depends on Mass and Speed

An object's kinetic energy can be found by the following equation:

$$kinetic\ energy = \frac{mv^2}{2}$$

The m stands for the object's mass in kilograms. The v stands for the object's speed. The faster something is moving, the more kinetic energy it has. Also, the greater the mass of a moving object, the greater its kinetic energy is.

A large car has more kinetic energy than a car that has less mass and that is moving at the same speed does. But as you can see from the equation, speed is squared. So speed has a greater effect on kinetic energy than mass does. For this reason, car crashes are much more dangerous at higher speeds than at lower speeds. A moving car has *4 times* the kinetic energy of the same car going half the speed! This is because it's going twice the speed of the slower car, and 2 squared is 4.

Figure 2 *When you swing a hammer, you give it kinetic energy, which does work on the nail.*

MATH FOCUS

Kinetic Energy What is the kinetic energy of a car that has a mass of 1,200 kg and is moving at a speed of 20 m/s?

Step 1: Write the equation for kinetic energy.

$$KE = \frac{mv^2}{2}$$

Step 2: Replace m and v with the measurements given, and solve.

$$KE = \frac{1{,}200\ \text{kg} \times (20\ \text{m/s})^2}{2}$$

$$KE = \frac{1{,}200\ \text{kg} \times 400\ \text{m}^2/\text{s}^2}{2}$$

$$KE = \frac{480{,}000\ \text{kg}\bullet\text{m}^2/\text{s}^2}{2}$$

$$KE = 240{,}000\ \text{kg}\bullet\text{m}^2/\text{s}^2 = 240{,}000\ \text{J}$$

Now It's Your Turn

1. What is the kinetic energy of a car that has a mass of 2,400 kg and is moving at 20 m/s? How does this kinetic energy compare to the kinetic energy of the car in the example given at left?
2. What is the kinetic energy of a 4,000 kg elephant that is running at 2 m/s? at 4 m/s? How do the two kinetic energies compare with one another?
3. What is the kinetic energy of a 2,000 kg bus that is moving at 30 m/s?
4. What is the kinetic energy of a 3,000 kg bus that is moving at 20 m/s?

Figure 3 *The stored potential energy of the bow and string allows them to do work on the arrow when the string is released.*

Potential Energy

Not all energy has to do with motion. **Potential energy** is the energy an object has because of its position. For example, the stretched bow shown in **Figure 3** has potential energy. The bow has energy because work has been done to change its shape. The energy of that work is turned into potential energy.

Gravitational Potential Energy

When you lift an object, you do work on it. You use a force that is against the force of gravity. When you do this, you transfer energy to the object and give the object *gravitational potential energy.* Books on a shelf have gravitational potential energy. So does your backpack after you lift it on to your back. The amount of gravitational potential energy that an object has depends on its weight and its height.

Calculating Gravitational Potential Energy

You can find gravitational potential energy by using the following equation:

$$\textit{gravitational potential energy} = \textit{weight} \times \textit{height}$$

Because weight is expressed in newtons and height in meters, gravitational potential energy is expressed in newton-meters (N•m), or joules (J).

Recall that *work* = *force* × *distance.* Weight is the amount of force that you must use on an object to lift it, and height is a distance. So, gravitational potential energy is equal to the amount of work done on the object to lift it to a certain height. Or, you can think of gravitational potential energy as equal to the work that would be done by the object if it were dropped from its height.

Gravitational Potential Energy What is the gravitational potential energy of a book with a weight of 13 N at a height of 1.5 m off the ground?

Step 1: Write the equation for gravitational potential energy (*GPE*).

$GPE = weight \times height$

Step 2: Replace the weight and height with the measurements given in the problem, and solve.

$GPE = 13 \text{ N} \times 1.5 \text{ m}$

$GPE = 19.5 \text{ N•m} = 19.5 \text{ J}$

Now It's Your Turn

1. What is the gravitational potential energy of a cat that weighs 40 N standing on a table that is 0.8 m above the ground?
2. What is the gravitational potential energy of a diver who weighs 500 N standing on a platform that is 10 m off the ground?
3. What is the gravitational potential energy of a diver who weighs 600 N standing on a platform that is 8 m off the ground?

Height Above What?

When you want to find out an object's gravitational potential energy, the "ground" that you measure the object's height from depends on where it is. For example, what if you want to measure the gravitational potential energy of an egg sitting on the kitchen counter? In this case, you would measure the egg's height from the floor. But if you were holding the egg over a balcony several stories from the ground, you would measure the egg's height from the ground! You can see that gravitational potential energy depends on your point of view. So, the height you use in calculating gravitational potential energy is a measure of how far an object has to fall.

potential energy the energy that an object has because of the position, shape, or condition of the object

mechanical energy the amount of work an object can do because of the object's kinetic and potential energies

Mechanical Energy

How would you describe the energy of the juggler's pins in **Figure 4**? To describe their total energy, you would state their mechanical energy. **Mechanical energy** is the total energy of motion and position of an object. Both potential energy and kinetic energy are kinds of mechanical energy. Mechanical energy can be all potential energy, all kinetic energy, or some of each. You can use the following equation to find mechanical energy:

$$mechanical\ energy = potential\ energy + kinetic\ energy$$

Reading Check **What two kinds of energy can make up the mechanical energy of an object?**

Mechanical Energy in a Juggler's Pin

The mechanical energy of an object remains the same unless it transfers some of its energy to another object. But even if the mechanical energy of an object stays the same, the potential energy or kinetic energy it has can increase or decrease.

Look at **Figure 4.** While the juggler is moving the pin with his hand, he is doing work on the pin to give it kinetic energy. But as soon as the pin leaves his hand, the pin's kinetic energy starts changing into potential energy. How can you tell that the kinetic energy is decreasing? The pin slows down as it moves upwards. Eventually, all of the pin's kinetic energy turns into potential energy, and it stops moving upward.

As the pin starts to fall back down again, its potential energy starts changing back into kinetic energy. More and more of its potential energy turns into kinetic energy. You can tell because the pin speeds up as it falls towards the ground.

Figure 4 *As a pin is juggled, its mechanical energy is the sum of its potential energy and its kinetic energy at any point.*

Figure 5 Thermal Energy in Water

The particles in an ice cube vibrate in fixed positions and do not have a lot of kinetic energy.

The particles of water in a lake can move more freely and have more kinetic energy than water particles in ice do.

The particles of water in steam move rapidly, so they have more energy than the particles in liquid water do.

Other Forms of Energy

Energy can come in a number of forms besides mechanical energy. These forms of energy include thermal, chemical, electrical, sound, light, and nuclear energy. As you read the next few pages, you will learn what these different forms of energy have to do with kinetic and potential energy.

Thermal Energy

All matter is made of particles that are always in random motion. Because the particles are in motion, they have kinetic energy. *Thermal energy* is all of the kinetic energy due to random motion of the particles that make up an object.

As you can see in **Figure 5,** particles move faster at higher temperatures than at lower temperatures. The faster the particles move, the greater their kinetic energy and the greater the object's thermal energy. Thermal energy also depends on the number of particles. Water in the form of steam has a higher temperature than water in a lake does. But the lake has more thermal energy because the lake has more water particles.

For another activity related to this chapter, go to **go.hrw.com** and type in the keyword **HP5ENGW.**

Chemical Energy

Where does the energy in food come from? Food is made of chemical compounds. When compounds such as sugar form, work is done to join the different atoms together. *Chemical energy* is the energy of a compound that changes as its atoms are rearranged. Chemical energy is a form of potential energy because it depends on the position and arrangement of the atoms in a compound.

Hear That Energy!

1. Make a simple drum by covering the open end of an **empty coffee can** with **wax paper.** Secure the wax paper with a **rubber band.**
2. Using the eraser end of a **pencil,** tap lightly on the wax paper. Describe how the paper responds. What do you hear?
3. Repeat step 2, but tap the paper a bit harder. Compare your results with those of step 2.
4. Cover half of the wax paper with one hand. Now, tap the paper. What happened? How can you describe sound energy as a form of mechanical energy?

Electrical Energy

The electrical outlets in your home allow you to use electrical energy. *Electrical energy* is the energy of moving electrons. Electrons are the negatively charged particles of atoms.

Suppose you plug an electrical device, such as the amplifier shown in **Figure 6,** into an outlet and turn it on. The electrons in the wires will transfer energy to different parts inside the amplifier. The electrical energy of moving electrons is used to do work that makes the sound that you hear from the amplifier.

The electrical energy used in your home comes from power plants. Huge generators turn magnets inside loops of wire. The changing position of a magnet makes electrical energy run through the wire. This electrical energy can be thought of as potential energy that is used when you plug in an electrical appliance and use it.

Figure 6 *The movement of electrons produces the electrical energy that an amplifier and a microphone use to produce sound.*

Sound Energy

Figure 7 shows how a vibrating object transmits energy through the air around it. Sound energy is caused by an object's vibrations. When you stretch a guitar string, the string stores potential energy. When you let the string go, this potential energy is turned into kinetic energy, which makes the string vibrate. The string also transmits some of this kinetic energy to the air around it. The air particles also vibrate, and transmit this energy to your ear. When the sound energy reaches your ear, you hear the sound of the guitar.

Reading Check **What does sound energy consist of?**

Figure 7 *As the guitar strings vibrate, they cause particles in the air to vibrate. These vibrations transmit sound energy.*

Figure 8 *The energy used to cook food in a microwave is a form of light energy.*

Light Energy

Light allows you to see, but did you know that not all light can be seen? **Figure 8** shows a type of light that we use but can't see. *Light energy* is produced by the vibrations of electrically charged particles. Like sound vibrations, light vibrations cause energy to be transmitted. But the vibrations that transmit light energy don't need to be carried through matter. In fact, light energy can move through a vacuum (an area where there is no matter).

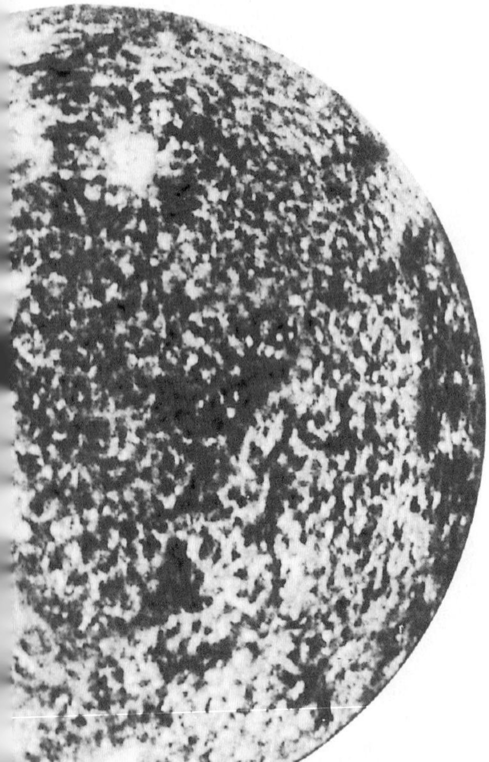

Nuclear Energy

There is a form of energy that comes from a tiny amount of matter. It is used to generate electrical energy, and it gives the sun its energy. It is *nuclear* (NOO klee uhr) *energy,* the energy that comes from changes in the nucleus (NOO klee uhs) of an atom.

Atoms store a lot of potential energy because of the positions of the particles in the nucleus of the atoms. When two or more small nuclei (NOO klee ie) join together, or when the nucleus of a large atom splits apart, energy is given off.

The energy given off by the sun comes from nuclear energy. In the sun, shown in **Figure 9,** hydrogen nuclei join together to make a larger helium nucleus. This reaction, known as *fusion,* gives off a huge amount of energy. The sun's light and heat come from these reactions.

Figure 9 *Without the nuclear energy from the sun, life on Earth would not be possible.*

When a nucleus of a heavy element such as uranium is split apart, the potential energy in the nucleus is given off. This kind of nuclear energy is called *fission.* Fission is used to generate electrical energy at nuclear power plants.

Reading Check **Where does nuclear energy come from?**

SECTION Review

Summary

- Energy is the ability to do work, and work equals the transfer of energy. Energy and work are expressed in units of joules (J).
- Kinetic energy is energy of motion and depends on speed and mass.
- Potential energy is energy of position. Gravitational potential energy depends on weight and height.
- Mechanical energy is the sum of kinetic energy and potential energy.
- Thermal energy and sound energy can be considered forms of kinetic energy.
- Chemical energy, electrical energy, and nuclear energy can be considered forms of potential energy.

Using Key Terms

1. In your own words, write a definition for the term *energy*.
2. Use the following terms in the same sentence: *kinetic energy, potential energy,* and *mechanical energy*.

Understanding Key Ideas

3. What determines an object's thermal energy?
   a. the motion of its particles
   b. its size
   c. its potential energy
   d. its mechanical energy
4. How are energy and work related?
5. What two factors determine gravitational potential energy?
6. Describe why chemical energy is a form of potential energy.

Critical Thinking

7. **Identifying Relationships** When you hit a nail into a board by using a hammer, the head of the nail gets warm. In terms of kinetic and thermal energy, describe why you think the nail head gets warm.
8. **Applying Concepts** Explain why a high-speed collision may cause more damage to vehicles than a low-speed collision does.

Interpreting Graphics

9. Which part of mechanical energy does the girl in the picture below have the most of?

SCI LINKS
NSTA
Developed and maintained by the National Science Teachers Association
For a variety of links related to this chapter, go to www.scilinks.org
Topic: What Is Energy? ; Forms of Energy
SciLinks code: HSM1660; HSM0612

SECTION 2

Energy Conversions

Imagine you're finishing a clay mug in art class. You turn around, and your elbow knocks the mug off the table. Luckily, you catch the mug before it hits the ground.

READING WARM-UP

Objectives

- Describe an energy conversion.
- Give examples of energy conversions for the different forms of energy.
- Explain how energy conversions make energy useful.
- Explain the role of machines in energy conversions.

Terms to Learn

energy conversion

READING STRATEGY

Brainstorming The key idea of this section is energy conversion. Brainstorm words and phrases related to energy conversion.

The mug has gravitational potential energy while it is on the table. As the mug falls, its potential energy changes into kinetic energy. This change is an example of an energy conversion. An **energy conversion** is a change from one form of energy to another. Any form of energy can change into any other form of energy. Often, one form of energy changes into more than one other form.

energy conversion a change from one form of energy to another

Kinetic Energy and Potential Energy

Look at **Figure 1.** At the instant this picture was taken, the skateboarder on the left side of the picture was hardly moving. How did he get up so high in the air? As you might guess, he was moving at a high speed on his way up the half-pipe. So, he had a lot of kinetic energy. What happened to that energy? His kinetic energy changed into potential energy. Imagine that the picture below is a freeze-frame of a video. What happens once the video starts running again? The skateboarder's potential energy will become kinetic energy once again as he speeds down the side of the half-pipe.

Figure 1 Potential Energy and Kinetic Energy

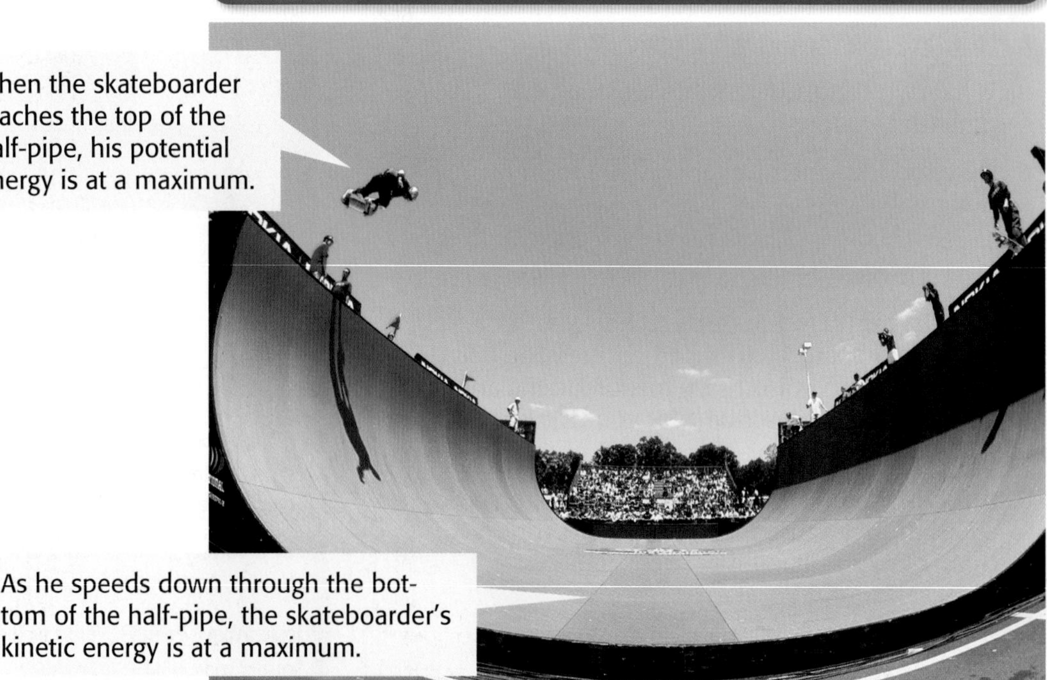

When the skateboarder reaches the top of the half-pipe, his potential energy is at a maximum.
As he speeds down through the bottom of the half-pipe, the skateboarder's kinetic energy is at a maximum.

Elastic Potential Energy

A rubber band can be used to show another example of an energy conversion. Did you know that energy can be stored in a rubber band? Look at **Figure 2.** The wound-up rubber band in the toy airplane has a kind of potential energy called *elastic potential energy.* When the rubber band is let go, the stored energy becomes kinetic energy, spins the propeller, and makes the airplane fly.

You can change the shape of a rubber band by stretching it. Stretching the rubber band takes a little effort. The energy you put into stretching it becomes elastic potential energy. Like the skateboarder at the top of the half-pipe, the stretched rubber band stores potential energy. When you let the rubber band go, it goes back to its original shape. It releases its stored-up potential energy as it does so, as you know if you have ever snapped a rubber band against your skin!

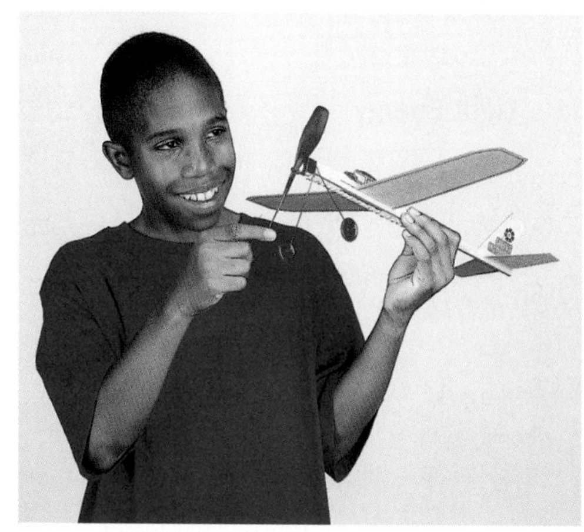

Figure 2 *The wound-up rubber band in this model airplane has potential energy because its shape has been changed.*

Reading Check **How is elastic potential energy stored and released?** (*See the Appendix for answers to Reading Checks.*)

Conversions Involving Chemical Energy

You may have heard someone say, "Breakfast is the most important meal of the day." Why is eating breakfast so important? As shown in **Figure 3,** chemical energy comes from the food you eat. Your body uses chemical energy to function. Eating breakfast gives your body the energy needed to help you start the day.

Figure 3 Chemical energy of food is converted into kinetic energy when you are active. It is converted into thermal energy to maintain body temperature.

Figure 4 From Light Energy to Chemical Energy

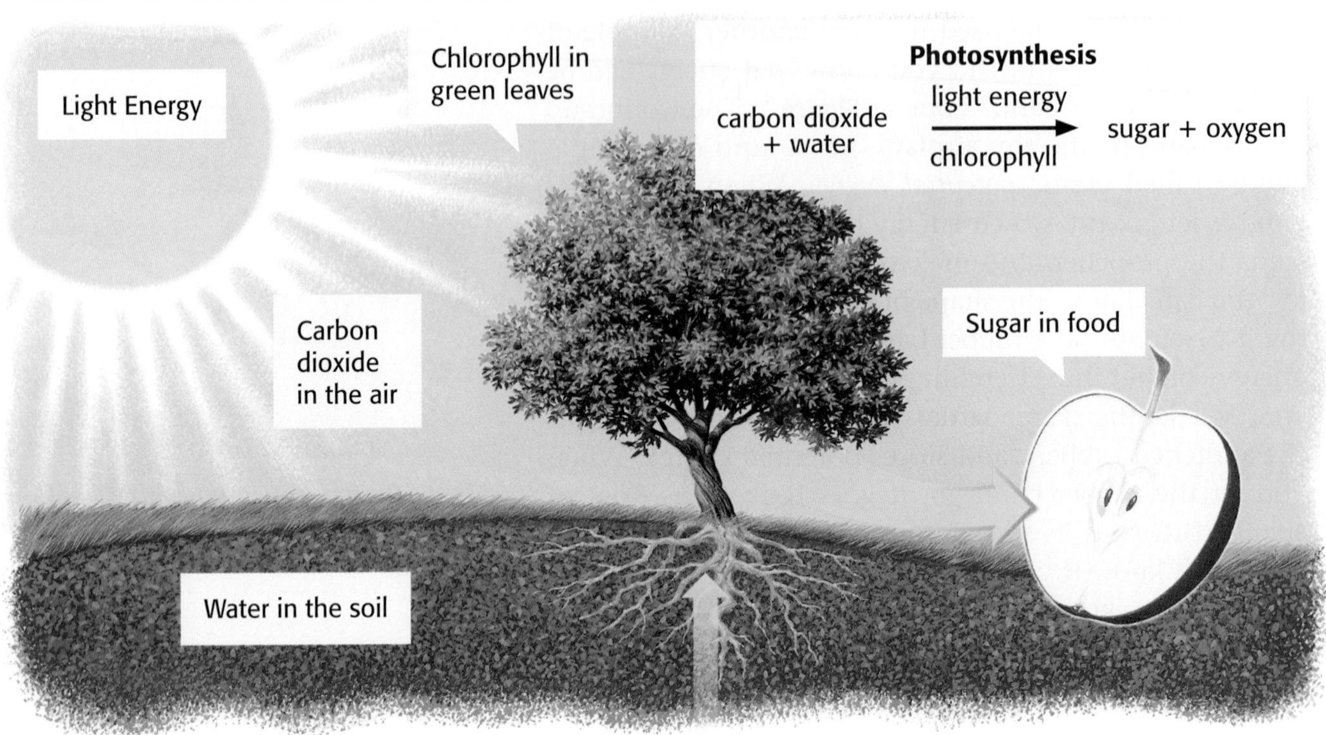

Energy Conversions in Plants

Did you know that the chemical energy in the food you eat comes from the sun's energy? When you eat fruits, vegetables, or grains, you are taking in chemical energy. This energy comes from a chemical change that was made possible by the sun's energy. When you eat meat from animals that ate plants, you are also taking in energy that first came from the sun.

As shown in **Figure 4,** photosynthesis (FOHT oh SIN thuh sis) uses light energy to make new substances that have chemical energy. In this way, light energy is changed into chemical energy. The chemical energy from a tree can be changed into thermal energy when you burn the tree's wood. So, if you follow the conversion of energy back far enough, the energy from a wood fire actually comes from the sun!

Reading Check **Where does the energy that plants use to grow come from?**

The Process Continues

Let's trace where the energy goes. Plants change light energy into chemical energy. The chemical energy in the food you eat is changed into another kind of chemical energy that your body can use. Your body then uses that energy to give you the kinetic energy that you use in everything you do. It's an endless process—energy is always going somewhere!

CONNECTION TO Biology

WRITING SKILL **Energy from Plants** All living things need energy. Plants play a major role in providing sources of energy that our bodies use, from the oxygen we breathe to the food we eat. Research the different ways that plants help provide the energy requirements of all living things, and write a one-page report in your **science journal** describing what you learn.

Figure 5 Energy Conversions in a Hair Dryer

1
Electrical energy enters the hair dryer and is converted into kinetic energy as a small electric motor spins a fan blade.
2
Electrical energy is also converted into thermal energy in a grid of wires that heats up.
3
The fan forces air across the hot wires, and hot air blows out of the nozzle of the hair dryer. You can hear the sound energy that also comes out.

Why Energy Conversions Are Important

Energy conversions are needed for everything we do. Heating our homes, getting energy from a meal, and many other things use energy conversions. Machines, such as the hair dryer shown in **Figure 5,** help harness energy and make that energy work for you. Electrical energy by itself won't dry your hair. But you can use a hair dryer to change electrical energy into the thermal energy that will help you dry your hair.

Conversions Involving Electrical Energy

You use electrical energy all of the time. Devices in your home convert electrical energy into other forms of energy. For example, electrical energy is changed into thermal energy and light energy by toasters, stoves, and lamps. Electrical energy can also be changed into sound energy by radios and TVs. Electrical energy can even be changed into chemical energy when you recharge batteries by using an electric charger.

Where does the electrical energy come from, and how does it reach your home? The energy comes from *electric generators* that convert mechanical energy into electrical energy. The energy is then transferred through electric circuits to your home. A *circuit* is a complete path of an electric current. Electrical energy can travel from one place to another only by way of a circuit.

Figure 6 *Some of the energy you transfer to a nutcracker is converted into sound energy as the nutcracker transfers energy to the nut.*

Energy and Machines

You've been learning about energy, its different forms, and the ways that it can change between forms. Another way to learn about energy is to look at how machines use energy. A machine can make work easier by changing the size or direction (or both) of the force needed to do the work.

Suppose you want to crack open a walnut. Using a nutcracker, such as the one shown in **Figure 6,** would be much easier (and less painful) than using your fingers. You transfer energy to the nutcracker, and it transfers energy to the nut. The nutcracker allows you to use less force over a greater distance to do the same amount of work as if you had used your bare hands. Another example of how energy is used by a machine is shown in **Figure 7.** Some machines change the energy put into them into other forms of energy.

Reading Check **What are two things that machines can do to force that is put into them?**

Figure 7 **Energy Conversions in a Bicycle**

For your bike to start and keep moving, energy must be transferred and converted.

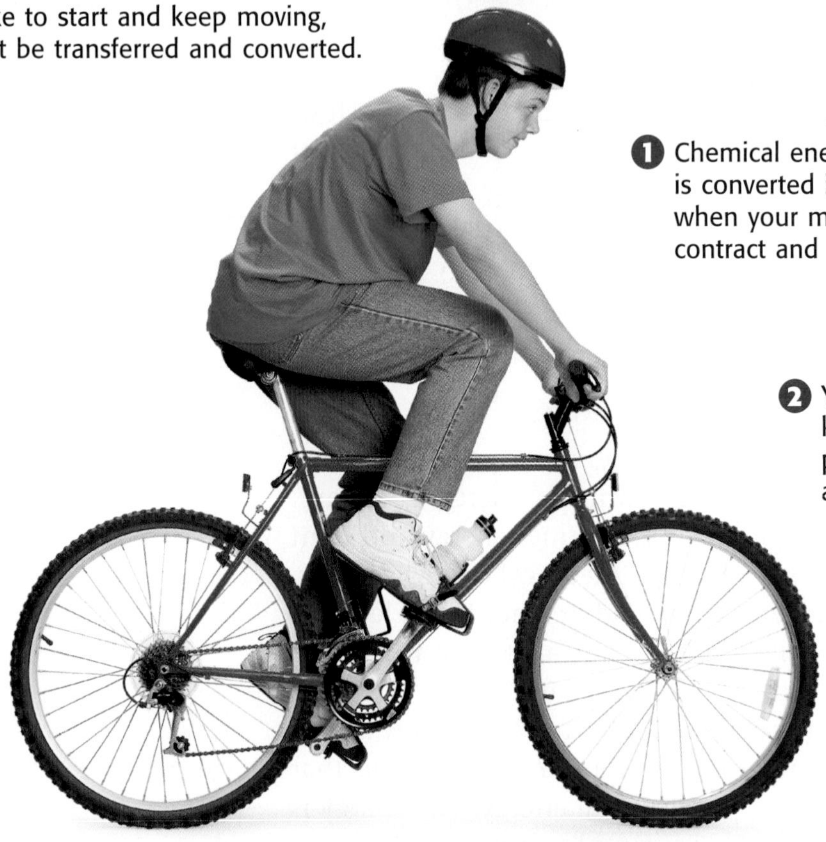

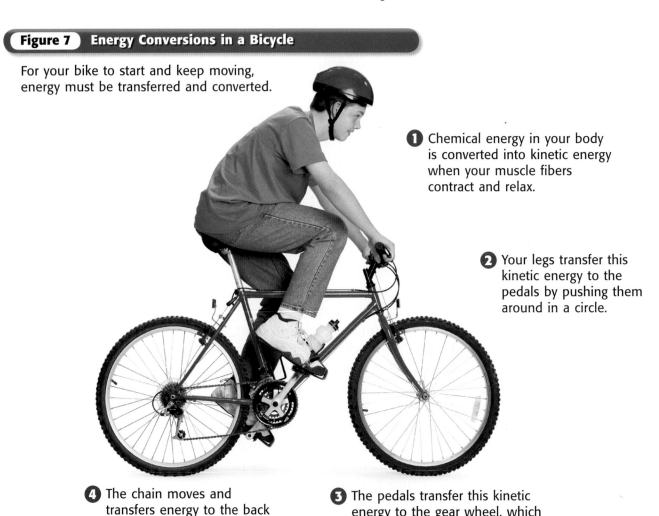

1. Chemical energy in your body is converted into kinetic energy when your muscle fibers contract and relax.
2. Your legs transfer this kinetic energy to the pedals by pushing them around in a circle.
3. The pedals transfer this kinetic energy to the gear wheel, which transfers kinetic energy to the chain.
4. The chain moves and transfers energy to the back wheel, which gets you moving!

Machines as Energy Converters

Machines help you use energy by converting it into the form that you need. **Figure 8** shows a device called a *radiometer*. It was invented to measure energy from the sun. Inside the glass bulb are four small vanes that absorb light energy. The vanes are dark on one side and light on the other. The dark sides absorb light energy better than the light sides do. As gases next to the dark sides of the vanes heat up, the gas molecules move faster, which causes the vanes to turn. The radiometer shows how a machine can convert energy from one form into another. It changes light energy into heat energy into kinetic energy.

Figure 8 *Machines can change energy into different forms. This radiometer converts light energy into kinetic energy.*

SECTION Review

Summary

- An energy conversion is a change from one form of energy to another. Any form of energy can be converted into any other form of energy.
- Kinetic energy is converted to potential energy when an object is moved against gravity.
- Elastic potential energy is another example of potential energy.
- Your body uses the food you eat to convert chemical energy into kinetic energy.
- Plants convert light energy into chemical energy.
- Machines can transfer energy and can convert energy into a more useful form.

Using Key Terms

1. In your own words, write a definition for the term *energy conversion*.

Understanding Key Ideas

2. In plants, energy is transformed from
   - **a.** kinetic to potential.
   - **b.** light to chemical.
   - **c.** chemical to electrical.
   - **d.** chemical to light.
3. Describe a case in which electrical energy is converted into thermal energy.
4. How does your body get the energy that it needs?
5. What is the role of machines in energy conversions?

Critical Thinking

6. **Applying Concepts** Describe the kinetic-potential energy conversions that occur when a basketball bounces.
7. **Applying Concepts** A car that brakes suddenly comes to a screeching halt. Is the sound energy produced in this conversion a useful form of energy? Explain your answer.

Interpreting Graphics

Look at the diagram below, and answer the following questions.

8. What kind of energy does the skier have at the top of the slope?
9. What happens to that energy after the skier races down the slope of the mountain?

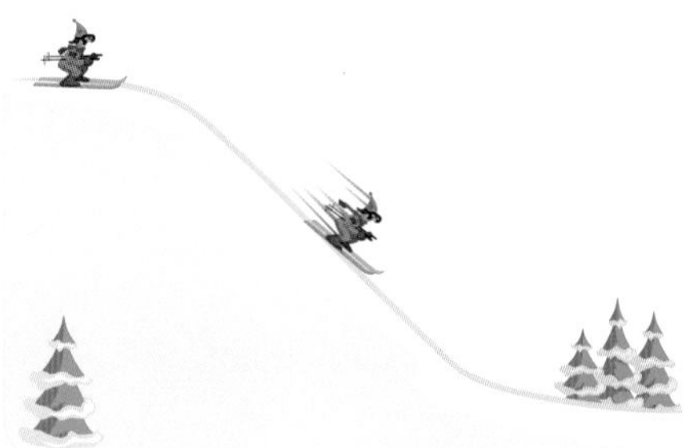

SCILINKS.
NSTA
Developed and maintained by the National Science Teachers Association
For a variety of links related to this chapter, go to www.scilinks.org
Topic: Energy Conversions
SciLinks code: HSM0511

Using Scientific Methods

Skills Practice Lab

Finding Energy

When you coast down a hill on a bike or skateboard, you may notice that you pick up speed, or go faster and faster. Because you are moving, you have kinetic energy—the energy of motion. Where does that energy come from? When you pedal the bike or push the skateboard, you are the source of the kinetic energy. But where does the kinetic energy come from when you roll down a hill without making any effort? In this lab, you will find out where such kinetic energy comes from.

OBJECTIVES

Form a hypothesis about where kinetic energy comes from.

Test your hypothesis by collecting and analyzing data.

MATERIALS

- books (2 or 3)
- masking tape
- meterstick
- metric balance
- rolling cart
- stopwatch
- wooden board

Ask a Question

1. Where does the kinetic energy come from when you roll down a hill?

Form a Hypothesis

2. Write a hypothesis that is a possible answer to the question above. Explain your reasoning.

Test the Hypothesis

3. Copy the Data Collection Table below.

Data Collection Table

Height of ramp (m)	Length of ramp (m)	Mass of cart (kg)	Weight of cart (N)	Time of trial (s)			Average time (s)
				1	2	3	

4. Use your books and board to make a ramp.
5. Use masking tape to mark a starting line at the top of the ramp. Be sure the starting line is far enough down from the top of the ramp to allow the cart to be placed behind the line.
6. Use masking tape to mark a finish line at the bottom of the ramp.
7. Find the height of the ramp by measuring the height of the starting line and subtracting the height of the finish line. Record the height of the ramp in your Data Collection Table.
8. Measure the distance in meters between the starting line and the finish line. In the Data Collection Table, record this distance as the length of the ramp.
9. Use the balance to find the mass of the cart in grams. Convert this measurement to kilograms by dividing it by 1,000. In your Data Collection Table, record the mass in kilograms.
10. Multiply the mass by 10 to get the weight of the cart in newtons. Record this weight in your Data Collection Table.
11. Set the cart behind the starting line, and release it. Use a stopwatch to time how long the cart takes to reach the finish line. Record the time in your Data Collection Table.
12. Repeat step 11 twice more, and average the results. Record the average time in your Data Collection Table.

Analyze the Results

1. **Organizing Data** Copy the Calculations Table shown at right onto a separate sheet of paper.
2. **Analyzing Data** Calculate and record the quantities for the cart in the Calculations Table by using your data and the four equations that follow.

Calculations Table

Average speed (m/s)	Final speed (m/s)	Kinetic energy at bottom (J)	Gravitational potential energy at top (J)
DO NOT WRITE IN BOOK			

$$\textit{average speed} = \frac{\textit{length of ramp}}{\textit{average time}}$$

Final speed = 2 × *average speed*
(This equation works because the cart accelerates smoothly from 0 m/s.)

$$\textit{kinetic energy} = \frac{\textit{mass} \times (\textit{final speed})^2}{2}$$

(Remember that 1 kg • m^2/s^2 = 1 J, the unit used to express energy.)

Gravitational potential energy = weight × height
(Remember that 1 N = 1 kg • m/s^2, so 1 N × 1 m = 1 kg • m^2/s^2 = 1 J)

Draw Conclusions

3. **Drawing Conclusions** How does the cart's gravitational potential energy at the top of the ramp compare with its kinetic energy at the bottom? Does this support your hypothesis? Explain your answer.
4. **Evaluating Data** You probably found that the gravitational potential energy of the cart at the top of the ramp was almost, but not exactly, equal to the kinetic energy of the cart at the bottom of the ramp. Explain this finding.
5. **Applying Conclusions** Suppose that while riding your bike, you coast down both a small hill and a large hill. Compare your final speed at the bottom of the small hill with your final speed at the bottom of the large hill. Explain your answer.

Chapter Review

USING KEY TERMS

1. Use the following term in a sentence: *energy*.

For each pair of terms, explain how the meanings of the terms differ.

2. *potential energy* and *kinetic energy*
3. *mechanical energy* and *energy conversion*

UNDERSTANDING KEY IDEAS

Multiple Choice

4. Kinetic energy depends on
   - **a.** mass and volume.
   - **b.** velocity and weight.
   - **c.** weight and height.
   - **d.** velocity and mass.
5. Gravitational potential energy depends on
   - **a.** mass and velocity.
   - **b.** weight and height.
   - **c.** mass and weight.
   - **d.** height and distance.
6. What kind of energy is related to the random motion of the particles that make up an object?
   - **a.** thermal energy
   - **b.** electrical energy
   - **c.** chemical energy
   - **d.** nuclear energy
7. Which of the following sentences describes a conversion from chemical energy to thermal energy?
   - **a.** Food is digested and used to regulate body temperature.
   - **b.** Charcoal is burned in a barbecue pit.
   - **c.** Coal is burned to produce steam.
   - **d.** All of the above
8. What can a machine do?
   - **a.** It can change the energy that is put into it into other forms of energy.
   - **b.** It can change the size of a force.
   - **c.** It can change the direction of a force.
   - **d.** All of the above

Short Answer

9. Name two forms of energy, and relate them to kinetic or potential energy.
10. Give three examples of one form of energy being converted into another form.
11. Where does the electrical energy that you use at home come from?
12. How does electrical energy reach your home?

Math Skills

13. A box has 400 J of gravitational potential energy.
    - **a.** How much work had to be done to give the box that energy?
    - **b.** If the box weighs 100 N, how far above the ground is it?

CRITICAL THINKING

14 **Concept Mapping** Use the following terms to create a concept map: *energy, machines, sound energy, hair dryer, electrical energy, energy conversions, thermal energy,* and *kinetic energy*.

15 **Applying Concepts** Describe what happens in terms of energy when you blow up a balloon and release it.

16 **Making Inferences** The city planners of your town want to build a new water storage tank. Some members of the planning team want to put the tank on top of a hill, but other members want to put the tank in a valley. Which place is better for the tank? Use your knowledge of gravitational potential energy to explain your answer.

17 **Analyzing Processes** Look at the photo below. Beginning with the pole vaulter's breakfast, trace the energy conversions necessary for the event shown to take place.

18 **Identifying Relationships** Dunk tanks are often found at fairs. To dunk a person, you throw a ball at a target. When the ball hits the target, the target moves and causes a bench above the water tank to drop. The person sitting on the bench then falls into the water. Explain the relationship between work and energy in the way that a dunk tank works. (Hint: Focus on what happens before the person falls.)

INTERPRETING GRAPHICS

Use the graphic below to answer the questions that follow.

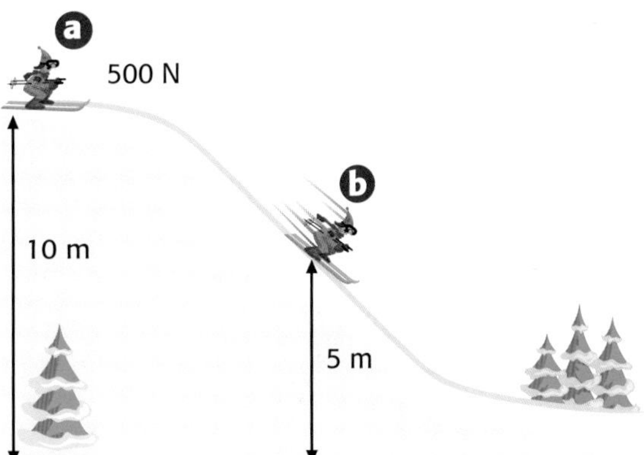

19 What is the skier's gravitational potential energy at point *A*?

20 What is the skier's gravitational potential energy at point *B*?

21 What is the skier's kinetic energy at point *B*? (Hint: mechanical energy = potential energy + kinetic energy)

Standardized Test Preparation

READING

Read each of the passages below. Then, answer the questions that follow each passage.

Passage 1 Gas hydrates are icy formations of water and methane. Methane is the main component of natural gas. The methane in gas hydrates is made by bacteria in the ocean. Large areas of hydrates have been found off the coasts of North Carolina and South Carolina in marine sediments. In just two areas that are each about the size of Rhode Island, scientists think there may be 70 times the amount of natural gas used by the United States in 1 year. The energy from gas hydrates could be used to drive machinery or generate electrical energy.

1. How large are each of the two gas hydrate deposits mentioned in this article?

A about the size of the United States
B about the size of South Carolina
C about the size of North Carolina
D about the size of Rhode Island

2. What are gas hydrates mainly made of?

F bacteria and sediments
G water and methane
H natural gas and water
I ice and sediments

3. How long could U.S. natural gas needs be met by all the gas in both deposits mentioned?

A 1 year
B 2 years
C 70 years
D 140 years

4. Where do methane gas hydrates come from?

F ocean water
G bacteria
H sediments
I ice

Passage 2 Two new technologies may reduce the price of electric cars. One is called a *hybrid electric vehicle*. This vehicle has a small gasoline engine that provides extra power and recharges the batteries. The other technology uses hydrogen fuel cells instead of batteries. These cells use the hydrogen present in more-conventional fuels, such as gasoline or ethanol, to produce an electric current that powers the car.

1. In this passage, what does *vehicle* mean?

A electric
B hybrid
C car
D current

2. Which of the following are conventional fuels?

F gasoline and ethanol
G hydrogen and ethanol
H gasoline and hydrogen
I only hydrogen

3. Which of the following is a fact in this passage?

A A hybrid electric vehicle runs partly on gasoline.
B All electric cars are hybrid.
C All electric cars use hydrogen fuel cells.
D Hydrogen fuel cells use conventional fuel.

4. What do the two new technologies described in the passage have in common?

F They do not use conventional fuels.
G They may reduce the price of electric cars.
H They use hybrid engines.
I They use hydrogen to produce an electric current.

INTERPRETING GRAPHICS

The pie chart below shows U.S. energy use by source of energy. Use the chart below to answer the questions that follow.

U.S. Energy Sources

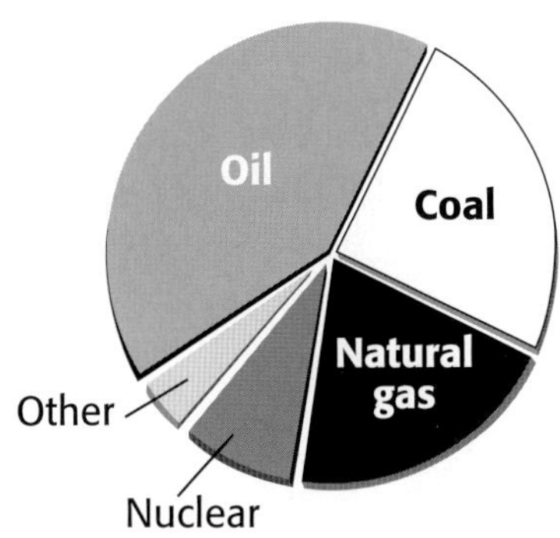

1. According to the graph, the United States relies on fossil fuels for about what percentage of its energy?
   A 30%
   B 45%
   C 60%
   D 80%

2. Nuclear energy represents about what percentage of U.S. energy sources?
   F 15%
   G 30%
   H 50%
   I 70%

3. Which energy source accounts for about 25% of U.S. energy?
   A oil
   B coal
   C natural gas
   D nuclear energy

MATH

Read each question below, and choose the best answer.

1. Gerald bought 2.5 kg of apples. How many grams of apples did he buy?
   A 0.0025 g
   B 0.25 g
   C 25 g
   D 2,500 g

2. Which group contains ratios that are equivalent to 3/8?
   F 6/16, 9/24, 12/32
   G 6/16, 12/24, 12/32
   H 6/24, 12/32, 15/40
   I 6/9, 9/24, 15/40

3. Carmen went to a bookstore. She bought three books for $7.99 each and four books for $3.35 each. Which number sentence can be used to find *c,* the total cost of the books?
   A $c = 3 + (7.99 \times 1) + (4 \times 3.35)$
   B $c = (1 \times 7.99) + (3 \times 3.35)$
   C $c = (3 \times 7.99) + (4 \times 3.35)$
   D $c = (3 \times 7.99) \times (4 \times 3.35)$

4. Rhonda's Mobile Car Washing charges $15 to wash a customer's car. Vacuuming the car costs an extra $10. Rhonda wants to know how much money she earned last week. When she looks at her appointment book, Rhonda finds that she washed a total of 50 cars. Only 20 of these cars were vacuumed after being washed. How much money did Rhonda earn last week?
   F $500
   G $750
   H $950
   I $1050

Science in Action

Science, Technology, and Society

Underwater Jet Engines

Almost all boats that have engines use propellers. But in 2002, a British company announced that it had developed an underwater jet engine.

The underwater jet engine works by producing steam in a gasoline-powered boiler. When the steam hits the water, it condenses to a very small volume, which creates a vacuum. This vacuum causes thrust by sucking in water from the front of the tube. The underwater jet engine is extremely energy-efficient, produces a great amount of thrust, and creates very little pollution.

Social Studies ACTIVITY

Research the kinds of water propulsion people have used throughout history. Note which kinds were improvements on previous technology and which were completely new.

Scientific Discoveries

$E = mc^2$

The famous 20th-century scientist Albert Einstein discovered an equation that is almost as famous as he is. That equation is $E = mc^2$. You may have heard of it before. But what does it mean?

The equation represents a relationship between mass and energy. E represents energy, m represents mass, and c represents the speed of light. So, $E = mc^2$ means that a small amount of mass has a very large amount of energy! Nuclear reactors harness this energy, which is given off when radioactive atoms split.

Math ACTIVITY

The speed of light is approximately 300,000,000 m/s. How much energy is equivalent to the mass of 0.00000002 g of hydrogen?

Careers

Cheryl Mele

Power-Plant Manager Cheryl Mele is the manager of the Decker Power Plant in Austin, Texas, where she is in charge of almost 1 billion watts of electric power generation. Most of the electric power is generated by a steam-driven turbine system that uses natural gas fuel. Gas turbines are also used. Together, the systems make enough electrical energy for many homes and businesses.

Cheryl Mele says her job as plant manager is to do "anything that needs doing." Her training as a mechanical engineer allows her to run tests and to find problems in the plant. Previously, Mele had a job helping to design more-efficient gas turbines. That job helped prepare her for the job of plant manager.

Mele believes that engineering and power-plant management are interesting jobs because they allow you to work with many new technologies. Mele thinks young people should pursue what interests them. "Be sure to connect the math you learn to the science you are doing," she says. "This will help you to understand both."

Language Arts ACTIVITY

Look up the word *energy* in a dictionary. Compare the different definitions you find to the definition given in this chapter.

go.hrw.com

To learn more about these Science in Action topics, visit **go.hrw.com** and type in the keyword **HP5ENGF.**

Current Science

Check out Current Science® articles related to this chapter by visiting go.hrw.com. Just type in the keyword HP5CS09.

The Energy of Waves

About the PHOTO

A surfer takes advantage of a wave's energy to catch an exciting ride. The ocean wave that this surfer is riding is just one type of wave. You are probably familiar with water waves. But did you know that light, sound, and even earthquakes are waves? From music to television, waves play an important role in your life every day.

PRE-READING ACTIVITY

Three-Panel Flip Chart

Before you read the chapter, create the FoldNote entitled "Three-Panel Flip Chart" described in the **Study Skills** section of the Appendix. Label the flaps of the three-panel flip chart with "The nature of waves," "Properties of waves," and "Wave interactions." As you read the chapter, write information you learn about each category under the appropriate flap.

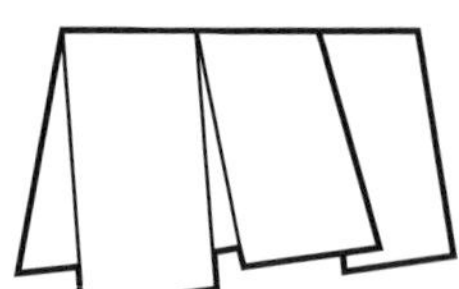

START-UP ACTIVITY

Energetic Waves

In this activity, you will observe the movement of a wave. Then, you will determine the source of the wave's energy.

Procedure

1. Tie one end of a **piece of rope** to the back of a **chair.**
2. Hold the other end in one hand, and stand away from the chair so that the rope is almost straight but is not pulled tight.
3. Move the rope up and down quickly to create a wave. Repeat this step several times. Record your observations.

Analysis

1. In which direction does the wave move?
2. How does the movement of the rope compare with the movement of the wave?
3. Where does the energy of the wave come from?

SECTION 1

The Nature of Waves

Imagine that your family has just returned home from a day at the beach. You had fun playing in the ocean under a hot sun. You put some cold pizza in the microwave for dinner, and you turn on the radio. Just then, the phone rings. It's your friend calling to ask about homework.

READING WARM-UP

Objectives

- Describe how waves transfer energy without transferring matter.
- Distinguish between waves that require a medium and waves that do not.
- Explain the difference between transverse and longitudinal waves.

Terms to Learn

wave	transverse wave
medium	longitudinal wave

READING STRATEGY

Discussion Read this section silently. Write down questions that you have about this section. Discuss your questions in a small group.

In the events described above, how many different waves were present? Believe it or not, there were at least five! Can you name them? Here's a hint: A **wave** is any disturbance that transmits energy through matter or empty space. Okay, here are the answers: water waves in the ocean; light waves from the sun; microwaves inside the microwave oven; radio waves transmitted to the radio; and sound waves from the radio, telephone, and voices. Don't worry if you didn't get very many. You will be able to name them all after you read this section.

Reading Check **What do all waves have in common?** (*See the Appendix for answers to Reading Checks.*)

wave a periodic disturbance in a solid, liquid, or gas as energy is transmitted through a medium

Wave Energy

Energy can be carried away from its source by a wave. You can observe an example of a wave if you drop a rock in a pond. Waves from the rock's splash carry energy away from the splash. However, the material through which the wave travels does not move with the energy. Look at **Figure 1.** Can you move a leaf on a pond if you are standing on the shore? You can make the leaf bob up and down by making waves that carry enough energy through the water. But you would not make the leaf move in the same direction as the wave.

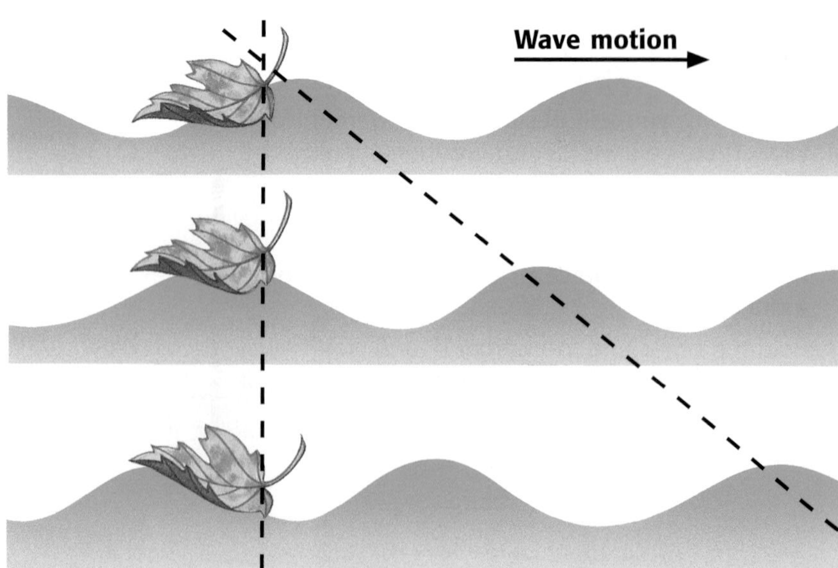

Figure 1 *Waves on a pond move toward the shore, but the water and the leaf floating on the surface only bob up and down.*

Waves and Work

As a wave travels, it does work on everything in its path. The waves in a pond do work on the water to make it move up and down. The waves also do work on anything floating on the water's surface. For example, boats and ducks bob up and down with waves. The fact that these objects move tells you that the waves are transferring energy.

Energy Transfer Through a Medium

Most waves transfer energy by the vibration of particles in a medium. A **medium** is a substance through which a wave can travel. A medium can be a solid, a liquid, or a gas. The plural of *medium* is *media*.

When a particle vibrates (moves back and forth, as in **Figure 2**), it can pass its energy to a particle next to it. The second particle will vibrate like the first particle does. In this way, energy is transmitted through a medium.

Waves that need a medium are called *mechanical waves*. Sound waves are mechanical waves. Sound energy travels by the vibration of particles in liquids, solids, and gases. If there are no particles to vibrate, no sound is possible.

Seismic waves are also mechanical waves. Seismic waves are caused by earthquakes and travel through the Earth's crust. Earthquakes happen when energy stored in the Earth's surface is released and the ground shakes. Seismic waves carry energy and spread away from the earthquake in all directions. **Figure 3** shows the effect of a seismic wave.

Figure 2 *A vibration is one complete back-and-forth motion of an object.*

medium a physical environment in which phenomena occur

Figure 3 *Earthquakes cause seismic waves to travel through Earth's crust. The energy they carry can be very destructive to anything on the ground.*

Figure 4 *Light waves are electromagnetic waves, which do not need a medium. Light waves from the Crab nebula, shown here, travel through the vacuum of space billions of miles to Earth, where they can be detected with a telescope.*

Energy Transfer Without a Medium

Some waves can transfer energy without going through a medium. Visible light is one example. Other examples include microwaves made by microwave ovens, TV and radio signals, and X rays used by dentists and doctors. These waves are *electromagnetic waves.*

Although electromagnetic waves do not need a medium, they can go through matter, such as air, water, and glass. The energy that reaches Earth from the sun comes through electromagnetic waves, which go through space. As shown in **Figure 4,** you can see light from stars because electromagnetic waves travel through space to Earth. Light is an electromagnetic wave that your eyes can see.

Reading Check **How do electromagnetic waves differ from mechanical waves?**

CONNECTION TO Astronomy

Light Speed Light waves from stars and galaxies travel great distances that are best expressed in light-years. A light-year is the distance a ray of light can travel in one year. Some of the light waves from these stars have traveled billions of light-years before reaching Earth. Do the following calculation in your **science journal:** If light travels at a speed of 300,000,000 m/s, what distance is a light-minute? (Hint: There are 60 s in a minute.)

ACTIVITY

Types of Waves

All waves transfer energy by repeated vibrations. However, waves can differ in many ways. Waves can be classified based on the direction in which the particles of the medium vibrate compared with the direction in which the waves move. The two main types of waves are *transverse waves* and *longitudinal* (LAHN juh TOOD'n uhl) *waves*. Sometimes, a transverse wave and a longitudinal wave can combine to form another kind of wave called a *surface wave*.

INTERNET ACTIVITY

For another activity related to this chapter, go to **go.hrw.com** and type in the keyword **HP5WAVW.**

Transverse Waves

Waves in which the particles vibrate in an up-and-down motion are called **transverse waves.** *Transverse* means "moving across." The particles in this kind of wave move across, or perpendicularly to, the direction that the wave is going. To be *perpendicular* means to be "at right angles."

transverse wave a wave in which the particles of the medium move perpendicularly to the direction the wave is traveling

A wave moving on a rope is an example of a transverse wave. In **Figure 5,** you can see that the points along the rope vibrate perpendicularly to the direction the wave is going. The highest point of a transverse wave is called a *crest,* and the lowest point between each crest is called a *trough* (TRAWF). Although electromagnetic waves do not travel by vibrating particles in a medium, all electromagnetic waves are considered transverse waves. The reason is that the waves are made of vibrations that are perpendicular to the direction of motion.

Figure 5 **Motion of a Transverse Wave**

A wave on a rope is a transverse wave because the particles of the medium vibrate perpendicularly to the direction the wave moves.

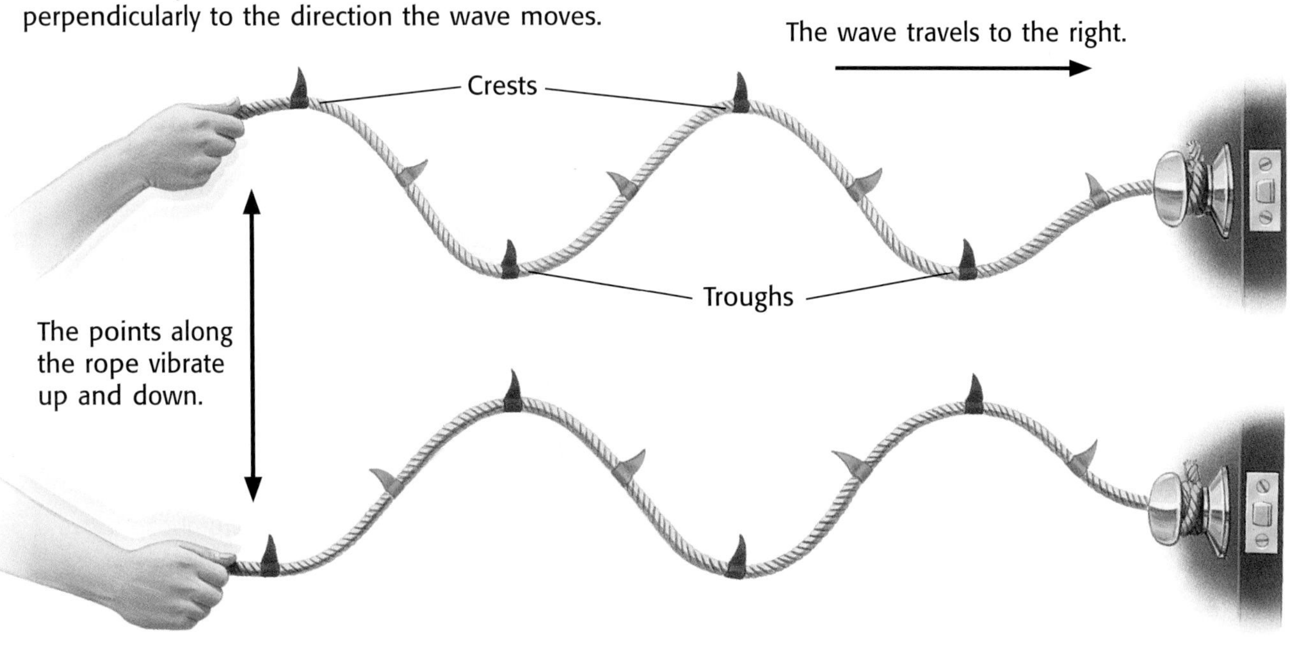

The wave travels to the right.

Crests

Troughs

The points along the rope vibrate up and down.

Figure 6 Comparing Longitudinal and Transverse Waves

Pushing a spring back and forth creates a longitudinal wave, much the same way that shaking a rope up and down creates a transverse wave.

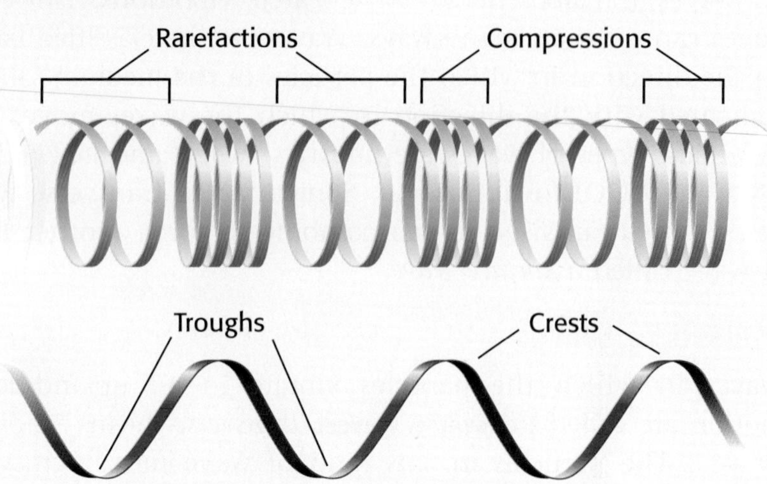

Longitudinal Waves

longitudinal wave a wave in which the particles of the medium vibrate parallel to the direction of wave motion

In a **longitudinal wave,** the particles of the medium vibrate back and forth along the path that the wave moves. You can make a longitudinal wave on a spring. When you push on the end of the spring, the coils of the spring crowd together. A part of a longitudinal wave where the particles are crowded together is called a *compression*. When you pull back on the end of the spring, the coils are pulled apart. A part where the particles are spread apart is a *rarefaction* (RER uh FAK shuhn). Compressions and rarefactions are like the crests and troughs of a transverse wave, as shown in **Figure 6.**

Sound Waves

A sound wave is an example of a longitudinal wave. Sound waves travel by compressions and rarefactions of air particles. **Figure 7** shows how a vibrating drum forms compressions and rarefactions in the air around it.

Reading Check What kind of wave is a sound wave?

Figure 7 *Sound energy is carried away from a drum by a longitudinal wave through the air.*

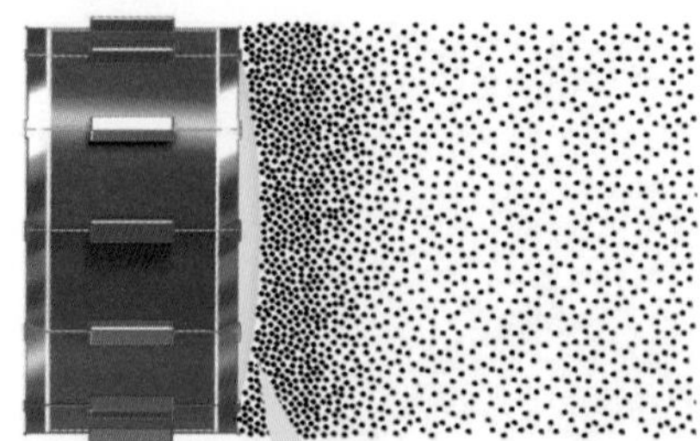

When the drumhead moves out after being hit, a compression is created in the air particles.

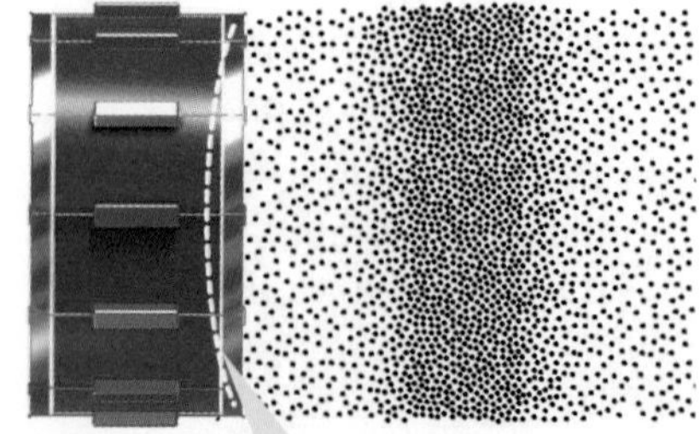

When the drumhead moves back in, a rarefaction is created.

Combinations of Waves

When waves form at or near the boundary between two media, a transverse wave and a longitudinal wave can combine to form a *surface wave*. An example is shown in **Figure 8.** Surface waves look like transverse waves, but the particles of the medium in a surface wave move in circles rather than up and down. The particles move forward at the crest of each wave and move backward at the trough.

Figure 8 *Ocean waves are surface waves. A floating bottle shows the circular motion of particles in a surface wave.*

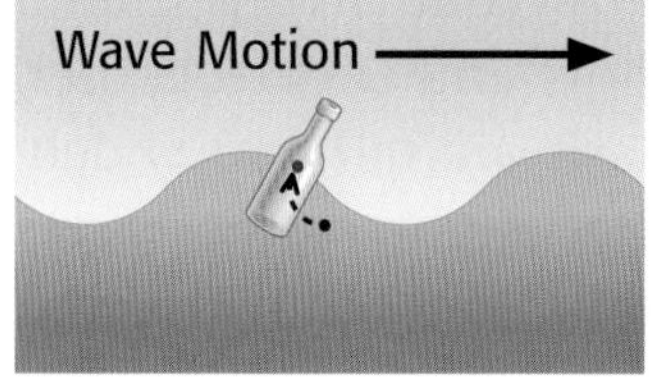

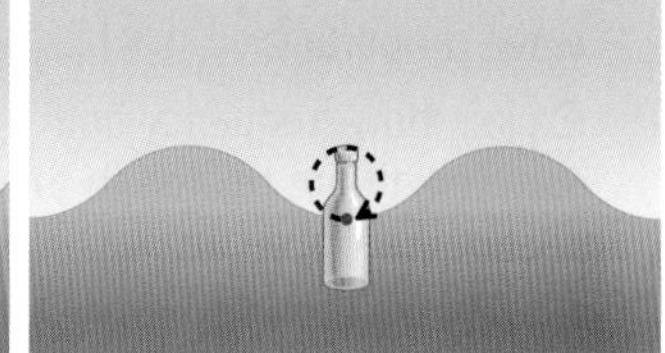

SECTION Review

Summary

- A wave is a disturbance that transmits energy.
- The particles of a medium do not travel with the wave.
- Mechanical waves require a medium, but electromagnetic waves do not.
- Particles in a transverse wave vibrate perpendicularly to the direction the wave travels.
- Particles in a longitudinal wave vibrate parallel to the direction that the wave travels.

Using Key Terms

Complete each of the following sentences by choosing the correct term from the word bank.

transverse wave	wave
longitudinal wave	medium

1. In a ___, the particles vibrate parallel to the direction that the wave travels.
2. Mechanical waves require a ___ through which to travel.
3. Any ___ transmits energy through vibrations.
4. In a ___, the particles vibrate perpendicularly to the direction that the wave travels.

Understanding Key Ideas

5. Waves transfer
   a. matter. **c.** particles.
   b. energy. **d.** water.
6. Name a kind of wave that does not require a medium.

Critical Thinking

7. **Applying Concepts** Sometimes, people at a sports event do "the wave." Is this a real example of a wave? Why or why not?
8. **Making Inferences** Why can supernova explosions in space be seen but not heard on Earth?

Interpreting Graphics

9. Look at the figure below. Which part of the wave is the crest? Which part of the wave is the trough?

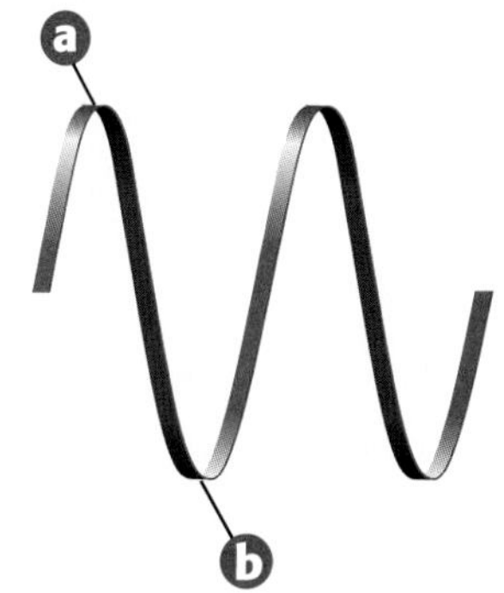

SCILINKS
NSTA
Developed and maintained by the National Science Teachers Association
For a variety of links related to this chapter, go to www.scilinks.org
Topic: The Nature of Waves; Types of Waves
SciLinks code: HSM1017; HSM1574

SECTION 2

Properties of Waves

You are in a swimming pool, floating on your air mattress, enjoying a gentle breeze. Your friend does a "cannonball" from the high dive nearby. Suddenly, your mattress is rocking wildly on the waves generated by the huge splash.

READING WARM-UP

Objectives

- Identify and describe four wave properties.
- Explain how frequency and wavelength are related to the speed of a wave.

Terms to Learn

amplitude frequency
wavelength wave speed

READING STRATEGY

Mnemonics As you read this section, create a mnemonic device to help you remember the wave equation.

The breeze generates waves in the water as well, but they are very different from the waves created by your diving friend. The waves made by the breeze are shallow and close together, while the waves from your friend's splash are tall and widely spaced. Properties of waves, such as the height of the waves and the distance between crests, are useful for comparing and describing waves.

Amplitude

If you tie one end of a rope to the back of a chair, you can create waves by moving the free end up and down. If you shake the rope a little, you will make a shallow wave. If you shake the rope hard, you will make a tall wave.

The **amplitude** of a wave is related to its height. A wave's amplitude is the maximum distance that the particles of a medium vibrate from their rest position. The rest position is the point where the particles of a medium stay when there are no disturbances. The larger the amplitude is, the taller the wave is. **Figure 1** shows how the amplitude of a transverse wave may be measured.

amplitude the maximum distance that the particles of a wave's medium vibrate from their rest position

Larger Amplitude—More Energy

When using a rope to make waves, you have to work harder to create a wave with a large amplitude than to create one with a small amplitude. The reason is that it takes more energy to move the rope farther from its rest position. Therefore, a wave with a large amplitude carries more energy than a wave with a small amplitude does.

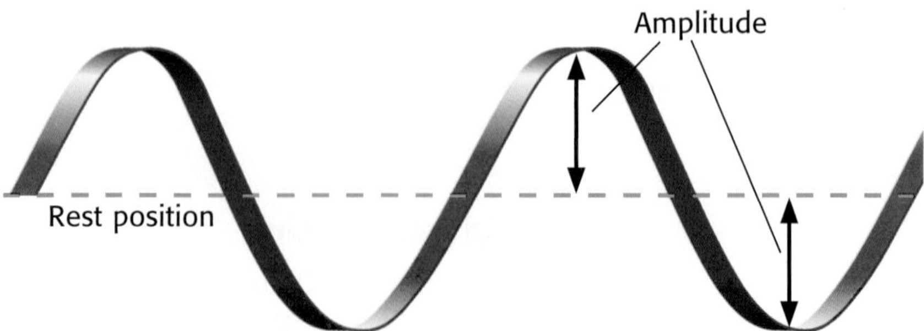

Figure 1 *The amplitude of a transverse wave is measured from the rest position to the crest or to the trough of the wave.*

Wavelength

Another property of waves is wavelength. A **wavelength** is the distance between any two crests or compressions next to each other in a wave. The distance between two troughs or rarefactions next to each other is also a wavelength. In fact, the wavelength can be measured from any point on a wave to the next corresponding point on the wave. Wavelength is measured the same way in both a longitudinal wave and a transverse wave, as shown in **Figure 2.**

wavelength the distance from any point on a wave to an identical point on the next wave

Shorter Wavelength—More Energy

If you are making waves on either a spring or a rope, the rate at which you shake it will determine whether the wavelength is short or long. If you shake it rapidly back and forth, the wavelength will be shorter. If you are shaking it rapidly, you are putting more energy into it than if you were shaking it more slowly. So, a wave with a shorter wavelength carries more energy than a wave with a longer wavelength does.

Reading Check **How does shaking a rope at different rates affect the wavelength of the wave that moves through the rope?** (*See the Appendix for answers to Reading Checks.*)

Springy Waves

1. Hold a coiled **spring toy** on the floor between you and a classmate so that the spring is straight. This is the rest position.
2. Move one end of the spring back and forth at a constant rate. Note the wavelength of the wave you create.
3. Increase the amplitude of the waves. What did you have to do? How did the change in amplitude affect the wavelength?
4. Now, shake the spring back and forth about twice as fast as you did before. What happens to the wavelength? Record your observations.

Figure 2 Measuring Wavelengths

Wavelength can be measured from any two corresponding points that are adjacent on a wave.

Longitudinal wave

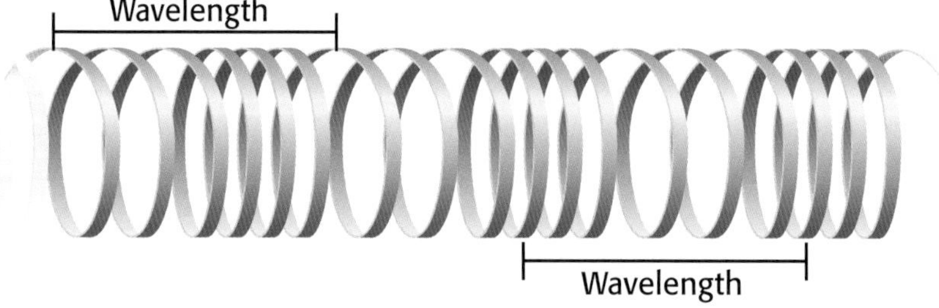

Transverse wave

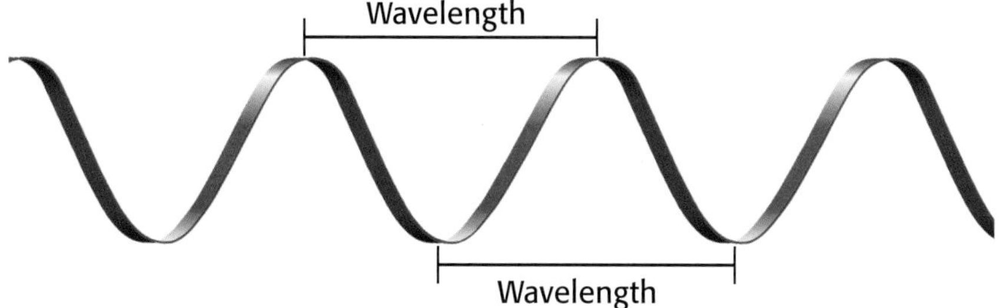

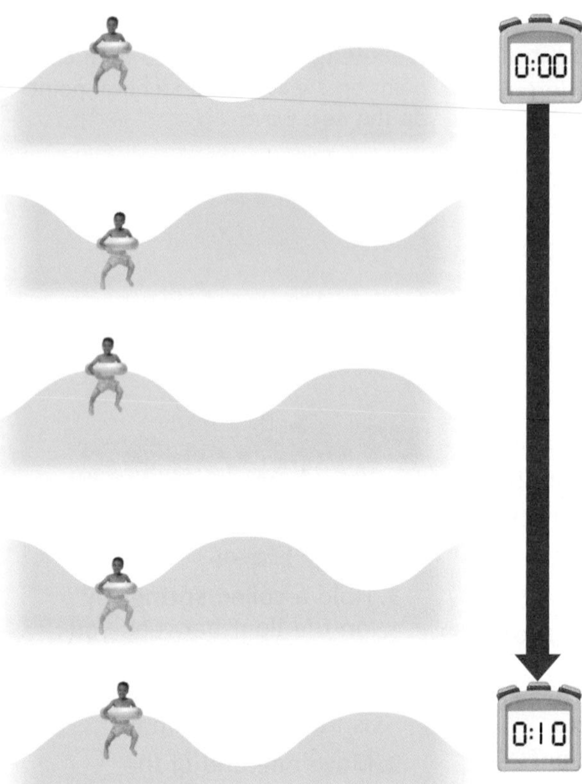

Figure 3 *Frequency can be measured by counting how many waves pass by in a certain amount of time. Here, two waves went by in 10 s, so the frequency is 2/ 10 s = 0.2 Hz.*

Frequency

Think about making rope waves again. The number of waves that you can make in 1 s depends on how quickly you move the rope. If you move the rope slowly, you make only a small number of waves each second. If you move it quickly, you make a large number of waves. The number of waves produced in a given amount of time is the **frequency** of the wave. Frequency is usually expressed in *hertz* (Hz). For waves, one hertz equals one wave per second (1 Hz = 1/s). **Figure 3** shows a wave with a frequency of 0.2 Hz.

Reading Check **If you make three rope waves per second, what is the frequency of the wave?**

Higher Frequency—More Energy

To make high-frequency waves in a rope, you must shake the rope quickly back and forth. To shake a rope quickly takes more energy than to shake it slowly. Therefore, if the amplitudes are equal, high-frequency waves carry more energy than low-frequency waves.

Wave Speed

Wave speed is the speed at which a wave travels. Wave speed (v) can be calculated using wavelength (λ, the Greek letter *lambda*) and frequency (f), by using the *wave equation,* which is shown below:

$$v = \lambda \times f$$

Wave Calculations Determine the wave speed of a wave that has a wavelength of 5 m and a frequency of 4 Hz.

Step 1: Write the equation for wave speed.

$$v = \lambda \times f$$

Step 2: Replace the λ and f with the values given in the problem, and solve.

$$v = 5 \text{ m} \times 4 \text{ Hz} = 20 \text{ m/s}$$

The equation for wave speed can also be rearranged to determine wavelength or frequency, as shown at top right.

$$\lambda = \frac{v}{f} \text{ (Rearranged by dividing by } f\text{.)}$$

$$f = \frac{v}{\lambda} \text{ (Rearranged by dividing by } \lambda\text{.)}$$

Now It's Your Turn

1. What is the frequency of a wave if the wave has a speed of 12 cm/s and a wavelength of 3 cm?
2. A wave has a frequency of 5 Hz and a wave speed of 18 m/s. What is its wavelength?

Frequency and Wavelength Relationship

Three of the basic properties of a wave are related to one another in the wave equation—wave speed, frequency, and wavelength. If you know any two of these properties of a wave, you can use the wave equation to find the third.

One of the things the wave equation tells you is the relationship between frequency and wavelength. If a wave is traveling a certain speed and you double its frequency, its wavelength will be cut in half. Or if you were to cut its frequency in half, the wavelength would be double what it was before. So, you can say that frequency and wavelength are *inversely* related. Think of a sound wave, traveling underwater at 1,440 m/s, given off by the sonar of a submarine like the one shown in **Figure 4.** If the sound wave has a frequency of 360 Hz, it will have a wavelength of 4.0 m. If the sound wave has twice that frequency, the wavelength will be 2.0 m, half as big.

The wave speed of a wave in a certain medium is the same no matter what the wavelength is. So, the wavelength and frequency of a wave depend on the wave speed, not the other way around.

Figure 4 *Submarines use sonar, sound waves in water, to locate underwater objects.*

frequency the number of waves produced in a given amount of time

wave speed the speed at which a wave travels through a medium

SECTION Review

Summary

- Amplitude is the maximum distance the particles of a medium vibrate from their rest position.
- Wavelength is the distance between two adjacent corresponding parts of a wave.
- Frequency is the number of waves that pass a given point in a given amount of time.
- Wave speed can be calculated by multiplying the wave's wavelength by the frequency.

Using Key Terms

1. In your own words, write a definition for each of the following terms: *amplitude, frequency,* and *wavelength.*

Understanding Key Ideas

2. Which of the following results in more energy in a wave?
   a. a smaller wavelength
   b. a lower frequency
   c. a shallower amplitude
   d. a lower speed
3. Draw a transverse wave, and label how the amplitude and wavelength are measured.

Math Skills

4. What is the speed (v) of a wave that has a wavelength (λ) of 2 m and a frequency (f) of 6 Hz?

Critical Thinking

5. **Making Inferences** A wave has a low speed but a high frequency. What can you infer about its wavelength?
6. **Analyzing Processes** Two friends blow two whistles at the same time. The first whistle makes a sound whose frequency is twice that of the sound made by the other whistle. Which sound will reach you first?

SCILINKS®
NSTA
Developed and maintained by the National Science Teachers Association
For a variety of links related to this chapter, go to www.scilinks.org
Topic: Properties of Waves
SciLinks code: HSM1236

SECTION 3

Wave Interactions

If you've ever seen a planet in the night sky, you may have had a hard time telling it apart from a star. Both planets and stars shine brightly, but the light waves that you see are from very different sources.

READING WARM-UP

Objectives

- Describe reflection, refraction, diffraction, and interference.
- Compare destructive interference with constructive interference.
- Describe resonance, and give examples.

Terms to Learn

reflection	interference
refraction	standing wave
diffraction	resonance

READING STRATEGY

Reading Organizer As you read this section, make a concept map by using the terms above.

All stars, including the sun, produce light. But planets do not produce light. So, why do planets shine so brightly? The planets and the moon shine because light from the sun *reflects* off them. Without reflection, you would not be able to see the planets. Reflection is one of the wave interactions that you will learn about in this section.

Reflection

Reflection happens when a wave bounces back after hitting a barrier. All waves—including water, sound, and light waves—can be reflected. The reflection of water waves is shown in **Figure 1.** Light waves reflecting off an object allow you to see that object. For example, light waves from the sun are reflected when they strike the surface of the moon. These reflected waves allow us to enjoy moonlit nights. A reflected sound wave is called an *echo.*

reflection the bouncing back of a ray of light, sound, or heat when the ray hits a surface that it does not go through

Waves are not always reflected when they hit a barrier. If all light waves were reflected when they hit your eyeglasses, you would not be able to see anything! A wave is *transmitted* through a substance when it passes through the substance.

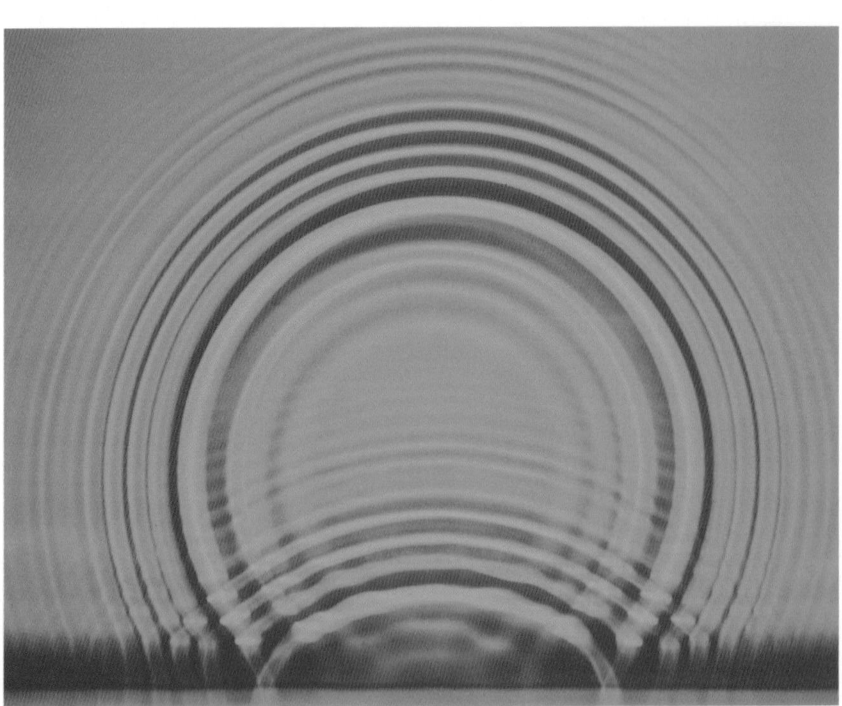

Figure 1 *These water waves are reflecting off the side of the container.*

Figure 2 *A light wave passing at an angle into a new medium—such as water—is refracted because the speed of the wave changes.*

Refraction

Try this simple activity: Place a pencil in a half-filled glass of water. Now, look at the pencil from the side. The pencil appears to be broken into two pieces! But as you can see when you take the pencil out of the water, it is still in one piece.

What you saw in this experiment was the result of the *refraction* of light waves. **Refraction** is the bending of a wave as the wave passes from one medium to another at an angle. Refraction of a flashlight beam as the beam passes from air to water is shown in **Figure 2.**

refraction the bending of a wave as the wave passes between two substances in which the speed of the wave differs

When a wave moves from one medium to another, the wave's speed changes. When a wave enters a new medium, the wave changes wavelength as well as speed. As a result, the wave bends and travels in a new direction.

Reading Check **What happens to a wave when it moves from one medium to another?** (*See the Appendix for answers to Reading Checks.*)

Refraction of Different Colors

When light waves from the sun pass through a droplet of water in a cloud or through a prism, the light is refracted. But the different colors in sunlight are refracted by different amounts, so the light is *dispersed,* or spread out, into its separate colors. When sunlight is refracted this way through water droplets, you can see a rainbow. Why does that happen?

Although all light waves travel at the same speed through empty space, when light passes through a medium such as water or glass, the speed of the light wave depends on the wavelength of the light wave. Because the different colors of light have different wavelengths, their speeds are different, and they are refracted by different amounts. As a result, the colors are spread out, so you can see them individually.

CONNECTION TO Language Arts

WRITING SKILL **The Colors of the Rainbow** People have always been fascinated by the beautiful array of colors that results when sunlight strikes water droplets in the air to form a rainbow. The knowledge science gives us about how they form makes them no less breathtaking.

In the library, find a poem that you like about rainbows. In your **science journal,** copy the poem, and write a paragraph in which you discuss how your knowledge of refraction affects your opinion about the poem.

Figure 3 Diffraction Through an Opening

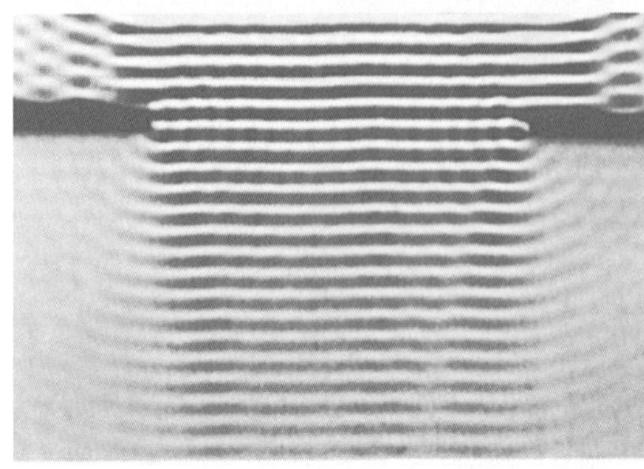

If the barrier or opening is larger than the wavelength of the wave, there is only a small amount of diffraction.

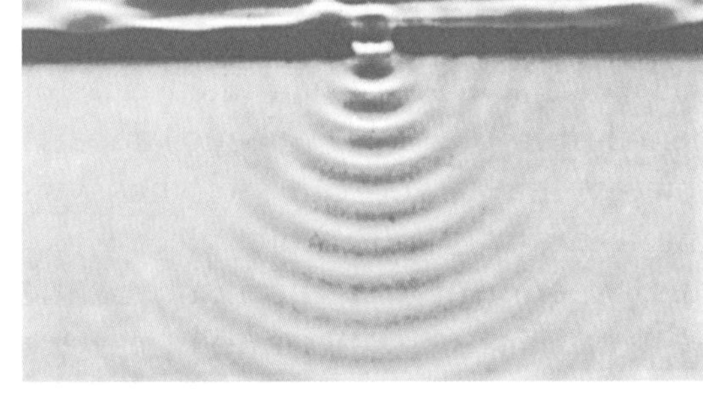

If the barrier or opening is the same size or smaller than the wavelength of an approaching wave, the amount of diffraction is large.

What if Light Diffracted?

With an adult, take a walk around your neighborhood. Light waves diffract around corners of buildings much less than sound waves do. Imagine what would happen if light waves diffracted around corners much more than sound waves did. Write a paragraph in your **science journal** describing how this would change what you see and hear as you walk around your neighborhood.

ACTIVITY

Diffraction

Suppose you are walking down a city street and you hear music. The sound seems to be coming from around the corner, but you cannot see where the music is coming from because a building on the corner blocks your view. Why do sound waves travel around a corner better than light waves do?

Most of the time, waves travel in straight lines. For example, a beam of light from a flashlight is fairly straight. But in some circumstances, waves curve or bend when they reach the edge of an object. The bending of waves around a barrier or through an opening is known as **diffraction.**

diffraction a change in the direction of a wave when the wave finds an obstacle or an edge, such as an opening

If You Can Hear It, Why Can't You See It?

The amount of diffraction of a wave depends on its wavelength and the size of the barrier or opening the wave encounters, as shown in **Figure 3.** You can hear music around the corner of a building because sound waves have long wavelengths and are able to diffract around corners. However, you cannot see who is playing the music because the wavelengths of light waves are much shorter than sound waves, so light is not diffracted very much.

Interference

You know that all matter has volume. Therefore, objects cannot be in the same space at the same time. But waves are energy, not matter. So, more than one wave can be in the same place at the same time. In fact, two waves can meet, share the same space, and pass through each other! When two or more waves share the same space, they overlap. The result of two or more waves overlapping is called **interference. Figure 4** shows what happens when waves occupy the same space and interfere with each other.

interference the combination of two or more waves that results in a single wave

Constructive Interference

Constructive interference happens when the crests of one wave overlap the crests of another wave or waves. The troughs of the waves also overlap. When waves combine in this way, the energy carried by the waves is also able to combine. The result is a new wave that has higher crests and deeper troughs than the original waves had. In other words, the resulting wave has a larger amplitude than the original waves had.

Reading Check How does constructive interference happen?

Figure 4 **Constructive and Destructive Interference**

Constructive Interference When waves combine by constructive interference, the combined wave has a larger amplitude.

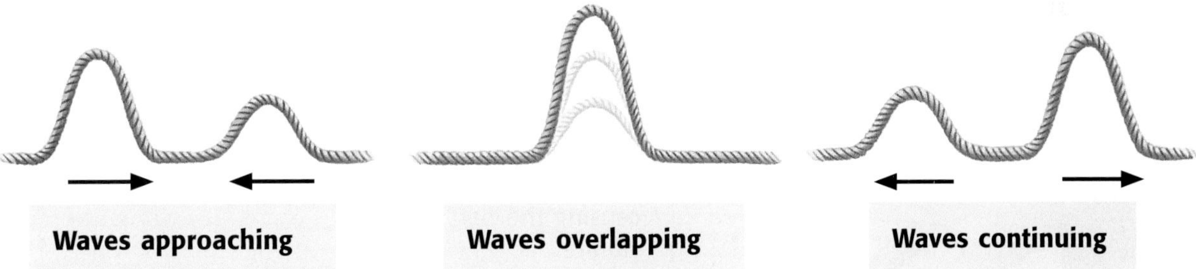

Waves approaching **Waves overlapping** **Waves continuing**

Destructive Interference When two waves with the same amplitude combine by destructive interference, they cancel each other out.

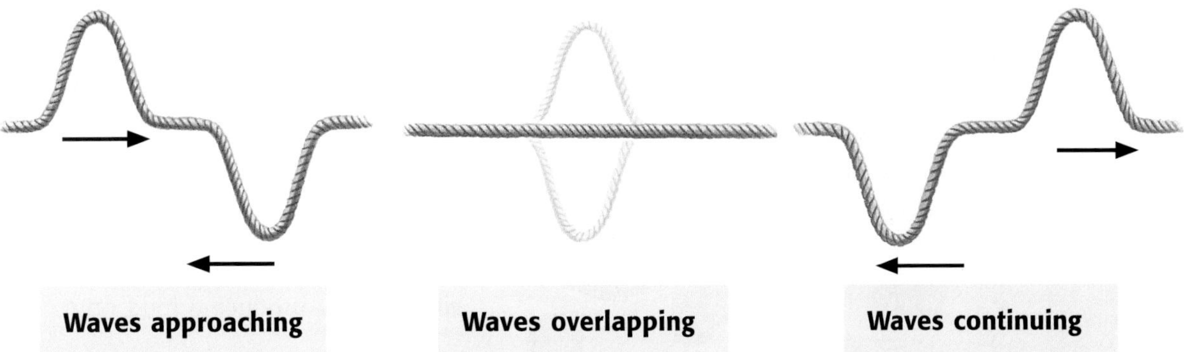

Waves approaching **Waves overlapping** **Waves continuing**

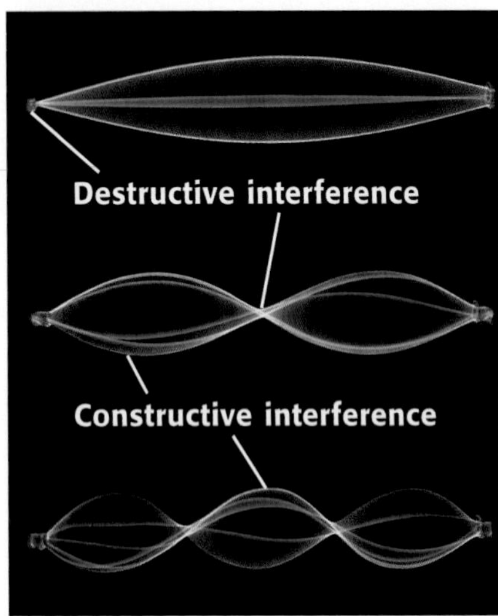

Figure 5 *When you move a rope at certain frequencies, you can create different standing waves.*

Destructive Interference

Destructive interference happens when the crests of one wave and the troughs of another wave overlap. The new wave has a smaller amplitude than the original waves had. When the waves involved in destructive interference have the same amplitude and meet each other at just the right time, the result is no wave at all.

Standing Waves

If you tie one end of a rope to the back of a chair and move the other end up and down, the waves you make go down the rope and are reflected back. If you move the rope at certain frequencies, the rope appears to vibrate in loops, as shown in **Figure 5.** The loops come from the interference between the wave you made and the reflected wave. The resulting wave is called a **standing wave.** In a standing wave, certain parts of the wave are always at the rest position because of total destructive interference between all the waves. Other parts have a large amplitude because of constructive interference.

A standing wave only *looks* as if it is standing still. Waves are actually going in both directions. Standing waves can be formed with transverse waves, such as when a musician plucks a guitar string, as well as with longitudinal waves.

Reading Check **How can interference and reflection cause standing waves?**

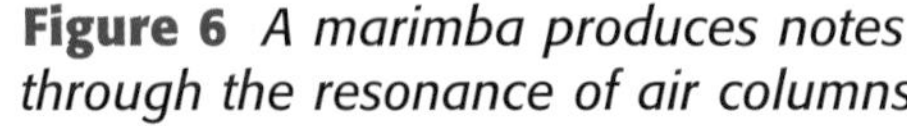

Figure 6 *A marimba produces notes through the resonance of air columns.*

a The marimba bars are struck with a mallet, causing the bars to vibrate.

b The vibrating bars cause the air in the columns to vibrate.

c The lengths of the columns have been adjusted so that the resonant frequency of the air column matches the frequency of the bar.

d The air column resonates with the bar, increasing the amplitude of the vibrations to produce a loud note.

Resonance

The frequencies at which standing waves are made are called *resonant frequencies.* When an object vibrating at or near the resonant frequency of a second object causes the second object to vibrate, **resonance** occurs. A resonating object absorbs energy from the vibrating object and vibrates, too. An example of resonance is shown in **Figure 6** on the previous page.

You may be familiar with another example of resonance at home—in your shower. When you sing in the shower, certain frequencies create standing waves in the air that fills the shower stall. The air resonates in much the same way that the air column in a marimba does. The amplitude of the sound waves becomes greater. So your voice sounds much louder.

standing wave a pattern of vibration that simulates a wave that is standing still

resonance a phenomenon that occurs when two objects naturally vibrate at the same frequency; the sound produced by one object causes the other object to vibrate

SECTION Review

Summary

- Waves reflect after hitting a barrier.
- Refraction is the bending of a wave when it passes through different media.
- Waves bend around barriers or through openings during diffraction.
- The result of two or more waves overlapping is called interference.
- Amplitude increases during constructive interference and decreases during destructive interference.
- Resonance occurs when a vibrating object causes another object to vibrate at one of its resonant frequencies.

Using Key Terms

Complete each of the following sentences by choosing the correct term from the word bank.

refraction reflection
diffraction interference

1. ___ happens when a wave passes from one medium to another at an angle.
2. The bending of a wave around a barrier is called ___.
3. We can see the moon because of the ___ of sunlight off it.

Understanding Key Ideas

4. The combining of waves as they overlap is known as
   a. interference.
   b. diffraction.
   c. refraction.
   d. resonance.
5. Name two wave interactions that can occur when a wave encounters a barrier.
6. Explain why you can hear two people talking even after they walk around a corner.
7. Explain what happens when two waves encounter one another in destructive interference.

Critical Thinking

8. **Making Inferences** Sometimes, when music is played loudly, you can feel your body shake. Explain what is happening in terms of resonance.
9. **Applying Concepts** How could two waves on a rope interfere so that the rope did not move at all?

Interpreting Graphics

10. In the image below, what sort of wave interaction is happening?

SCILINKS.
NSTA
Developed and maintained by the National Science Teachers Association
For a variety of links related to this chapter, go to www.scilinks.org
Topic: Interactions of Waves
SciLinks code: HSM0304

SECTION 4

Interactions of Light Waves

Have you ever seen a cat's eyes glow in the dark when light shines on them? Cats have a special layer of cells in the back of their eyes that reflects light.

This layer helps the cat see better by giving the eyes another chance to detect the light. Reflection is one interaction of electromagnetic waves. Because we can see visible light, it is easier to explain all wave interactions by using visible light.

READING WARM-UP

Objectives

- Describe how reflection allows you to see things.
- Describe absorption and scattering.
- Explain how refraction can create optical illusions and separate white light into colors.
- Explain the relationship between diffraction and wavelength.
- Compare constructive and destructive interference of light.

Terms to Learn

reflection
absorption
scattering
refraction
diffraction
interference

READING STRATEGY

Reading Organizer As you read this section, make a concept map by using the terms above.

Reflection

Reflection happens when light waves bounce off an object. Light reflects off objects all around you. When you look in a mirror, you are seeing light that has been reflected twice—first from you and then from the mirror. If light is reflecting off everything around you, why can't you see your image on a wall? To answer this question, you must learn the law of reflection.

The Law of Reflection

Light reflects off surfaces the same way that a ball bounces off the ground. If you throw the ball straight down against a smooth surface, it will bounce straight up. If you bounce it at an angle, it will bounce away at an angle. The *law of reflection* states that the angle of incidence is equal to the angle of reflection. *Incidence* is the arrival of a beam of light at a surface. **Figure 1** shows this law.

Reading Check What is the law of reflection? (*See the Appendix for answers to Reading Checks.*)

Figure 1 The Law of Reflection

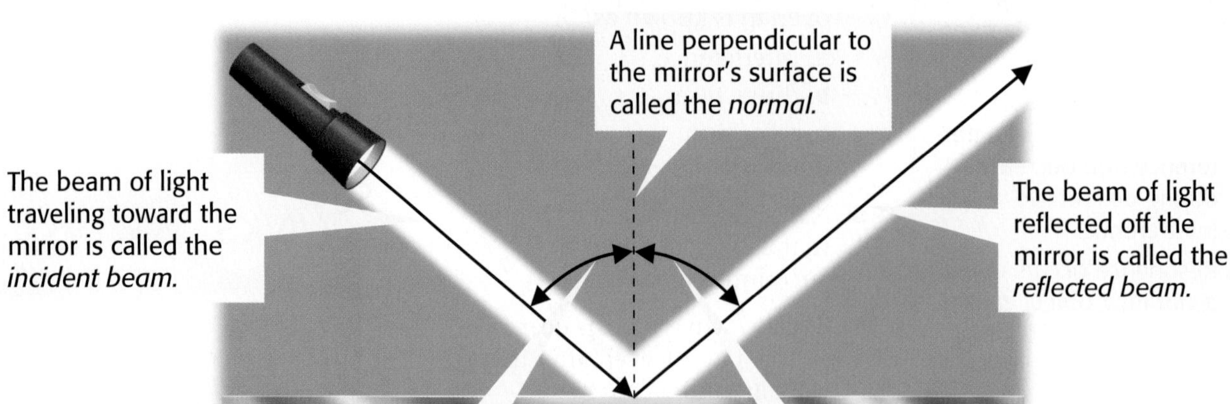

A line perpendicular to the mirror's surface is called the *normal.*
The beam of light traveling toward the mirror is called the *incident beam.*
The beam of light reflected off the mirror is called the *reflected beam.*
The angle between the incident beam and the normal is called the *angle of incidence.*
The angle between the reflected beam and the normal is called the *angle of reflection.*

Figure 2 **Regular Reflection Vs. Diffuse Reflection**

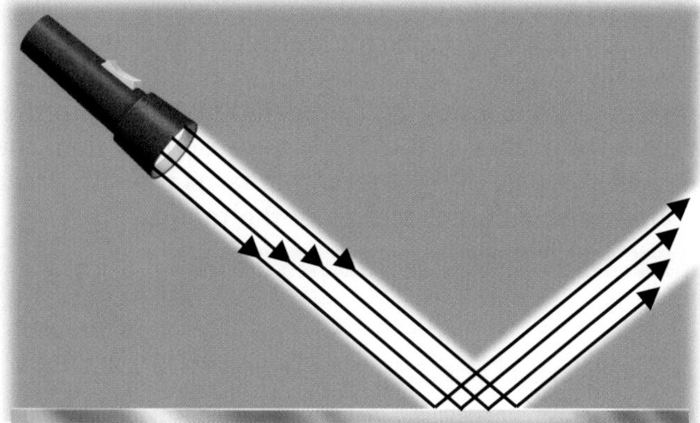

Regular reflection occurs when light beams are reflected at the same angle. When your eye detects the reflected beams, you can see a reflection on the surface.

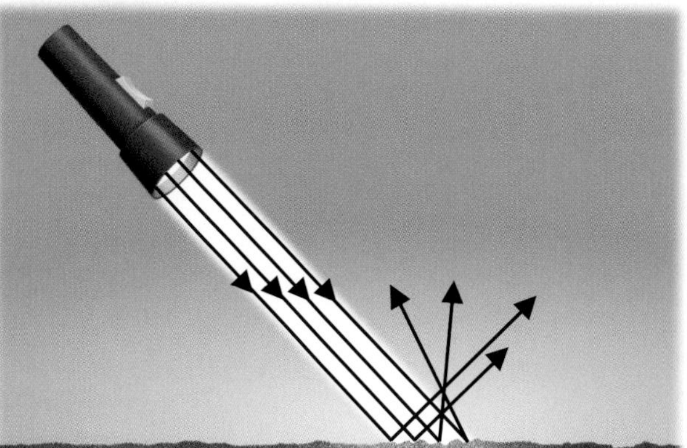

Diffuse reflection occurs when light beams reflect at many different angles. You can't see a reflection because not all of the reflected light is directed toward your eyes.

Types of Reflection

So, why can you see your image in a mirror but not in a wall? The answer has to do with the differences between the two surfaces. A mirror's surface is very smooth. Thus, light beams reflect off all points of the mirror at the same angle. This kind of reflection is called *regular reflection.* A wall's surface is slightly rough. Light beams will hit the wall's surface and reflect at many different angles. This kind of reflection is called *diffuse reflection.* **Figure 2** shows the difference between the two kinds of reflection.

reflection the bouncing back of a ray of light, sound, or heat when the ray hits a surface that it does not go through

Light Source or Reflection?

If you look at a TV set in a bright room, you see the cabinet around the TV and the image on the screen. But if you look at the same TV in the dark, you see only the image on the screen. The difference is that the screen is a light source, but the cabinet around the TV is not.

You can see a light source even in the dark because its light passes directly into your eyes. The tail of the firefly in **Figure 3** is a light source. Flames, light bulbs, and the sun are also light sources. Objects that produce visible light are called *luminous* (LOO muh nuhs).

Most things around you are not light sources. But you can still see them because light from light sources reflects off the objects and then travels to your eyes. A visible object that is not a light source is *illuminated.*

Reading Check List four different light sources.

Figure 3 *You can see the tail of this firefly because it is luminous. But you see its body because it is illuminated.*

CONNECTION TO
Astronomy

Moonlight? Sometimes, the moon shines so brightly that you might think there is a lot of "moonlight." But did you know that moonlight is actually sunlight? The moon does not give off light. You can see the moon because it is illuminated by light from the sun. You see different phases of the moon because light from the sun shines only on the part of the moon that faces the sun. Make a poster that shows the different phases of the moon.

ACTIVITY

Absorption and Scattering

absorption in optics, the transfer of light energy to particles of matter

scattering an interaction of light with matter that causes light to change its energy, direction of motion, or both

Have you noticed that when you use a flashlight, the light shining on things closer to you appears brighter than the light shining on things farther away? The light is less bright the farther it travels from the flashlight. The light is weaker partly because the beam spreads out and partly because of absorption and scattering.

Absorption of Light

The transfer of energy carried by light waves to particles of matter is called **absorption.** When a beam of light shines through the air, particles in the air absorb some of the energy from the light. As a result, the beam of light becomes dim. The farther the light travels from its source, the more it is absorbed by particles, and the dimmer it becomes.

Figure 4 *A beam of light becomes dimmer partly because of scattering.*

Scattering of Light

Scattering is an interaction of light with matter that causes light to change direction. Light scatters in all directions after colliding with particles of matter. Light from the ship shown in **Figure 4** is scattered out of the beam by air particles. This scattered light allows you to see things that are outside the beam. But, because light is scattered out of the beam, the beam becomes dimmer.

Scattering makes the sky blue. Light with shorter wavelengths is scattered more than light with longer wavelengths. Sunlight is made up of many different colors of light, but blue light (which has a very short wavelength) is scattered more than any other color. So, when you look at the sky, you see a background of blue light.

Reading Check Why can you see things outside a beam of light?

Scattering Milk

1. Fill a **2 L clear plastic bottle** with **water.**
2. Turn the lights off, and shine a **flashlight** through the water. Look at the water from all sides of the bottle. Write a description of what you see.
3. Add **3 drops of milk** to the water, and shake the bottle to mix it up.
4. Repeat step 2. Describe any color changes. If you don't see any, add more milk until you do.
5. How is the water-and-milk mixture like air particles in the atmosphere? Explain your answer.

Refraction

Imagine that you and a friend are at a lake. Your friend wades into the water. You look at her, and her feet appear to have separated from her legs! What has happened? You know her feet did not fall off, so how can you explain what you see? The answer has to do with refraction.

Refraction and Material

Refraction is the bending of a wave as it passes at an angle from one substance, or material, to another. **Figure 5** shows a beam of light refracting twice. Refraction of light waves occurs because the speed of light varies depending on the material through which the waves are traveling. In a vacuum, light travels at 300,000 km/s, but it travels more slowly through matter. When a wave enters a new material at an angle, the part of the wave that enters first begins traveling at a different speed from that of the rest of the wave.

refraction the bending of a wave as the wave passes between two substances in which the speed of the wave differs

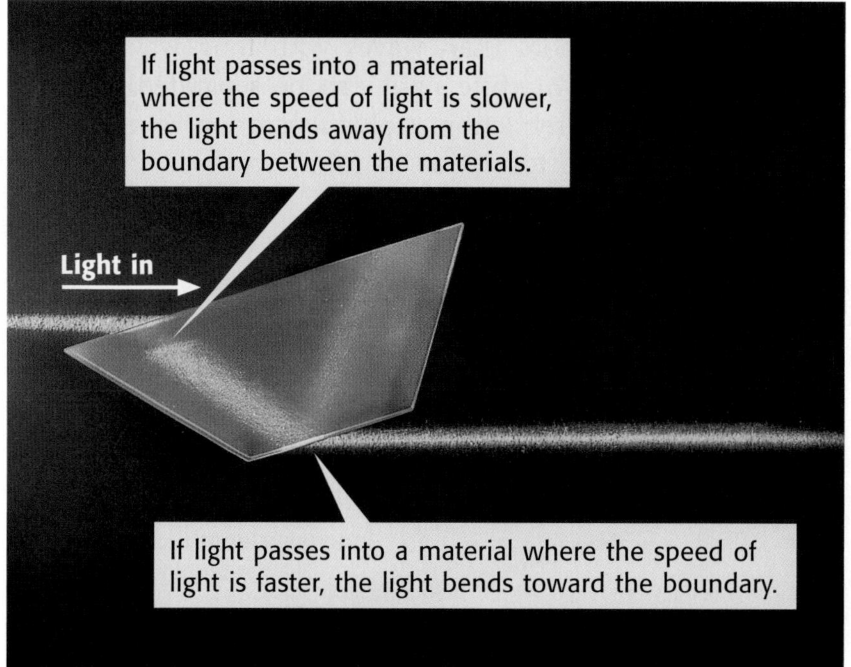

If light passes into a material where the speed of light is slower, the light bends away from the boundary between the materials.
Light in
If light passes into a material where the speed of light is faster, the light bends toward the boundary.

Figure 5 *Light travels more slowly through glass than it does through air. So, light refracts as it passes at an angle from air to glass or from glass to air. Notice that the light is also reflected inside the prism.*

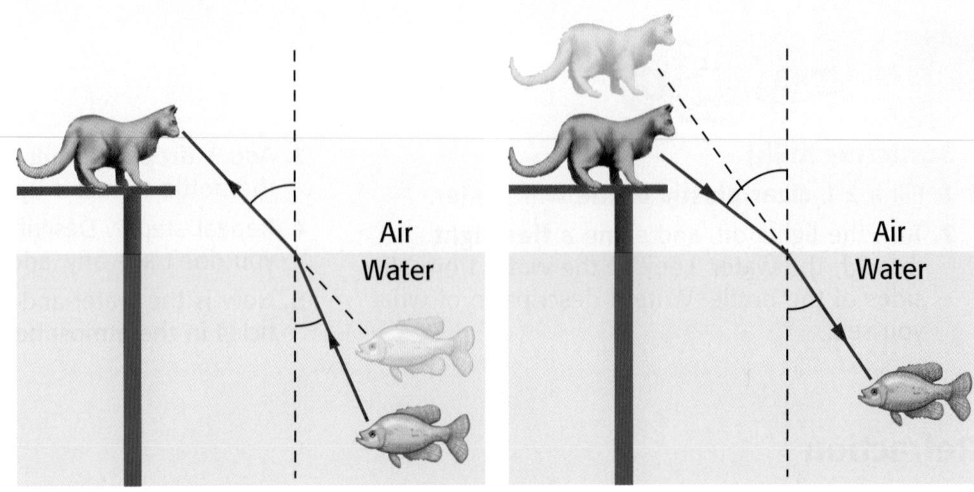

Figure 6 *Because of refraction, the cat and the fish see optical illusions. To the cat, the fish appears closer than it really is. To the fish, the cat appears farther away than it actually is.*

Refraction and Optical Illusions

Usually, when you look at an object, the light reflecting off the object travels in a straight line from the object to your eye. Your brain always interprets light as traveling in straight lines. But when you look at an object that is underwater, the light reflecting off the object does not travel in a straight line. Instead, it refracts. **Figure 6** shows how refraction creates an optical illusion. This kind of illusion causes a person's feet to appear separated from the legs when the person is wading.

Refraction and Color Separation

White light is made up of a mixture of many different colors of light, even though it is perceived as almost white. The different wavelengths of visible light are seen by humans as different colors. When white light is refracted, the amount that the light bends depends on its wavelength. Waves with short wavelengths bend more than waves with long wavelengths. As shown in **Figure 7,** white light can be separated into different colors during refraction. Color separation by refraction is responsible for the formation of rainbows.

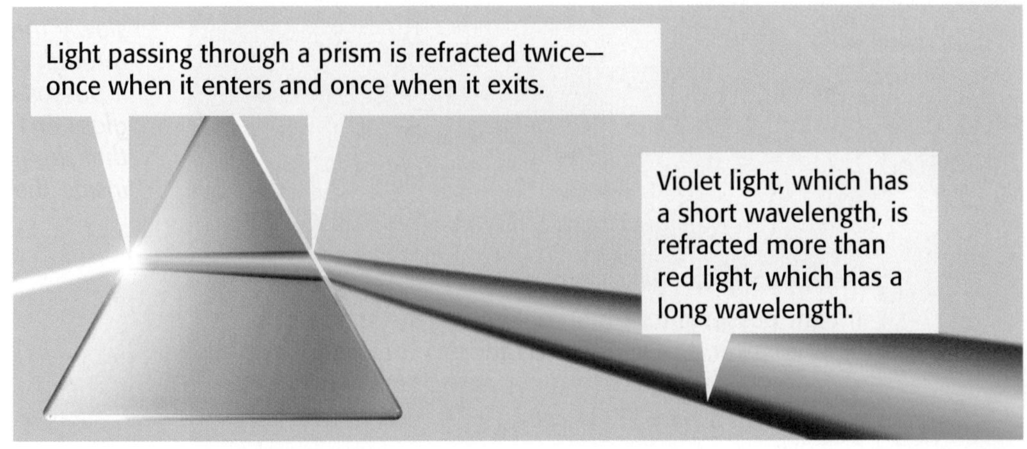

Light passing through a prism is refracted twice—
once when it enters and once when it exits.
Violet light, which has a short wavelength, is refracted more than red light, which has a long wavelength.

Figure 7 *A prism is a piece of glass that separates white light into the colors of visible light by refraction.*

Refraction Rainbow

1. **Tape** a **piece of construction paper** over the end of a **flashlight.** Use **scissors** to cut a slit in the paper.
2. Turn on the flashlight, and lay it on a table. Place a **prism** on end in the beam of light.
3. Slowly rotate the prism until you can see a rainbow on the surface of the table. Draw a diagram of the light beam, the prism, and the rainbow.

Diffraction

Refraction isn't the only way light waves are bent. **Diffraction** is the bending of waves around barriers or through openings. The amount a wave diffracts depends on its wavelength and the size of the barrier or the opening. The greatest amount of diffraction occurs when the barrier or opening is the same size or smaller than the wavelength.

diffraction a change in the direction of a wave when the wave finds an obstacle or an edge, such as an opening

Reading Check **The amount a wave diffracts depends on what two things?**

Diffraction and Wavelength

The wavelength of visible light is very small—about 100 times thinner than a human hair! So, a light wave cannot bend very much by diffraction unless it passes through a narrow opening, around sharp edges, or around a small barrier, as shown in **Figure 8.**

Light waves cannot diffract very much around large obstacles, such as buildings. Thus, you can't see around corners. But light waves always diffract a small amount. You can observe light waves diffracting if you examine the edges of a shadow. Diffraction causes the edges of shadows to be blurry.

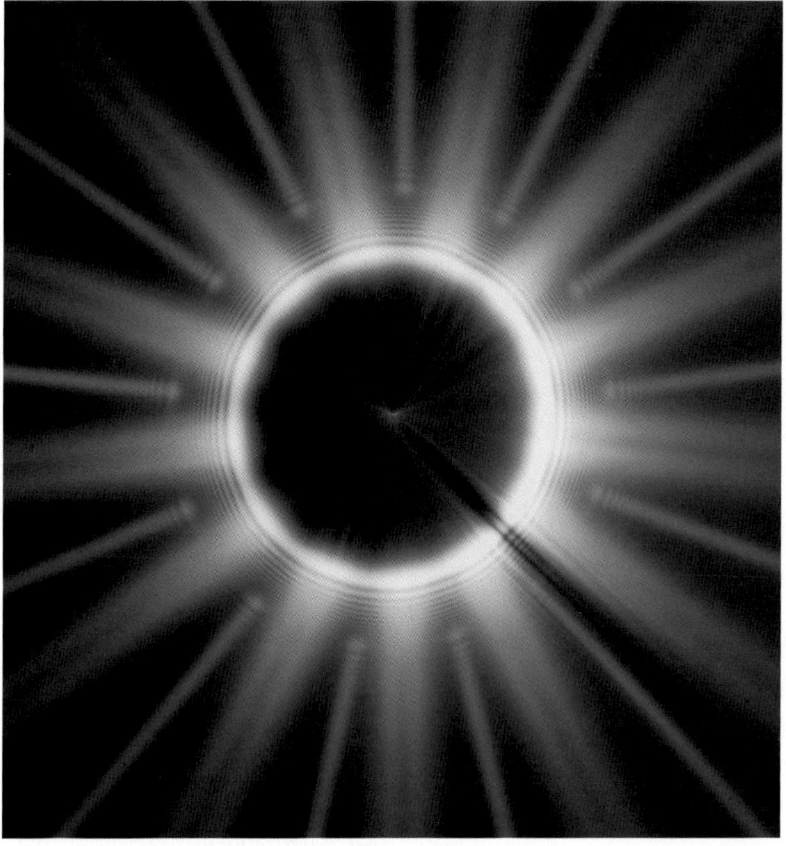

Figure 8 *This diffraction pattern is made by light of a single wavelength shining around the edges of a very tiny disk.*

Interference

interference the combination of two or more waves that results in a single wave

Interference is a wave interaction that happens when two or more waves overlap. Overlapping waves can combine by constructive or destructive interference.

Constructive Interference

When waves combine by *constructive interference,* the resulting wave has a greater amplitude, or height, than the individual waves had. Constructive interference of light waves can be seen when light of one wavelength shines through two small slits onto a screen. The light on the screen will appear as a series of alternating bright and dark bands, as shown in **Figure 9.** The bright bands result from light waves combining through constructive interference.

Reading Check What is constructive interference?

Destructive Interference

When waves combine by *destructive interference,* the resulting wave has a smaller amplitude than the individual waves had. So, when light waves interfere destructively, the result will be dimmer light. Destructive interference forms the dark bands seen in **Figure 9.**

You do not see constructive or destructive interference of white light. To understand why, remember that white light is composed of waves with many different wavelengths. The waves rarely line up to combine in total destructive interference.

Figure 9 **Constructive and Destructive Interference**

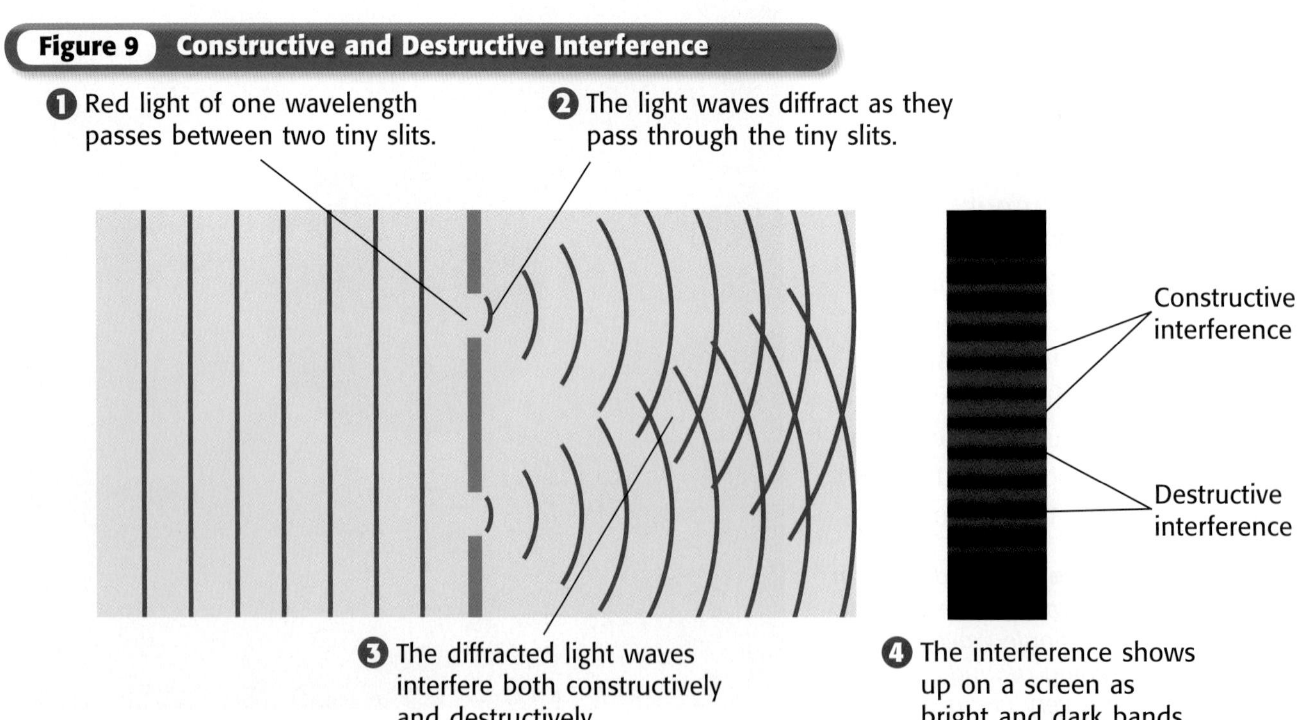

1 Red light of one wavelength passes between two tiny slits.
2 The light waves diffract as they pass through the tiny slits.
Constructive interference
Destructive interference
3 The diffracted light waves interfere both constructively and destructively.
4 The interference shows up on a screen as bright and dark bands.

SECTION Review

Summary

- The law of reflection states that the angle of incidence is equal to the angle of reflection.
- Things that are luminous can be seen because they produce their own light. Things that are illuminated can be seen because light reflects off them.
- Absorption is the transfer of light energy to particles of matter. Scattering is an interaction of light with matter that causes light to change direction.
- Refraction of light waves can create optical illusions and can separate white light into separate colors.
- How much light waves diffract depends on the light's wavelength. Light waves diffract more when traveling through a narrow opening.
- Interference can be constructive or destructive. Interference of light waves can cause bright and dark bands.

Using Key Terms

For each pair of terms, explain how the meanings of the terms differ.

1. *refraction* and *diffraction*
2. *absorption* and *scattering*

Understanding Key Ideas

3. Which light interaction explains why you can see things that do not produce their own light?
   a. absorption
   b. reflection
   c. refraction
   d. scattering
4. Describe how absorption and scattering can affect a beam of light.
5. Why do objects that are underwater look closer than they actually are?
6. How does a prism separate white light into different colors?
7. What is the relationship between diffraction and the wavelength of light?

Critical Thinking

8. **Applying Concepts** Explain why you can see your reflection on a spoon but not on a piece of cloth.
9. **Making Inferences** The planet Mars does not produce light. Explain why you can see Mars shining like a star at night.
10. **Making Comparisons** Compare constructive interference and destructive interference.

Interpreting Graphics

Use the image below to answer the questions that follow.

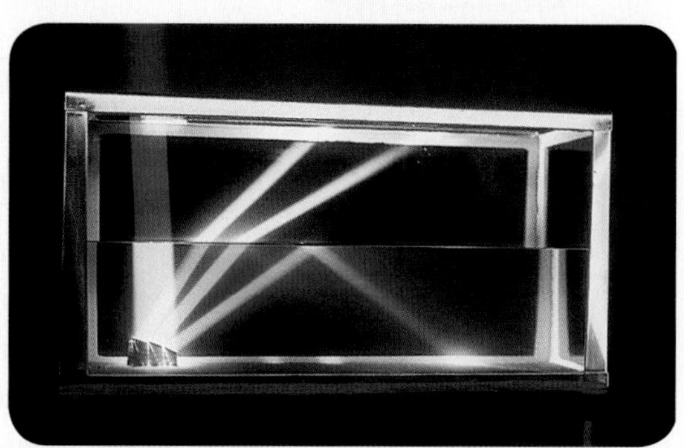

11. Why doesn't the large beam of light bend like the two beams in the middle of the tank?
12. Which light interaction explains what is happening to the bottom light beam?

SCiLINKS.
NSTA
Developed and maintained by the National Science Teachers Association
For a variety of links related to this chapter, go to www.scilinks.org
Topic: Reflection and Refraction
SciLinks code: HSM1283

Using Scientific Methods

Skills Practice Lab

Wave Energy and Speed

If you threw a rock into a pond, waves would carry energy away from the point of origin. But if you threw a large rock into a pond, would the waves carry more energy away from the point of origin than waves caused by a small rock? And would a large rock make waves that move faster than waves made by a small rock? In this lab, you'll answer these questions.

OBJECTIVES

Form hypotheses about the energy and speed of waves.

Test your hypotheses by performing an experiment.

MATERIALS

- beaker, small
- newspaper
- pan, shallow, approximately 20 cm × 30 cm
- pencils (2)
- stopwatch
- water

SAFETY

Ask a Question

1. In this lab, you will answer the following questions: Do waves made by a large disturbance carry more energy than waves made by a small disturbance? Do waves created by a large disturbance travel faster than waves created by a small disturbance?

Form a Hypothesis

2. Write a few sentences that answer the questions above.

Test the Hypothesis

3. Place the pan on a few sheets of newspaper. Using the small beaker, fill the pan with water.
4. Make sure that the water is still. Tap the surface of the water with the eraser end of one pencil. This tap represents the small disturbance. Record your observations about the size of the waves that are made and the path they take.

5. Repeat step 4. This time, use the stopwatch to record the amount of time it takes for one of the waves to reach the side of the pan. Record your data.

6. Using two pencils at once, repeat steps 4 and 5. These taps represent the large disturbance. (Try to use the same amount of force to tap the water that you used with just one pencil.) Observe and record your results.

Analyze the Results

1. **Describing Events** Compare the appearance of the waves created by one pencil with that of the waves created by two pencils. Were there any differences in amplitude (wave height)?

2. **Describing Events** Compare the amount of time required for the waves to reach the side of the pan. Did the waves travel faster when two pencils were used?

Draw Conclusions

3. **Drawing Conclusions** Do waves made by a large disturbance carry more energy than waves made by a small one? Explain your answer, using your results to support your answer. (Hint: Remember the relationship between amplitude and energy.)

4. **Drawing Conclusions** Do waves made by a large disturbance travel faster than waves made by a small one? Explain your answer.

Applying Your Data

A tsunami is a giant ocean wave that can reach a height of 30 m. Tsunamis that reach land can cause injury and enormous property damage. Using what you learned in this lab about wave energy and speed, explain why tsunamis are so dangerous. How do you think scientists can predict when tsunamis will reach land?

Chapter Review

USING KEY TERMS

For each pair of terms, explain how the meanings of the terms differ.

1. *longitudinal wave* and *transverse wave*
2. *wavelength* and *amplitude*
3. *reflection* and *refraction*

UNDERSTANDING KEY IDEAS

Multiple Choice

4. You can see yourself in a mirror because of
   a. absorption.
   b. scattering.
   c. regular reflection.
   d. diffuse reflection.

5. Waves transfer
   a. matter.
   b. energy.
   c. particles.
   d. water.

6. Refraction occurs when a wave enters a new medium at an angle because
   a. the frequency changes.
   b. the amplitude changes.
   c. the wave speed changes.
   d. None of the above

7. The wave property that is related to the height of a wave is the
   a. wavelength.
   b. amplitude.
   c. frequency.
   d. wave speed.

8. During constructive interference,
   a. the amplitude increases.
   b. the frequency decreases.
   c. the wave speed increases.
   d. All of the above

9. Waves that don't require a medium are
   a. longitudinal waves.
   b. electromagnetic waves.
   c. surface waves.
   d. mechanical waves.

Short Answer

10. Draw a transverse wave and a longitudinal wave. Label a crest, a trough, a compression, a rarefaction, and wavelengths. Also, label the amplitude on the transverse wave.

11. What is the relationship between frequency, wave speed, and wavelength?

Math Skills

12. A fisherman in a row boat notices that one wave crest passes his fishing line every 5 s. He estimates the distance between the crests to be 1.5 m and estimates that the crests of the waves are 0.5 m above the troughs. Using this data, determine the amplitude and speed of the waves.

CRITICAL THINKING

13. **Concept Mapping** Use the following terms to create a concept map: *wave, refraction, transverse wave, longitudinal wave, wavelength, wave speed,* and *diffraction.*

14. **Analyzing Ideas** You have lost the paddles for the canoe you rented, and the canoe has drifted to the center of a pond. You need to get it back to the shore, but you do not want to get wet by swimming in the pond. Your friend suggests that you drop rocks behind the canoe to create waves that will push the canoe toward the shore. Will this solution work? Why or why not?

15. **Applying Concepts** Some opera singers can use their powerful voices to break crystal glasses. To do this, they sing one note very loudly and hold it for a long time. While the opera singer holds the note, the walls of the glass move back and forth until the glass shatters. Explain in terms of resonance how the glass shatters.

16. **Analyzing Processes** After setting up stereo speakers in your school's music room, you notice that in certain areas of the room, the sound from the speakers is very loud. In other areas, the sound is very soft. Using the concept of interference, explain why the sound levels in the music room vary.

17. **Applying Concepts** A tern is a type of bird that dives underwater to catch fish. When a young tern begins learning to catch fish, the bird is rarely successful. The tern has to learn that when a fish appears to be in a certain place underwater, the fish is actually in a slightly different place. Why does the tern see the fish in the wrong place?

INTERPRETING GRAPHICS

18. Look at the waves below. Rank the waves from highest energy to lowest energy, and explain your reasoning.

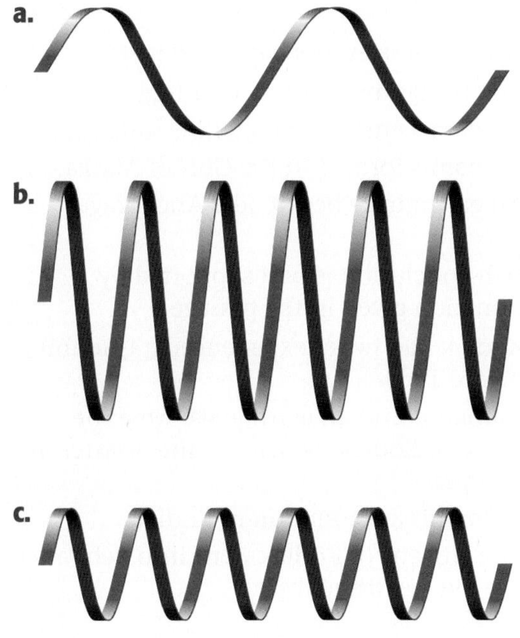

Standardized Test Preparation

READING

Read each of the passages below. Then, answer the questions that follow each passage.

Passage 1 On March 27, 1964, a powerful earthquake rocked Alaska. The earthquake started on land near Anchorage, and the seismic waves spread quickly in all directions. The earthquake created a series of ocean waves called tsunamis in the Gulf of Alaska. In the deep water of the gulf, the tsunamis were short and far apart. But as these waves entered the shallow water surrounding Kodiak Island, off the coast of Alaska, they became taller and closer together. Some reached heights of nearly 30 m! The destructive forces of the earthquake and tsunamis killed 21 people and caused $10 million in damage to Kodiak, which made this marine disaster the worst in the town's 200-year history.

1. In the passage, what does *tsunami* mean?

- **A** a seismic wave
- **B** an earthquake
- **C** an ocean wave
- **D** a body of water

2. Which of these events happened first?

- **F** The tsunamis became closer together.
- **G** Tsunamis entered the shallow water.
- **H** Tsunamis formed in the Gulf of Alaska.
- **I** An earthquake began near Anchorage.

3. Which conclusion is **best** supported by information given in the passage?

- **A** Kodiak had never experienced a tsunami before 1964.
- **B** Tsunamis and an earthquake were the cause of Kodiak's worst marine disaster in 200 years.
- **C** Tsunamis are common in Kodiak.
- **D** The citizens of Kodiak went into debt after the 1964 earthquake.

Passage 2 Resonance was partially responsible for the destruction of the Tacoma Narrows Bridge, in Washington. The bridge opened in July 1940 and soon earned the nickname Galloping Gertie because of its wavelike motions. These motions were created by wind that blew across the bridge. The wind caused vibrations that were close to a resonant frequency of the bridge. Because the bridge was in resonance, it absorbed a large amount of energy from the wind, which caused it to vibrate with a large amplitude. On November 7, 1940, a supporting cable slipped, and the bridge began to twist. The twisting of the bridge, combined with high winds, further increased the amplitude of the bridge's motion. Within hours, the amplitude became so great that the bridge collapsed. Luckily, all of the people on the bridge that day were able to escape before it crashed into the river below.

1. What caused wavelike motions in the Tacoma Narrows Bridge?

- **A** wind that caused vibrations that were close to the resonant frequency of the bridge
- **B** vibrations from cars going over the bridge
- **C** twisting of a broken support cable
- **D** an earthquake

2. Why did the bridge collapse?

- **F** A supporting cable slipped.
- **G** It absorbed a great amount of energy from the wind.
- **H** The amplitude of the bridge's vibrations became great enough.
- **I** Wind blew across it.

INTERPRETING GRAPHICS

Use the figure below to answer the questions that follow.

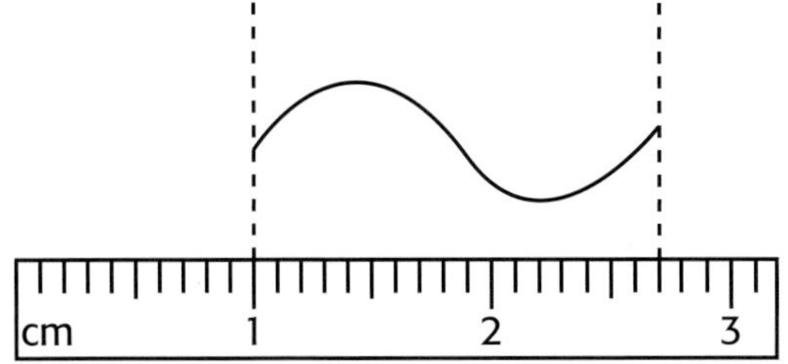

1. This wave was generated in a laboratory investigation. What is the wavelength of the wave?

A 1.5 cm
B 1.7 cm
C 2.0 cm
D 2.7 cm

2. If the frequency of the wave shown were doubled, what would the wavelength of the wave be?

F 0.85 cm
G 1.35 cm
H 3.4 cm
I 5.4 cm

3. What is the amplitude of the wave shown?

A 0.85 cm
B 1.7 cm
C 2.7 cm
D There is not enough information to determine the answer.

MATH

Read each question below, and choose the best answer.

1. How is the product of 5 × 5 × 5 × 2 × 2 × 2 × 2 expressed in exponential notation?

A $3^5 \times 4^2$
B $5^3 \times 2^4$
C $5^7 \times 2^7$
D 10^7

2. Mannie purchased 8.9 kg of dog food from the veterinarian. How many grams of dog food did he purchase?

F 8,900 g
G 890 g
H 89 g
I 0.89 g

3. What is the area of a rectangle whose sides are 3 cm long and 7.5 cm long?

A 10.5 cm^2
B 12 cm^2
C 21 cm^2
D 22.5 cm^2

4. An underwater sound wave traveled 1.5 km in 1 s. How far would it travel in 4 s?

F 5.0 km
G 5.5 km
H 6.0 km
I 6.5 km

5. During a tennis game, the person serving the ball is allowed only 2 serves to start a point. Hannah plays a tennis match and is able to use 50 of her 63 first serves to start a point. What is the **best** estimate of Hannah's first-service percentage?

A 126%
B 88%
C 81.5%
D 79%

Science in Action

Science, Technology, and Society

The Ultimate Telescope

The largest telescopes in the world don't depend on visible light, lenses, or mirrors. Instead, they collect radio waves from the far reaches of outer space. One radio telescope, called the Very Large Array (VLA), is located in a remote desert in New Mexico.

Just as you can detect light waves from stars with your eyes, radio waves emitted from objects in space can be detected with radio telescopes. The Very Large Array consists of 27 radio telescopes like the ones in the photo above.

Math Activity

Radio waves travel about 300,000,000 m/s. The M100 galaxy is about 5.68×10^{23} m away from Earth. How long, in years, does it take radio waves from M100 to be detected by the VLA?

Scientific Discoveries

The Wave Nature of Light

Have you ever wondered what light really is? Many early scientists did. One of them, the great 17th-century scientist Isaac Newton, did some experiments and decided that light consisted of particles. But when experimenting with lenses, Newton observed some things that he could not explain.

Around 1800, the scientist Thomas Young did more experiments on light and found that it diffracted when it passed through slits. Young concluded that light could be thought of as waves. Although scientists were slow to accept this idea, they now know that light is both particle-like and wavelike.

Language Arts Activity

WRITING SKILL Thomas Young said, "The nature of light is a subject of no material importance to the concerns of life or to the practice of the arts, but it is in many other respects extremely interesting." Write a brief essay in which you answer the following questions: What do you think Young meant? Do you agree with him? How would you respond to his statement?

Careers

Estela Zavala

Ultrasonographer Estela Zavala is a registered diagnostic medical ultrasonographer who works at Austin Radiological Association in Austin, Texas. Most people have seen a picture of a sonogram showing an unborn baby inside its mother's womb. Ultrasound technologists make these images with an ultrasound machine, which sends harmless, high-frequency sound waves into the body. Zavala uses ultrasound to form images of organs in the body. Zavala says about her education, "After graduating from high school, I went to an X-ray school to be licensed as an X-ray technologist. First, I went to an intensive one-month training program. After that, I worked for a licensed radiologist for about a year. Finally, I attended a year-long ultrasound program at a local community college before becoming fully licensed." What Zavala likes best about her job is being able to help people by finding out what is wrong with them without surgery. Before ultrasound, surgery was the only way to find out about the health of someone's organs.

Social Studies ACTIVITY

WRITING SKILL Research the different ways in which ultrasound technology is used in medical practice today. Write a few paragraphs about what you learn.

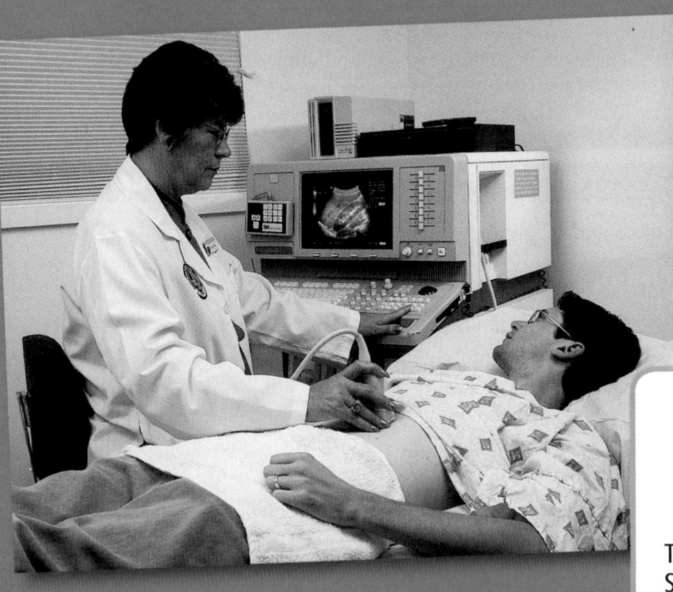

To learn more about these Science in Action topics, visit **go.hrw.com** and type in the keyword **HP5WAVF.**

Current Science

Check out Current Science® articles related to this chapter by visiting go.hrw.com. Just type in the keyword HP5CS20.

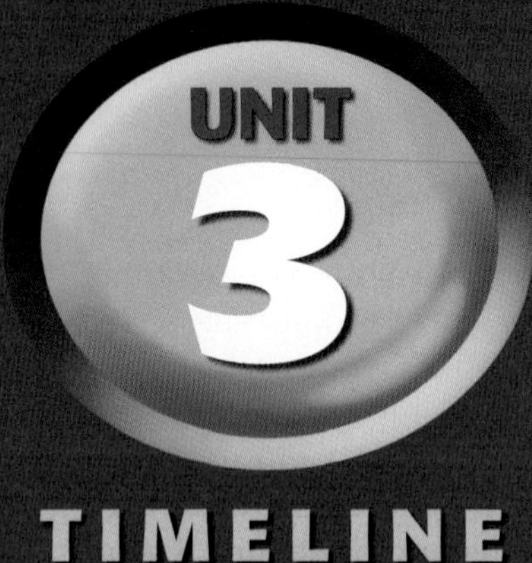

TIMELINE

Life Science

People have always searched for answers about life. Life science is the study of living things—from cells to communities of living things.

In this unit, you will learn about cells and about how living things are classified based on their characteristics. You will study the systems of your body and how your body protects itself and fights illness. You will also learn how all living things on Earth are interconnected.

This timeline includes a few of the many people who have studied living things and a few events that have shaped the history of life science.

1620
The Pilgrims settle Plymouth Colony.

1665
Robert Hooke discovers cells after observing a thin piece of cork under a microscope.

1861
The American Civil War begins.

1952
Martha Chase and Alfred Hershey demonstrate that DNA is the hereditary material.

1831

Robert Brown discovers the nucleus in a plant cell.

1838

Matthias Schleiden discovers that all plant tissue is made up of cells.

1839

Theodor Schwann shows that all animal tissue is made up of cells.

1858

Rudolf Virchow determines that all cells are produced from cells.

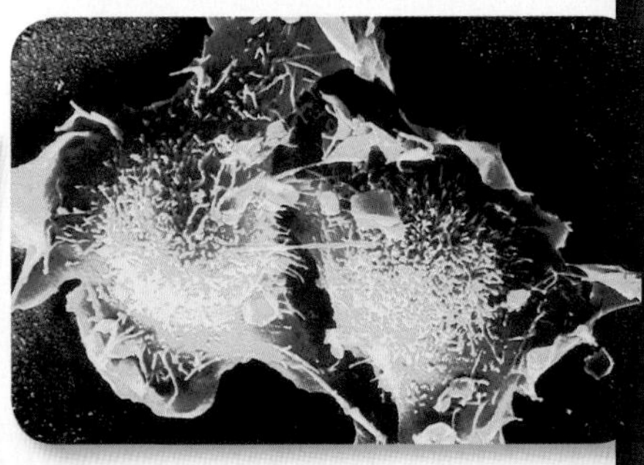

1873

Anton Schneider observes and accurately describes mitosis.

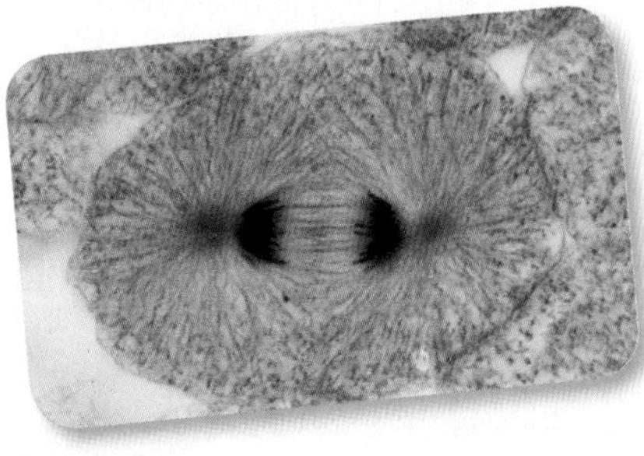

1937

The Golden Gate Bridge opens in San Francisco.

1941

George Beadle and Edward Tatum discover that genes control the chemical reactions in cells by directing protein production.

1956

The manufacture of protein in the cell is found to occur in ribosomes.

1971

Lynn Margulis proposes the endosymbiotic theory of the origin of cell organelles.

1997

A sheep named Dolly becomes the first animal to be cloned from a single body cell.

2002

Scientists test a cancer vaccine that can be given orally. Tests on mice lead scientists to be hopeful that the vaccine can be tested on humans.

Cells: The Basic Units of Life

Harmful bacteria may invade your body and make you sick. But wait—your white blood cells come to the rescue! In this image, a white blood cell (the large, yellowish cell) reaches out its pseudopod to destroy bacteria (the purple cells). The red discs are red blood cells.

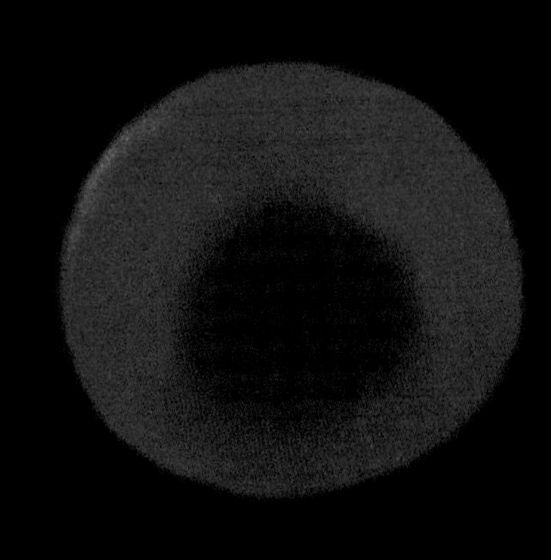

PRE-READING ACTIVITY

Key-Term Fold Before you read the chapter, create the FoldNote entitled "Key-Term Fold" described in the **Study Skills** section of the Appendix. Write a key term from the chapter on each tab of the key-term fold. Under each tab, write the definition of the key term.

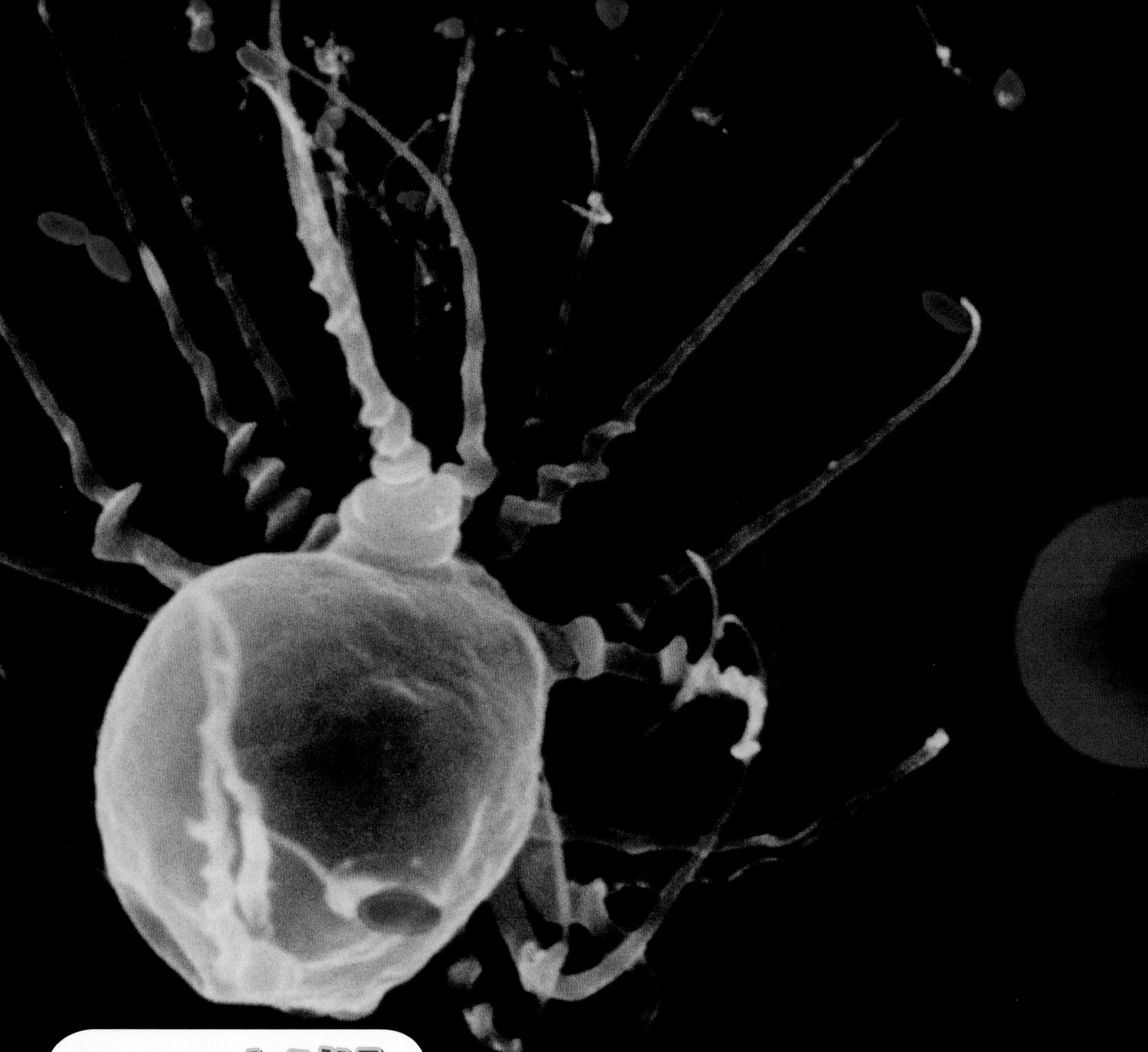

START-UP ACTIVITY

What Are Plants Made Of?

All living things, including plants, are made of cells. What do plant cells look like? Do this activity to find out.

Procedure

1. Tear off a **small leaf** from near the tip of an **Elodea sprig.**
2. Using **forceps,** place the whole leaf in a **drop of water** on a **microscope slide.**
3. Place a **coverslip** on top of the water drop by putting one edge of the coverslip on the slide near the water drop. Next, lower the coverslip slowly so that the coverslip does not trap air bubbles.
4. Place the slide on your **microscope.**
5. Using the lowest-powered lens first, find the plant cells. When you can see the cells under the lower-powered lens, switch to a higher-powered lens.
6. Draw a picture of what you see.

Analysis

1. Describe the shape of the *Elodea* cells. Are all of the cells in the *Elodea* the same?
2. Do you think human cells look like *Elodea* cells? How do you think they are different? How might they be similar?

SECTION 1

The Diversity of Cells

Most cells are so small they can't be seen by the naked eye. So how did scientists find cells? By accident, that's how! The first person to see cells wasn't even looking for them.

READING WARM-UP

Objectives

- State the parts of the cell theory.
- Explain why cells are so small.
- Describe the parts of a cell.
- Describe how eubacteria are different from archaebacteria.
- Explain the difference between prokaryotic cells and eukaryotic cells.

Terms to Learn

cell	nucleus
cell membrane	prokaryote
organelle	eukaryote

READING STRATEGY

Reading Organizer As you read this section, create an outline of the section. Use the headings from the section in your outline.

All living things are made of tiny structures called cells. A **cell** is the smallest unit that can perform all the processes necessary for life. Because of their size, cells weren't discovered until microscopes were invented in the mid-1600s.

Cells and the Cell Theory

Robert Hooke was the first person to describe cells. In 1665, he built a microscope to look at tiny objects. One day, he looked at a thin slice of cork. Cork is found in the bark of cork trees. The cork looked like it was made of little boxes. Hooke named these boxes *cells,* which means "little rooms" in Latin. Hooke's cells were really the outer layers of dead cork cells. Hooke's microscope and his drawing of the cork cells are shown in **Figure 1.**

Hooke also looked at thin slices of living plants. He saw that they too were made of cells. Some cells were even filled with "juice." The "juicy" cells were living cells.

Hooke also looked at feathers, fish scales, and the eyes of houseflies. But he spent most of his time looking at plants and fungi. The cells of plants and fungi have cell walls. This makes them easy to see. Animal cells do not have cell walls. This absence of cell walls makes it harder to see the outline of animal cells. Because Hooke couldn't see their cells, he thought that animals weren't made of cells.

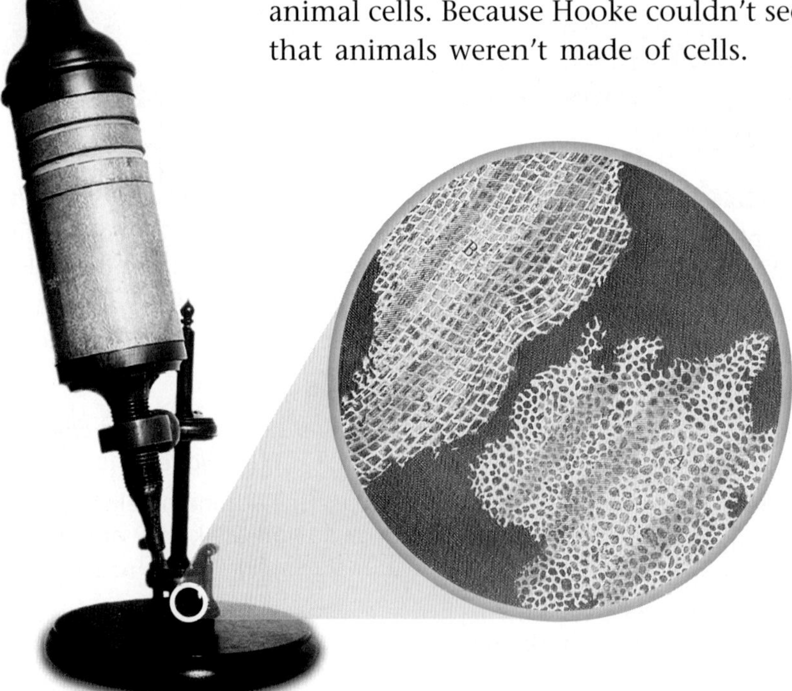

Figure 1 *Hooke discovered cells using this microscope. Hooke's drawing of cork cells is shown to the right of his microscope.*

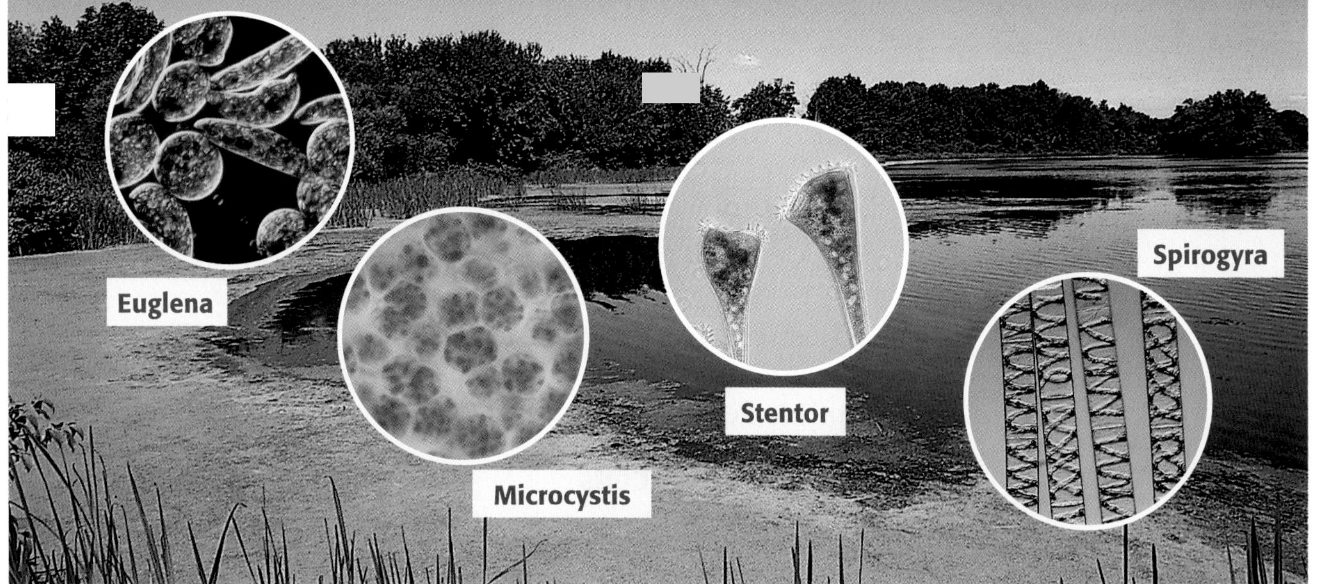

Finding Cells in Other Organisms

In 1673, Anton van Leeuwenhoek (LAY vuhn HOOK), a Dutch merchant, made his own microscopes. Leeuwenhoek used one of his microscopes to look at pond scum. Leeuwenhoek saw small organisms in the water. He named these organisms *animalcules,* which means "little animals." Today, we call these single-celled organisms protists (PROH tists). Pond scum and some of the protists it contains are shown in **Figure 2.**

Leeuwenhoek also looked at animal blood. He saw differences in blood cells from different kinds of animals. For example, blood cells in fish, birds, and frogs are oval. Blood cells in humans and dogs are round and flat. Leeuwenhoek was also the first person to see bacteria. And he discovered that yeasts that make bread dough rise are single-celled organisms.

Figure 2 *The green area at the edge of the pond is a layer of pond scum. This pond scum contains organisms called* protists, *such as those shown above.*

cell in biology, the smallest unit that can perform all life processes; cells are covered by a membrane and have DNA and cytoplasm

The Cell Theory

Almost 200 years passed before scientists concluded that cells are present in all living things. Scientist Matthias Schleiden (mah THEE uhs SHLIE duhn) studied plants. In 1838, he concluded that all plant parts were made of cells. Theodor Schwann (TAY oh dohr SHVAHN) studied animals. In 1839, Schwann concluded that all animal tissues were made of cells. Soon after that, Schwann wrote the first two parts of what is now known as the *cell theory*.

- All organisms are made of one or more cells.
- The cell is the basic unit of all living things.

Later, in 1858, Rudolf Virchow (ROO dawlf FIR koh), a doctor, stated that all cells could form only from other cells. Virchow then added the third part of the cell theory.

- All cells come from existing cells.

Reading Check **What are the three parts of the cell theory?** (*See the Appendix for answers to Reading Checks.*)

CONNECTION TO Physics

Microscopes The microscope Hooke used to study cells was much different from microscopes today. Research different kinds of microscopes, such as light microscopes, scanning electron microscopes (SEMs), and transmission electron microscopes (TEMs). Select one type of microscope. Make a poster or other presentation to show to the class. Describe how the microscope works and how it is used. Be sure to include images.

ACTIVITY

Cell Size

Most cells are too small to be seen without a microscope. It would take 50 human cells to cover the dot on this letter *i*.

A Few Large Cells

Most cells are small. A few, however, are big. The yolk of a chicken egg, shown in **Figure 3**, is one big cell. The egg can be this large because it does not have to take in more nutrients.

Figure 3 *The white and yolk of this chicken egg provide nutrients for the development of a chick.*

Many Small Cells

There is a physical reason why most cells are so small. Cells take in food and get rid of wastes through their outer surface. As a cell gets larger, it needs more food and produces more waste. Therefore, more materials pass through its outer surface.

As the cell's volume increases, its surface area grows too. But the cell's volume grows faster than its surface area. If a cell gets too large, the cell's surface area will not be large enough to take in enough nutrients or pump out enough wastes. So, the area of a cell's surface—compared with the cell's volume—limits the cell's size. The ratio of the cell's outer surface area to the cell's volume is called the *surface area–to-volume ratio,* which can be calculated by using the following equation:

$$\textit{surface area–to-volume ratio} = \frac{\textit{surface area}}{\textit{volume}}$$

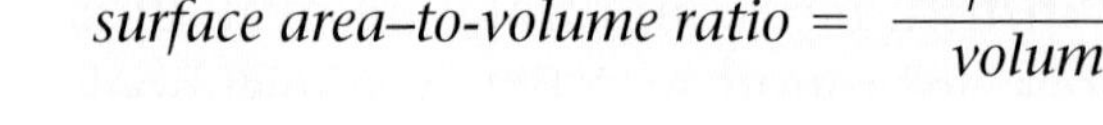

Reading Check Why are most cells small?

MATH FOCUS

Surface Area–to-Volume Ratio Calculate the surface area–to-volume ratio of a cube whose sides measure 2 cm.

Step 1: Calculate the surface area.

$$\textit{surface area of cube} = \textit{number of sides} \times \textit{area of side}$$

$$\textit{surface area of cube} = 6 \times (2 \text{ cm} \times 2 \text{ cm})$$

$$\textit{surface area of cube} = 24 \text{ cm}^2$$

Step 2: Calculate the volume.

$$\textit{volume of cube} = \textit{side} \times \textit{side} \times \textit{side}$$

$$\textit{volume of cube} = 2 \text{ cm} \times 2 \text{ cm} \times 2 \text{ cm}$$

$$\textit{volume of cube} = 8 \text{ cm}^3$$

Step 3: Calculate the surface area–to-volume ratio.

$$\textit{surface area–to-volume ratio} = \frac{\textit{surface area}}{\textit{volume}} = \frac{24}{8} = \frac{3}{1}$$

Now It's Your Turn

1. Calculate the surface area–to-volume ratio of a cube whose sides are 3 cm long.
2. Calculate the surface area–to-volume ratio of a cube whose sides are 4 cm long.
3. Of the cubes from questions 1 and 2, which has the greater surface area–to-volume ratio?
4. What is the relationship between the length of a side and the surface area–to-volume ratio of a cell?

Parts of a Cell

Cells come in many shapes and sizes. Cells have many different functions. But all cells have the following parts in common.

The Cell Membrane and Cytoplasm

All cells are surrounded by a cell membrane. The **cell membrane** is a protective layer that covers the cell's surface and acts as a barrier. It separates the cell's contents from its environment. The cell membrane also controls materials going into and out of the cell. Inside the cell is a fluid. This fluid and almost all of its contents are called the *cytoplasm* (SIET oh PLAZ uhm).

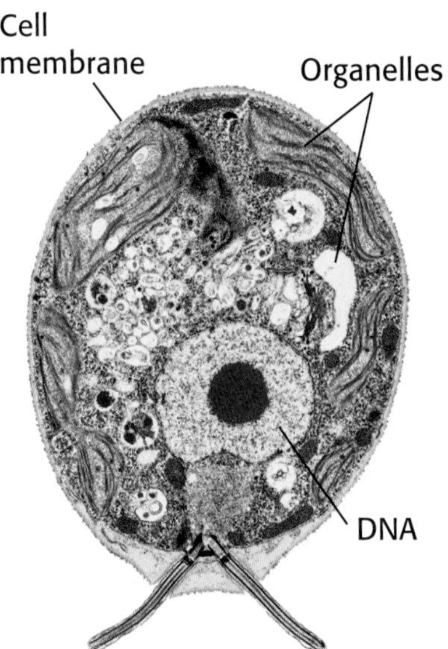

Figure 4 *This green alga has organelles. The organelles and the fluid surrounding them make up the cytoplasm.*

Organelles

Cells have organelles that carry out various life processes. **Organelles** are structures that perform specific functions within the cell. Different types of cells have different organelles. Most organelles are surrounded by membranes. For example, the algal cell in **Figure 4** has membrane-bound organelles. Some organelles float in the cytoplasm. Other organelles are attached to membranes or other organelles.

Reading Check What are organelles?

Genetic Material

All cells contain DNA (**d**eoxyribo**n**ucleic **a**cid) at some point in their life. *DNA* is the genetic material that carries information needed to make new cells and new organisms. DNA is passed on from parent cells to new cells and controls the activities of a cell. **Figure 5** shows the DNA of a bacterium.

In some cells, the DNA is enclosed inside an organelle called the **nucleus.** For example, your cells have a nucleus. In contrast, bacterial cells do not have a nucleus.

In humans, mature red blood cells lose their DNA. Red blood cells are made inside bones. When red blood cells are first made, they have a nucleus with DNA. But before they enter the bloodstream, red blood cells lose their nucleus and DNA. They survive with no new instructions from their DNA.

cell membrane a phospholipid layer that covers a cell's surface; acts as a barrier between the inside of a cell and the cell's environment

organelle one of the small bodies in a cell's cytoplasm that are specialized to perform a specific function

nucleus in a eukaryotic cell, a membrane-bound organelle that contains the cell's DNA and that has a role in processes such as growth, metabolism, and reproduction

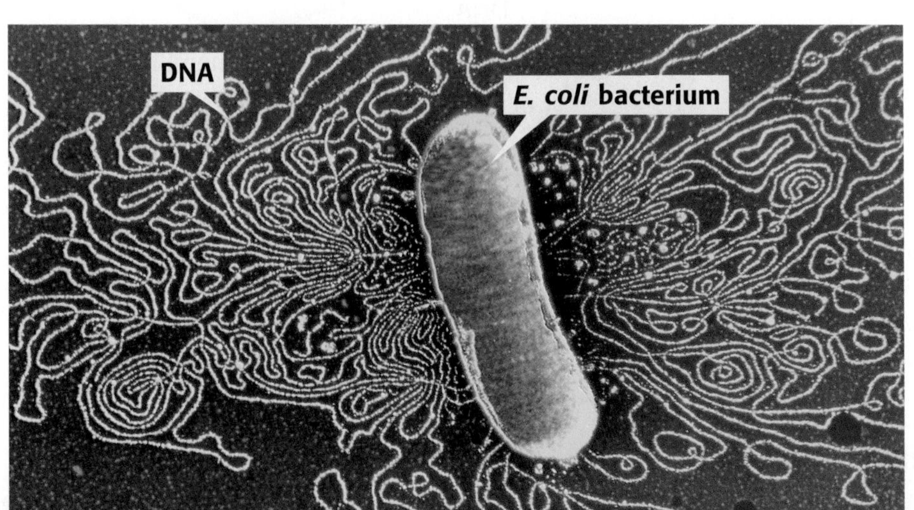

Figure 5 *This photo shows an* Escherichia coli *bacterium. The bacterium's cell membrane has been treated so that the cell's DNA is released.*

Bacteria in Your Lunch?

Most of the time, you don't want bacteria in your food. Many bacteria make toxins that will make you sick. However, some foods–such as yogurt–are supposed to have bacteria in them! The bacteria in these foods are not dangerous.

In yogurt, masses of rod-shaped bacteria feed on the sugar (lactose) in milk. The bacteria convert the sugar into lactic acid. Lactic acid causes milk to thicken. This thickened milk makes yogurt.

1. Using a **cotton swab,** put a **small dot of yogurt** on a **microscope slide.**
2. Add a **drop of water.** Use the cotton swab to stir.
3. Add a **coverslip**.
4. Use a **microscope** to examine the slide. Draw what you observe.

Two Kinds of Cells

All cells have cell membranes, organelles, cytoplasm, and DNA in common. But there are two basic types of cells—cells without a nucleus and cells with a nucleus. Cells with no nucleus are *prokaryotic* (proh KAR ee AHT ik) *cells*. Cells that have a nucleus are *eukaryotic* (yoo KAR ee AHT ik) *cells*. Prokaryotic cells are further classified into two groups: *eubacteria* (yoo bak TIR ee uh) and *archaebacteria* (AHR kee bak TIR ee uh).

Prokaryotes: Eubacteria and Archaebacteria

Eubacteria and archaebacteria are prokaryotes (pro KAR ee OHTS). **Prokaryotes** are single-celled organisms that do not have a nucleus or membrane-bound organelles.

prokaryote an organism that consists of a single cell that does not have a nucleus

Eubacteria

The most common prokaryotes are eubacteria (or just *bacteria*). Bacteria are the world's smallest cells. These tiny organisms live almost everywhere. Bacteria do not have a nucleus, but they do have DNA. A bacteria's DNA is a long, circular molecule, shaped sort of like a rubber band. Bacteria have no membrane-covered organelles. But they do have ribosomes. *Ribosomes* are tiny, round organelles made of protein and other material.

Bacteria also have a strong, weblike exterior cell wall. This wall helps the cell retain its shape. A bacterium's cell membrane is just inside the cell wall. Together, the cell wall and cell membrane allow materials into and out of the cell.

Some bacteria live in the soil and water. Others live in, or on, other organisms. For example, you have bacteria living on your skin and teeth. You also have bacteria living in your digestive system. These bacteria help the process of digestion. A typical bacterial cell is shown in **Figure 6.**

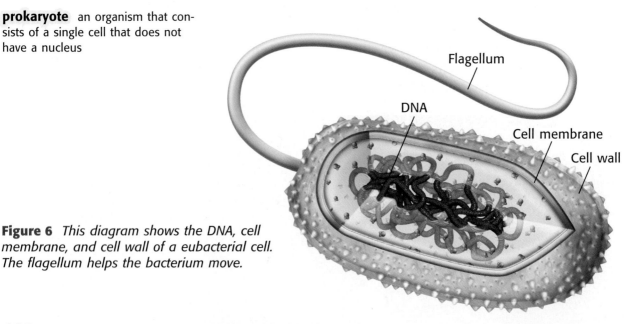

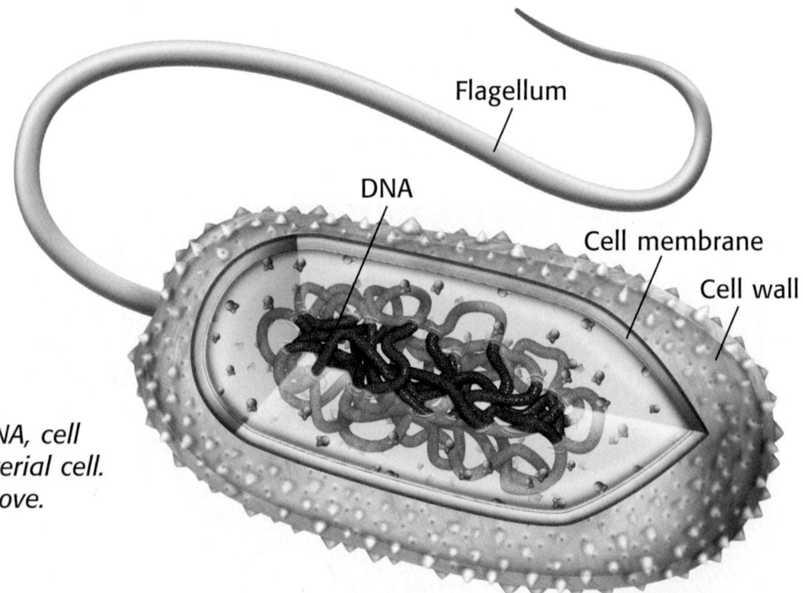

Figure 6 *This diagram shows the DNA, cell membrane, and cell wall of a eubacterial cell. The flagellum helps the bacterium move.*

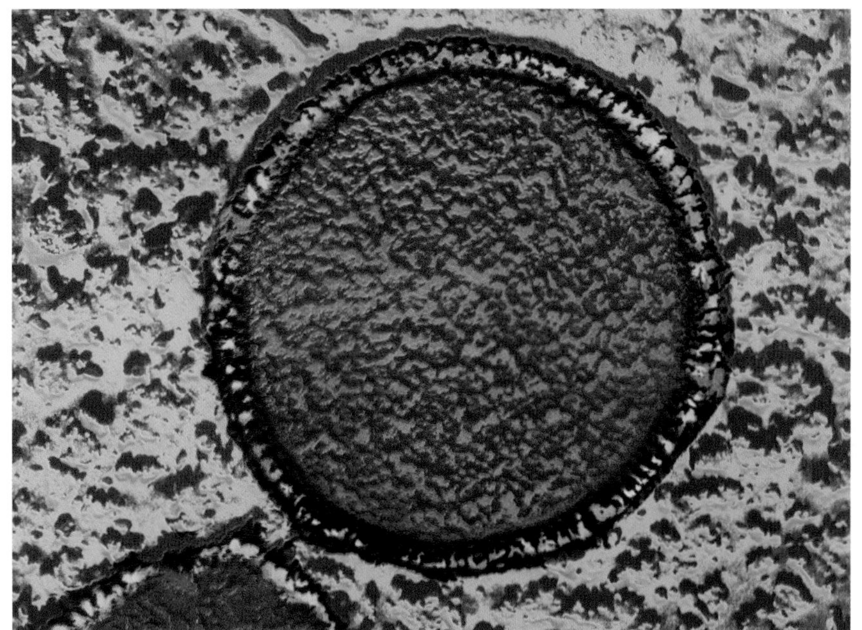

Figure 7 *This photograph, taken with an electron microscope, is of an archaebacterium that lives in the very high temperatures of deep-sea volcanic vents. The photograph has been colored so that the cell wall is green and the cell contents are pink.*

Archaebacteria

The second kind of prokaryote are the archaebacteria. These organisms are also called *archaea* (ahr KEE uh). Archaebacteria are similar to bacteria in some ways. For example, both are single-celled organisms. Both have ribosomes, a cell membrane, and circular DNA. And both lack a nucleus and membrane-bound organelles. But archaebacteria are different from bacteria. For example, archaebacterial ribosomes are different from eubacterial ribosomes.

Archaebacteria are similar to eukaryotic cells in some ways, too. For example, archaebacterial ribosomes are more like the ribosomes of eukaryotic cells. But archaebacteria also have some features that no other cells have. For example, the cell wall and cell membranes of archaebacteria are different from the cell walls of other organisms. And some archaebacteria live in places where no other organisms could live.

Three types of archaebacteria are *heat-loving, salt-loving,* and *methane-making.* Methane is a kind of gas frequently found in swamps. Heat-loving and salt-loving archaebacteria are sometimes called extremophiles. *Extremophiles* live in places where conditions are extreme. They live in very hot water, such as in hot springs, or where the water is extremely salty. **Figure 7** shows one kind of methane-making archaebacteria that lives deep in the ocean near volcanic vents. The temperature of the water from those vents is extreme: it is above the boiling point of water at sea level.

Reading Check **What is one difference between eubacteria and archaebacteria?**

CONNECTION TO Social Studies

Where Do They Live? While most archaebacteria live in extreme environments, scientists have found that archaebacteria live almost everywhere. Do research about archaebacteria. Select one kind of archaebacteria. Create a poster showing the geographical location where the organism lives, describing its physical environment, and explaining how it survives in its environment.

ACTIVITY

Eukaryotic Cells and Eukaryotes

eukaryote an organism made up of cells that have a nucleus enclosed by a membrane; eukaryotes include animals, plants, and fungi, but not archaebacteria or eubacteria

Eukaryotic cells are the largest cells. Most eukaryotic cells are still microscopic, but they are about 10 times larger than most bacterial cells. A typical eukaryotic cell is shown in **Figure 8.**

Unlike bacteria and archaebacteria, eukaryotic cells have a nucleus. The nucleus is one kind of membrane-bound organelle. A cell's nucleus holds the cell's DNA. Eukaryotic cells have other membrane-bound organelles as well. Organelles are like the different organs in your body. Each kind of organelle has a specific job in the cell. Together, organelles, such as the ones shown in **Figure 8,** perform all the processes necessary for life.

All living things that are not bacteria or archaebacteria are made of one or more eukaryotic cells. Organisms made of eukaryotic cells are called **eukaryotes.** Many eukaryotes are multicellular. *Multicellular* means "many cells." Multicellular organisms are usually larger than single-cell organisms. So, most organisms you see with your naked eye are eukaryotes. There are many types of eukaryotes. Animals, including humans, are eukaryotes. So are plants. Some protists, such as amoebas, are single-celled eukaryotes. Other protists, including some types of green algae, are multicellular eukaryotes. Fungi are organisms such as mushrooms or yeasts. Mushrooms are multicellular eukaryotes. Yeasts are single-celled eukaryotes.

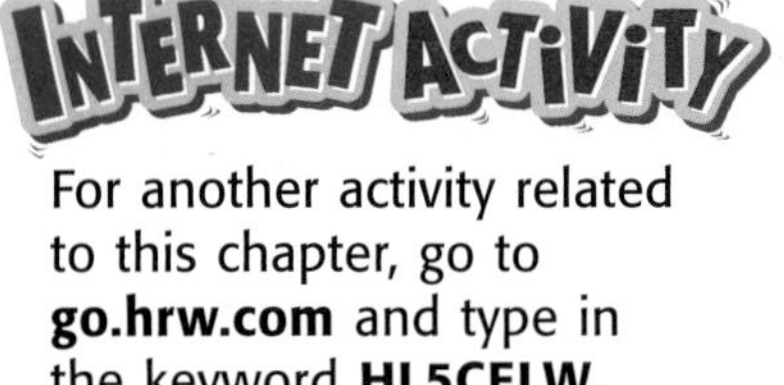

For another activity related to this chapter, go to **go.hrw.com** and type in the keyword **HL5CELW.**

Reading Check How are eukaryotes different from prokaryotes?

Figure 8 **Organelles in a Typical Eukaryotic Cell**

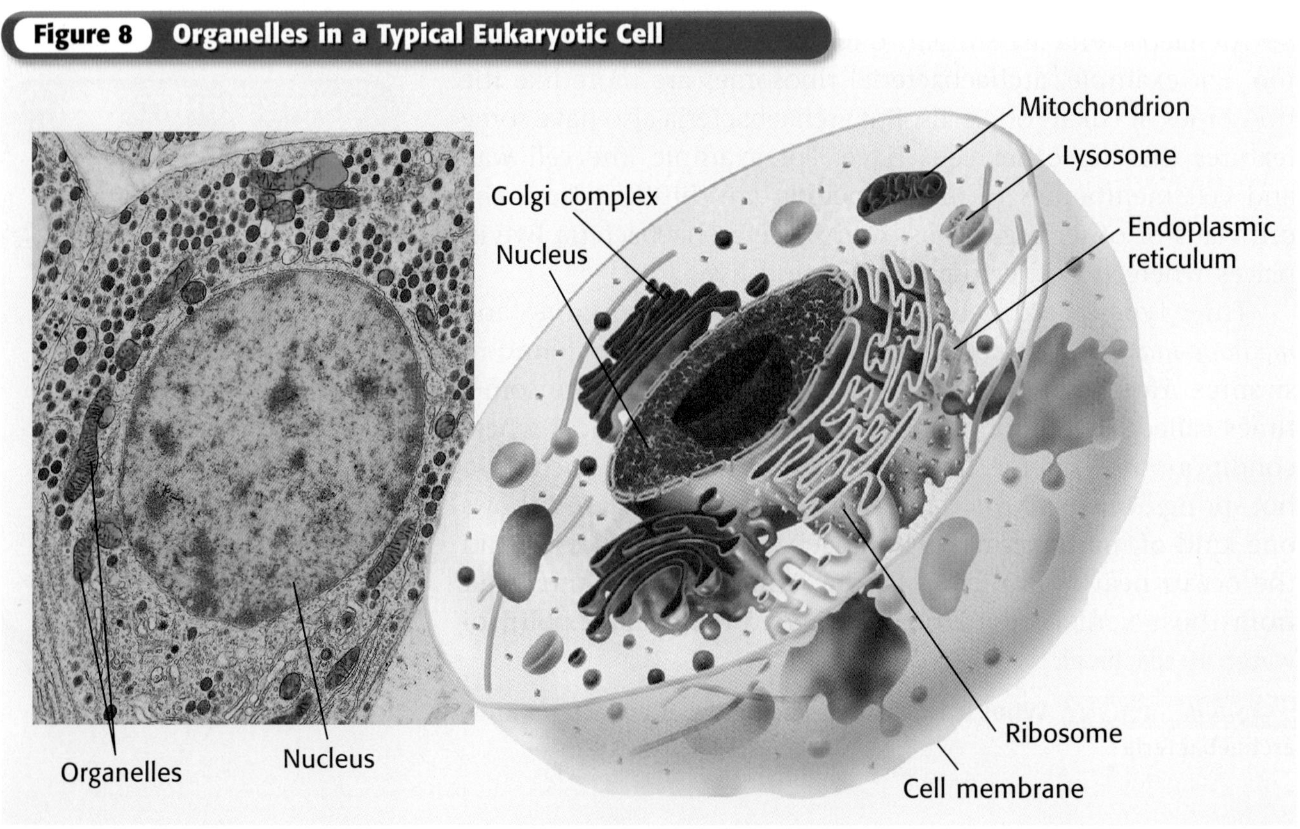

SECTION Review

Summary

- Cells were not discovered until microscopes were invented in the 1600s.
- Cell theory states that all organisms are made of cells, the cell is the basic unit of all living things, and all cells come from other cells.
- All cells have a cell membrane, cytoplasm, and DNA.
- Most cells are too small to be seen with the naked eye. A cell's surface area–to-volume ratio limits the size of a cell.
- The two basic kinds of cells are prokaryotic cells and eukaryotic cells. Eukaryotic cells have a nucleus and membrane-bound organelles. Prokaryotic cells do not.
- Prokaryotes are classified as archaebacteria and eubacteria.
- Archaebacterial cell walls and ribosomes are different from the cell walls and ribosomes of other organisms.
- Eukaryotes can be single-celled or multicellular.

Using Key Terms

1. In your own words, write a definition for the term *organelle*.
2. Use the following terms in the same sentence: *prokaryotic, nucleus,* and *eukaryotic.*

Understanding Key Ideas

3. Cell size is limited by the
   a. thickness of the cell wall.
   b. size of the cell's nucleus.
   c. cell's surface area–to-volume ratio.
   d. amount of cytoplasm in the cell.
4. What are the three parts of the cell theory?
5. Name three structures that every cell has.
6. Give two ways in which archaebacteria are different from bacteria.

Critical Thinking

7. **Applying Concepts** You have discovered a new single-celled organism. It has a cell wall, ribosomes, and long, circular DNA. Is it a eukaryote or a prokaryote cell? Explain.
8. **Identifying Relationships** One of your students brings you a cell about the size of the period at the end of this sentence. It is a single cell, but it also forms chains. What characteristics would this cell have if the organism is a eukaryote? If it is a prokaryote? What would you look for first?

Interpreting Graphics

The picture below shows a particular organism. Use the picture to answer the questions that follow.

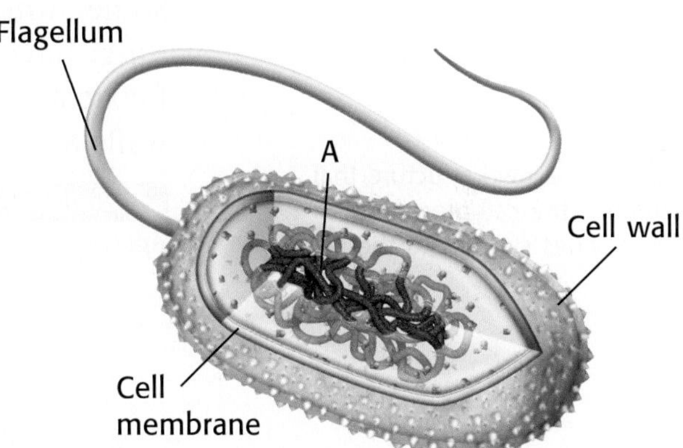

9. What type of organism does the picture represent? How do you know?
10. Which structure helps the organism move?
11. What part of the organism does the letter *A* represent?

SCILINKS.
NSTA
Developed and maintained by the National Science Teachers Association
For a variety of links related to this chapter, go to www.scilinks.org
Topic: Prokaryotic Cells
SciLinks code: HSM1225

SECTION 2

Eukaryotic Cells

Most eukaryotic cells are small. For a long time after cells were discovered, scientists could not see what was going on inside cells. They did not know how complex cells are.

READING WARM-UP

Objectives

- Identify the different parts of a eukaryotic cell.
- Explain the function of each part of a eukaryotic cell.

Terms to Learn

cell wall
ribosome
endoplasmic reticulum
mitochondrion
Golgi complex
vesicle
lysosome

READING STRATEGY

Reading Organizer As you read this section, make a table comparing plant cells and animal cells.

Now, scientists know a lot about eukaryotic cells. These cells have many parts that work together and keep the cell alive.

Cell Wall

Some eukaryotic cells have cell walls. A **cell wall** is a rigid structure that gives support to a cell. The cell wall is the outermost structure of a cell. Plants and algae have cell walls made of cellulose (SEL yoo LOHS) and other materials. *Cellulose* is a complex sugar that most animals can't digest.

The cell walls of plant cells allow plants to stand upright. In some plants, the cells must take in water for the cell walls to keep their shape. When such plants lack water, the cell walls collapse and the plant droops. **Figure 1** shows a cross section of a plant cell and a close-up of the cell wall.

Fungi, including yeasts and mushrooms, also have cell walls. Some fungi have cell walls made of *chitin* (KIE tin). Other fungi have cell walls made from a chemical similar to chitin. Eubacteria and archaebacteria also have cell walls, but those walls are different from plant or fungal cell walls.

cell wall a rigid structure that surrounds the cell membrane and provides support to the cell

Reading Check What types of cells have cell walls? (*See the Appendix for answers to Reading Checks.*)

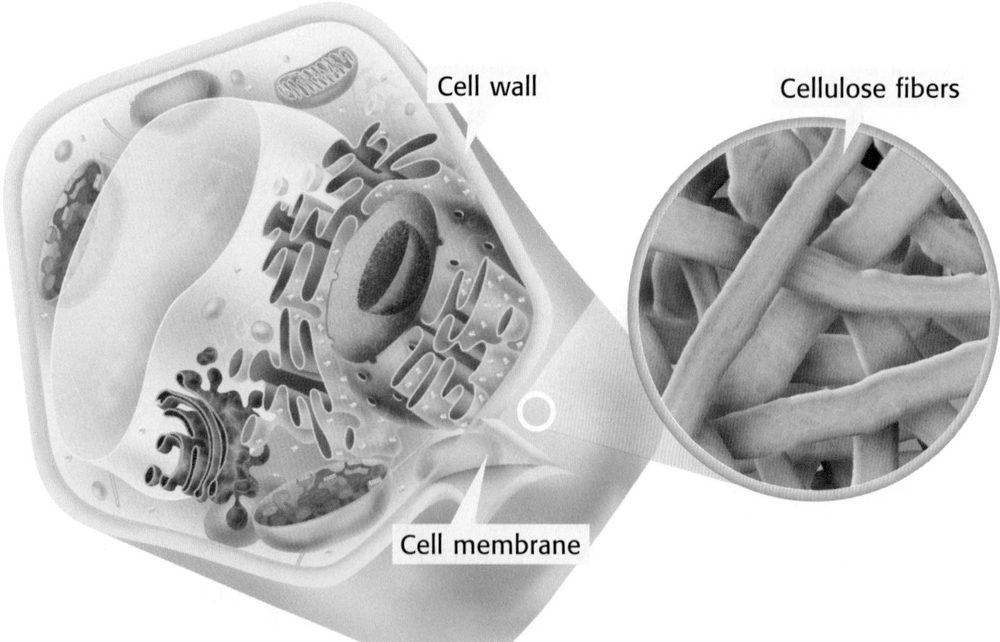

Figure 1 *The cell walls of plant cells help plants retain their shape. Plant cell walls are made of cellulose.*

Cell Membrane

All cells have a cell membrane. The *cell membrane* is a protective barrier that encloses a cell. It separates the cell's contents from the cell's environment. The cell membrane is the outermost structure in cells that lack a cell wall. In cells that have a cell wall, the cell membrane lies just inside the cell wall.

The cell membrane contains proteins, lipids, and phospholipids. *Lipids,* which include fats and cholesterol, are a group of compounds that do not dissolve in water. The cell membrane has two layers of phospholipids (FAHS foh LIP idz), shown in **Figure 2.** A *phospholipid* is a lipid that contains phosphorus. Lipids are "water fearing," or *hydrophobic*. Lipid ends of phospholipids form the inner part of the membrane. Phosphorus-containing ends of the phospholipids are "water loving," or *hydrophilic*. Much of the fluid inside and outside of a cell is made up of water. In fact, as much as 70% of a cell's mass is made up of water. Therefore, the hydrophilic ends of the phospholipid form the outside of the membrane.

Some of the proteins and lipids control the movement of materials into and out of the cell. Some of the proteins form passageways. Nutrients and water move into the cell, and wastes move out of the cell, through these protein passageways.

Reading Check What are two functions of a cell membrane?

CONNECTION TO Chemistry

Osmosis The movement of water across the cell membrane is called *osmosis*. Osmosis is very important to cell processes. Research osmosis, and draw a diagram describing what takes place when pure water is separated from a solution of salt water by a membrane that allows water molecules to pass.

Figure 2 *The cell membrane is made of two layers of phospholipids. It allows nutrients to enter and wastes to exit the cell.*

Cytoskeleton

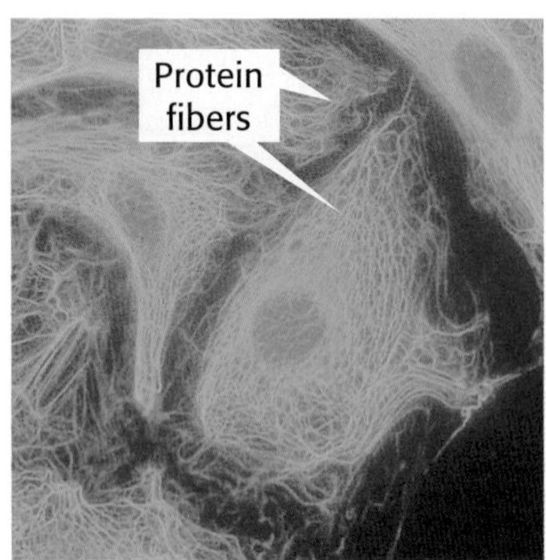

Figure 3 *The cytoskeleton, made of protein fibers, helps a cell retain its shape, move in its environment, and move its organelles.*

The *cytoskeleton* (SIET oh SKEL uh tuhn) is a web of proteins in the cytoplasm. The cytoskeleton, shown in **Figure 3,** acts as both a muscle and a skeleton. It keeps the cell's membranes from collapsing. The cytoskeleton also helps some cells move.

The cytoskeleton is made of three types of protein. One protein is a hollow tube. The other two are long, stringy fibers. One of the stringy proteins is also found in muscle cells.

Reading Check **What is the cytoskeleton?**

Nucleus

All eukaryotic cells have the same basic membrane-bound organelles, starting with the nucleus. The *nucleus* is a large organelle in a eukaryotic cell. It contains the cell's DNA, or genetic material. DNA contains the information on how to make a cell's proteins. Proteins control the chemical reactions in a cell. They also provide structural support for cells and tissues. But proteins are not made in the nucleus. Messages for how to make proteins are copied from the DNA. These messages are then sent out of the nucleus through the membranes.

The nucleus is covered by two membranes. Materials cross this double membrane by passing through pores. **Figure 4** shows a nucleus and nuclear pores. The nucleus of many cells has a dark area called the nucleolus (noo KLEE uh luhs). The *nucleolus* is where a cell begins to make its ribosomes.

Figure 4 *The nucleus contains the cell's DNA. Pores allow materials to move between the nucleus and the cytoplasm.*

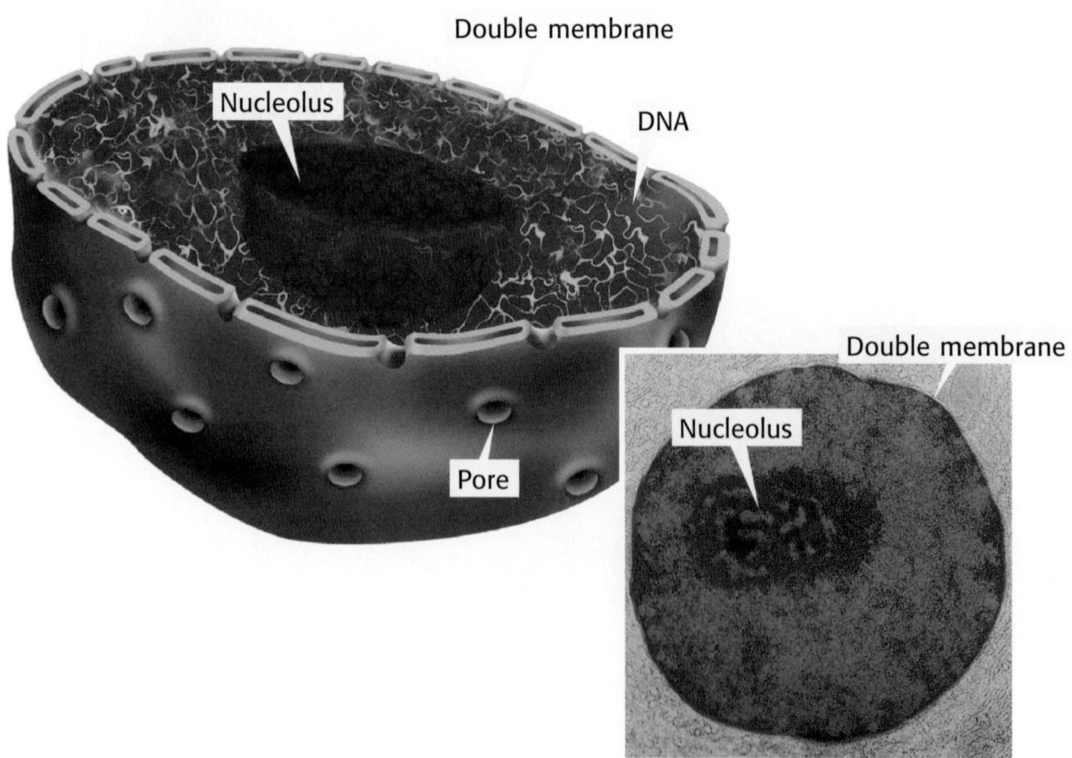

Ribosomes

Organelles that make proteins are called **ribosomes.** Ribosomes are the smallest of all organelles. And there are more ribosomes in a cell than there are any other organelles. Some ribosomes float freely in the cytoplasm. Others are attached to membranes or the cytoskeleton. Unlike most organelles, ribosomes are not covered by a membrane.

Proteins are made within the ribosomes. Proteins are made of amino acids. An *amino acid* is any one of about 20 different organic molecules that are used to make proteins. All cells need proteins to live. All cells have ribosomes.

ribosome cell organelle composed of RNA and protein; the site of protein synthesis

endoplasmic reticulum a system of membranes that is found in a cell's cytoplasm and that assists in the production, processing, and transport of proteins and in the production of lipids

Endoplasmic Reticulum

Many chemical reactions take place in a cell. Many of these reactions happen on or in the endoplasmic reticulum (EN doh PLAZ mik ri TIK yuh luhm). The **endoplasmic reticulum,** or ER, is a system of folded membranes in which proteins, lipids, and other materials are made. The ER is shown in **Figure 5.**

The ER is part of the internal delivery system of the cell. Its folded membrane contains many tubes and passageways. Substances move through the ER to different places in the cell.

Endoplasmic reticulum is either rough ER or smooth ER. The part of the ER covered in ribosomes is rough ER. Rough ER is usually found near the nucleus. Ribosomes on rough ER make many of the cell's proteins. The ER delivers these proteins throughout the cell. ER that lacks ribosomes is smooth ER. The functions of smooth ER include making lipids and breaking down toxic materials that could damage the cell.

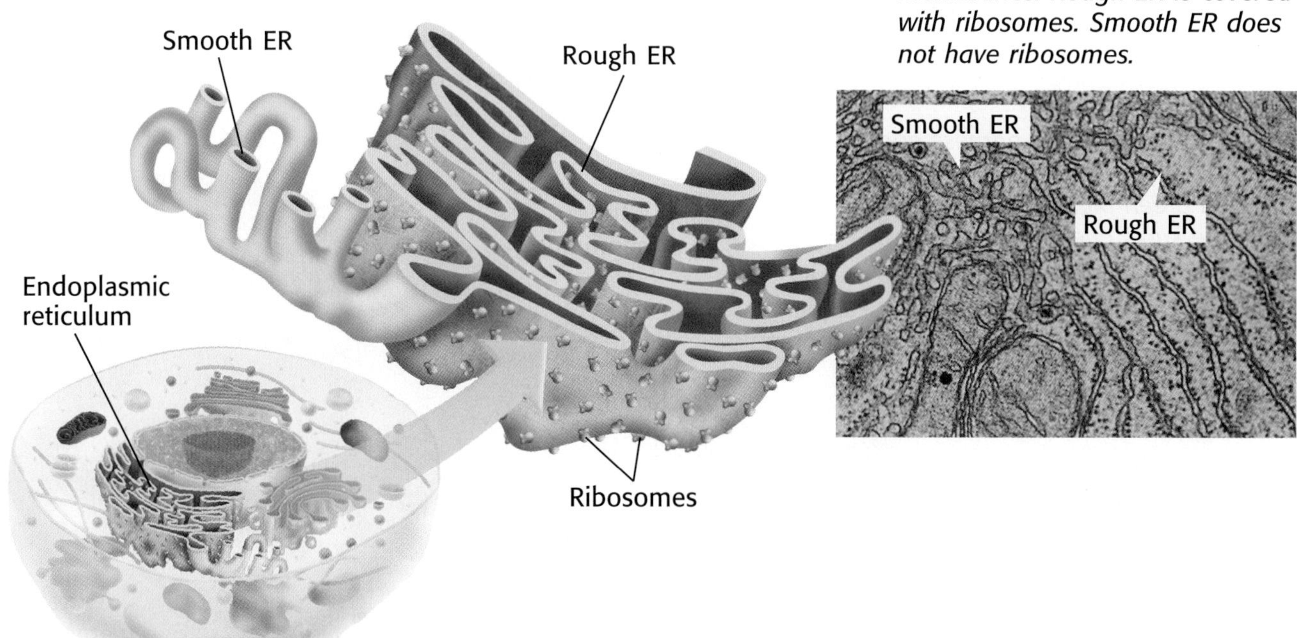

Figure 5 *The endoplasmic reticulum (ER) is a system of membranes. Rough ER is covered with ribosomes. Smooth ER does not have ribosomes.*

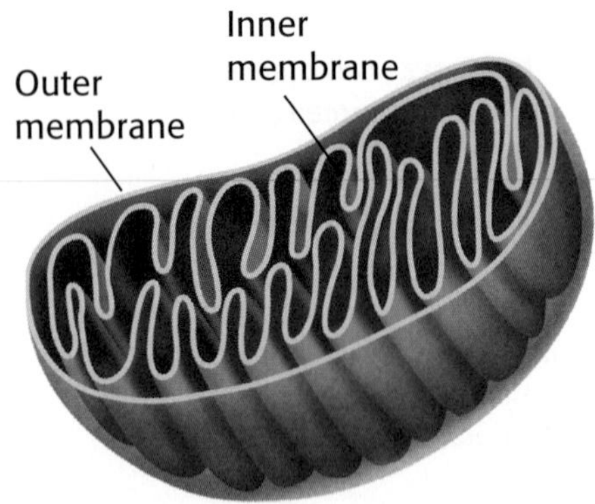

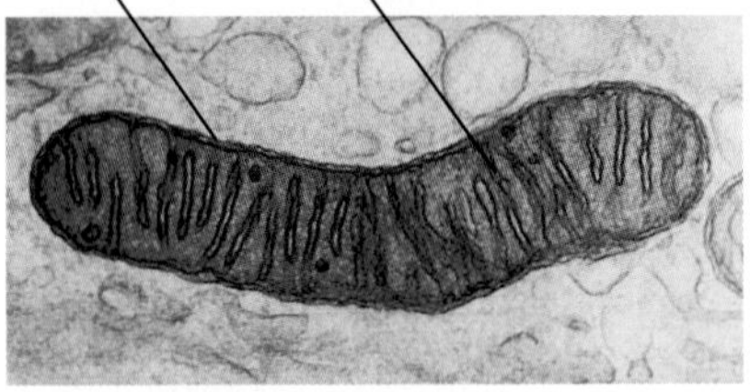

Figure 6 *Mitochondria break down sugar and make ATP. ATP is produced on the inner membrane.*

Mitochondria

A mitochondrion (MIET oh KAHN dree uhn) is the main power source of a cell. A **mitochondrion** is the organelle in which sugar is broken down to produce energy. Mitochondria are covered by two membranes, as shown in **Figure 6.** Energy released by mitochondria is stored in a substance called *ATP* (**a**denosine **t**ri**p**hosphate). The cell then uses ATP to do work. ATP can be made at several places in a cell. But most of a cell's ATP is made in the inner membrane of the cell's mitochondria.

Most eukaryotic cells have mitochondria. Mitochondria are the size of some bacteria. Like bacteria, mitochondria have their own DNA, and mitochondria can divide within a cell.

Reading Check **Where is most of a cell's ATP made?**

mitochondrion in eukaryotic cells, the cell organelle that is surrounded by two membranes and that is the site of cellular respiration

Chloroplasts

Animal cells cannot make their own food. Plants and algae are different. They have chloroplasts (KLAWR uh PLASTS) in some of their cells. *Chloroplasts* are organelles in plant and algae cells in which photosynthesis takes place. Like mitochondria, chloroplasts have two membranes and their own DNA. A chloroplast is shown in **Figure 7.** *Photosynthesis* is the process by which plants and algae use sunlight, carbon dioxide, and water to make sugar and oxygen.

Chloroplasts are green because they contain *chlorophyll,* a green pigment. Chlorophyll is found inside the inner membrane of a chloroplast. Chlorophyll traps the energy of sunlight, which is used to make sugar. The sugar produced by photosynthesis is then used by mitochondria to make ATP.

Figure 7 *Chloroplasts harness and use the energy of the sun to make sugar. A green pigment–chlorophyll–traps the sun's energy.*

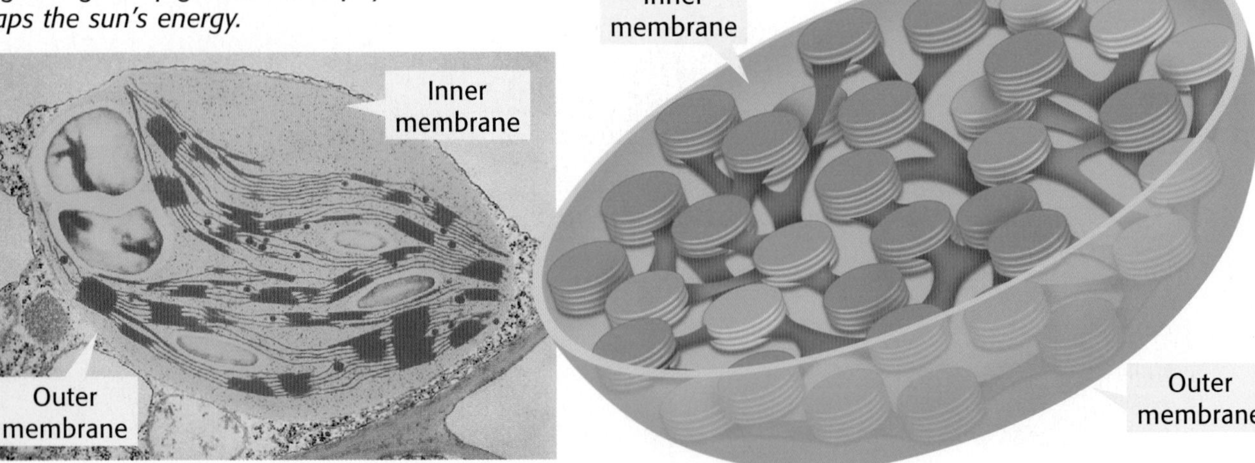

Golgi Complex

The organelle that packages and distributes proteins is called the **Golgi complex** (GOHL jee KAHM pleks). It is named after Camillo Golgi, the Italian scientist who first identified the organelle.

The Golgi complex looks like smooth ER, as shown in **Figure 8.** Lipids and proteins from the ER are delivered to the Golgi complex. There, the lipids and proteins may be modified to do different jobs. The final products are enclosed in a piece of the Golgi complex's membrane. This membrane pinches off to form a small bubble. The bubble transports its contents to other parts of the cell or out of the cell.

Golgi complex cell organelle that helps make and package materials to be transported out of the cell

vesicle a small cavity or sac that contains materials in a eukaryotic cell

Cell Compartments

The bubble that forms from the Golgi complex's membrane is a vesicle. A **vesicle** (VES i kuhl) is a small sac that surrounds material to be moved into or out of a cell. All eukaryotic cells have vesicles. Vesicles also move material within a cell. For example, vesicles carry new protein from the ER to the Golgi complex. Other vesicles distribute material from the Golgi complex to other parts of the cell. Some vesicles form when part of the cell membrane surrounds an object outside the cell.

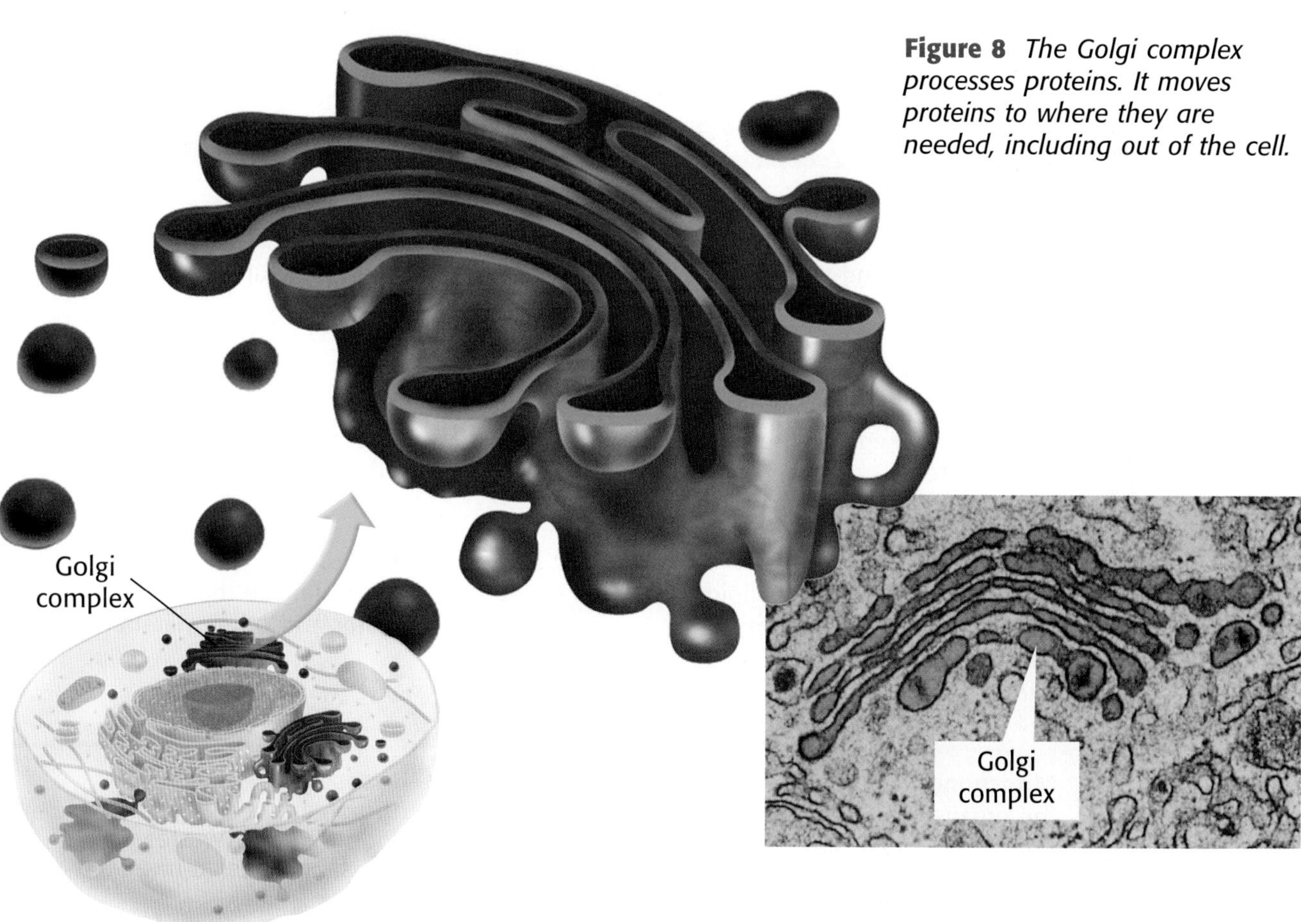

Figure 8 *The Golgi complex processes proteins. It moves proteins to where they are needed, including out of the cell.*

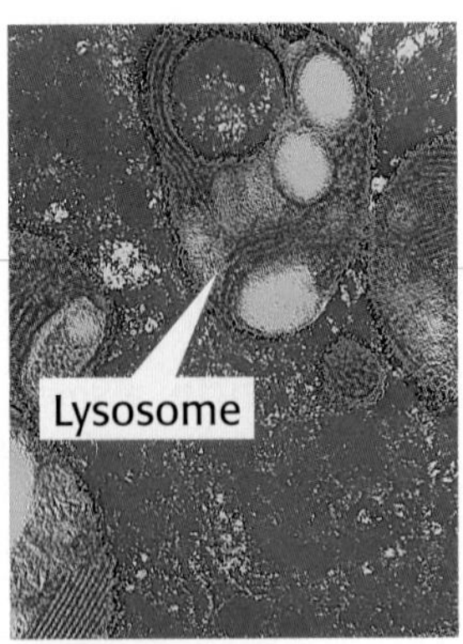

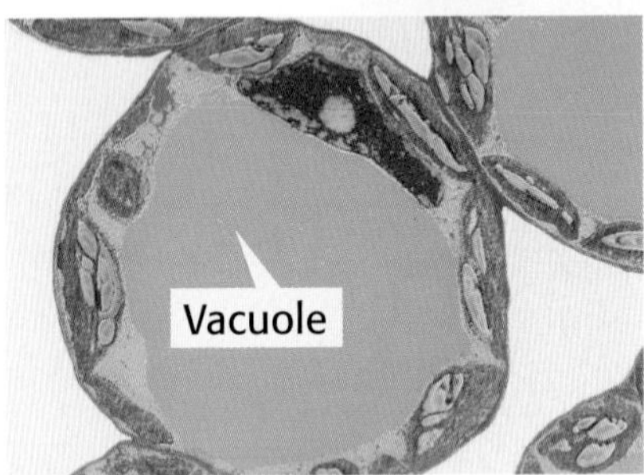

Figure 9 *Lysosomes digest materials inside a cell. In plant and fungal cells, vacuoles often perform the same function.*

Cellular Digestion

Lysosomes (LIE suh SOHMZ) are vesicles that are responsible for digestion inside a cell. **Lysosomes** are organelles that contain digestive enzymes. They destroy worn-out or damaged organelles, get rid of waste materials, and protect the cell from foreign invaders. Lysosomes, which come in a wide variety of sizes and shapes, are shown in **Figure 9.**

Lysosomes are found mainly in animal cells. When eukaryotic cells engulf particles, they enclose the particles in vesicles. Lysosomes bump into these vesicles and pour enzymes into them. These enzymes digest the particles in the vesicles.

Reading Check Why are lysosomes important?

lysosome a cell organelle that contains digestive enzymes

Vacuoles

A *vacuole* (VAK yoo OHL) is a large vesicle. In plant and fungal cells, some vacuoles act like large lysosomes. They store digestive enzymes and aid in digestion within the cell. Other vacuoles in plant cells store water and other liquids. Vacuoles that are full of water, such as the one in **Figure 9,** help support the cell. Some plants wilt when their vacuoles lose water. **Table 1** shows some organelles and their functions.

Table 1 Organelles and Their Functions

Organelle	Function	Organelle	Function
Nucleus	the organelle that contains the cell's DNA and is the control center of the cell	**Chloroplast**	the organelle that uses the energy of sunlight to make food
Ribosome	the organelle in which amino acids are hooked together to make proteins	**Golgi complex**	the organelle that processes and transports proteins and other materials out of cell
Endoplasmic reticulum	the organelle that makes lipids, breaks down drugs and other substances, and packages proteins for Golgi complex	**Vacuole**	the organelle that stores water and other materials
Mitochondria	the organelle that breaks down food molecules to make ATP	**Lysosome**	the organelle that digests food particles, wastes, cell parts, and foreign invaders

SECTION Review

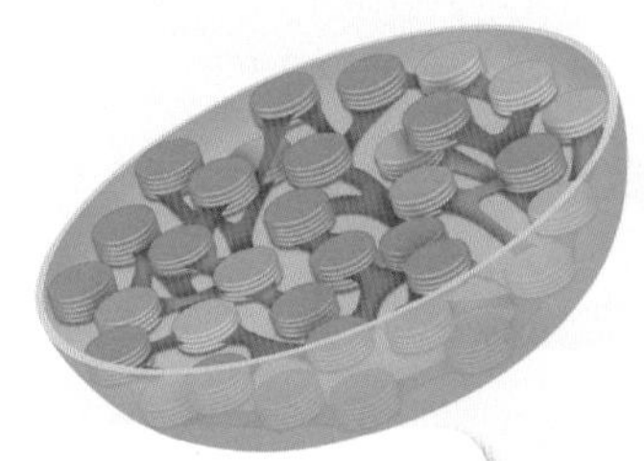

Summary

- Eukaryotic cells have organelles that perform functions that help cells remain alive.
- All cells have a cell membrane. Some cells have a cell wall. Some cells have a cytoskeleton.
- The nucleus of a eukaryotic cell contains the cell's genetic material, DNA.
- Ribosomes are the organelles that make proteins. Ribosomes are not covered by a membrane.
- The endoplasmic reticulum (ER) and the Golgi complex make and process proteins before the proteins are transported to other parts of the cell or out of the cell.
- Mitochondria and chloroplasts are energy-producing organelles.
- Lysosomes are organelles responsible for digestion within a cell. In plant cells, organelles called *vacuoles* store cell materials and sometimes act like large lysosomes.

Using Key Terms

1. In your own words, write a definition for each of the following terms: *ribosome, lysosome,* and *cell wall.*

Understanding Key Ideas

2. Which of the following are found mainly in animal cells?
   a. mitochondria
   b. lysosomes
   c. ribosomes
   d. Golgi complexes
3. What is the function of a Golgi complex? What is the function of the endoplasmic reticulum?

Critical Thinking

4. **Making Comparisons** Describe three ways in which plant cells differ from animal cells.
5. **Applying Concepts** Every cell needs ribosomes. Explain why.
6. **Predicting Consequences** A certain virus attacks the mitochondria in cells. What would happen to a cell if all of its mitochondria were destroyed?
7. **Expressing Opinions** Do you think that having chloroplasts gives plant cells an advantage over animal cells? Support your opinion.

Interpreting Graphics

Use the diagram below to answer the questions that follow.

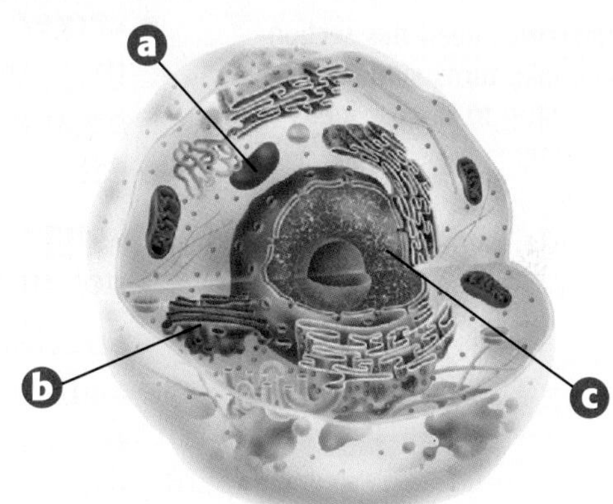

8. Is this a diagram of a plant cell or an animal cell? Explain how you know.
9. What organelle does the letter *b* refer to?

SCLINKS
NSTA
Developed and maintained by the National Science Teachers Association
For a variety of links related to this chapter, go to www.scilinks.org
Topic: Eukaryotic Cells
SciLinks code: HSM0541

SECTION 3

The Organization of Living Things

READING WARM-UP

Objectives

- List three advantages of being multicellular.
- Describe the four levels of organization in living things.
- Explain the relationship between the structure and function of a part of an organism.

Terms to Learn

tissue	organism
organ	structure
organ system	function

READING STRATEGY

Paired Summarizing Read this section silently. In pairs, take turns summarizing the material. Stop to discuss ideas that seem confusing.

In some ways, organisms are like machines. Some machines have just one part. But most machines have many parts. Some organisms exist as a single cell. Other organisms have many—even trillions—of cells.

Most cells are smaller than the period that ends this sentence. Yet, every cell in every organism performs all the processes of life. So, are there any advantages to having many cells?

The Benefits of Being Multicellular

You are a *multicellular organism*. This means that you are made of many cells. Multicellular organisms grow by making more small cells, not by making their cells larger. For example, an elephant is bigger than you are, but its cells are about the same size as yours. An elephant just has more cells than you do. Some benefits of being multicellular are the following:

- **Larger Size** Many multicellular organisms are small. But they are usually larger than single-celled organisms. Larger organisms are prey for fewer predators. Larger predators can eat a wider variety of prey.
- **Longer Life** The life span of a multicellular organism is not limited to the life span of any single cell.
- **Specialization** Each type of cell has a particular job. Specialization makes the organism more efficient. For example, the cardiac muscle cell in **Figure 1** is a specialized muscle cell. Heart muscle cells contract and make the heart pump blood.

Reading Check **List three advantages of being multicellular.** *(See the Appendix for answers to Reading Checks.)*

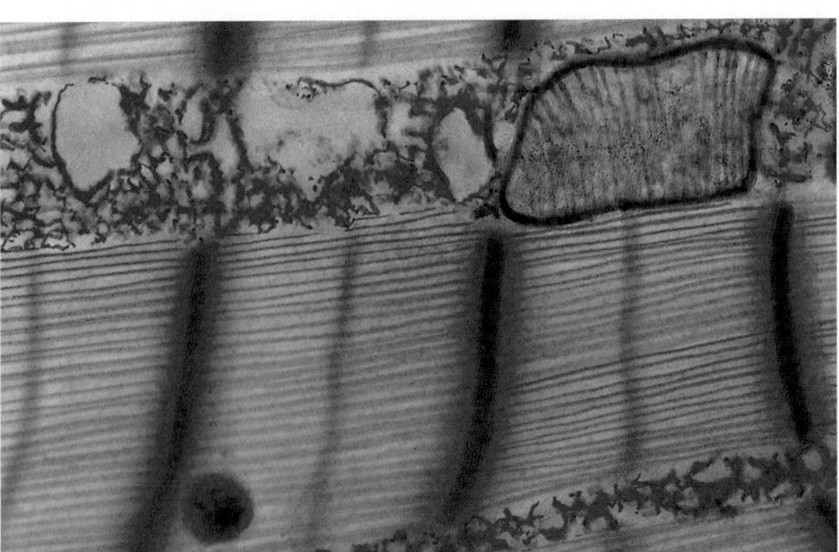

Figure 1 *This photomicrograph shows a small part of one heart muscle cell. The green line surrounds one of many mitochondria, the powerhouses of the cell. The pink areas are muscle filaments.*

Figure 2 *This photomicrograph shows cardiac muscle tissue. Cardiac muscle tissue is made up of many cardiac cells.*

Cells Working Together

A **tissue** is a group of cells that work together to perform a specific job. The material around and between the cells is also part of the tissue. The cardiac muscle tissue, shown in **Figure 2,** is made of many cardiac muscle cells. Cardiac muscle tissue is just one type of tissue in a heart.

Animals have four basic types of tissues: nerve tissue, muscle tissue, connective tissue, and protective tissue. In contrast, plants have three types of tissues: transport tissue, protective tissue, and ground tissue. Transport tissue moves water and nutrients through a plant. Protective tissue covers the plant. It helps the plant retain water and protects the plant against damage. Photosynthesis takes place in ground tissue.

tissue a group of similar cells that perform a common function

organ a collection of tissues that carry out a specialized function of the body

Tissues Working Together

A structure that is made up of two or more tissues working together to perform a specific function is called an **organ.** For example, your heart is an organ. It is made mostly of cardiac muscle tissue. But your heart also has nerve tissue and tissues of the blood vessels that all work together to make your heart the powerful pump that it is.

Another organ is your stomach. It also has several kinds of tissue. In the stomach, muscle tissue makes food move in and through the stomach. Special tissues make chemicals that help digest your food. Connective tissue holds the stomach together, and nervous tissue carries messages back and forth between the stomach and the brain. Other organs include the intestines, brain, and lungs.

Plants also have different kinds of tissues that work together as organs. A leaf is a plant organ that contains tissue that traps light energy to make food. Other examples of plant organs are stems and roots.

Reading Check What is an organ?

A Pet Protist

Imagine that you have a tiny box-shaped protist for a pet. To care for your pet protist properly, you have to figure out how much to feed it. The dimensions of your protist are roughly 25 µm × 20 µm × 2 µm. If seven food particles per second can enter through each square micrometer of surface area, how many particles can your protist eat in 1 min?

Organs Working Together

A group of organs working together to perform a particular function is called an **organ system.** Each organ system has a specific job to do in the body.

For example, the digestive system is made up of several organs, including the stomach and intestines. The digestive system's job is to break down food into small particles. Other parts of the body then use these small particles as fuel. In turn, the digestive system depends on the respiratory and cardiovascular systems for oxygen. The cardiovascular system, shown in **Figure 3,** includes organs and tissues such as the heart and blood vessels. Plants also have organ systems. They include leaf systems, root systems, and stem systems.

Reading Check List the levels of organization in living things.

organ system a group of organs that work together to perform body functions

organism a living thing; anything that can carry out life processes independently

structure the arrangement of parts in an organism

function the special, normal, or proper activity of an organ or part

Organisms

Anything that can perform life processes by itself is an **organism.** An organism made of a single cell is called a *unicellular organism.* Bacteria, most protists, and some kinds of fungi are unicellular. Although some of these organisms live in colonies, they are still unicellular. They are unicellular organisms living together, and all of the cells in the colony are the same. Each cell must carry out all life processes in order for that cell to survive. In contrast, even the simplest multicellular organism has specialized cells that depend on each other for the organism to survive.

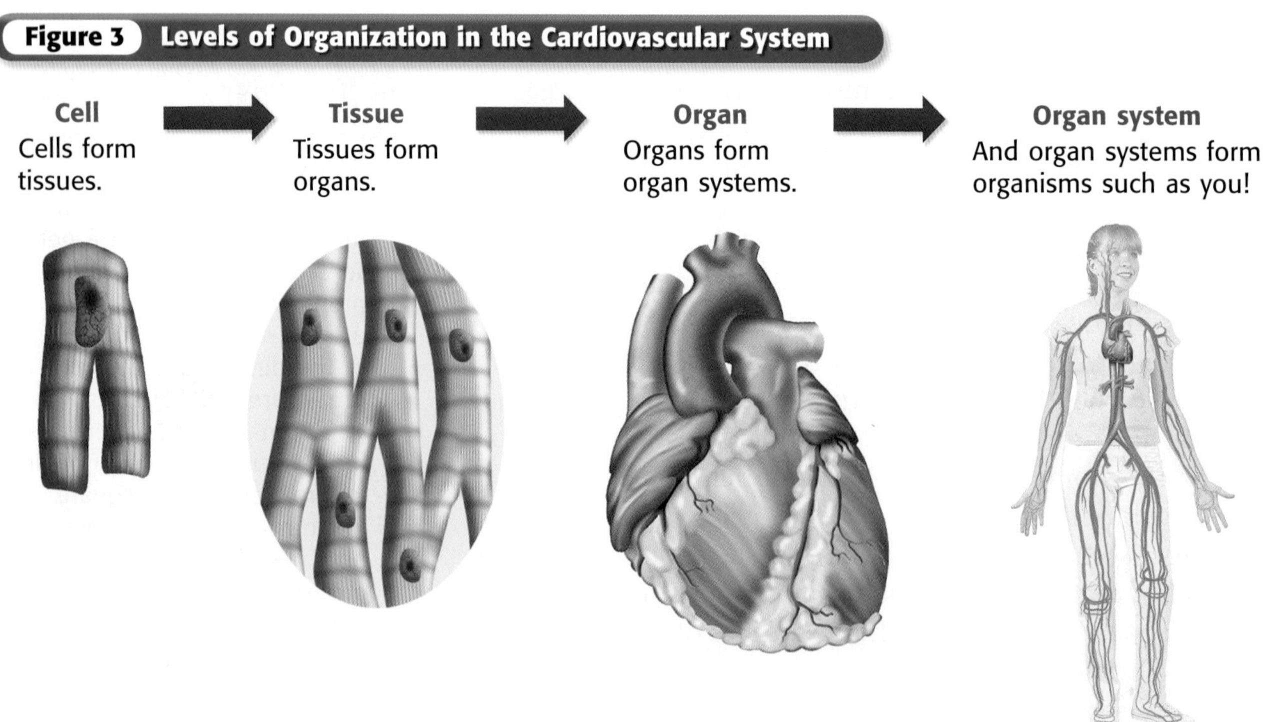
Cell
Cells form tissues.
Tissue
Tissues form organs.
Organ
Organs form organ systems.
Organ system
And organ systems form organisms such as you!

Figure 3 Levels of Organization in the Cardiovascular System

Structure and Function

In organisms, structure and function are related. **Structure** is the arrangement of parts in an organism. It includes the shape of a part and the material of which the part is made. **Function** is the job the part does. For example, the structure of the lungs is a large, spongy sac. In the lungs, there are millions of tiny air sacs called *alveoli*. Blood vessels wrap around the alveoli, as shown in **Figure 4.** Oxygen from air in the alveoli enters the blood. Blood then brings oxygen to body tissues. Also, in the alveoli, carbon dioxide leaves the blood and is exhaled.

The structures of alveoli and blood vessels enable them to perform a function. Together, they bring oxygen to the body and get rid of its carbon dioxide.

Figure 4 The Structure and Function of Alveoli

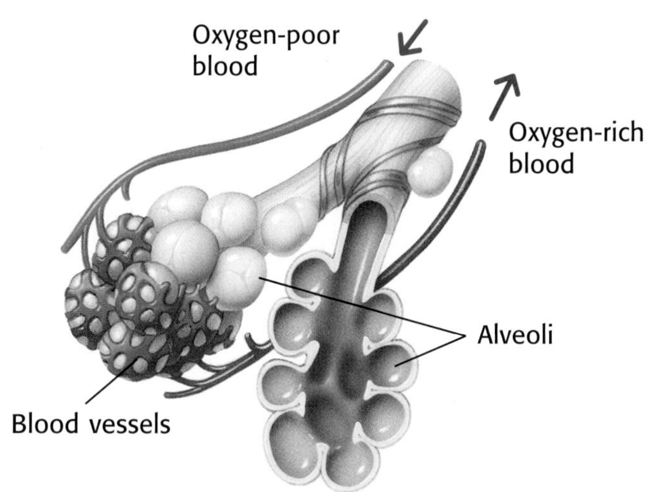

SECTION Review

Summary

- Advantages of being multicellular are larger size, longer life, and cell specialization.
- Four levels of organization are cell, tissue, organ, and organ system.
- A *tissue* is a group of cells working together. An *organ* is two or more tissues working together. An *organ system* is two or more organs working together.
- In organisms, a part's structure and function are related.

Using Key Terms

1. Use each of the following terms in a separate sentence: *tissue, organ,* and *function.*

Understanding Key Ideas

2. What are the four levels of organization in living things?
   - **a.** cell, multicellular, organ, organ system
   - **b.** single cell, multicellular, tissue, organ
   - **c.** larger size, longer life, specialized cells, organs
   - **d.** cell, tissue, organ, organ system

Math Skills

3. One multicellular organism is a cube. Each of its sides is 3 cm long. Each of its cells is 1 cm^3. How many cells does it have? If each side doubles in length, how many cells will it then have?

Critical Thinking

4. **Applying Concepts** Explain the relationship between structure and function. Use alveoli as an example. Be sure to include more than one level of organization.

5. **Making Inferences** Why can multicellular organisms be more complex than unicellular organisms? Use the three advantages of being multicellular to help explain your answer.

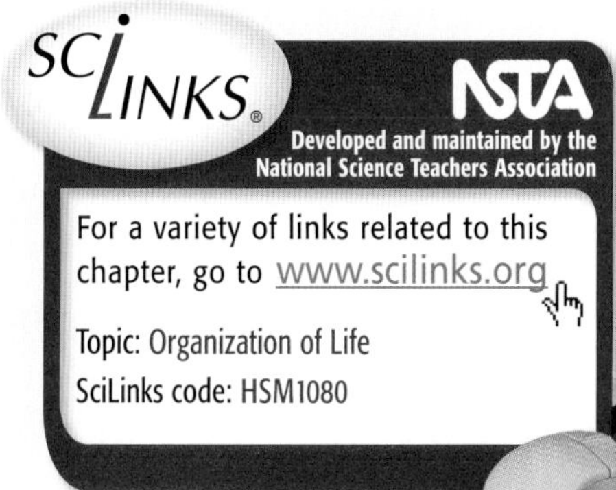

For a variety of links related to this chapter, go to www.scilinks.org

Topic: Organization of Life
SciLinks code: HSM1080

Model-Making Lab

Elephant-Sized Amoebas?

OBJECTIVES

Explore why a single-celled organism cannot grow to the size of an elephant.

Create a model of a cell to illustrate the concept of surface area–to-volume ratio.

MATERIALS

- calculator (optional)
- cubic cell patterns
- heavy paper or poster board
- sand, fine
- scale or balance
- scissors
- tape, transparent

SAFETY

An amoeba is a single-celled organism. Like most cells, amoebas are microscopic. Why can't amoebas grow as large as elephants? If an amoeba grew to the size of a quarter, the amoeba would starve to death. To understand how this can be true, build a model of a cell and see for yourself.

Procedure

1. Use heavy paper or poster board to make four cube-shaped cell models from the patterns supplied by your teacher. Cut out each cell model, fold the sides to make a cube, and tape the tabs on the sides. The smallest cell model has sides that are each one unit long. The next larger cell has sides of two units. The next cell has sides of three units, and the largest cell has sides of four units. These paper models represent the cell membrane, the part of a cell's exterior through which food and wastes pass.

Data Table for Measurements				
Length of side	Area of one side (A = S × S)	Total surface area of cube cell (TA = S × S × 6)	Volume of cube cell (V = S × S × S)	Mass of filled cube cell
1 unit	1 unit^2	6 unit^2	1 unit^3	
2 unit				
3 unit				
4 unit				

Key to Formula Symbols

S = the length of one side

A = area

6 = number of sides

V = volume

TA = total area

2. Copy the data table shown above. Use each formula to calculate the data about your cell models. Record your calculations in the table. Calculations for the smallest cell have been done for you.
3. Carefully fill each model with fine sand until the sand is level with the top edge of the model. Find the mass of the filled models by using a scale or a balance. What does the sand in your model represent?
4. Record the mass of each filled cell model in your Data Table for Measurements. (Always remember to use the appropriate mass unit.)

Analyze the Results

1. **Constructing Tables** Make a data table like the one shown at right.
2. **Organizing Data** Use the data from your Data Table for Measurements to find the ratios for each of your cell models. For each of the cell models, fill in the Data Table for Ratios .

Draw Conclusions

3. **Interpreting Information** As a cell grows larger, does the ratio of total surface area to volume increase, decrease, or stay the same?
4. **Interpreting Information** As a cell grows larger, does the total surface area–to-mass ratio increase, decrease, or stay the same?
5. **Drawing Conclusions** Which is better able to supply food to all the cytoplasm of the cell: the cell membrane of a small cell or the cell membrane of a large cell? Explain your answer.
6. **Evaluating Data** In the experiment, which is better able to feed all of the cytoplasm of the cell: the cell membrane of a cell that has high mass or the cell membrane of a cell that has low mass? You may explain your answer in a verbal presentation to the class, or you may choose to write a report and illustrate it with drawings of your models.

Data Table for Ratios		
Length of side	Ratio of total surface area to volume	Ratio of total surface area to mass
1 unit		
2 unit		
3 unit		
4 unit		

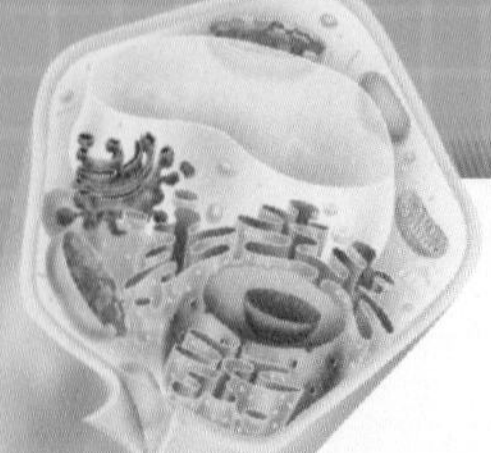

Chapter Review

USING KEY TERMS

Complete each of the following sentences by choosing the correct term from the word bank.

cell	organ
cell membrane	prokaryote
organelles	eukaryote
cell wall	tissue
structure	function

1. A(n) ___ is the most basic unit of all living things.
2. The job that an organ does is the ___ of that organ.
3. Ribosomes and mitochondria are types of ___.
4. A(n) ___ is an organism whose cells have a nucleus.
5. A group of cells working together to perform a specific function is a(n) ___.
6. Only plant cells have a(n) ___.

UNDERSTANDING KEY IDEAS

Multiple Choice

7. Which of the following best describes an organ?
   - **a.** a group of cells that work together to perform a specific job
   - **b.** a group of tissues that belong to different systems
   - **c.** a group of tissues that work together to perform a specific job
   - **d.** a body structure, such as muscles or lungs

8. The benefits of being multicellular include
   - **a.** small size, long life, and cell specialization.
   - **b.** generalized cells, longer life, and ability to prey on small animals.
   - **c.** larger size, more enemies, and specialized cells.
   - **d.** longer life, larger size, and specialized cells.

9. In eukaryotic cells, which organelle contains the DNA?
   - **a.** nucleus
   - **b.** Golgi complex
   - **c.** smooth ER
   - **d.** vacuole

10. Which of the following statements is part of the cell theory?
    - **a.** All cells suddenly appear by themselves.
    - **b.** All cells come from other cells.
    - **c.** All organisms are multicellular.
    - **d.** All cells have identical parts.

11. The surface area–to-volume ratio of a cell limits
    - **a.** the number of organelles that the cell has.
    - **b.** the size of the cell.
    - **c.** where the cell lives.
    - **d.** the types of nutrients that a cell needs.

12. Two types of organisms whose cells do not have a nucleus are
    - **a.** prokaryotes and eukaryotes.
    - **b.** plants and animals.
    - **c.** eubacteria and archaebacteria.
    - **d.** single-celled and multicellular organisms.

Short Answer

13. Explain why most cells are small.

14. Describe the four levels of organization in living things.

15. What is the difference between the structure of an organ and the function of the organ?

16. Name two functions of a cell membrane.

17. What are the structure and function of the cytoskeleton in a cell?

CRITICAL THINKING

18. **Concept Mapping** Use the following terms to create a concept map: *cells, organisms, Golgi complex, organ systems, organs, nucleus, organelle,* and *tissues*.

19. **Making Comparisons** Compare and contrast the functions of the endoplasmic reticulum and the Golgi complex.

20. **Identifying Relationships** Explain how the structure and function of an organism's parts are related. Give an example.

21. **Evaluating Hypotheses** One of your classmates states a hypothesis that all organisms must have organ systems. Is your classmate's hypothesis valid? Explain your answer.

22. **Predicting Consequences** What would happen if all of the ribosomes in your cells disappeared?

23. **Expressing Opinions** Scientists think that millions of years ago the surface of the Earth was very hot and that the atmosphere contained a lot of methane. In your opinion, which type of organism, a eubacterium or an archaebacterium, is the older form of life? Explain your reasoning.

INTERPRETING GRAPHICS

Use the diagram below to answer the questions that follow.

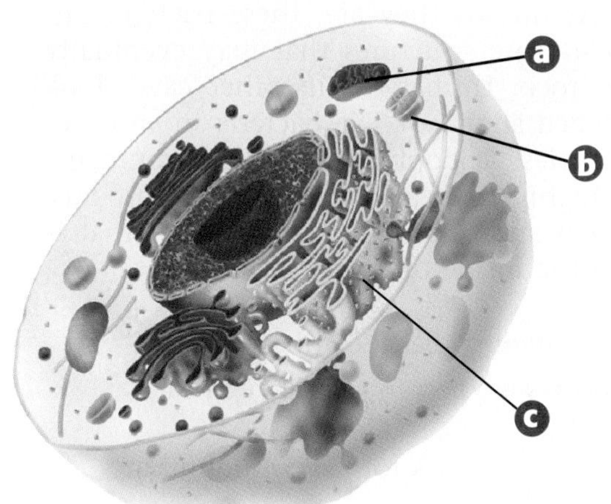

24. What is the name of the structure identified by the letter *a*?

25. Which letter identifies the structure that digests food particles and foreign invaders?

26. Which letter identifies the structure that makes proteins, lipids, and other materials and that contains tubes and passageways that enable substances to move to different places in the cell?

Standardized Test Preparation

READING

Read each of the passages below. Then, answer the questions that follow each passage.

Passage 1 Exploring caves can be dangerous but can also lead to interesting discoveries. For example, deep in the darkness of Cueva de Villa Luz, a cave in Mexico, are slippery formations called *snottites*. They were named snottites because they look just like a two-year-old's runny nose. If you use an electron microscope to look at them, you see that snottites are bacteria; thick, sticky fluids; and small amounts of minerals produced by the bacteria. As tiny as they are, these bacteria can build up snottite structures that may eventually turn into rock. Formations in other caves look like hardened snottites. The bacteria in snottites are acidophiles. Acidophiles live in environments that are highly acidic. Snottite bacteria produce sulfuric acid and live in an environment that is similar to the inside of a car battery.

1. Which statement best describes snottites?

- **A** Snottites are bacteria that live in car batteries.
- **B** Snottites are rock formations found in caves.
- **C** Snottites were named for a cave in Mexico.
- **D** Snottites are made of bacteria, sticky fluids, and minerals.

2. Based on this passage, which conclusion about snottites is most likely to be correct?

- **F** Snottites are found in caves everywhere.
- **G** Snottite bacteria do not need sunlight.
- **H** You could grow snottites in a greenhouse.
- **I** Snottites create other bacteria in caves.

3. What is the main idea of this passage?

- **A** Acidophiles are unusual organisms.
- **B** Snottites are strange formations.
- **C** Exploring caves is dangerous.
- **D** Snottites are large, slippery bacteria.

Passage 2 The world's smallest mammal may be a bat about the size of a jelly bean. The scientific name for this tiny animal, which was unknown until 1974, is *Craseonycteris thonglongyai*. It is so small that it is sometimes called the *bumblebee bat*. Another name for this animal is the *hog-nosed bat*. Hog-nosed bats were given their name because one of their distinctive features is a piglike muzzle. Hog-nosed bats differ from other bats in another way: they do not have a tail. But, like other bats, hog-nosed bats do eat insects that they catch in mid-air. Scientists think that the bats eat small insects that live on the leaves at the tops of trees. Hog-nosed bats live deep in limestone caves and have been found in only one country, Thailand.

1. According to the passage, which statement about hog-nosed bats is most accurate?

- **A** They are the world's smallest animal.
- **B** They are about the size of a bumblebee.
- **C** They eat leaves at the tops of trees.
- **D** They live in hives near caves in Thailand.

2. Which of the following statements describes distinctive features of hog-nosed bats?

- **F** The bats are very small and eat leaves.
- **G** The bats live in caves and have a tail.
- **H** The bats live in Thailand and are birds.
- **I** The bats have a piglike muzzle and no tail.

3. From the information in this passage, which conclusion is most likely to be correct?

- **A** Hog-nosed bats are similar to other bats.
- **B** Hog-nosed bats are probably rare.
- **C** Hog-nosed bats can sting like a bumblebee.
- **D** Hog-nosed bats probably eat fruit.

INTERPRETING GRAPHICS

The diagrams below show two kinds of cells. Use these cell diagrams to answer the questions that follow.

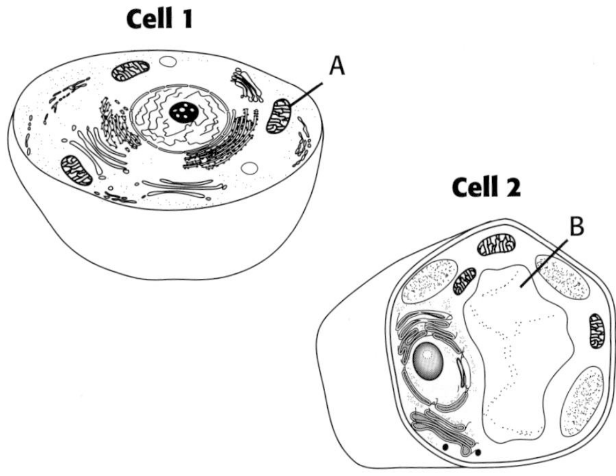

1. What is the name of the organelle labeled *A* in Cell 1?
   - **A** endoplasmic reticulum
   - **B** mitochondrion
   - **C** vacuole
   - **D** nucleus

2. What type of cell is Cell 1?
   - **F** a bacterial cell
   - **G** a plant cell
   - **H** an animal cell
   - **I** a prokaryotic cell

3. What is the name and function of the organelle labeled *B* in Cell 2?
   - **A** The organelle is a vacuole, and it stores water and other materials.
   - **B** The organelle is the nucleus, and it contains the DNA.
   - **C** The organelle is the cell wall, and it gives shape to the cell.
   - **D** The organelle is a ribosome, where proteins are put together.

4. What type of cell is Cell 2? How do you know?
   - **F** prokaryotic; because it does not have a nucleus
   - **G** eukaryotic; because it does not have a nucleus
   - **H** prokaryotic; because it has a nucleus
   - **I** eukaryotic; because it has a nucleus

MATH

Read each question below, and choose the best answer.

1. What is the surface area–to-volume ratio of the rectangular solid shown in the diagram below?

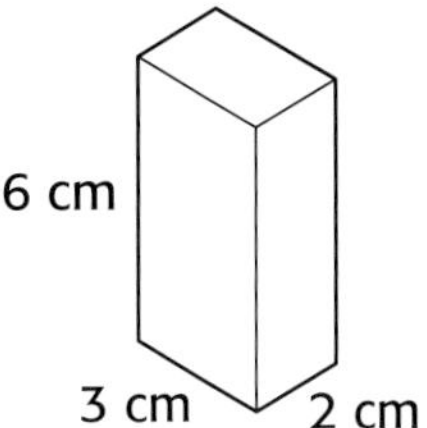

   - **A** 0.5:1
   - **B** 2:1
   - **C** 36:1
   - **D** 72:1

2. Look at the diagram of the cell below. Three molecules of food per cubic unit of volume per minute are required for the cell to survive. One molecule of food can enter through each square unit of surface area per minute. What will happen to this cell?

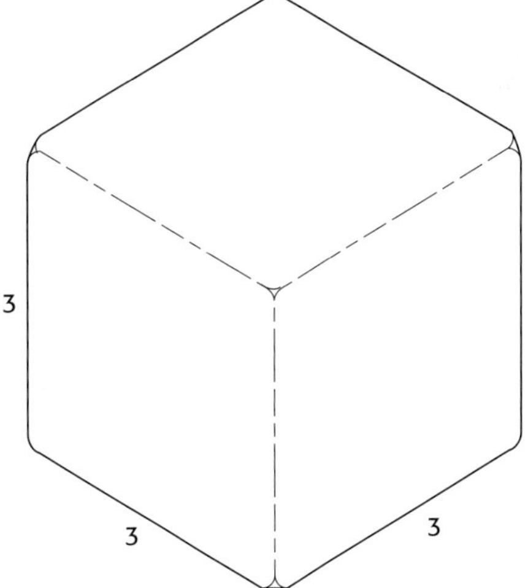

   - **F** The cell is too small, and it will starve.
   - **G** The cell is too large, and it will starve.
   - **H** The cell is at a size that will allow it to survive.
   - **I** There is not enough information to determine the answer.

Standardized Test Preparation

Science in Action

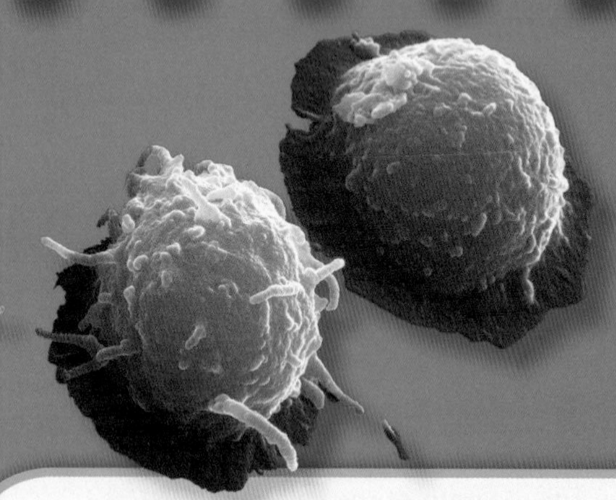

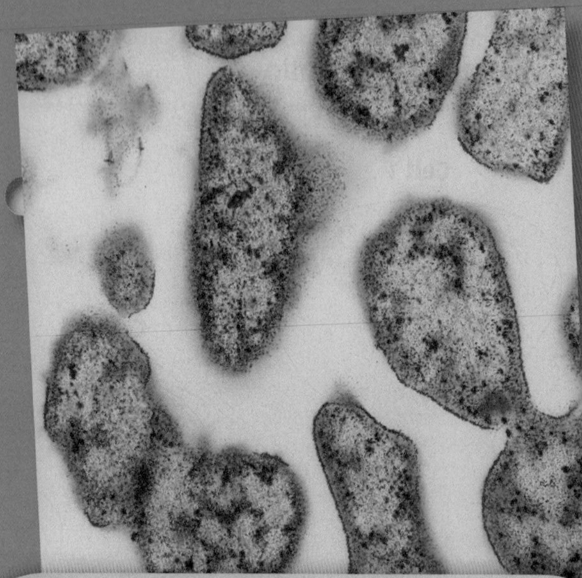

Scientific Discoveries

Discovery of the Stem Cell

What do Parkinson's disease, diabetes, aplastic anemia, and Alzheimer's disease have in common? All of these diseases are diseases for which stem cells may provide treatment or a cure. Stem cells are unspecialized cells from which all other kinds of cells can grow. And research on stem cells has been going on almost since microscopes were invented. But scientists have been able to culture, or grow, stem cells in laboratories for only about the last 20 years. Research during these 20 years has shown scientists that stem cells can be useful in treating—and possibly curing—a variety of diseases.

Language Arts ACTIVITY

WRITING SKILL Imagine that you are a doctor who treats diseases such as Parkinson's disease. Design and create a pamphlet or brochure that you could use to explain what stem cells are. Include in your pamphlet a description of how stem cells might be used to treat one of your patients who has Parkinson's disease. Be sure to include information about Parkinson's disease.

Weird Science

Extremophiles

Are there organisms on Earth that can give scientists clues about possible life elsewhere? Yes, there are! These organisms are called *extremophiles,* and they live where the environment is extreme. For example, some extremophiles live in the hot volcanic thermal vents deep in the ocean. Other extremophiles live in the extreme cold of Antarctica. But these organisms do not live only in extreme environments. Research shows that extremophiles may be abundant in plankton in the ocean. And not all extremophiles are archaebacteria; some extremophiles are eubacteria.

Social Studies ACTIVITY

Choose one of the four types of extremophiles. Do some research about the organism you have chosen and make a poster showing what you learned about it, including where it can be found, under what conditions it lives, how it survives, and how it is used.

People in Science

Caroline Schooley

Microscopist Imagine that your assignment is the following: Go outside. Look at 1 ft^2 of the ground for 30 min. Make notes about what you observe. Be prepared to describe what you see. If you look at the ground with just your naked eyes, you may quickly run out of things to see. But what would happen if you used a microscope to look? How much more would you be able to see? And how much more would you have to talk about? Caroline Schooley could tell you.

Caroline Schooley joined a science club in middle school. That's when her interest in looking at things through a microscope began. Since then, Schooley has spent many years studying life through a microscope. She is a microscopist. A *microscopist* is someone who uses a microscope to look at small things. Microscopists use their tools to explore the world of small things that cannot be seen by the naked eye. And with today's powerful electron microscopes, microscopists can study things we could never see before, things as small as atoms.

Math Activity

An average bacterium is about 0.000002 m long. A pencil point is about 0.001 m wide. Approximately how many bacteria would fit on a pencil point?

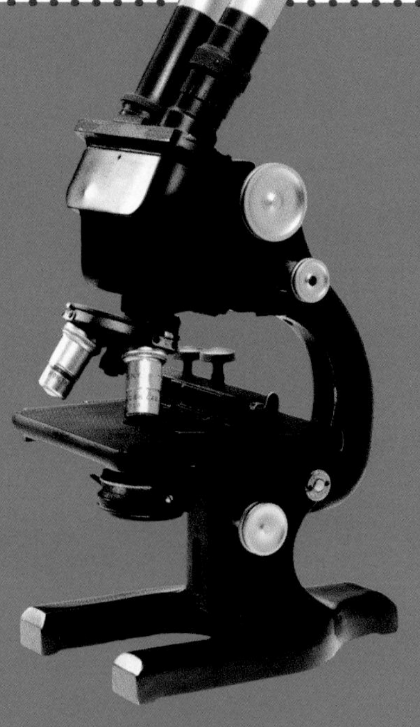

To learn more about these Science in Action topics, visit **go.hrw.com** and type in the keyword **HL5CELF.**

Current Science

Check out Current Science® articles related to this chapter by visiting go.hrw.com. Just type in the keyword HL5CS03.

15

Classification

About the PHOTO

Look at the katydids, grasshoppers, and mantids in the photo. A scientist is classifying these insects. Every insect has a label describing the insect. These descriptions will be used to help the scientist know if each insect has already been discovered and named. When scientists discover a new insect or other organism, they have to give the organism a name. The name chosen is unique and should help other scientists understand some basic facts about the organism.

PRE-READING ACTIVITY

FOLDNOTES **Booklet** Before you read the chapter, create the FoldNote entitled "Booklet" described in the **Study Skills** section of the Appendix. Label each page of the booklet with a main idea from the chapter. As you read the chapter, write what you learn about each main idea on the appropriate page of the booklet.

Short Answer

12 Why is the use of scientific names important in biology?

13 What kind of evidence is used by modern taxonomists to classify organisms based on evolutionary relationships?

14 Is a eubacterium a type of eukaryote? Explain your answer.

15 Scientists used to classify organisms as either plants or animals. Why doesn't that classification system work?

CRITICAL THINKING

16 **Concept Mapping** Use the following terms to create a concept map: *kingdom, fern, lizard, Animalia, Fungi, algae, Protista, Plantae,* and *mushroom.*

17 **Analyzing Methods** Explain how the levels of classification depend on the similarities and differences between organisms.

18 **Making Inferences** Explain why two species that belong to the same genus, such as white oak (*Quercus alba*) and cork oak (*Quercus suber*), also belong to the same family.

19 **Identifying Relationships** What characteristic do the members of all six kingdoms have in common?

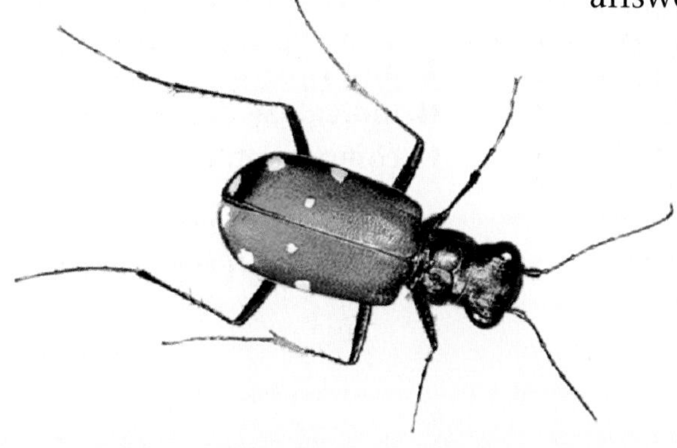

INTERPRETING GRAPHICS

Use the branching diagram of selected primates below to answer the questions that follow.

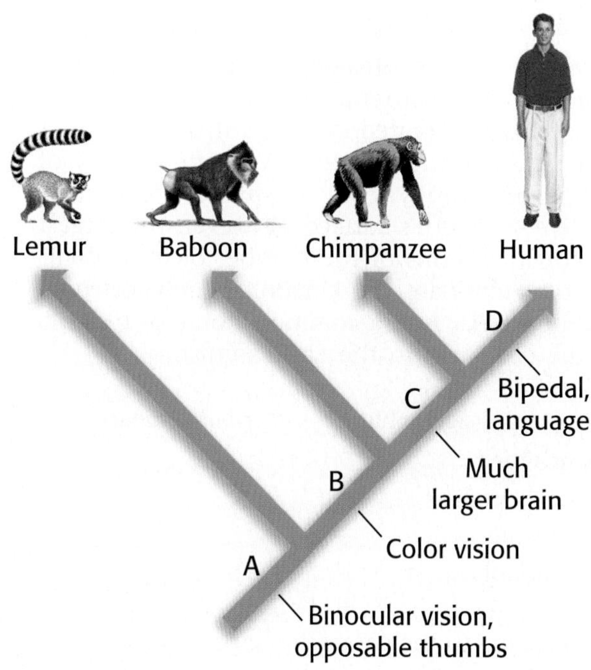

20 Which primate is the closest relative to the common ancestor of all primates?

21 Which primate shares the most traits with humans?

22 Do both lemurs and humans have the characteristics listed at point D? Explain your answer.

23 What characteristic do baboons have that lemurs do not have? Explain your answer.

Standardized Test Preparation

READING

Read each of the passages below. Then, answer the questions that follow each passage.

Passage 1 When organizing life on Earth into categories, we must remember that organisms are not equally distributed throughout the categories of our classification system. We often think of Earth's living things as only the plants and animals that live on Earth's surface. However, the largest kingdoms in terms of the number of individuals and total mass are the kingdoms Archaebacteria and Eubacteria. And a common home of bacteria may be deep within the Earth's crust.

1. In the passage, what does *distributed* mean?

- **A** divided
- **B** important
- **C** visible
- **D** variable

2. According to the passage, what are most of the organisms living on Earth?

- **F** plants
- **G** animals
- **H** fungi
- **I** bacteria

3. Which of the following statements is a fact according to the passage?

- **A** All organisms are equally distributed over Earth's surface.
- **B** Plants are the most important organisms on Earth.
- **C** Many bacteria may live deep within Earth's crust.
- **D** Bacteria are equally distributed over Earth's surface.

Passage 2 When you think of an animal, what do you imagine? You may think of a dog, a cat, or a parrot. All of those organisms are animals. But the animal kingdom also includes some members that might surprise you, such as worms, insects, corals, and sponges.

1. In the passage, what is coral?

- **A** a kind of animal
- **B** a kind of insect
- **C** a color similar to pink
- **D** an organism found in lakes and streams

2. What can you infer from the passage?

- **F** All members of the animal kingdom are visible.
- **G** Parrots make good pets.
- **H** Not all members of the animal kingdom have DNA.
- **I** Members of the animal kingdom come in many shapes and sizes.

3. Which of the following can you infer from the passage?

- **A** Worms and corals make good pets.
- **B** Corals and cats have some traits in common.
- **C** All organisms are animals.
- **D** Worms, corals, insects, and sponges are in the same family.

4. In the passage, what does *members* mean?

- **F** teammates
- **G** limbs
- **H** individuals admitted to a club
- **I** components

INTERPRETING GRAPHICS

The Venn diagrams below show two classification systems. Use the diagrams to answer the questions that follow.

Classification system A

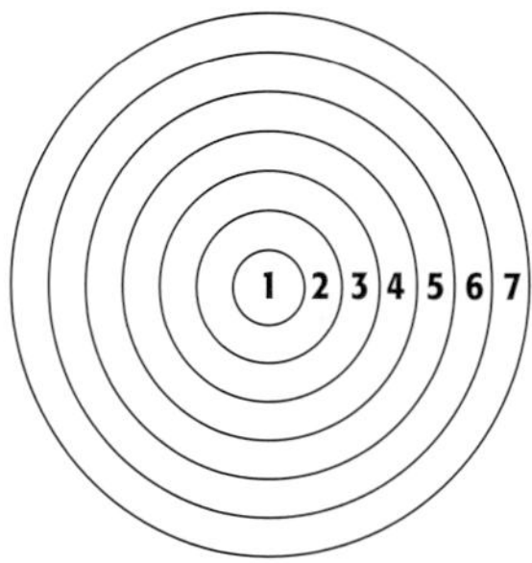

Classification system B

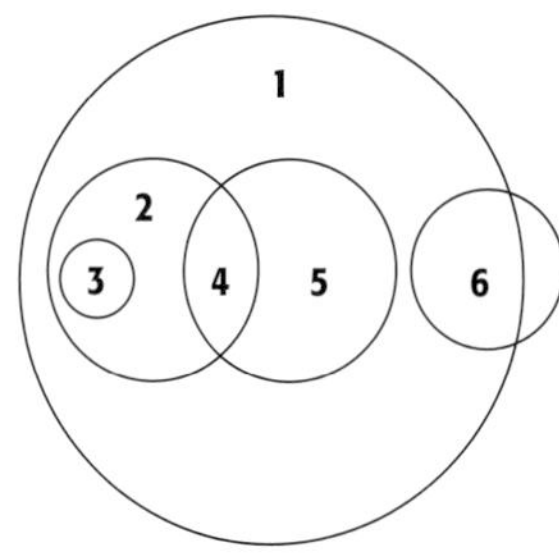

1. For Classification system A, which of the following statements is true?

A All organisms in group 6 are in group 7.
B All organisms in group 5 are in group 4.
C All organisms in group 6 are in group 1.
D All organisms in group 2 are in group 1.

2. For Classification system A, which of the following statements is true?

F All organisms in group 3 are in group 2.
G All organisms in group 3 are in group 4.
H All organisms in group 3 are in group 1.
I All organisms in group 3 are in every other group.

3. For Classification system B, which of the following statements is true?

A All organisms in group 1 are in group 6.
B All organisms in group 6 are in group 1.
C All organisms in group 3 are in group 1.
D All organisms in group 2 are in group 5.

4. For Classification system B, which of the following statements is true?

F All organisms in group 4 are in group 1, 2, and 5.
G All organisms in group 4 are in groups 3 and 5.
H All organisms in group 4 are in groups 5 and 6.
I All organisms in group 4 are in groups 1, 5, and 6.

5. In Classification system B, which group contains organisms that are not in group 1?

A 2
B 4
C 5
D 6

MATH

Read each question below, and choose the best answer.

1. Scientists estimate that millions of species have not yet been discovered and classified. About 1.8 million species have been discovered and classified. If scientists think that this 1.8 million makes up only 10% of the total number of species on Earth, how many species do scientists think exist on Earth?

A 180 million
B 18 million
C 1.8 million
D 180,000

2. Sequoia trees can grow to more than 90 m in height. There are 3.28 feet in 1 meter. How many feet are in 90 m?

F 27.4 ft
G 95.2 ft
H 270 ft
I 295.2 ft

Science in Action

Scientific Debate

Birds and Dinosaurs

Did birds evolve from dinosaurs? Some scientists think that birds evolved from small, carnivorous dinosaurs such as *Velociraptor* about 115 million to 150 million years ago. This idea is based on similarities of modern birds and these small dinosaurs. These similarities include the size, shape, and number of toes and "fingers," the location and shape of the breastbone and shoulder, and the presence of a hollow bone structure. Many scientists find this evidence convincing.

However, some scientists think that birds developed 100 million years before *Velociraptor* and its relatives did. These scientists point out that *Velociraptor* and its relatives were ground dwellers and were the wrong shape and size for flying.

Math ACTIVITY

Velociraptor lived between 115 million and 150 million years ago. Find the average of these two numbers. Use that average to answer the following questions: How many weeks ago did *Velociraptor* live on Earth? How many days ago did *Velociraptor* live on Earth?

Scientific Discovery

A New Insect Order

In 2001, Oliver Zompro was studying a fossil insect preserved in amber. Although the fossil insect resembled a grasshopper or a walking stick, it was unique and could not be classified in the same group as either one. Zompro wondered if he might be seeing a new type of insect or an insect that was now thought to be extinct. The fossil insect was less than 4 cm long. Its spiny appearance earned the insect the nickname "gladiator." The gladiator bug that Zompro discovered is so unusual that it cannot be classified in any of the 30 existing orders of insects. Instead, the gladiator bug constitutes its own new order, which has been named *Mantophasmatodea*.

Language Arts ACTIVITY

WRITING SKILL Give the gladiator bug a new nickname. Write a short essay about why you chose that particular name for the insect.

People in Science

Michael Fay

Crossing Africa Finding and classifying wild animals takes a great deal of perseverance. Just ask Michael Fay, who spent 15 months crossing 2,000 miles of uninhabited rain forest in the Congo River Basin of West Africa. He used video, photography, and old-fashioned note taking to record the types of animals and vegetation that he encountered along the way.

To find and classify wild animals, Fay often had to think like an animal. When coming across a group of monkeys swinging high above him in the emerald green canopy, Fay would greet the monkeys with his imitation of the crowned eagle's high-pitched, whistling cry. When the monkeys responded with their own distinctive call, Fay could identify exactly what species they were and would jot it down in one of his 87 waterproof notebooks. Fay also learned other tricks, such as staying downwind of an elephant to get as close to the elephant as possible. He could then identify its size, its age, and the length of its tusks.

Social Studies ACTIVITY

WRITING SKILL Many organizations around the world are committed to helping preserve biodiversity. Conduct some Internet and library research to find out about an organization that works to keep species safe from extinction. Create a poster that describes the organization and some of the species that the organization protects.

To learn more about these Science in Action topics, visit **go.hrw.com** and type in the keyword **HL5CLSF.**

Current Science

Check out Current Science® articles related to this chapter by visiting go.hrw.com. Just type in the keyword HL5CS09.

Structure and Function

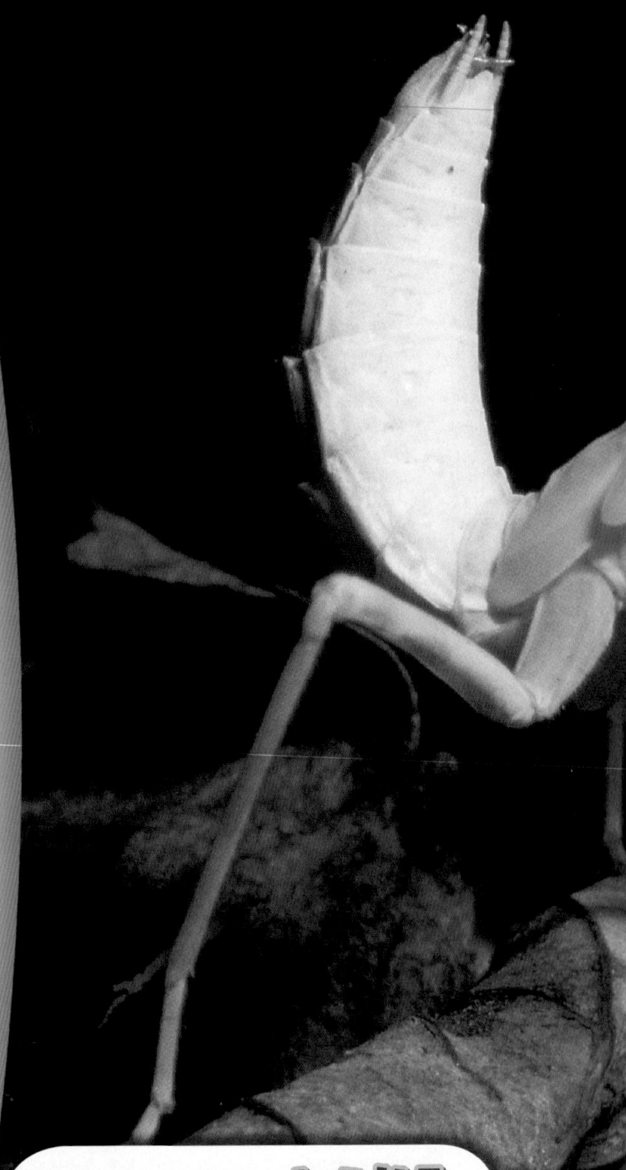

About the PHOTO

A mantis is a very efficient predator that captures and eats a wide variety of insects and other small prey. Its head can rotate 180 degrees while the mantis waits for a meal. The mantis's two front legs are highly specialized. A hunting mantis assumes a "praying" position, before it strikes out to capture its prey. The upper insides of its legs have long, sharp spines that get a good grip on prey.

PRE-READING ACTIVITY

FOLDNOTES **Booklet** Before you read the chapter, create the FoldNote entitled "Booklet" described in the **Study Skills** section of the Appendix. Label each page of the booklet with a main idea from the chapter. As you read the chapter, write what you learn about each main idea on the appropriate page of the booklet.

People in Science

George Archibald

Dancing with Cranes Imagine a man flapping his arms in a dance with a whooping crane. Does this sound funny? When Dr. George Archibald danced with a crane named Tex, he wasn't joking around. To help this endangered species survive, Archibald wanted cranes to mate in captivity so that he could release cranes into the wild. But the captive cranes wouldn't do their courtship dance. Archibald's cranes had imprinted on the humans that raised them. *Imprinting* is a process in which birds learn to recognize their species by looking at their parents. The birds saw humans as their own species, and could only reproduce if a human did the courtship dance. So, Archibald decided to dance. His plan worked! After some time, Tex hatched a baby crane.

After that, Archibald found a way to help the captive cranes imprint on other cranes. He and his staff now feed baby cranes with hand puppets that look like crane heads. They play recordings of real crane sounds for the young cranes. They even wear crane suits when they are near older birds. These cranes are happy to do their courtship dance with each other instead of with Archibald.

Math ACTIVITY

Suppose you want to drive a group of cranes from Madison, Wisconsin, to Orlando, Florida. Find and measure this distance on a map. If your truck goes 500 km per gas tank and a tank costs $30, how much would gas cost on your trip?

To learn more about these Science in Action topics, visit go.hrw.com and type in the keyword **HT5D6BSFF.**

Current Science

Check out Current Science® articles related to this chapter by visiting go.hrw.com. Just type in the keyword HL5CS14.

17

Human Body Systems

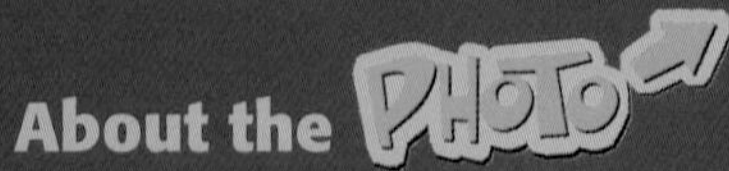

About the PHOTO

Lance Armstrong has won the Tour de France several times. These victories are especially remarkable because he was diagnosed with cancer in 1996. But with medicine and hard work, he grew strong enough to win one of the toughest events in all of sports.

PRE-READING ACTIVITY

Four-Corner Fold Before you read the chapter, create the FoldNote entitled "Four-Corner Fold" described in the **Study Skills** section of the Appendix. Label the flaps of the four-corner fold with "Body organization," "The digestive system," "The circulatory system" and "The endocrine system." Write what you know about each topic under the appropriate flap. As you read the chapter, add other information that you learn.

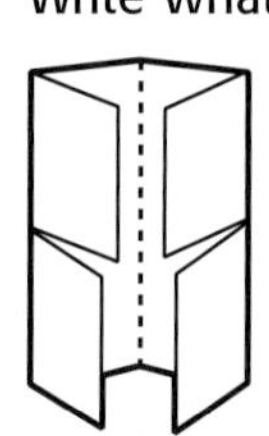

START-UP ACTIVITY

Too Cold for Comfort

Your nervous system sends you messages about your body. For example, if someone steps on your toe, your nervous system sends you a message. The pain you feel is a message that tells you to move your toe to safety. Try this exercise to watch your nervous system in action.

Procedure

1. Hold **a few pieces of ice** in one hand. Allow the melting water to drip into a **dish.** Hold the ice until the cold is uncomfortable. Then, release the ice into the dish.
2. Compare the hand that held the ice with your other hand. Describe the changes you see.

Analysis

1. What message did you receive from your nervous system while you held the ice?
2. How quickly did the cold hand return to normal?
3. What organ systems do you think helped restore your hand to normal?
4. Think of a time when your nervous system sent you a message, such as an uncomfortable feeling of heat, cold, or pain. How did your body react?

SECTION 1

Body Organization

Imagine jumping into a lake. At first, your body feels very cold. You may even shiver. But eventually you get used to the cold water. How?

READING WARM-UP

Objectives

- Describe how tissues, organs, and organ systems are related.
- List 12 organ systems.
- Identify how organ systems work together to maintain homeostasis.

Terms to Learn

homeostasis
organ
tissue

READING STRATEGY

Reading Organizer As you read this section, make a concept map by using the terms above.

Your body gets used to cold water because it returns to *homeostasis*. **Homeostasis** (HOH mee OH STAY sis) is the maintenance of a stable internal environment in the body. When you jump into a lake, homeostasis helps your body adapt to the cold water.

homeostasis the maintenance of a constant internal state in a changing environment

tissue a group of similar cells that perform a common function

Cells, Tissues, and Organs

Maintaining homeostasis is not easy. Your internal environment is always changing. Your cells need nutrients and oxygen to survive. Your cells need wastes removed. If homeostasis is disrupted, cells may not get the materials they need. So, cells may be damaged or may die.

Your cells must do many jobs to maintain homeostasis. Fortunately, each of your cells does not have to do all of those jobs. Just as each person on a soccer team has a role during a game, each cell in your body has a job in maintaining homeostasis. Your cells are organized into groups. A group of similar cells working together forms a **tissue.** Your body has four main kinds of tissue. The four kinds of tissue are shown in **Figure 1.**

Figure 1 Four Kinds of Tissue

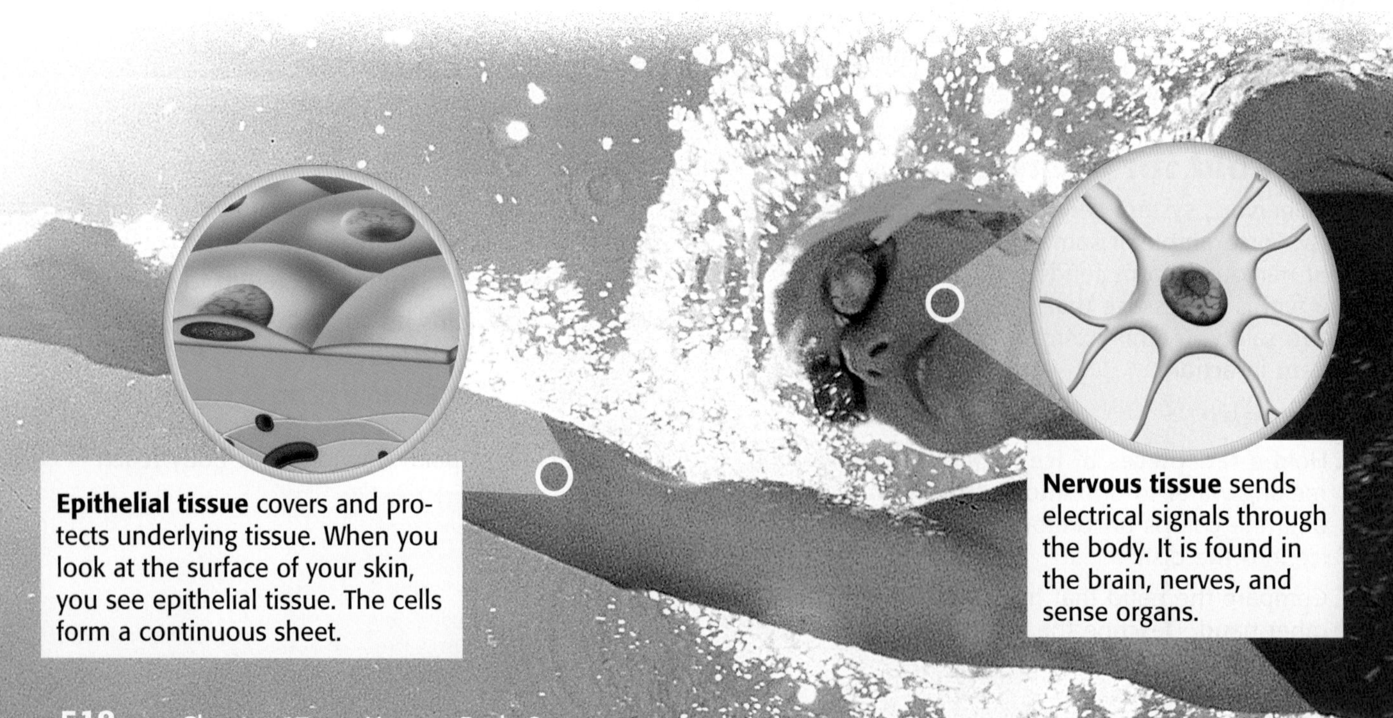

Epithelial tissue covers and protects underlying tissue. When you look at the surface of your skin, you see epithelial tissue. The cells form a continuous sheet.

Nervous tissue sends electrical signals through the body. It is found in the brain, nerves, and sense organs.

Figure 2 **Organization of the Stomach**

The stomach is an organ. The four kinds of tissue work together so that the stomach can carry out digestion.

Nervous tissue in the stomach partly controls the production of acids that aid in the digestion of food. Nervous tissue signals when the stomach is full.

Epithelial tissue lines the stomach.

Blood and another **connective tissue** called *collagen* are found in the wall of the stomach.

Layers of **muscle tissue** break up stomach contents.

Tissues Form Organs

One kind of tissue alone cannot do all of the things that several kinds of tissue working together can do. Two or more tissues working together form an **organ.** Your stomach, shown in **Figure 2,** uses all four kinds of tissue to carry out digestion.

organ a collection of tissues that carry out a specialized function of the body

Organs Form Systems

Your stomach does a lot to help you digest your food. But the stomach doesn't do it all. Your stomach works with other organs, such as the small and large intestines, to digest your food. Organs that work together make up an *organ system.*

Reading Check **How is the stomach part of an organ system?** (*See the Appendix for answers to Reading Checks.*)

Muscle tissue is made of cells that contract and relax to produce movement.
Connective tissue joins, supports, protects, insulates, nourishes, and cushions organs. It also keeps organs from falling apart.

Working Together

Your body has 12 major organ systems, shown in **Figure 3.** Some organ systems help you get and use energy. Other organ systems defend against disease, coordinate body functions, and help people reproduce. Organ systems work together to maintain homeostasis. For example, the circulatory and cardiovascular systems work closely together. They contain some of the same organs. Together, these two systems deliver materials that your cells need to survive. They also help remove cell wastes.

Reading Check **Give an example of how organ systems work together in the body.**

Figure 3 Organ Systems

Integumentary System Your skin protects you from disease and regulates body temperature.

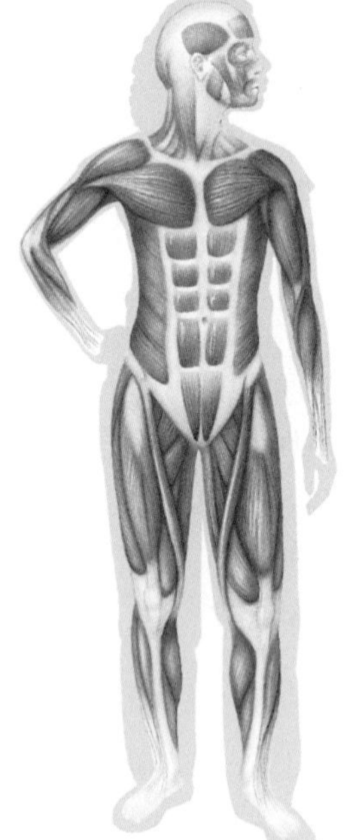

Muscular System Your muscular system works with the skeletal system to help you move.

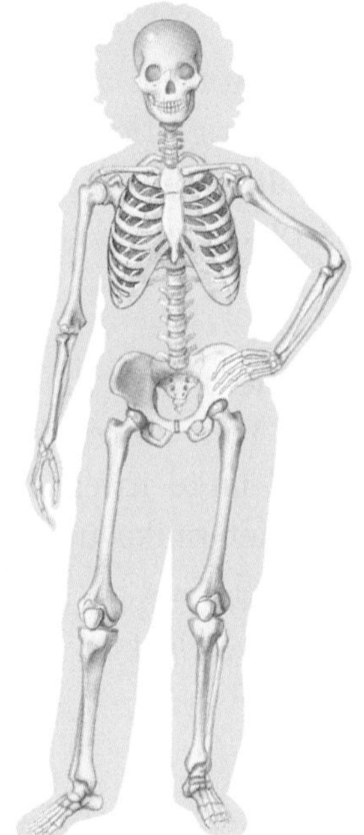

Skeletal System Your bones provide a frame to support and protect your body parts.

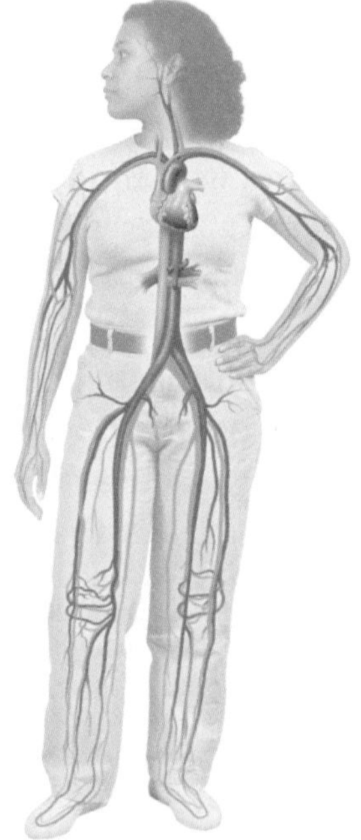

Cardiovascular and Circulatory Systems Your heart pumps blood through all of your blood vessels.

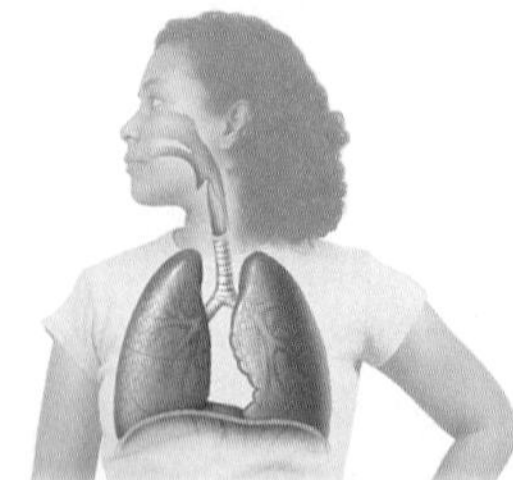

Respiratory System Your lungs absorb oxygen and release carbon dioxide.

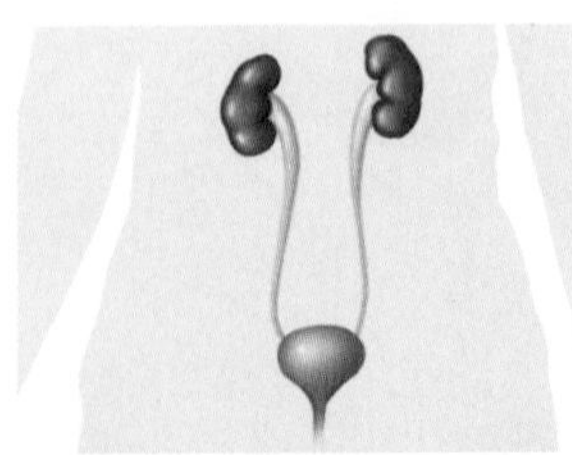

Urinary System Your urinary system removes wastes from the blood and regulates your body's fluids.

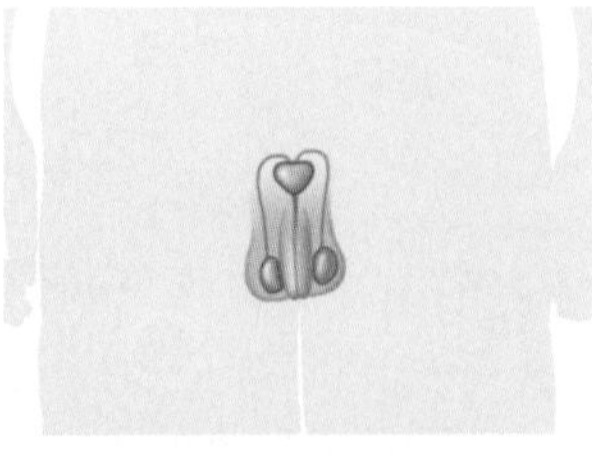

Male Reproductive System The male reproductive system produces and delivers sperm.

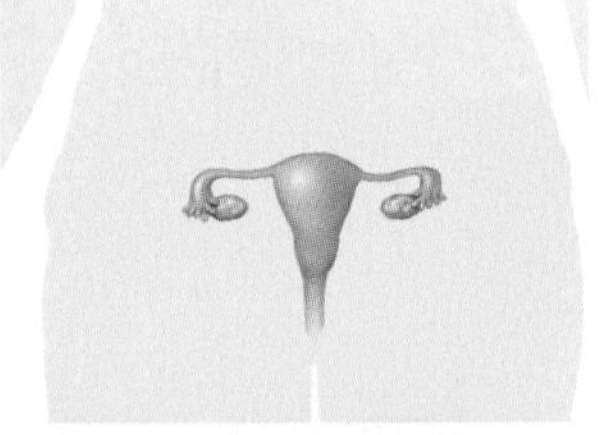

Female Reproductive System The female reproductive system produces eggs and nourishes and protects the fetus.

Careers

Christy Krames

Medical Illustrator Christy Krames is a medical illustrator. For 19 years, she has created detailed illustrations of the inner workings of the human body. Medical illustrations allow doctors and surgeons to share concepts, theories, and techniques with colleagues and allow students to learn about the human body.

Medical illustrators often draw tiny structures or body processes that would be difficult or impossible to photograph. For example, a photograph of a small intestine can show the entire organ. But a medical illustrator can add to the photograph an enlarged drawing of the tiny villi inside the intestine. Adding details helps to better explain how small parts of organs work together so that the organs can function.

Medical illustration requires knowledge of both art and science. So, Christy Krames studied both art and medicine in college. Often, Krames must do research before she draws a subject. Her research may include reading books, observing surgical procedures, or even dissecting a pig's heart. This research results in accurate and educational drawings of the inner body.

Language Arts ACTIVITY

WRITING SKILL Pretend you are going to publish an atlas of the human body. Write a classified advertisement to hire medical illustrators. Describe the job, and describe the qualities that the best candidates will have. As you write the ad, remember you are trying to persuade the best illustrators to contact you.

To learn more about these Science in Action topics, visit go.hrw.com and type in the keyword **HT5D6HBSF.**

Current Science

Check out Current Science® articles related to this chapter by visiting go.hrw.com. Just type in the keyword HL5CS24.

Reproduction and Development

About the PHOTO

If someone had taken your picture when your mother was about 13 weeks pregnant with you, that picture would have looked much like this photograph. You have changed a lot since then, haven't you? You started out as a single cell, and you became a complete person. And you haven't stopped growing and changing yet. In fact, you will continue to change for the rest of your life.

PRE-READING ACTIVITY

Graphic Organizer

Spider Map Before you read the chapter, create the graphic organizer entitled "Spider Map" described in the **Study Skills** section of the Appendix. Label the circle "Reproduction and Development." Create a leg for each section title. As you read the chapter, fill in the map with details about reproduction and development from each section.

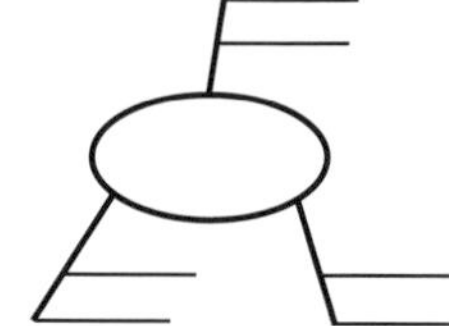

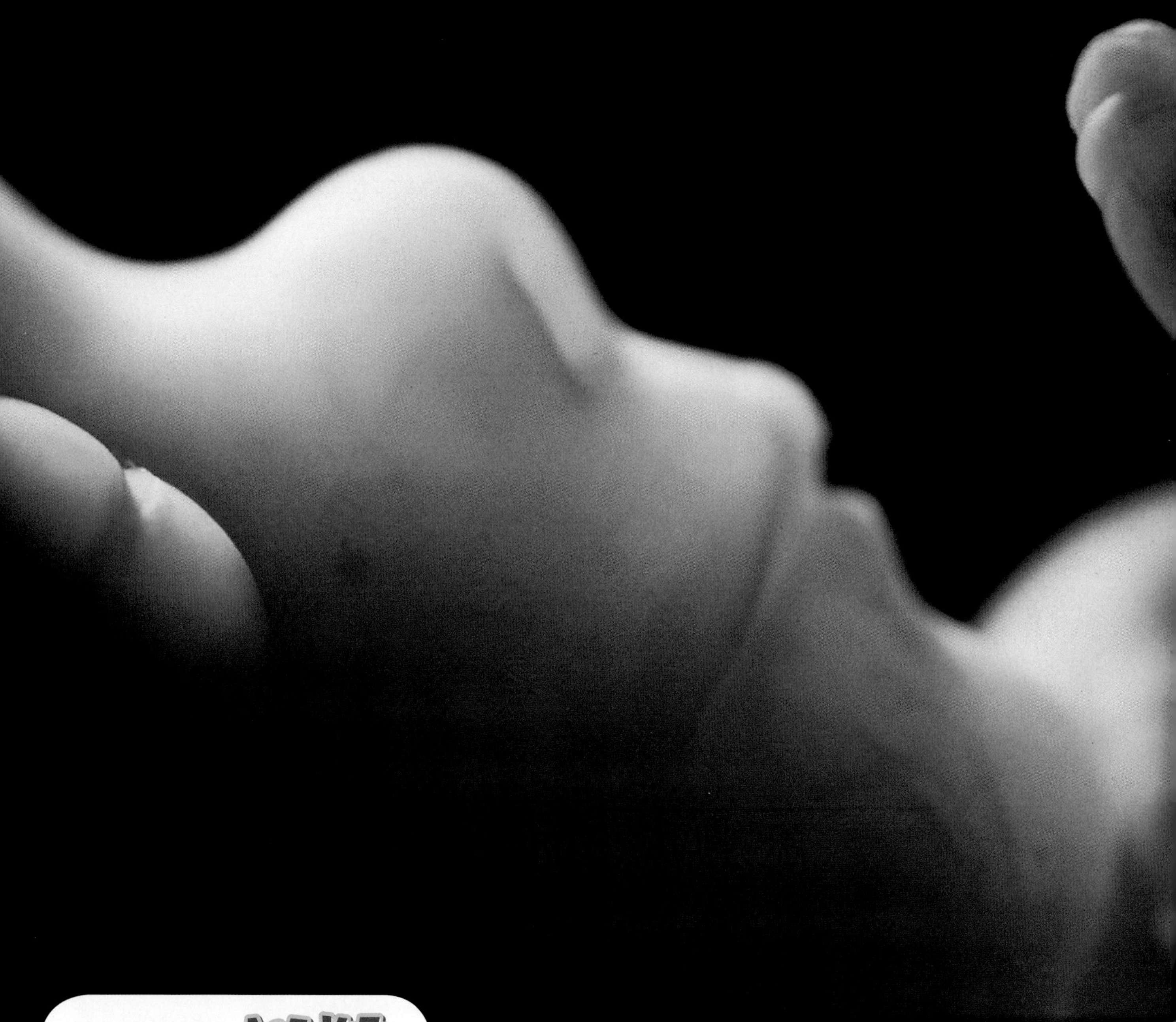

START-UP ACTIVITY

How Grows It?

As you read this paragraph, you are slowly aging. Your body is growing into the body of an adult. But does your body have the same proportions that an adult's body has? Complete this activity to find out.

Procedure

1. Have a classmate use a **tape measure** and **meter-stick** to measure your total height, head height, and leg length. Your teacher will tell you how to take these measurements.
2. Use the following equations to calculate your head height–to–total body height proportion and your leg length–to–total body height proportion.

$$\text{head proportion} = \frac{\text{head height}}{\text{body height}} \times 100$$

$$\text{leg proportion} = \frac{\text{leg length}}{\text{body height}} \times 100$$

3. Your teacher will give you the head, body, and leg measurements of three adults. Calculate the head-body and leg-body proportions of each of the three adults. Record all of the measurements and calculations.

Analysis

1. Compare your proportions with the proportions of the three adults.

SECTION 1

Human Reproduction

About nine months after a human sperm and egg combine, a mother gives birth to her baby. But how do humans make eggs and sperm?

READING WARM-UP

Objectives

- Identify the structures and functions of the male and female reproductive systems.
- Describe two reproductive system problems.

Terms to Learn

testes, penis, ovary, uterus, vagina

READING STRATEGY

Reading Organizer As you read this section, create an outline of the section. Use the headings from the section in your outline.

The Male Reproductive System

The male reproductive system, shown in **Figure 1,** produces sperm and delivers it to the female reproductive system. The **testes** (singular, *testis*) are a pair of organs that make sperm and testosterone (tes TAHS tuhr OHN). Testosterone is the main male sex hormone. It helps regulate the production of sperm and the development of male characteristics.

As sperm leave a testis, they are stored in a tube called an *epididymis* (EP uh DID i mis). Sperm mature in the epididymis. Another tube, called a *vas deferens* (vas DEF uh RENZ), passes from the epididymis into the body and through the *prostate gland*. The prostate gland surrounds the neck of the bladder. As sperm move through the vas deferens, they mix with fluids from several glands, including the prostate gland. This mixture of sperm and fluids is called *semen*.

To leave the body, semen passes through the vas deferens into the *urethra* (yoo REE thruh). The urethra is the tube that runs through the penis. The **penis** is the external organ that transfers semen into the female's body.

testes the primary male reproductive organs, which produce sperm and testosterone (singular, *testis*)

penis the male organ that transfers sperm to a female and that carries urine out of the body

Reading Check **Describe the path that sperm take from the testes to the penis.** (*See the Appendix for answers to Reading Checks.*)

Figure 1 **The Male Reproductive System**

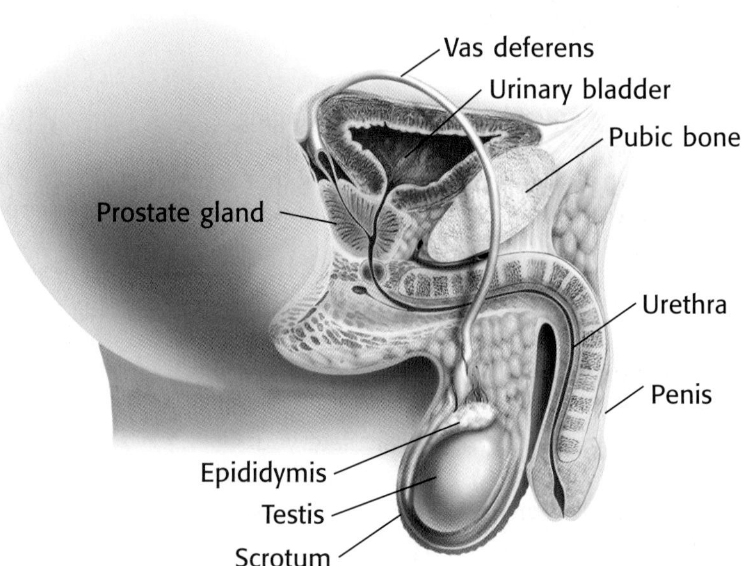

Figure 2 The Female Reproductive System

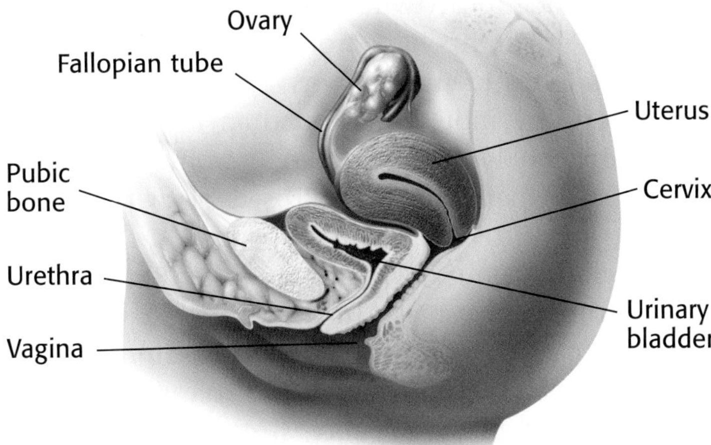

The Female Reproductive System

The female reproductive system, shown in **Figure 2,** produces eggs, nurtures fertilized eggs (zygotes), and gives birth. The two **ovaries** are the organs that make eggs. Ovaries also release estrogen (ES truh juhn) and progesterone (proh JES tuhr OHN), the main female sex hormones. These hormones regulate the release of eggs and development of female characteristics.

ovary in the female reproductive system of animals, an organ that produces eggs

uterus in female mammals, the hollow, muscular organ in which a fertilized egg is embedded and in which the embryo and fetus develop

vagina the female reproductive organ that connects the outside of the body to the uterus

The Egg's Journey

During *ovulation* (AHV yoo LAY shuhn), an egg is released from an ovary and passes into a *fallopian* (fuh LOH pee uhn) *tube.* A fallopian tube leads from each ovary to the uterus. The egg passes through the fallopian tube into the uterus. Fertilization usually happens in the fallopian tube. If the egg is fertilized, the resulting zygote enters the uterus. The zygote may become embedded in the thickened lining of the uterus. The **uterus** is the organ in which a zygote develops into a baby.

When a baby is born, he or she passes from the uterus through the vagina and emerges outside the body. The **vagina** is the canal between the outside of the body and the uterus.

Menstrual Cycle

From puberty through her late 40s or early 50s, a woman's reproductive system goes through monthly changes. These changes prepare the body for pregnancy and are called the *menstrual cycle* (MEN struhl SIE kuhl). The first day of *menstruation* (MEN STRAY shuhn), the monthly discharge of blood and tissue from the uterus, is counted as the first day of the cycle. Menstruation lasts about 5 days. When menstruation ends, the lining of the uterus thickens. Ovulation occurs on about the 14th day of the cycle. If the egg is not fertilized within a few days, menstruation begins and flushes the egg away. The cycle—which usually takes about 28 days—starts again.

Counting Eggs

1. The average woman ovulates each month from about age 12 to about age 50. How many mature eggs could she produce from age 18 to age 50?
2. A female's ovaries typically contain 2 million immature eggs. If she ovulates regularly from age 12 to age 50, what percentage of her eggs will mature?

Figure 3 *Identical twins have genes that are exactly the same. Many identical twins who are raised apart have similar personalities and interests.*

Multiple Births

Have you ever seen identical twins? Sometimes, they are so similar that even their parents have trouble telling them apart. The boys in **Figure 3** are identical twins. Fraternal twins, the other type of twins, are more common than identical twins are. Fraternal twins can look very different from each other. In every 1,000 births, there are about 30 sets of twins. About one-third of all twin births are identical twins.

Twins are the most common multiple births. But humans sometimes have triplets (3 babies). In the United States, there are about two sets of triplets in every 1,000 births. Humans also have quadruplets (4 babies), quintuplets (5 babies), and more. These types of multiple births are rare. Births of quintuplets or more happen only once in about 53,000 births.

Reading Check **What is the frequency of twin births?**

Reproductive System Problems

In most cases, the reproductive system functions flawlessly. But like any body system, the reproductive system sometimes has problems. These problems include disease and infertility.

STDs

Chlamydia, herpes, and hepatitis B are common sexually transmitted diseases. A *sexually transmitted disease,* or STD, is a disease that can pass from a person who is infected with the STD to an uninfected person during sexual contact. STDs are also called *sexually transmitted infections,* or STIs. These diseases affect many people each year, as shown in **Table 1.**

An STD you may have heard of is *acquired immune deficiency syndrome* (AIDS). AIDS is caused by *human immunodeficiency virus* (HIV). But you may not have heard of the STD *hepatitis B,* a liver disease also caused by a virus. This virus is spread in several ways, including sexual contact. In the United States, about 140,000 new cases of hepatitis B happen each year.

Twins and More

With a parent, discuss some challenges that are created by the birth of twins, triplets, quadruplets, or other multiples. Include financial, mental, emotional, and physical challenges.

Create a poster that shows these challenges and ways to meet them.

If twins or other multiples are in your family, discuss how the individuals differ and how they are alike.

Table 1 **The Spread of STDs in the United States**

STD	Approximate number of new cases each year
Chlamydia	3 to 10 million
Genital HPV (human papillomavirus)	5.5 million
Genital herpes	1 million
Gonorrhea	650,000
Syphilis	70,000
HIV/AIDS	40,000 to 50,000

Cancer

Sometimes, cancer happens in reproductive organs. *Cancer* is a disease in which cells grow at an uncontrolled rate. Cancer cells start out as normal cells. Then, something triggers uncontrolled cell growth. Different kinds of cancer have different triggers.

In men, the two most common reproductive system cancers are cancer of the testes and cancer of the prostate gland. In women, the two most common reproductive system cancers are breast cancer and cancer of the cervix. The *cervix* is the lower part, or neck, of the uterus. The cervix opens to the vagina.

Infertility

In the United States, about 15% of married couples have difficulty producing offspring. Many of these couples are *infertile,* or unable to have children. Men may be infertile if they do not produce enough healthy sperm. Women may be infertile if they do not ovulate normally.

Sexually transmitted diseases, such as gonorrhea and chlamydia, can lead to infertility in women. STD-related infertility occurs in men, but not as commonly as it does in women.

CONNECTION TO Social Studies

Understanding STDs Select one of the STDs in **Table 1.** Make a poster or brochure that identifies the cause of the disease, describes its symptoms, explains how it affects the body, and tells how it can be treated. Include a bar graph that shows the number of cases in different age groups.

ACTIVITY

SECTION Review

Summary

- The male reproductive system produces sperm and delivers it to the female reproductive system.
- The female reproductive system produces eggs, nurtures zygotes, and gives birth.
- Humans usually have one child per birth, but multiple births, such as those of twins or triplets, are possible.
- Human reproduction can be affected by cancer, infertility, and disease.

Using Key Terms

1. Use the following terms in the same sentence: *uterus* and *vagina.*

Understanding Key Ideas

2. Describe two problems of the reproductive system.
3. Identify the structures and functions of the male and female reproductive systems.
4. Identical twins happen once in 250 births. How many pairs of these twins might be at a school with 2,750 students?
   - **a.** 1
   - **b.** 11
   - **c.** 22
   - **d.** 250

Math Skills

5. In one country, 7 out of 1,000 infants die before their first birthday. Convert this figure to a percentage. Is your answer greater than or less than 1%?

Critical Thinking

6. **Making Inferences** What is the purpose of the menstrual cycle?
7. **Applying Concepts** Twins can happen when a zygote splits in two or when two eggs are fertilized. How can these two ways of twin formation explain how identical twins differ from fraternal twins?
8. **Predicting Consequences** How might cancer of the testes affect a man's ability to make sperm?

SCILINKS
NSTA
Developed and maintained by the National Science Teachers Association
For a variety of links related to this chapter, go to www.scilinks.org
Topic: Reproduction System Irregularities or Disorders
SciLinks code: HSM1298

SECTION 2

Growth and Development

Every one of us started out as a single cell. How did that cell become a person made of trillions of cells?

READING WARM-UP

Objectives

- Summarize the processes of fertilization and implantation.
- Describe the development of the embryo and the fetus.
- Identify the stages of human development from birth to death.

Terms to Learn

embryo
placenta
umbilical cord
fetus

READING STRATEGY

Discussion Read this section silently. Write down questions that you have about this section. Discuss your questions in a small group.

A single cell divides many times and develops into a baby. But the development of a baby from a single cell is only the first stage of human development. Think about how you will change between now and when you become a grandparent!

From Fertilization to Embryo

Ordinarily, the process of human development starts when a man deposits millions of sperm into a woman's vagina. A few hundred sperm make it through the uterus into a fallopian tube. There, a few sperm cover the egg. Usually, only one sperm gets through the outer coating of the egg. When this happens, it triggers a response—a membrane forms around the egg to keep other sperm from entering. When the sperm's nucleus joins with the nucleus of the egg, the egg becomes fertilized.

The fertilized egg, or zygote, travels down the fallopian tube toward the uterus. This journey takes 5 to 6 days. During the trip, the zygote undergoes cell division many times. Eleven to 12 days after fertilization, the zygote has become a tiny ball of cells called an **embryo.** The embryo implants itself in the uterus. *Implantation* happens when the zygote embeds itself in the thick, nutrient-rich lining of the uterus. Fertilization and implantation are outlined in **Figure 1.**

embryo a developing human, from fertilization through the first 8 weeks of development (the 10th week of pregnancy)

placenta the partly fetal and partly maternal organ by which materials are exchanged between a fetus and the mother

Reading Check **Describe the processes of fertilization and implantation.** (*See the Appendix for answers to Reading Checks.*)

Figure 1 Fertilization and Implantation

b The egg is fertilized in the fallopian tube by a sperm.
a The egg is released from the ovary.
c The embryo implants itself in the uterus's wall.

CRITICAL THINKING

16 **Concept Mapping** Use the following terms to create a concept map: *testes, penis, ovary, uterus, vagina, embryo, placenta, reproductive organs,* and *umbilical cord.*

17 **Applying Concepts** What is the function of the uterus? How is this function related to the menstrual cycle?

18 **Making Inferences** As the number of babies in a multiple birth increases, the type of multiple birth becomes less common. For example, the birth of twins is the most common type of multiple birth—30 sets of twins are born for every 1,000 births. But the birth of quintuplets is very rare—1 set of quintuplets is born in about 53,000 births. Why might multiple births in which a large number of babies are born be less common than multiple births in which a small number of babies are born?

19 **Drawing Conclusions** Menstruation is affected by a hormone called *estrogen.* A woman who produces very little estrogen may not have a menstrual cycle. In turn, the production of estrogen is affected by body fat. A woman who has very little body fat usually produces less estrogen. What might happen to the menstrual cycle of a female athlete who exercises a great deal?

INTERPRETING GRAPHICS

The following graph illustrates the cycles of the female hormone estrogen and the male hormone testosterone. The blue line shows the estrogen level in a female over 28 days. The red line shows the testosterone level in a male over the same amount of time. Use the graph below to answer the questions that follow.

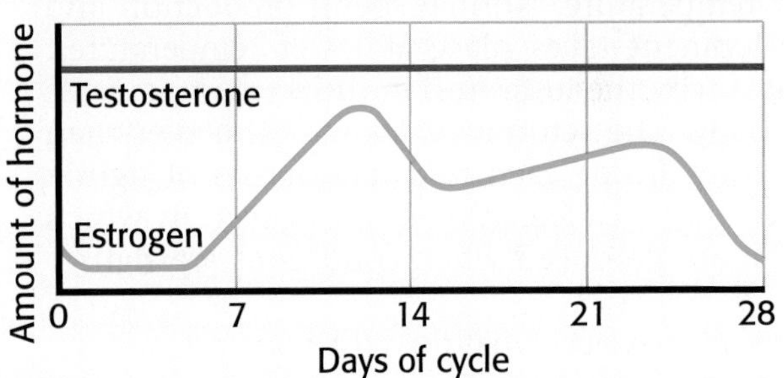

20 What is the major difference between the levels of the two hormones over the 28 days?

21 What cycle do you think estrogen affects?

22 Why might the level of testosterone stay the same?

23 Do you think that the above estrogen cycle would change in a pregnant woman? Explain your answer.

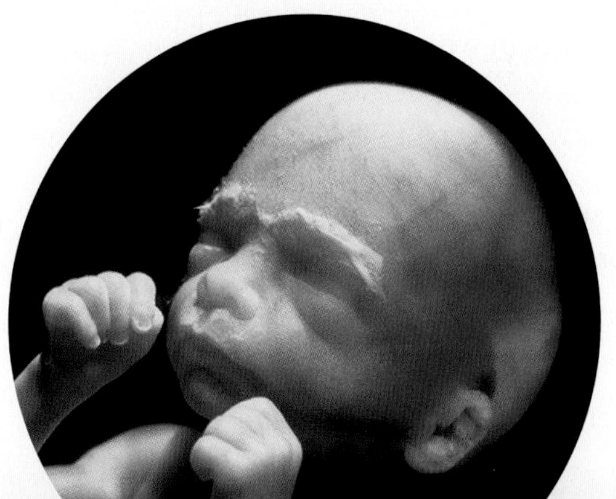

Standardized Test Preparation

READING

Read each of the passages below. Then, answer the questions that follow each passage.

Passage 1 The male reproductive system is made up of internal and external organs. The external organs of this system are the penis and the scrotum. The scrotum is a skin-covered sac that hangs outside the body. Normal human body temperature is about 37°C. Normal sperm production and development cannot take place at that temperature. Normal sperm production and development takes place at lower temperatures. That is why the testes rest in the scrotum, outside the body. The scrotum is about 2°C cooler than the body. Inside each testis are masses of tightly coiled tubes, called *seminiferous tubules,* in which sperm are produced when conditions are right.

1. In this passage, what does the word *external* mean?

- **A** not part of the body
- **B** outside the body
- **C** inside the body
- **D** lasting a long time

2. Which of the following statements is a fact according to the passage?

- **F** The temperature in the scrotum is higher than body temperature.
- **G** Testes are internal organs of the male reproductive system.
- **H** Normal sperm production cannot take place at normal body temperature.
- **I** Normal human body temperature is about 37°F.

3. What are the tubes in which sperm are made called?

- **A** testes
- **B** scrotum
- **C** seminiferous tubules
- **D** external organs

Passage 2 In a normal pregnancy, the fertilized egg travels to the uterus and implants itself in the uterus's wall. But in about 7 out of 1,000 pregnancies in the United States, a woman has an ectopic pregnancy. The term *ectopic* is from two Greek words meaning "out of place." In an ectopic pregnancy, the fertilized egg implants itself in an ovary, a fallopian tube, or another area of the female reproductive system that is not the lining of the uterus. Because the zygote cannot develop properly outside of the uterus, an ectopic pregnancy can be very dangerous for both the mother and zygote. As the zygote grows, it causes the mother pain and bleeding. For example, an ectopic pregnancy in a fallopian tube can rupture the tube and cause abdominal bleeding. If an ectopic pregnancy is not treated quickly enough, the mother may die.

1. In the passage, what does the term *ectopic pregnancy* probably mean?

- **A** a pregnancy that takes place at the wrong time
- **B** a type of pregnancy that happens about 7 out of 100 times in the United States
- **C** a type of pregnancy caused by a problem with a fallopian tube
- **D** a pregnancy in which the zygote implants itself in the wrong place

2. Which of the following statements is a fact according to the passage?

- **F** Ectopic pregnancies take place in about 7% of all pregnancies.
- **G** The ectopic pregnancy rate in the United States is less than 1%.
- **H** Ectopic pregnancies take place in the uterus.
- **I** An ectopic pregnancy is harmless.

INTERPRETING GRAPHICS

Use the diagrams below to answer the questions that follow.

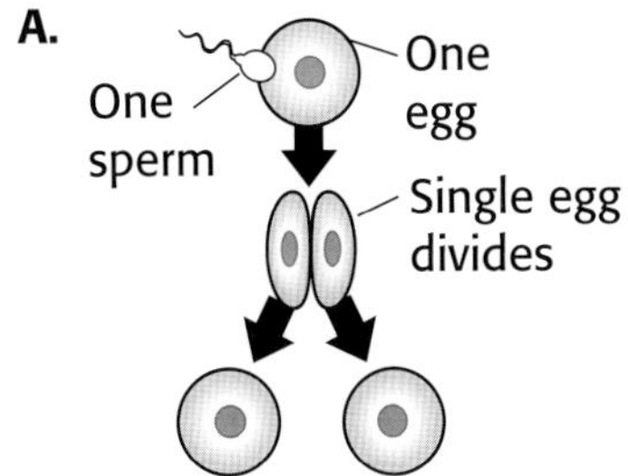

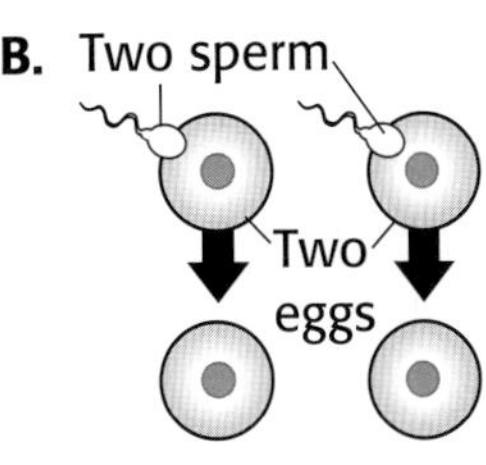

1. Which diagram of cell division would produce identical twins: A or B?

A diagram B, because each egg is fertilized by a separate sperm cell

B both diagram A and diagram B, because twins result in both cases

C diagram A, because a single fertilized egg separates into two halves

D diagram B, because two eggs are released by an ovary

2. Which of the following could describe fraternal twins?

F both boys

G both girls

H one girl and one boy

I any of these combinations

3. Which diagram of cell division could explain triplets, two of whom are identical and one of whom is fraternal?

A diagram A

B diagram B

C either diagram A or diagram B

D neither diagram A or diagram B

MATH

Read each question below, and choose the best answer.

1. Identify the group that contains equivalent fractions, decimals, and percents.

A 7/10, 0.7, 7%

B 1/2, 0.5, 50%

C 3/8, 0.38, 38%

D 3/100, 0.3, 33%

2. A geologist was exploring a cave. She spent 2.7 h exploring on Saturday and twice as many hours exploring on Sunday. Which equation could be used to find *n,* the total number of hours the geologist spent exploring the cave on those 2 days?

F $n = 2 \div 2.7$

G $n = 2.7 + (2 \times 2.7)$

H $n = 2.7 + 2.7 + 2$

I $n = 2 \times 2.7$

3. Which of the following story problems can be solved by the equation below?

$$(60 + 70 + 68 + 80 + x) \div 5 = 70$$

A The heights of four buildings in South Braintree are 60 ft, 70 ft, 68 ft, and 80 ft. Find *x,* the average height of the buildings.

B The weights of four dogs Jason is raising are 60 lb, 70 lb, 68 lb, and 80 lb. Find *x,* the sum of the weights of the four dogs.

C Kayla's first four handmade bracelets sold for $60, $70, $68, and $80. Find *x,* the amount for which Kayla needs to sell her fifth bracelet to have an average selling price of $70.

D The times it took Taylor to complete each of four 100 m practice swims were 60 s, 70 s, 68 s, and 80 s. Find *x,* the average time it took Taylor to complete his practice swims.

Science in Action

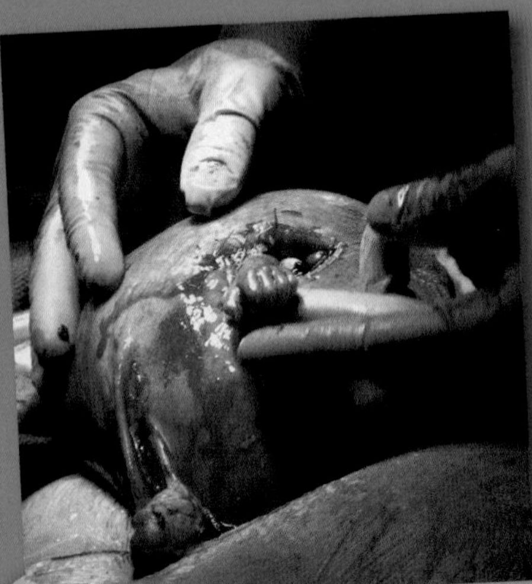

Doctors operated on a fetus, whose hand is visible in this photo, to correct spina bifida.

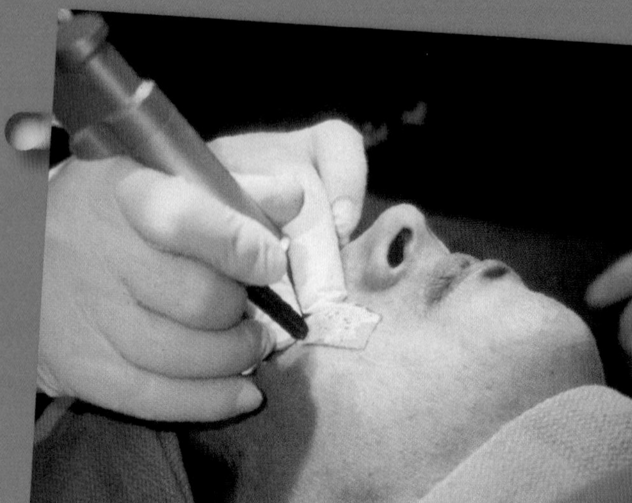

Science, Technology, and Society

Fetal Surgery

Sometimes, a developing fetus has a serious medical problem. In many cases, surgery after birth can correct the problem. But some problems can be treated while the fetus is still in the uterus. For example, fetal surgery may be used to correct spina bifida (part of the spinal cord is exposed because the backbone doesn't form properly). Doctors now can fix several types of problems before a baby is born.

Social Studies ACTIVITY

WRITING SKILL Research the causes of spina bifida. Write a brochure telling expectant mothers what precautions they can take to prevent spina bifida.

Scientific Discoveries

Lasers and Acne

Many people think that acne affects only teenagers, but acne can strike at any age. Some acne is mild, but some is severe. Now, for some severe cases of acne, lasers may provide relief. That's right—lasers can be used to treat acne! Surgeons who specialize in the health and diseases of the skin use laser light to treat acne.

In addition, laser treatments may stimulate the skin cells that produce collagen. Collagen is a protein found in connective tissue. Increased production of collagen in the skin improves the skin's texture and helps smooth out acne scars.

Language Arts ACTIVITY

WRITING SKILL Write a story about how severe acne affects a teen's life. Tell what happens when a doctor refers the teen to a specialist for laser treatment and how the successful treatment changes the teen's life.

Careers

Reva Curry

Diagnostic Medical Sonographer Sounds are everywhere in our world. But only some of those sounds—such as your favorite music playing on the stereo or the dog barking next door—are sounds that we can hear. There are sound waves whose frequency is too high for us to hear. These high-pitched sounds are called *ultrasound*. Some animals, such as bats, use ultrasound to hunt and to avoid midair collisions.

Humans use ultrasound, too. Ultrasound machines can peer inside the human body to look at hearts, blood vessels, and fetuses. Diagnostic medical sonographers are people who use sonography equipment to diagnose medical problems and to follow the growth and development of a fetus before it is born. One of the leading professionals in the field of diagnostic medical sonography is Dr. Reva Curry. Dr. Curry spent many years as a sonographer. Her primary job was to use high-tech instruments to create ultrasound images of parts of the body and interpret the results for other medical professionals. Today, Dr. Curry works with students as the dean of a community college.

Math Activity

At 20°C, the speed of sound in water is 1,482 m/s and in steel is 5,200 m/s. How long would it take a sound to travel 815.1 m in water? In that same length of time, how far would a sound travel in a steel beam?

To learn more about these Science in Action topics, visit go.hrw.com and type in the keyword **HL5BD5F.**

Current Science

Check out Current Science® articles related to this chapter by visiting go.hrw.com. Just type in the keyword HL5CS26.

Body Defenses and Disease

About the PHOTO

No, this photo is not from a sci-fi movie. It is not an alien insect soldier. This is, in fact, a greatly enlarged image of a house dust mite that is tinier than the dot of an *i*. Huge numbers of these creatures live in carpets, beds, and sofas in every home. Dust mites often cause problems for people who have asthma or allergies. The body's immune system fights diseases and alien factors, such as dust mites, that cause allergies.

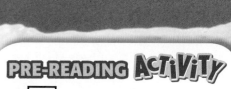

Tri-Fold Before you read the chapter, create the FoldNote entitled "Tri-Fold" described in the **Study Skills** section of the Appendix. Write what you know about the body's defenses in the column labeled "Know." Then, write what you want to know in the column labeled "Want." As you read the chapter, write what you learn about the body's defenses in the column labeled "Learn."

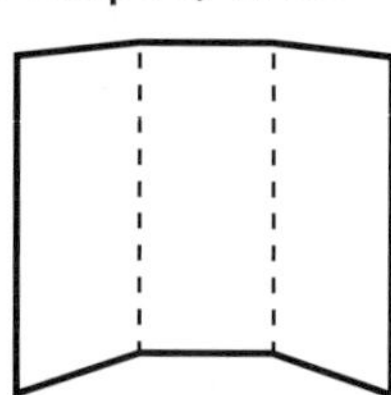

Careers

Terrel Shepherd III

Nurse Terrel Shepherd III is a registered nurse (RN) at Texas Children's Hospital in Houston, Texas. RNs have many responsibilities. These responsibilities include giving patients their medications, assessing patients' health, and establishing intravenous access. Nurses also serve as a go-between for the patient and the doctor. Although most nurses work in hospitals or clinics, some nurses work for corporations. Pediatric nurses such as Shepherd work specifically with infants, children, and adolescents. The field of nursing offers a wide variety of job opportunities including home-care nurses, traveling nurses, and flight nurses. The hospital alone has many areas of expertise for nurses, including geriatrics (working with the elderly), intensive care, administration, and surgery. Traditionally, nursing has been considered to be a woman's career. However, since nursing began as a profession, men and women have practiced nursing. A career in nursing is possible for anyone who does well in science, enjoys people, and wants to make a difference in people's lives.

Language Arts ACTIVITY

WRITING SKILL Create a brochure that persuades people to consider a career in nursing. Describe nursing as a career, the benefits of becoming a nurse, and the education needed to be a nurse. Illustrate the brochure with pictures of nurses from the Internet or from magazines.

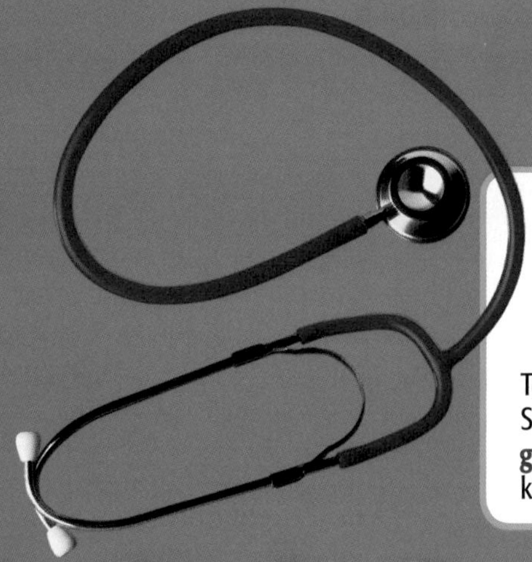

To learn more about these Science in Action topics, visit **go.hrw.com** and type in the keyword **HL5BD6F.**

Current Science

Check out Current Science® articles related to this chapter by visiting go.hrw.com. Just type in the keyword HL5CS27.

20

Interactions of Living Things

About the PHOTO

A chameleon is about to grab an insect using its long tongue. A chameleon's body can change color to match its surroundings. Blending in helps the chameleon sneak up on its prey and also keeps the chameleon safe from animals that would like to make a snack out of a chameleon.

PRE-READING ACTIVITY

FOLDNOTES **Tri-Fold** Before you read the chapter, create the FoldNote entitled "Tri-Fold" described in the **Study Skills** section of the Appendix. Write what you know about the interactions of living things in the column labeled "Know." Then, write what you want to know in the column labeled "Want." As you read the chapter, write what you learn about the interactions of living things in the column labeled "Learn."

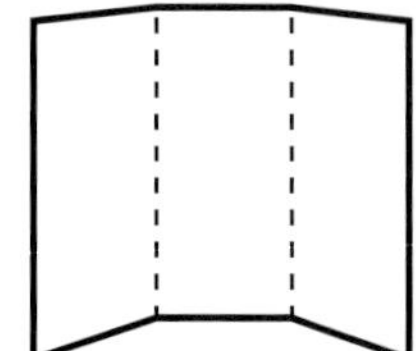

START-UP ACTIVITY

Who Eats Whom?

In this activity, you will learn how organisms interact when finding (or becoming) the next meal.

Procedure

1. On each of **five index cards,** print the name of one of the following organisms: killer whale, cod fish, krill shrimp, algae, and leopard seal.
2. On your desk, arrange the cards in a chain to show who eats whom.
3. Record the order of your cards.
4. In nature, would you expect to see more killer whales or cod? Arrange the cards in order of most individuals in an organism group to fewest.

Analysis

1. What might happen to the other organisms if algae were removed from this group? What might happen if the killer whales were removed?
2. Are there any organisms in this group that eat more than one kind of food? (Hint: What else might a seal, a fish, or a killer whale eat?) How could you change the order of your cards to show this information? How could you use pieces of string to show these relationships?

SECTION 1

Everything Is Connected

READING WARM-UP

Objectives

- Distinguish between the biotic and abiotic parts of the environment.
- Explain how populations and communities are related.
- Describe how the abiotic parts of the environment affect ecosystems.

Terms to Learn

ecology
biotic
abiotic
population
community
ecosystem
biosphere

READING STRATEGY

Reading Organizer As you read this section, create an outline of the section. Use the headings from the section in your outline.

An alligator drifts in a weedy Florida river, watching a long, thin fish called a gar. *The gar swims too close to the alligator. Then, in a rush of murky water, the alligator swallows the gar whole and slowly swims away.*

It is clear that two organisms have interacted when one eats the other. But organisms have many interactions other than simply "who eats whom." For example, alligators dig underwater holes to escape from the heat. After the alligators abandon these holes, fish and other aquatic organisms live in the holes during the winter dry period.

Studying the Web of Life

All living things are connected in a web of life. Scientists who study the web of life specialize in the science of ecology. **Ecology** is the study of the interactions of organisms with one another and with their environment.

The Two Parts of an Environment

An organism's environment consists of all the things that affect the organism. These things can be divided into two groups. All of the organisms that live together and interact with one another make up the **biotic** part of the environment. The **abiotic** part of the environment consists of the nonliving factors, such as water, soil, light, and temperature. How many biotic parts and abiotic parts do you see in **Figure 1?**

Figure 1 *The alligator affects, and is affected by, many organisms in its environment.*

Organization in the Environment

At first glance, the environment may seem disorganized. However, the environment can be arranged into different levels, as shown in **Figure 2.** The first level is made of an individual organism. The second level is larger and is made of similar organisms, which form a population. The third level is made of different populations, which form a community. The fourth level is made of a community and its abiotic environment, which form an ecosystem. The fifth and final level contains all ecosystems, which form the biosphere.

ecology the study of the interactions of living organisms with one another and with their environment

biotic describes living factors in the environment

abiotic describes the nonliving part of the environment, including water, rocks, light, and temperature

Figure 2 **The Five Levels of Environmental Organization**

Meeting the Neighbors

1. Explore two or three blocks of your neighborhood.
2. Draw a map of the area's biotic and abiotic features. For example, map the location of sidewalks, large rocks, trees, water features, and any animals you see. Remember to approach all plants and animals with caution. Use your map to answer the following questions.
3. How are the biotic factors affected by the abiotic factors?
4. How are the abiotic factors affected by the biotic factors?

population a group of organisms of the same species that live in a specific geographical area

community all the populations of species that live in the same habitat and interact with each other

Populations

A salt marsh, such as the one shown in **Figure 3,** is a coastal area where grasslike plants grow. Within the salt marsh are animals. Each animal is a part of a **population,** or a group of individuals of the same species that live together. For example, all of the seaside sparrows that live in the same salt marsh are members of a population. The individuals in the population often compete with one another for food, nesting space, and mates.

Communities

A **community** consists of all of the populations of species that live and interact in an area. The animals and plants you see in **Figure 3** form a salt-marsh community. The populations in a community depend on each other for food, shelter, and many other things.

Figure 3 *Examine the picture of a salt marsh. Try to find examples of each level of organization in this environment.*

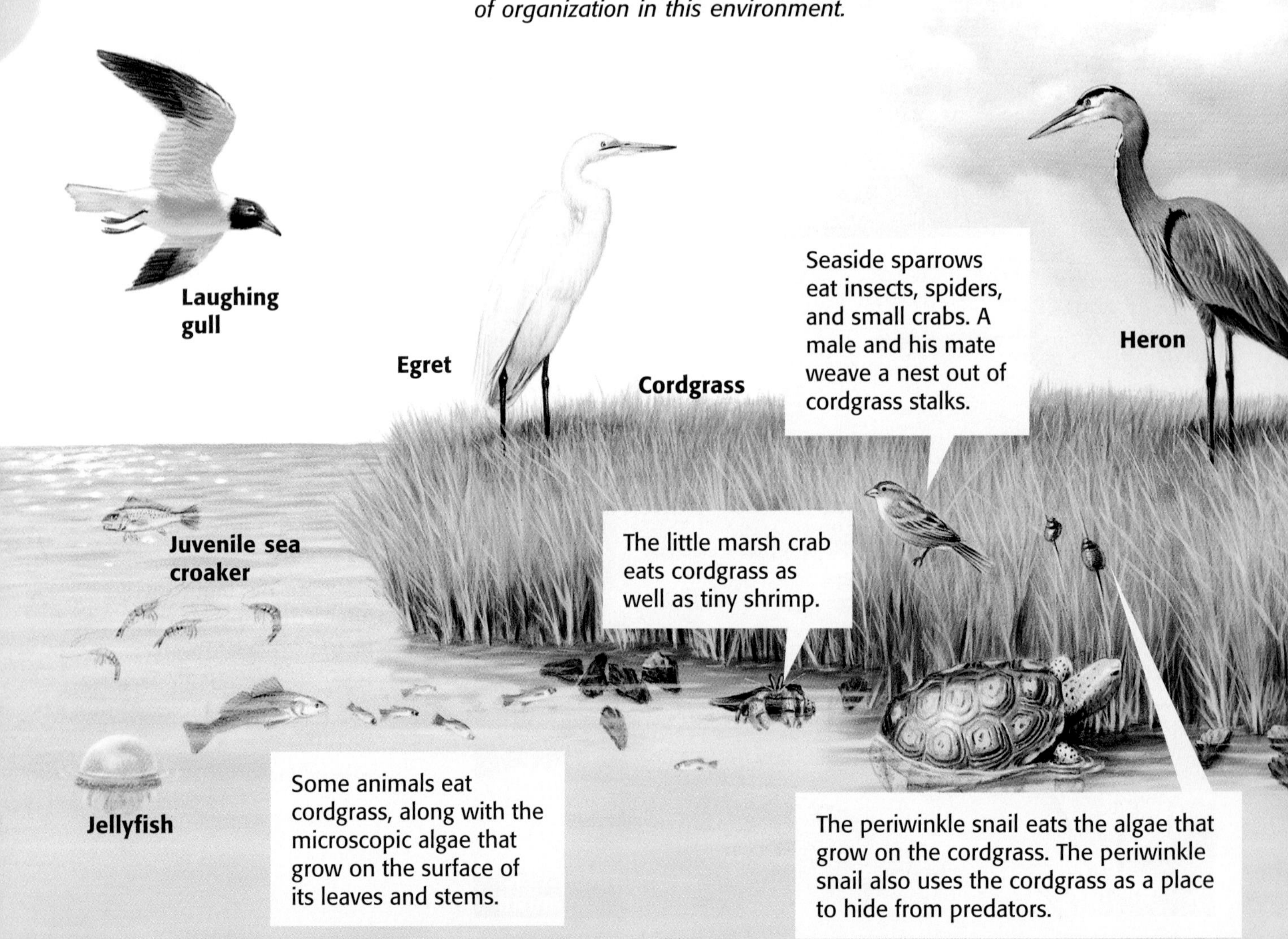

Laughing gull
Egret
Cordgrass
Seaside sparrows eat insects, spiders, and small crabs. A male and his mate weave a nest out of cordgrass stalks.
Heron
Juvenile sea croaker
The little marsh crab eats cordgrass as well as tiny shrimp.
Jellyfish
Some animals eat cordgrass, along with the microscopic algae that grow on the surface of its leaves and stems.
The periwinkle snail eats the algae that grow on the cordgrass. The periwinkle snail also uses the cordgrass as a place to hide from predators.

Careers

Dalton Dockery

Horticulture Specialist Did you know that instead of using pesticides to get rid of insects that are eating the plants in your garden, you can use other insects? "It is a healthy way of growing vegetables without the use of chemicals and pesticides, and it reduces the harmful effects pesticides have on the environment," says Dalton Dockery, a horticulture specialist in North Carolina. Some insects, such as ladybugs and praying mantises, are natural predators of many insects that are harmful to plants. They will eat other bugs but leave your precious plants in peace. Using bugs to drive off pests is just one aspect of natural gardening. Natural gardening takes advantage of relationships that already exist in nature and uses these interactions to our benefit. For Dockery, the best parts about being a horticultural specialist are teaching people how to preserve the environment, getting to work outside regularly, and having the opportunity to help people on a daily basis.

Social Studies ACTIVITY

WRITING SKILL Research gardening or farming techniques in other cultures. Do other cultures use any of the same aspects of natural gardening as horticultural specialists? Write a short report describing your findings.

To learn more about these Science in Action topics, visit **go.hrw.com** and type in the keyword **HL5INTF**.

Current Science

Check out Current Science® articles related to this chapter by visiting go.hrw.com. Just type in the keyword HL5CS18.

21

The Earth's Ecosystems

About the PHOTO

Is this animal a movie monster? No! The thorny devil is a lizard that lives in the desert of Australia. The thorny devil's rough skin is an adaptation that helps it survive in the hot, dry desert. Grooves in the thorny devil's skin collect water that the lizard later drinks. Water lands on its back and runs along the tiny grooves to the thorny devil's mouth.

PRE-READING ACTIVITY

FOLDNOTES

Three-Panel Flip Chart

Before you read the chapter, create the FoldNote entitled "Three-Panel Flip Chart" described in the **Study Skills** section of the Appendix. Label the flaps of the three-panel flip chart with "Land biomes," "Marine ecosystems," and "Freshwater ecosystems." As you read the chapter, write information you learn about each category under the appropriate flap.

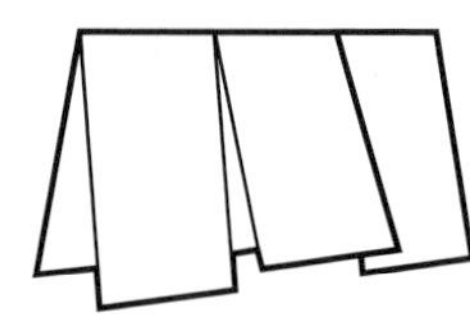

START-UP ACTIVITY

A Mini-Ecosystem

In this activity, you will build and observe a miniature ecosystem.

Procedure

1. Place a layer of **gravel** at the bottom of a **container,** such as a **large, wide-mouthed jar** or a **2 L soda bottle** with the top cut off. Then, add a layer of **soil.**
2. Add a variety of **plants** that need similar growing conditions. Choose small plants that will not grow too quickly.
3. Spray **water** inside the container to moisten the soil.
4. Loosely cover the container with a **lid** or **plastic wrap.** Place the container in indirect light.
5. Describe the appearance of your ecosystem.
6. Let your mini-ecosystem grow for 6 weeks. Add more water when the soil is dry.
7. Observe your mini-ecosystem every week. Record your observations.

Analysis

1. List the nonliving factors that make up the ecosystem that you built.
2. List the living factors that make up your ecosystem.
3. How is your mini-ecosystem similar to a real ecosystem? How is it different?

SECTION 1

Land Biomes

What do you think of when you think of polar bears? You probably imagine them in a snow-covered setting. Why don't polar bears live in the desert?

READING WARM-UP

Objectives

- Distinguish between abiotic factors and biotic factors in biomes.
- Identify seven land biomes on Earth.

Terms to Learn

biome
savanna
desert
tundra

READING STRATEGY

Reading Organizer As you read this section, create an outline of the section. Use the headings from the section in your outline.

Different ecosystems are home to different kinds of organisms. Polar bears don't live in the desert because they are adapted to very cold environments. Polar bears have thick fur. This fur keeps polar bears warm. It also hides them in the snow.

The Earth's Land Biomes

Imagine yourself in a hot, dry, dusty place. You see a cactus on your right. A lizard sits on a rock to your left. Where are you? You may not know exactly, but you probably think you are in a desert.

A desert is different from other places because of its abiotic (AY bie AHT ik) factors and biotic (bie AHT ik) factors. *Abiotic factors* are the nonliving parts of an environment. Soil, water, and climate are abiotic factors. Climate is the average weather conditions for an area over a long period of time. *Biotic factors* are the living parts of an environment. Plants and animals are biotic factors. Areas that have similar abiotic factors usually have similar biotic factors. A **biome** (BIE OHM) is a large area characterized by its climate and the plants and animals that live in the area. A biome contains related ecosystems. For example, a tropical rain forest biome contains treetop ecosystems and forest-floor ecosystems. The major land biomes on Earth are shown in **Figure 1.**

biome a large region characterized by a specific type of climate and certain types of plant and animal communities

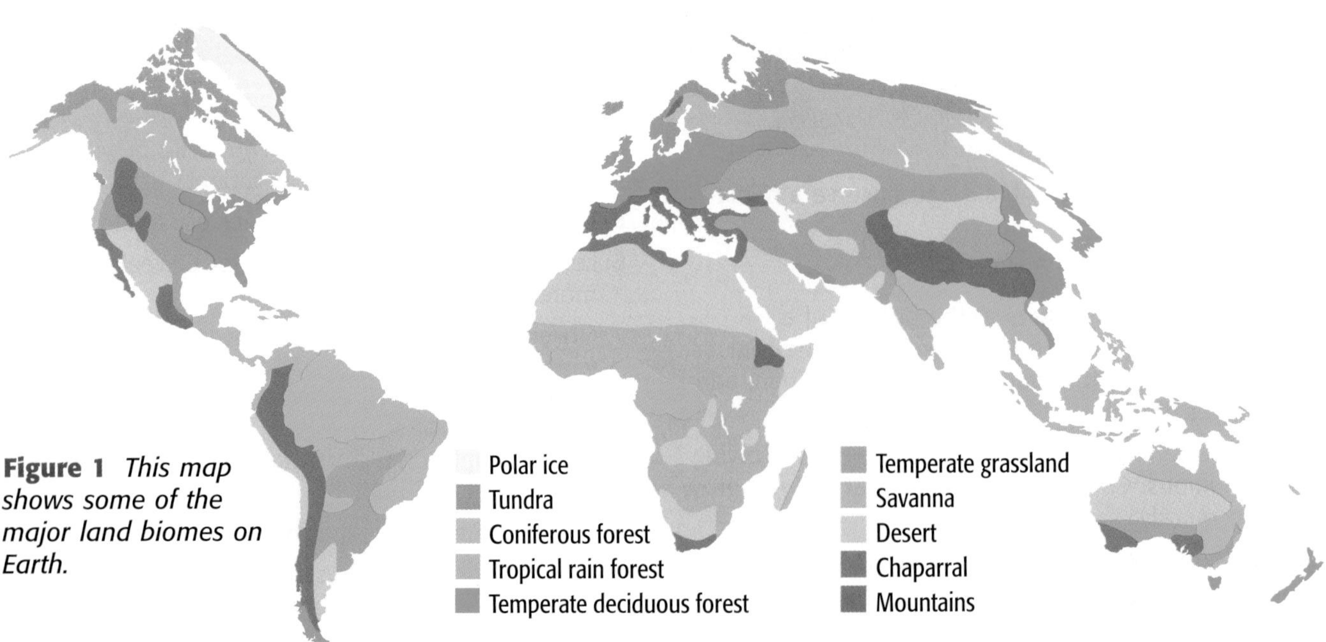

Figure 1 *This map shows some of the major land biomes on Earth.*

In forests, plant growth happens in layers. The leafy tops of the trees reach high above the forest floor, where the leaves can get sunlight.
Woody shrubs catch the light that filters through the trees.
Ferns and mosses are scattered across the forest floor. Flowering plants often bloom in early spring, before the trees grow new leaves.
Temperate Deciduous Forest
• Average Yearly Rainfall 75 to 125 cm (29.5 to 49 in.)
• Average Temperatures Summer: 28°C (82°F) Winter: 6°C (43°F)

Figure 2 *In a temperate deciduous forest, mammals, birds, and reptiles thrive on the many leaves, seeds, nuts, and insects.*

Forests

Forest biomes are often found in areas that have mild temperatures and plenty of rain. The kind of forest biome that develops depends on an area's temperatures and rainfall. Three forest biomes are temperate deciduous (dee SIJ oo uhs) forests, coniferous (koh NIF uhr uhs) forests, and tropical rain forests.

Temperate Deciduous Forests

Have you seen leaves change colors in the fall? Have you seen trees lose all of their leaves? If so, you have seen trees that are deciduous. The word *deciduous* comes from a Latin word that means "to fall off." Deciduous trees shed their leaves to save water during the winter or during the dry season. As shown in **Figure 2,** a variety of animals, such as bears, snakes, and woodpeckers, live in temperate deciduous forests.

Reading Check **How does the word *deciduous* describe temperate deciduous forests?** (*See the Appendix for answers to Reading Checks.*)

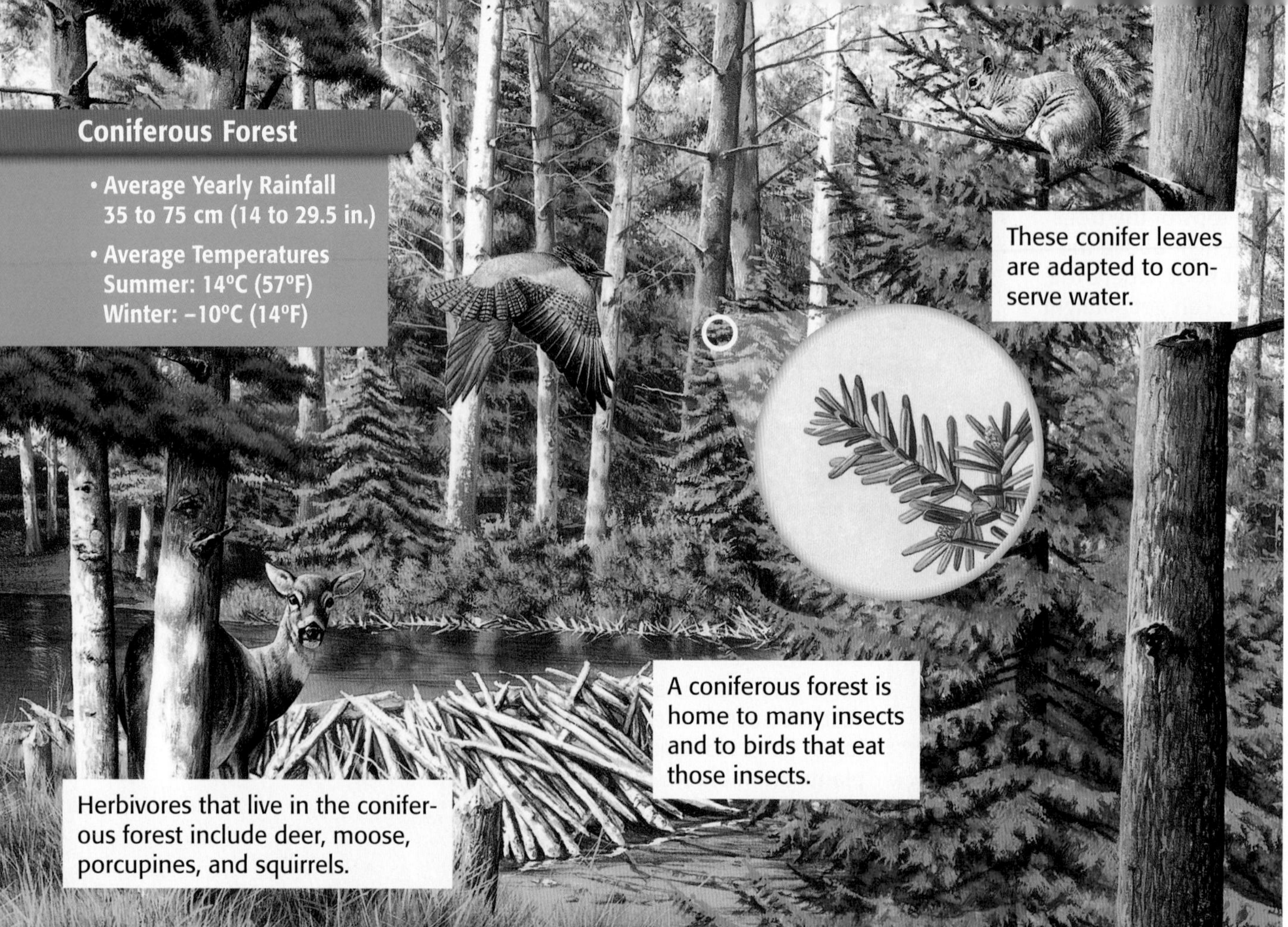

Coniferous Forest
• Average Yearly Rainfall
35 to 75 cm (14 to 29.5 in.)
• Average Temperatures
Summer: 14°C (57°F)
Winter: –10°C (14°F)
These conifer leaves are adapted to conserve water.
A coniferous forest is home to many insects and to birds that eat those insects.
Herbivores that live in the coniferous forest include deer, moose, porcupines, and squirrels.

Figure 3 *Many animals that live in a coniferous forest survive the harsh winters by hibernating or migrating to a warmer climate for the winter.*

Coniferous Forests

Most of the trees in a coniferous forest are called *conifers*. Conifers produce seeds in cones. Conifers also have special leaves that are shaped like needles. The leaves have a thick, waxy coating. This waxy coating has three functions. First, it helps keep conifer leaves from drying out. Second, the waxy coating protects needles from being damaged by cold winter temperatures. Finally, the waxy coating allows most conifers to keep many of their leaves year-round. So, most conifers do not change very much from summer to winter. Trees that stay green all year and do not lose all of their leaves at one time are known as *evergreen trees*.

Figure 3 shows a coniferous forest and some of the animals that live there. Squirrels and insects live in coniferous forests. Birds, such as finches, chickadees, and jays, are common in these forests. Herbivores, such as porcupines, elk, and moose, also live in coniferous forests. The ground beneath large conifers is often covered by a thick layer of needles. Also, very little light reaches the ground. So, few large plants can grow beneath these trees.

Reading Check **What is another name for most conifers? What are some animals that live in coniferous forests?**

The Oceanic Zone

In the oceanic zone, the sea floor drops sharply. This zone contains the deep water of the open ocean. Plankton can be found near the water surface. Animals, such as fishes, whales, and sharks, are found in the oceanic zone. Some animals in this zone live in very deep water. These animals often get food from material that sinks down from the ocean surface.

The Benthic Zone

The benthic zone is the ocean floor. The deepest parts of the benthic zone do not get any sunlight. They are also very cold. Animals, such as fishes, worms, and crabs, have special adaptations to the deep, dark water. Many of these organisms get food by eating material that sinks from above. Some organisms, such as bacteria, get energy from chemicals that escape from thermal vents on the ocean floor. Thermal vents form at cracks in the Earth's crust.

Reading Check How do animals in the benthic zone get food?

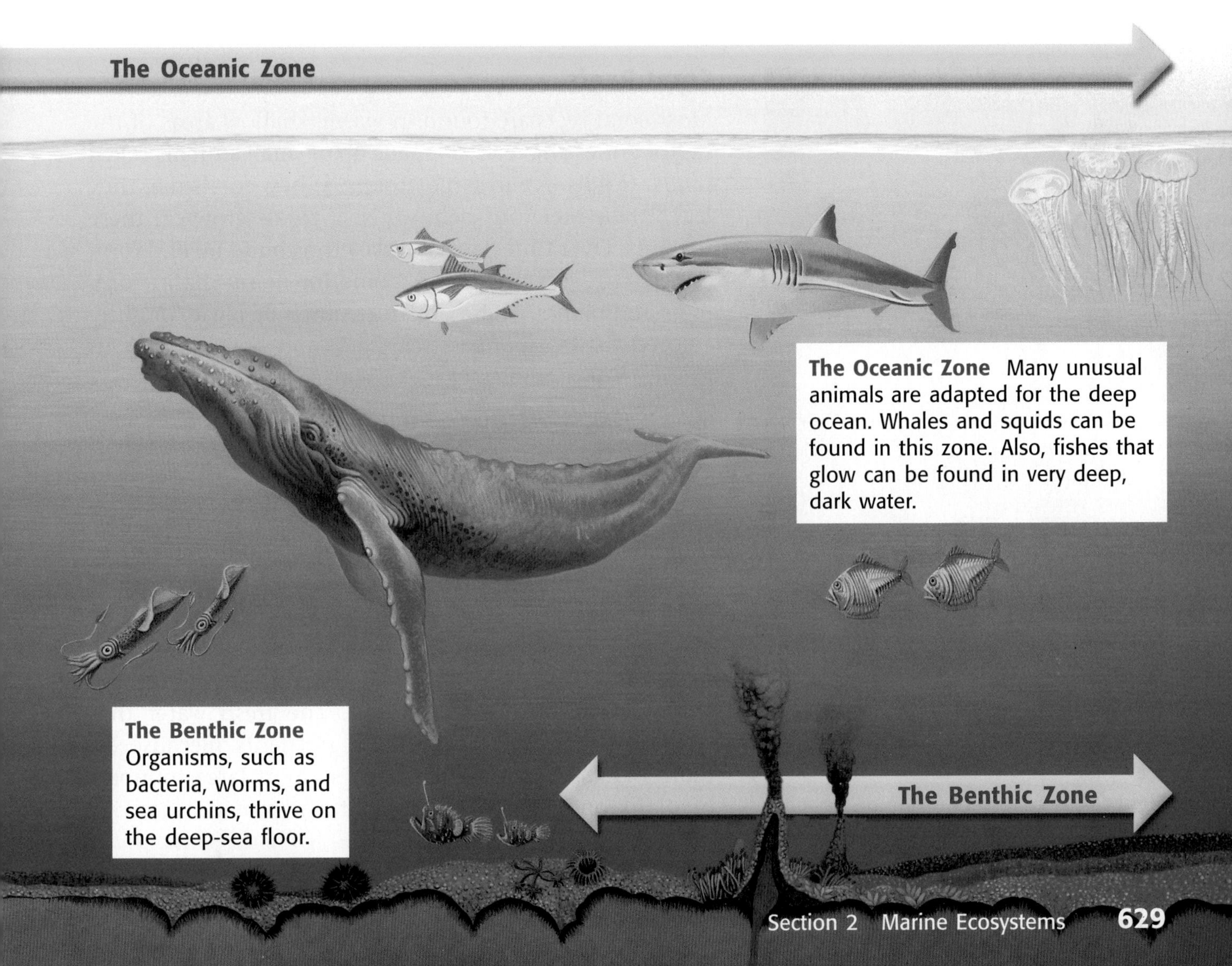

The Oceanic Zone Many unusual animals are adapted for the deep ocean. Whales and squids can be found in this zone. Also, fishes that glow can be found in very deep, dark water.

The Benthic Zone Organisms, such as bacteria, worms, and sea urchins, thrive on the deep-sea floor.

A Closer Look

Life on Earth depends on the ocean. Through evaporation, the ocean provides most of the water that makes up Earth's precipitation. Ocean temperatures and currents can affect world climates and wind patterns. Humans and many animals depend on the ocean for food.

Many ecosystems exist in the ocean. Some of these ecosystems are found on or near the shore. Other ecosystems are found in the middle of the ocean or near the poles.

Intertidal Areas

estuary an area where fresh water from rivers mixes with salt water from the ocean

Intertidal areas are found near the shore. These areas include mudflats, sandy beaches, and rocky shores. Intertidal organisms must be able to live both underwater and out of water. The organisms that live in mudflats include worms and crabs. Shorebirds feed on these animals. Organisms that live on sandy beaches include worms, clams, crabs, and plankton. On rocky shores, organisms have adaptations to keep from being swept away by crashing waves. Some organisms use rootlike structures called *holdfasts* to attach themselves to the rocks. Other organisms attach themselves to rocks by releasing a special glue.

Figure 4 *A coral reef is one of the most biologically diverse ecosystems on Earth.*

Coral Reefs

Most coral reefs are found in warm, shallow areas of the neritic zone. The reefs are made up of small animals called *corals*. Corals live in large groups. When corals die, they leave their skeletons behind. New corals grow on these remains. Over time, layers of skeletons build up and form a reef. This reef provides a home for many marine animals and plants. These organisms include algae, brightly colored fishes, sponges, sea stars, and sea urchins. An example of a coral reef is shown in **Figure 4.**

Reading Check How do coral reefs develop?

Estuaries

An area where fresh water from streams and rivers spills into the ocean is called an **estuary** (ES tyoo er ee). In estuaries, the fresh water from rivers and the salt water from the ocean are always mixing. Therefore, the amount of salt in the water is always changing. Plants and animals that live in estuaries must be able to survive the changing concentrations of salt. The fresh water that spills into an estuary is rich in nutrients. Because estuaries are so nutrient rich, they support large numbers of plankton. The plankton, in turn, provide food for many animals.

The Sargasso Sea

An ecosystem called the *Sargasso Sea* (sahr GAS oh SEE) is found in the middle of the Atlantic Ocean. This ecosystem contains floating rafts of algae called *sargassum* (sahr GAS uhm). Many of the animals that live in the Sargasso Sea are the same color as sargassum, which helps the animals hide from predators.

Polar Ice

The Arctic Ocean and the ocean around Antarctica make up another marine ecosystem. These icy waters are rich in nutrients, which support large numbers of plankton. Many fishes, birds, and mammals rely on the plankton for food. Animals, such as polar bears and penguins, live on the polar ice.

SECTION Review

Summary

- Abiotic factors that affect marine ecosystems are water temperature, water depth, and the amount of light that passes into the water.
- Plankton form the base of the ocean's food chains.
- Four ocean zones are the intertidal zone, the neritic zone, the oceanic zone, and the benthic zone.
- The ocean contains unique ecosystems, including intertidal areas, coral reefs, estuaries, the Sargasso Sea, and polar ice.

Using Key Terms

1. Use each of the following terms in a separate sentence: *plankton* and *estuary*.

Understanding Key Ideas

2. Water temperature
   - **a.** has no effect on the animals in a marine ecosystem.
   - **b.** affects the types of organisms that can live in a marine ecosystem.
   - **c.** decreases gradually as water gets deeper.
   - **d.** increases as water gets deeper.
3. What are three abiotic factors that affect marine ecosystems?
4. Describe four major ocean zones.
5. Describe five marine ecosystems. For each ecosystem, list an organism that lives there.

Math Skills

6. The ocean covers about 71% of the Earth's surface. If the total surface area of the Earth is about 510 million square kilometers, how many square kilometers are covered by the ocean?

Critical Thinking

7. **Making Inferences** Animals in the Sargasso Sea hide from predators by blending in with the sargassum. Color is only one way to blend in. What is another way that animals can blend in with sargassum?
8. **Identifying Relationships** Many fishes and other organisms that live in the deep ocean produce light. What are two ways in which this light might be useful?
9. **Applying Concepts** Imagine that you are studying animals that live in intertidal zones. You just discovered a new animal. Describe the animal and adaptations the animal has to survive in the intertidal zone.

SCILINKS.
NSTA
Developed and maintained by the National Science Teachers Association
For a variety of links related to this chapter, go to www.scilinks.org
Topic: Marine Ecosystems
SciLinks code: HSM0911

SECTION 3

Freshwater Ecosystems

A brook bubbles over rocks. A mighty river thunders through a canyon. A calm swamp echoes with the sounds of frogs and birds. What do these places have in common?

READING WARM-UP

Objectives

- Describe one abiotic factor that affects freshwater ecosystems.
- Describe the three zones of a lake.
- Describe two wetland ecosystems.
- Explain how a lake becomes a forest.

Terms to Learn

littoral zone	wetland
open-water zone	marsh
deep-water zone	swamp

READING STRATEGY

Paired Summarizing Read this section silently. In pairs, take turns summarizing the material. Stop to discuss ideas that seem confusing.

Brooks, rivers, and swamps are examples of freshwater ecosystems. The water in brooks and rivers is often fast moving. In swamps, water moves very slowly. Also, water in swamps is often found in standing pools.

Stream and River Ecosystems

The water in brooks, streams, and rivers may flow from melting ice or snow. Or the water may come from a spring. A spring is a place where water flows from underground to the Earth's surface. Each stream of water that joins a larger stream is called a *tributary* (TRIB yoo TER ee). As more tributaries join a stream, the stream contains more water. The stream becomes stronger and wider. A very strong, wide stream is called a *river*. **Figure 1** shows how a river develops.

Like other ecosystems, freshwater ecosystems are characterized by their abiotic factors. An important abiotic factor in freshwater ecosystems is how quickly water moves.

Streams and rivers are full of life. Plants line the edges of streams and rivers. Fish live in the open waters. And clams and snails live in the mud at the bottom of a stream or river. Organisms that live in fast-moving water have adaptations to keep from being washed away. Some producers, such as algae and moss, are attached to rocks. Consumers, such as tadpoles, use suction disks to hold themselves to rocks. Other consumers, such as insects, live under rocks.

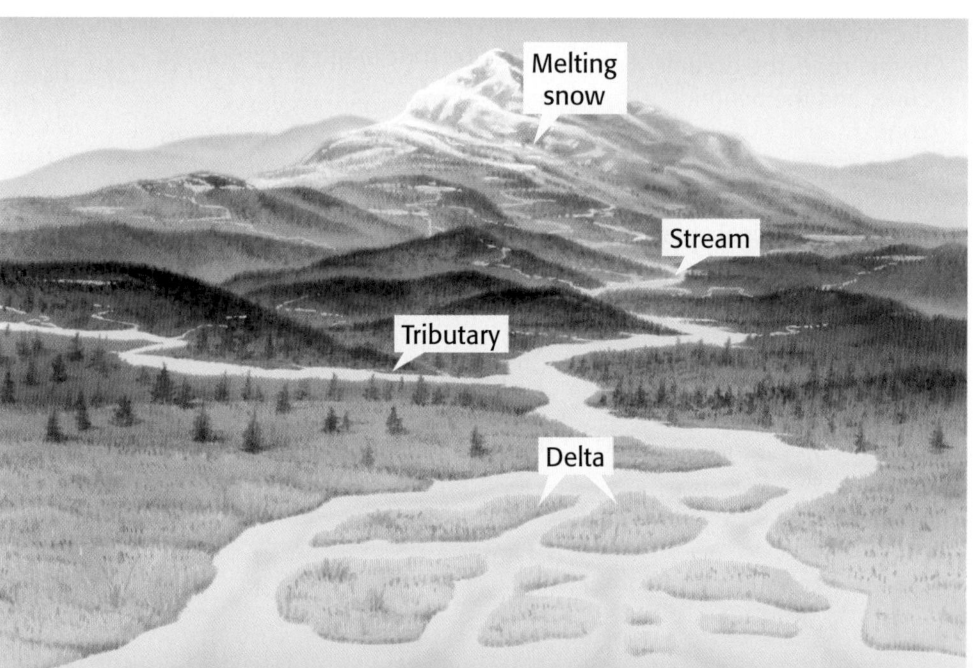

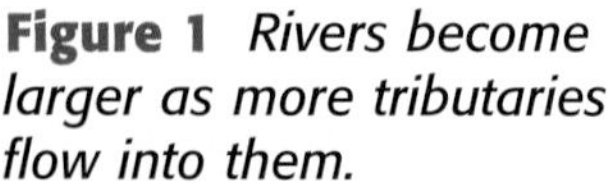

Figure 1 *Rivers become larger as more tributaries flow into them.*

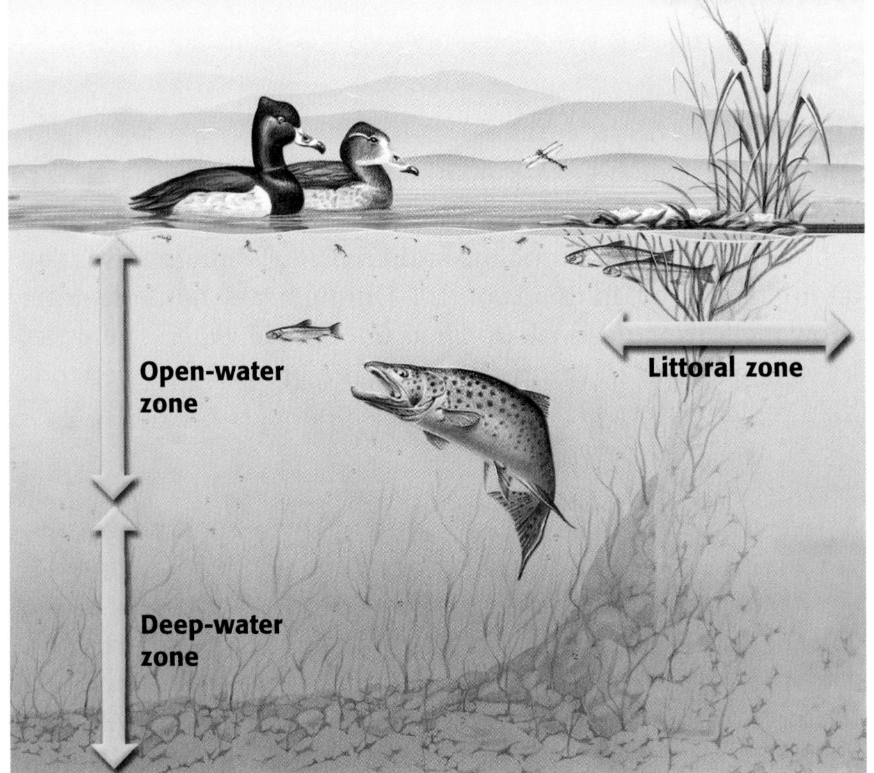

Figure 2 *Ponds and lakes can be divided into three zones. Each zone has different organisms and abiotic factors.*

Pond and Lake Ecosystems

Ponds and lakes have different ecosystems than streams and rivers do. **Figure 2** shows the zones of a typical lake.

Life near Shore

The area of water closest to the edge of a lake or pond is called the **littoral zone** (LIT uh ruhl ZOHN). Sunlight reaches the bottom of the littoral zone. This sunlight makes it possible for algae and plants to grow in the littoral zone. Algae grow beneath the surface of the water in the littoral zone. Plants that grow near the shore include cattails and rushes. Floating leaf plants, such as water lilies, grow farther from the shore. The plants of the littoral zone are home to small animals, such as snails and insects. Clams and worms bury themselves in the mud. Frogs, salamanders, turtles, fish, and snakes also live in this zone.

Life Away from Shore

The area of a lake or pond that extends from the littoral zone across the top of the water is called the **open-water zone.** The open-water zone goes as deep as sunlight can reach. This zone is home to bass, lake trout, and other fishes. Many photosynthetic plankton also live in this area. Beneath the open-water zone is the **deep-water zone,** where no sunlight reaches. Catfish, carp, worms, crustaceans, fungi, and bacteria live here. These organisms often feed on dead organisms that sink from above.

Reading Check **Describe the three zones of a lake.** (*See the Appendix for answers to Reading Checks.*)

Pond-Food Relationships

1. On **index cards,** write the names of some of the plants and animals that live in a typical freshwater pond or small lake. Write one type of organism on each card.
2. Use **yarn** or **string** to connect each organism to its food sources.
3. Describe the food relationships in a pond.

littoral zone the shallow zone of a lake or pond where light reaches the bottom and nurtures plants

open-water zone the zone of a pond or lake that extends from the littoral zone and that is only as deep as light can reach

deep-water zone the zone of a lake or pond below the open-water zone, where no light reaches

Figure 3 *This painted turtle suns itself on a log in a freshwater marsh.*

Wetland Ecosystems

An area of land that is sometimes underwater or whose soil contains a great deal of moisture is called a **wetland.** Wetlands support many different plants and animals. Wetlands also play an important role in flood control. During heavy rains or spring snow melt, wetlands soak up large amounts of water. The water in wetlands also moves deeper into the ground. So, wetlands help replenish underground water supplies.

Marshes

A treeless wetland ecosystem where plants, such as grasses, grow is called a **marsh.** A freshwater marsh is shown in **Figure 3.** Freshwater marshes are often found in shallow areas along the shores of lakes, ponds, rivers, and streams. The plants in a marsh vary depending on the depth of the water and the location of the marsh. Grasses, reeds, bulrushes, and wild rice are common marsh plants. Muskrats, turtles, frogs, and birds also live in marshes.

wetland an area of land that is periodically underwater or whose soil contains a great deal of moisture

marsh a treeless wetland ecosystem where plants such as grasses grow

swamp a wetland ecosystem in which shrubs and trees grow

Swamps

A wetland ecosystem in which trees and vines grow is called a **swamp.** Swamps, as shown in **Figure 4,** are found in low-lying areas and beside slow-moving rivers. Most swamps are flooded part of the year, depending on rainfall. Willows, bald cypresses, and oaks are common swamp trees. Vines, such as poison ivy, grow up tree trunks. Plants, such as orchids, may hang from tree branches. Water lilies and other plants grow in standing water. Many fishes, snakes, and birds also live in swamps.

Reading Check What is a swamp?

CONNECTION TO Language Arts

Compound Words A compound word is a word made up of two or more single words. In your **science journal,** define the two words that make up the word *wetland.* Then, define three more compound words.

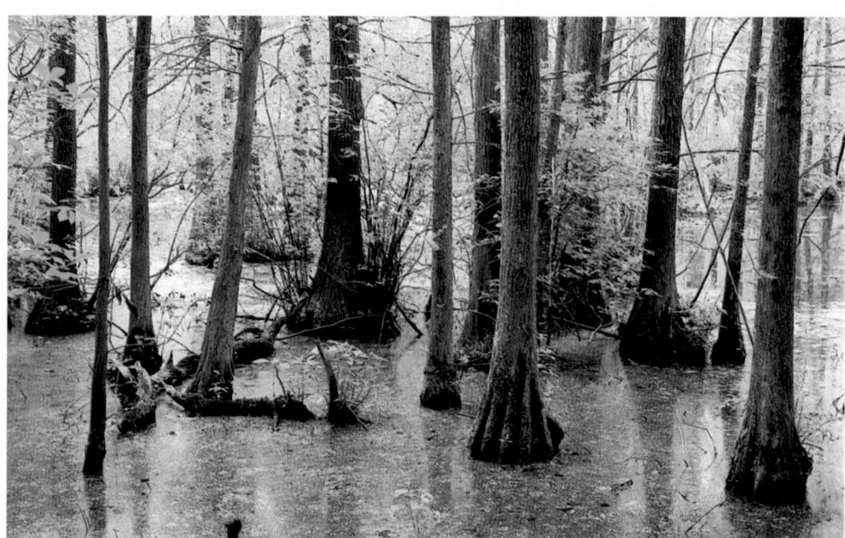

Figure 4 *The trunks of these trees are adapted to give the trees more support in the wet, soft soil of a swamp.*

From a Lake to a Forest

Did you know that a lake or pond can disappear? How can this happen? Water entering a standing body of water usually carries nutrients and sediment. These materials settle to the bottom of the pond or lake. Dead leaves from overhanging trees and decaying plant and animal life also settle to the bottom. Then, bacteria decompose this material. This process uses oxygen in the water. The loss of oxygen affects the kinds of animals that can survive in the pond or lake. For example, many fishes would not be able to survive with less oxygen in the water.

Over time, the pond or lake is filled with sediment. Plants grow in the new soil. Shallow areas fill in first. So, plants slowly grow closer and closer to the center of the pond or lake. What is left of the lake or pond becomes a wetland, such as a marsh or swamp. Eventually, the wetland can become a forest.

Reading Check **What happens to some of the animals in a pond as the pond becomes a forest?**

For another activity related to this chapter, go to **go.hrw.com** and type in the keyword **HL5ECOW.**

SECTION Review

Summary

- An important abiotic factor in freshwater ecosystems is how quickly water moves.
- The three zones of a pond or lake are the littoral zone, the open-water zone, and the deep-water zone.
- Wetlands include marshes and swamps.
- Sediments and decaying plant and animal matter build up in a pond. Over time, the pond may fill completely and become a forest.

Using Key Terms

1. Use the following terms in the same sentence: *wetland, marsh,* and *swamp.*

Understanding Key Ideas

2. A major abiotic factor in freshwater ecosystems is the
   a. source of the water.
   b. speed of the water.
   c. width of the stream or river.
   d. None of the above
3. Describe the three zones of a lake.
4. Explain how a lake can become a forest over time.

Math Skills

5. Sunlight can penetrate a certain lake to a depth of 15 m. The lake is five and a half times deeper than the depth to which light can penetrate. In meters, how deep is the lake?

Critical Thinking

6. **Making Inferences** When bacteria decompose material in a pond, the oxygen in the water may be used up. So, fishes in the pond die. How might the absence of fish lead to a pond filling faster?
7. **Applying Concepts** Imagine a steep, rocky stream. What kinds of adaptations might animals living in this stream have? Explain your answer.

SCILINKS
NSTA
Developed and maintained by the National Science Teachers Association
For a variety of links related to this chapter, go to www.scilinks.org
Topic: Freshwater Ecosystems
SciLinks code: HSM0621

Skills Practice Lab

Too Much of a Good Thing?

Plants need nutrients, such as phosphates and nitrates, to grow. Phosphates are often found in detergents. Nitrates are often found in animal wastes and fertilizers. When large amounts of these nutrients enter rivers and lakes, algae and plants grow rapidly and then die off. Microorganisms that decompose the dead matter use up oxygen in the water. Without oxygen, fish and other animals die. In this activity, you will observe the effect of fertilizers on organisms that live in pond water.

OBJECTIVES

Draw common pond-water organisms.

Observe the effect of fertilizer on pond-water organisms.

Describe how fertilizer affects the number and type of pond-water organisms over time.

MATERIALS

- beaker, 500 mL
- distilled water, 2.25 L
- eyedropper
- fertilizer
- gloves, protective
- graduated cylinder, 100 mL
- jars, 1 qt or 1 L (3)
- microscope
- microscope slides with coverslips
- pencil, wax
- plastic wrap
- pond water containing living organisms, 300 mL
- stirring rod

SAFETY

Procedure

1. Label one jar "Control," the second jar "Fertilizer," and the third jar "Excess fertilizer."
2. Pour 750 mL of distilled water into each jar. To the "Fertilizer" jar, add the amount of fertilizer recommended for 750 mL of water. To the "Excess fertilizer" jar, add 10 times the amount recommended for 750 mL of water. Stir the contents of each jar to dissolve the fertilizer.
3. Obtain a sample of pond water. Stir it gently to make sure that the organisms in it are evenly distributed. Pour 100 mL of pond water into each of the three jars.
4. Observe a drop of water from each jar under the microscope. Draw at least four of the organisms. Determine whether the organisms you see are producers, which are usually green, or consumers, which are usually able to move. Describe the number and type of organisms in the pond water.

Common Pond-Water Organisms

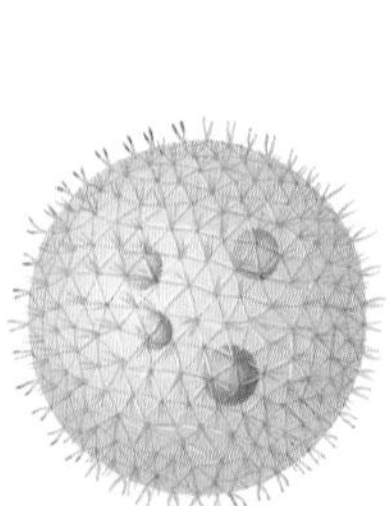

Volvox (producer)

Spirogyra (producer)

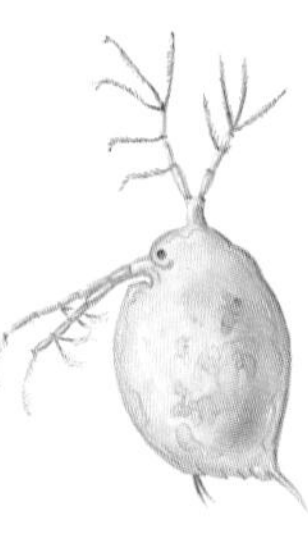

Daphnia (consumer)

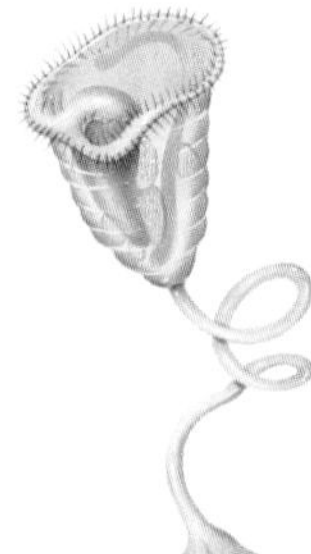

Vorticella (consumer)

5. Cover each jar loosely with plastic wrap. Place the jars near a sunny window but not in direct sunlight.

6. Make a prediction about how the pond organisms will grow in each of the three jars.

7. Make three data tables. Title one table "Control," as shown below. Title another table "Fertilizer," and title the third table "Excess fertilizer."

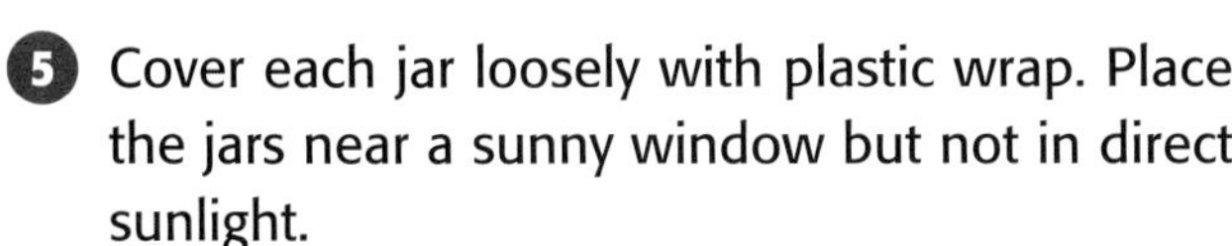

Control			
Date	Color	Odor	Other observations

8. Observe the jars when you first set them up and once every 3 days for the next 3 weeks. Note the color, the odor, and the presence of organisms. Record your observations.

9. When organisms become visible in the jars, use an eyedropper to remove a sample from each jar. Observe the sample under the microscope. How have the number and type of organisms changed since you first looked at the pond water?

10. At the end of the 3-week period, observe a sample from each jar under the microscope. Draw at least four of the most abundant organisms, and describe how the number and type of organisms have changed since your last microscope observation.

Analyze the Results

1. **Describing Events** After 3 weeks, which jar has the most abundant growth of algae?

2. **Analyzing Data** Did you observe any effects on organisms (other than algae) in the jar with the most abundant algal growth? Explain your answer.

Draw Conclusions

3. **Drawing Conclusions** What may have caused increased growth in the jars?

4. **Evaluating Results** Did your observations match your predictions? Explain your answer.

5. **Interpreting Information** Decaying plant and animal life contribute to the filling of lakes and ponds. How might the rapid filling of lakes and ponds be prevented or slowed?

Chapter Review

USING KEY TERMS

1. In your own words, write a definition for the following terms: *biome* and *tundra*.

2. Use each of the following terms in a separate sentence: *intertidal zone, neritic zone,* and *oceanic zone.*

For each pair of terms, explain how the meanings of the terms differ.

3. *savanna* and *desert*

4. *open-water zone* and *deep-water zone*

5. *marsh* and *swamp*

UNDERSTANDING KEY IDEAS

Multiple Choice

6. Trees that lose their leaves in the winter are called
   - **a.** evergreen trees.
   - **b.** coniferous trees.
   - **c.** deciduous trees.
   - **d.** None of the above

7. In which major ocean zone are plants and animals exposed to air for part of the day?
   - **a.** intertidal zone
   - **b.** neritic zone
   - **c.** oceanic zone
   - **d.** benthic zone

8. An abiotic factor that affects marine ecosystems is
   - **a.** the temperature of the water.
   - **b.** the depth of the water.
   - **c.** the amount of sunlight that passes through the water.
   - **d.** All of the above

9. _____ is a marine ecosystem that includes mudflats, sandy beaches, and rocky shores.
   - **a.** An intertidal area
   - **b.** Polar ice
   - **c.** A coral reef
   - **d.** The Sargasso Sea

Short Answer

10. What are seven land biomes?

11. Explain how a small lake can become a forest.

12. What are two factors that characterize biomes?

13. Describe the three zones of a lake.

14. How do rivers form?

15. What are three abiotic factors in land biomes? three abiotic factors in marine ecosystems? an abiotic factor in freshwater ecosystems?

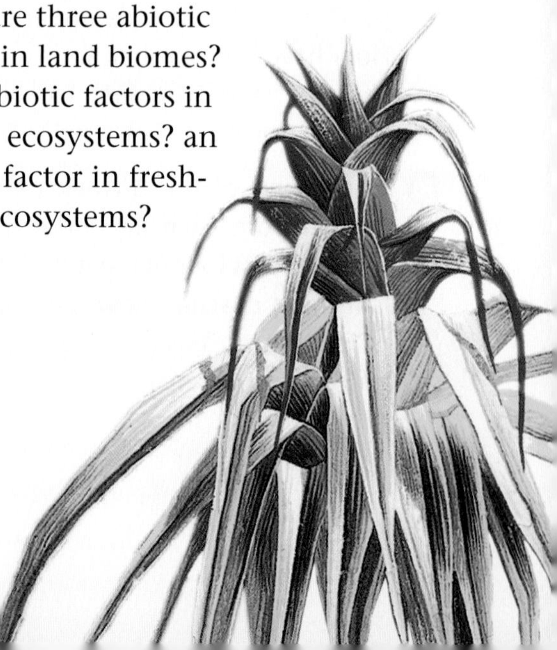

CRITICAL THINKING

16 **Concept Mapping** Use the following terms to create a concept map: *plants and animals, tropical rain forest, tundra, biomes, permafrost, canopy, desert,* and *abiotic factors.*

17 **Making Inferences** Plankton use photosynthesis to make their own food. They need sunlight for photosynthesis. Which of the four major ocean zones can support plankton growth? Explain your answer.

18 **Predicting Consequences** Wetlands, such as marshes and swamps, play an important role in flood control. Wetlands also help replenish underground water supplies. Predict what might happen if a wetland dries out.

19 **Analyzing Ideas** A scientist has a new hypothesis. He or she thinks that savannas and deserts are part of one biome rather than two separate biomes. Based on what you've learned, decide if the scientist's hypothesis is correct. Explain your answer.

20 **Applying Concepts** Imagine that you are a scientist. You are studying an area that gets about 100 cm of rain each year. The average summer temperatures are near 30°C. What biome are you in? What are some plants and animals you will likely encounter? If you stayed in this area for the winter, what kind of preparations might you need to make?

INTERPRETING GRAPHICS

Use the graphs below to answer the questions that follow.

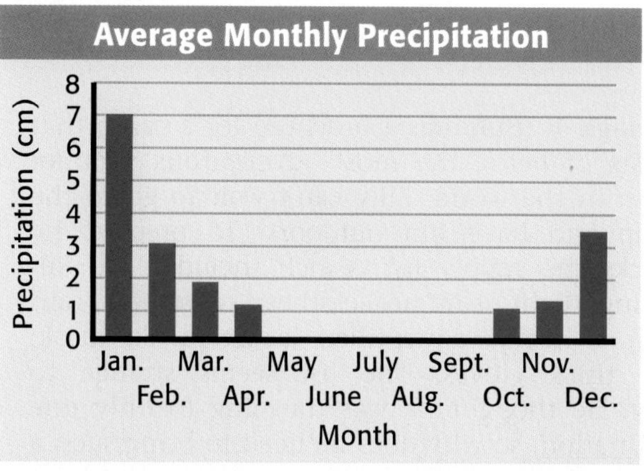

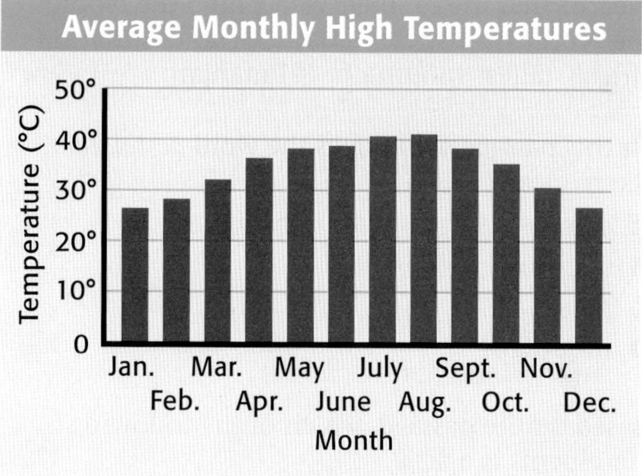

21 Which biome is most likely found in the region described by the graphs above? Explain your answer.

22 How many centimeters of rain fell in the region during the course of the year?

23 Which month is the hottest in the region? the coolest in the region?

24 What is the average monthly precipitation for the month that has the highest average high temperature?

Standardized Test Preparation

READING

Read each of the passages below. Then, answer the questions that follow each passage.

Passage 1 Billy has a brochure for a camp that boasts of being the most adventurous summer camp in the world. Billy can't wait to go to the camp and have fun outdoors. To prepare, he checks the supply list, which includes the following: light, summer clothes; sunscreen; rain gear; a heavy, down-filled jacket; a ski mask; and thick gloves. The list seems strange to Billy. He thought he was traveling to only one destination, so why does he need to bring such a wide variety of clothes? Billy rereads the brochure and learns that the campers will "climb the biomes of the world in just three days." The destination is Africa's tallest mountain, Kilimanjaro.

1. In this passage, what does the word *destination* likely mean?

- **A** camp
- **B** vacation
- **C** place
- **D** mountain

2. Based on the passage, which of the following statements is a fact?

- **F** People ski on Kilimanjaro.
- **G** Kilimanjaro is Africa's tallest mountain.
- **H** It rains a lot on Kilimanjaro.
- **I** The summers are cold on Kilimanjaro.

3. Why might Billy wonder if the brochure was advertising only one location?

- **A** The brochure called the camp the most adventurous summer camp in the world.
- **B** The brochure said that he would need light, summer clothes and sunscreen.
- **C** The brochure said that he would need light, summer clothes and a heavy, down-filled jacket.
- **D** The brochure said that the summers are cold on Kilimanjaro.

Passage 2 The layer of soil above the permafrost is too shallow for plants with deep roots to live. Grasses and shrubs can survive there because they have shallow roots. A sheet of mosses and lichens grows beneath these plants. When the soil above the permafrost thaws, the soil becomes muddy. Muddy soil is an excellent place for insects, such as mosquitoes, to lay eggs. Many birds spend the summer in the tundra to feed on these insects. Tundra animals include caribou, musk oxen, wolves, and other large mammals. Smaller animals, such as lemmings, shrews, and hares, also live in the tundra.

1. Based on the passage, what is one reason for the lack of trees on the tundra?

- **A** Trees need more sunlight than is available.
- **B** The roots of trees need more room than is available.
- **C** The soil above the permafrost becomes too muddy for trees.
- **D** Trees need more water than is available.

2. Based on the passage, which of the following statements about permafrost is true?

- **F** It is a thawed layer of soil.
- **G** It is always moist.
- **H** It is always frozen.
- **I** It is shallow.

3. Based on the passage, which of the following statements is a fact?

- **A** Muddy soil is an excellent place for mosses and lichens to grow.
- **B** Birds fly north to reach the tundra in the summer.
- **C** Caribou and oxen are some of the large mammals that live in the tundra.
- **D** The tundra is a beautiful biome that is home to diverse communities.

INTERPRETING GRAPHICS

The map below shows the biomes of Australia. Use the map to answer the questions that follow.

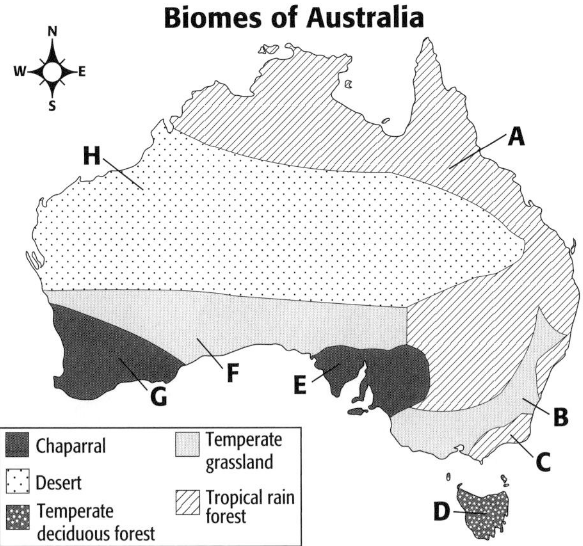

1. Which letters on the map correspond to areas that are chaparral?

A A and C
B B and F
C C and E
D E and G

2. If you lived in the area marked F, which biome would you live in?

F desert
G temperate grassland
H temperate deciduous forest
I tropical rain forest

3. If you wanted to live in a forest, which letters correspond to areas where you could live?

A A, B, and D
B A, C, and D
C B, C, and D
D C, D, and E

4. Which letter corresponds to desert?

F A
G D
H F
I H

MATH

Read each question below, and choose the best answer.

1. Larry wants to buy a glass tabletop for his science lab at home. The glass tabletop is 1 m wide and 2 m long. How many square meters is the surface of the glass tabletop?

A 2 m
B 2 m^2
C 3 m^2
D 6 m^2

2. A scuba diver was exploring a coral reef. She spent 1.5 h exploring on Friday and spent twice as many hours exploring on Saturday. Which equation could be used to find n, the total number of hours that the scuba diver spent exploring on Friday and Saturday?

F $n = 2 \div 1.5$
G $n = 1.5 + (2 \times 1.5)$
H $n = 1.5 + 1.5 + 2$
I $n = 2 \times 1.5$

3. How do you express $5 \times 5 \times 5 \times 5 \times 2 \times 2 \times 2$ in exponential notation?

A $(5 \times 4) + (2 \times 3)$
B $5^4 \times 2^3$
C $4^5 \times 3^2$
D $5^7 \times 2^7$

4. The tropical rain forest receives up to 400 cm of rain per year. The desert receives up to 25 cm of rain per year. Which of the following simplified fractions compares rainfall in the desert to rainfall in the rain forest?

F 1/400
G 1/25
H 1/16
I 16

Science in Action

Scientific Debate

Developing Wetlands

Wetlands are home to many flowering plants, birds, and turtles. Wetlands also play important roles in flood control and maintaining water quality. However, as more people need homes, grocery stores, and other facilities, some wetlands are being developed for construction. State governments often regulate the development of wetlands. Development is not allowed on many environmentally sensitive wetlands. But it is sometimes allowed on wetlands that are less sensitive. However, some people think that all wetlands should be protected, regardless of how sensitive an area is.

Language Arts ACTIVITY

WRITING SKILL Research wetland development on your own. Then, write a letter in which you describe your opinion about the development of wetlands.

Scientific Discoveries

Ocean Vents

Imagine the deepest parts of the ocean. There is no light at all, and it is very cold. Some of the animals that live here have found a unique place to live—vents on the ocean floor. Water seeps into the Earth between plates on the ocean floor. The water is heated and absorbs sulfuric gases. When the water blasts up through ocean vents, it raises the temperature of the ocean hundreds of degrees! Bacteria use the gases from the ocean vents to survive. In turn, mussels and clams feed on the bacteria. Without ocean vents, it would be much more difficult for these organisms to survive.

Math ACTIVITY

A thermal vent increases the temperature of the water around it to 360°C. If the temperature of the water was 2°C, what is the difference in temperature? By what percentage did the water temperature increase?

Careers

Alfonso Alonso-Mejía

Ecologist During the winter, ecologist Alfonso Alonso-Mejía visits sites in central Mexico where millions of monarch butterflies spend the winter. Unfortunately, the monarchs' winter habitat is threatened by human activity. Only nine of the monarchs' wintering sites remain. Five of the sites are set aside as sanctuaries for monarchs, but these sites are threatened by people who cut down fir trees for firewood or for commercial purposes.

Alonso-Mejía discovered that monarchs depend on understory vegetation, bushlike plants that grow beneath fir trees, to survive. When the temperature is low, monarchs can climb understory vegetation until they are at least 10 cm above the ground. This tiny difference in elevation can ensure that monarchs are warm enough to survive. Because of Alonso-Mejía's discovery, Mexican conservationists are working to protect understory vegetation and monarchs.

Social Studies ACTIVITY

Use your school library or the Internet to research the routes that monarchs use to migrate to Mexico. Draw a map illustrating your findings.

To learn more about these Science in Action topics, visit **go.hrw.com** and type in the keyword **HL5ECOF.**

Current Science

Check out Current Science® articles related to this chapter by visiting go.hrw.com. Just type in the keyword HL5CS20.

LabBook

Contents

Skills Practice Lab

Mysterious Minerals

Imagine sitting on a rocky hilltop, gazing at the ground below you. You can see dozens of different types of rocks. How can scientists possibly identify the countless variations? It's a mystery!

In this activity, you'll use your powers of observation and a few simple tests to determine the identities of rocks and minerals. Take a look at the Mineral Identification Key on the next page. That key will help you use clues to discover the identity of several minerals.

MATERIALS

- gloves, protective
- iron filings
- minerals, samples
- slides, microscope, glass
- streak plate

SAFETY

Procedure

1. On a separate sheet of paper, create a data chart like the one below.
2. Choose one mineral sample, and locate its column in your data chart.
3. Follow the Mineral Identification Key to find the identity of your sample. When you are finished, record the mineral's name and primary characteristics in the appropriate column in your data chart. **Caution:** Put on your safety goggles and gloves when scratching the glass slide.
4. Select another mineral sample, and repeat steps 2 and 3 until your data table is complete.

Analyze the Results

1. Were some minerals easier to identify than others? Explain.
2. A streak test is a better indicator of a mineral's true color than visual observation is. Why isn't a streak test used to help identify every mineral?
3. On a separate sheet of paper, summarize what you learned about the various characteristics of each mineral sample you identified.

Mineral Summary Chart

Characteristics	1	2	3	4	5	6
Mineral name						
Luster						
Color						
Streak						
Hardness						
Cleavage						
Special properties						

Mineral Identification Key
1. a. If your mineral has a metallic luster, **GO TO STEP 2.** **b.** If your mineral has a nonmetallic luster, **GO TO STEP 3.**
2. a. If your mineral is black, **GO TO STEP 4.** **b.** If your mineral is yellow, it is **PYRITE.** **c.** If your mineral is silver, it is **GALENA.**
3. a. If your mineral is light in color, **GO TO STEP 5.** **b.** If your mineral is dark in color, **GO TO STEP 6.**
4. a. If your mineral leaves a red-brown line on the streak plate, it is **HEMATITE.** **b.** If your mineral leaves a black line on the streak plate, it is **MAGNETITE.** Test your sample for its magnetic properties by holding it near some iron filings.
5. a. If your mineral scratches the glass microscope slide, **GO TO STEP 7.** **b.** If your mineral does not scratch the glass microscope slide, **GO TO STEP 8.**
6. a. If your mineral scratches the glass slide, **GO TO STEP 9.** **b.** If your mineral does not scratch the glass slide, **GO TO STEP 10.**
7. a. If your mineral shows signs of cleavage, it is **ORTHOCLASE FELDSPAR.** **b.** If your mineral does not show signs of cleavage, it is **QUARTZ.**
8. a. If your mineral shows signs of cleavage, it is **MUSCOVITE.** Examine this sample for twin sheets. **b.** If your mineral does not show signs of cleavage, it is **GYPSUM.**
9. a. If your mineral shows signs of cleavage, it is **HORNBLENDE.** **b.** If your mineral does not show signs of cleavage, it is **GARNET.**
10. a. If your mineral shows signs of cleavage, it is **BIOTITE.** Examine your sample for twin sheets. **b.** If your mineral does not show signs of cleavage, it is **GRAPHITE.**

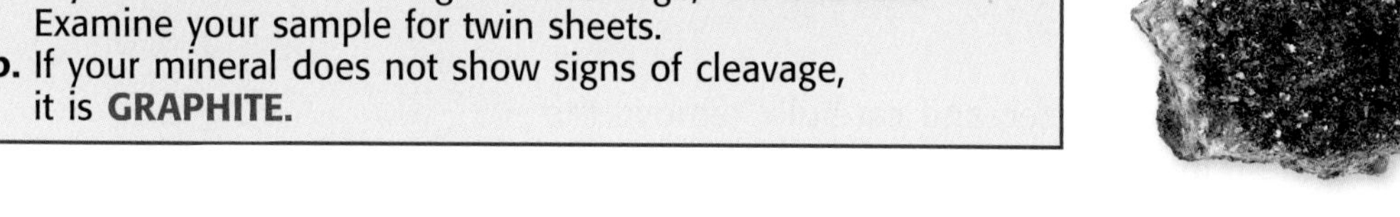

Applying Your Data

Using your textbook and other reference books, research other methods of identifying different types of minerals. Based on your findings, create a new identification key. Give the key and a few sample minerals to a friend, and see if your friend can unravel the mystery!

Using Scientific Methods

Skills Practice Lab

Great Ice Escape

Did you know that ice acts as a natural wrecking ball? Even rocks don't stand a chance against the power of ice. When water trapped in rock freezes, a process called *ice wedging* occurs. The water volume increases, and the rock cracks to "get out of the way." This expansion can fragment a rock into several pieces. In this exercise, you will see how this natural wrecker works, and you will try to stop the great ice escape.

MATERIALS

- bags, sandwich resealable (3)
- freezer
- jars, hard plastic with screw-on lids, such as spice containers (3)
- ruler, metric
- tape, strings, rubber bands, and other items to bind or reinforce the jars
- water

SAFETY

Ask a Question

1. If a plastic jar is filled with water, is there a way to prevent the jar from breaking when the water freezes?

Form a Hypothesis

2. Write a hypothesis that is a possible answer to the question above. Explain your reasoning.

Test the Hypothesis

3. Fill three identical jars to overflowing with water, and close two of them securely.
4. Measure the height of the water in the unsealed container. Record the height.
5. Tightly wrap one of the closed jars with tape, string, or other items to reinforce the jar. These items must be removable.
6. Place all three jars in resealable sandwich bags, and leave them in the freezer overnight. (Make sure the open jar does not spill.)
7. Remove the jars from the freezer, and carefully remove the wrapping from the reinforced jar.
8. Did your reinforced jar crack? Why or why not?
9. What does each jar look like? Record your observations.
10. Record the height of the ice in the unsealed jar. How does the new height compare with the height you measured in step 4?

Analyze the Results

1. Do you think it is possible to stop the ice from breaking the sealed jars? Why or why not?
2. How could ice wedging affect soil formation?

Using Scientific Methods

Skills Practice Lab

Clean Up Your Act

When you wash dishes, the family car, the bathroom sink, or your clothes, you wash them with water. But have you ever wondered how water gets clean? Two major methods of purifying water are filtration and evaporation. In this activity, you will use both of these methods to test how well they remove pollutants from water. You will test detritus (decaying plant matter), soil, vinegar, and detergent. Your teacher may also ask you to test other pollutants.

Form a Hypothesis

1. Form a hypothesis about whether filtration and evaporation will clean each of the four pollutants from the water and how well they might do it. Then, use the procedures below to test your hypothesis.

Part A: Filtration

Filtration is a common method of removing various pollutants from water. Filtration requires very little energy—gravity pulls water down through the layers of filter material. See how well this energy-efficient method works to clean your sample of polluted water.

Test the Hypothesis

2. Put on your gloves and goggles. Use scissors to carefully cut the bottom out of the empty soda bottle.
3. Using a small nail and hammer, carefully punch four or five small holes through the plastic cap of the bottle. Screw the plastic cap onto the bottle.
4. Turn the bottle upside down, and set its neck in a ring on a ring stand, as shown on the next page. Put a handful of gravel into the inverted bottle. Add a layer of activated charcoal, followed by thick layers of sand and gravel. Place a 400 mL beaker under the neck of the bottle.
5. Fill each of the large beakers with 1,000 mL of clean water. Set one beaker aside to serve as the control. Add three or four spoonfuls of each of the following pollutants to the other beaker: detritus, soil, household vinegar, and dishwashing detergent.
6. Copy the table on the next page, and record your observations for each beaker in the columns labeled "Before cleaning."
7. Observe the color of the water in each beaker.
8. Use a hand lens to examine the water for visible particles.

MATERIALS

Part A

- charcoal, activated
- goggles
- gravel
- hammer and small nail
- sand
- scissors
- soda bottle, plastic, with cap, 2 L

Part B

- bag, plastic sandwich, sealable
- flask, Erlenmeyer
- gloves, heat-resistant
- hot plate
- ice
- stopper, rubber, one-hole, with a glass tube
- tubing, plastic, 1.5 m

Parts A and B

- beaker, 400 mL
- beaker, 1,000 mL (2)
- detergent, dishwashing
- detritus (grass and leaf clippings)
- hand lens
- pH test strips
- ring stand with ring
- soil
- spoons, plastic (2)
- vinegar, household
- water, 2,000 mL

SAFETY

9. Smell the water, and note any unusual odors.
10. Stir the water in each beaker rapidly with a plastic spoon, and check for suds. Use a different spoon for each sample.
11. Use a pH test strip to find the pH of the water.
12. Gently stir the clean water, and then pour half of it through the filtration device.
13. Observe the water in the collection beaker for color, particles, odors, suds, and pH. Be patient. It may take several minutes for the water to travel through the filtration device.
14. Record your observations in the appropriate "After filtration" column in your table.
15. Repeat steps 12–14 using the polluted water.

Analyze the Results

1. How did the color of the polluted water change after the filtration? Did the color of the clean water change?
2. Did the filtration method remove all of the particles from the polluted water? Explain.
3. How much did the pH of the polluted water change? Did the pH of the clean water change? Was the final pH of the polluted water the same as the pH of the clean water before cleaning? Explain.

Results Table

	Before cleaning (clean water)	Before cleaning (polluted water)	After filtration (clean water)	After filtration (polluted water)	After evaporation (clean water)	After evaporation (polluted water)
Color						
Particles						
Odor						
Suds						
pH						

DO NOT WRITE IN BOOK

Part B: Evaporation

Cleaning water by evaporation is more expensive than cleaning water by filtration. Evaporation requires more energy, which can come from a variety of sources. In this activity, you will use an electric hot plate as the energy source. See how well this method works to clean your sample of polluted water.

Form a Hypothesis

1. Write a hypothesis about which method you think will work better for water purification. Explain your reasoning.

Test the Hypothesis

2. Fill an Erlenmeyer flask with about 250 mL of the clean water, and insert the rubber stopper and glass tube into the flask.
3. Wearing goggles and gloves, connect about 1.5 m of plastic tubing to the glass tube.
4. Set the flask on the hot plate, and run the plastic tubing up and around the ring and down into a clean, empty 400 mL collection beaker.
5. Fill the sandwich bag with ice, seal the bag, and place the bag on the ring stand. Be sure the plastic bag and the tubing touch, as shown below.
6. Bring the water in the flask to a slow boil. As the water vapor passes by the bag of ice, the vapor will condense and drip into the collection beaker.
7. Observe the water in the collection beaker for color, particles, odor, suds, and pH. Record your observations in the "After evaporation" column in your data table.
8. Repeat steps 2–7 using the polluted water.

Analyze the Results

1. How did the color of the polluted water change after evaporation? Did the color of the clean water change after evaporation?
2. Did the evaporation method remove all of the particles from the polluted water? Explain.
3. How much did the pH of the polluted water change? Did the pH of the final clean water change? Was the final pH of the polluted water the same as the pH of the clean water before it was cleaned? Explain.

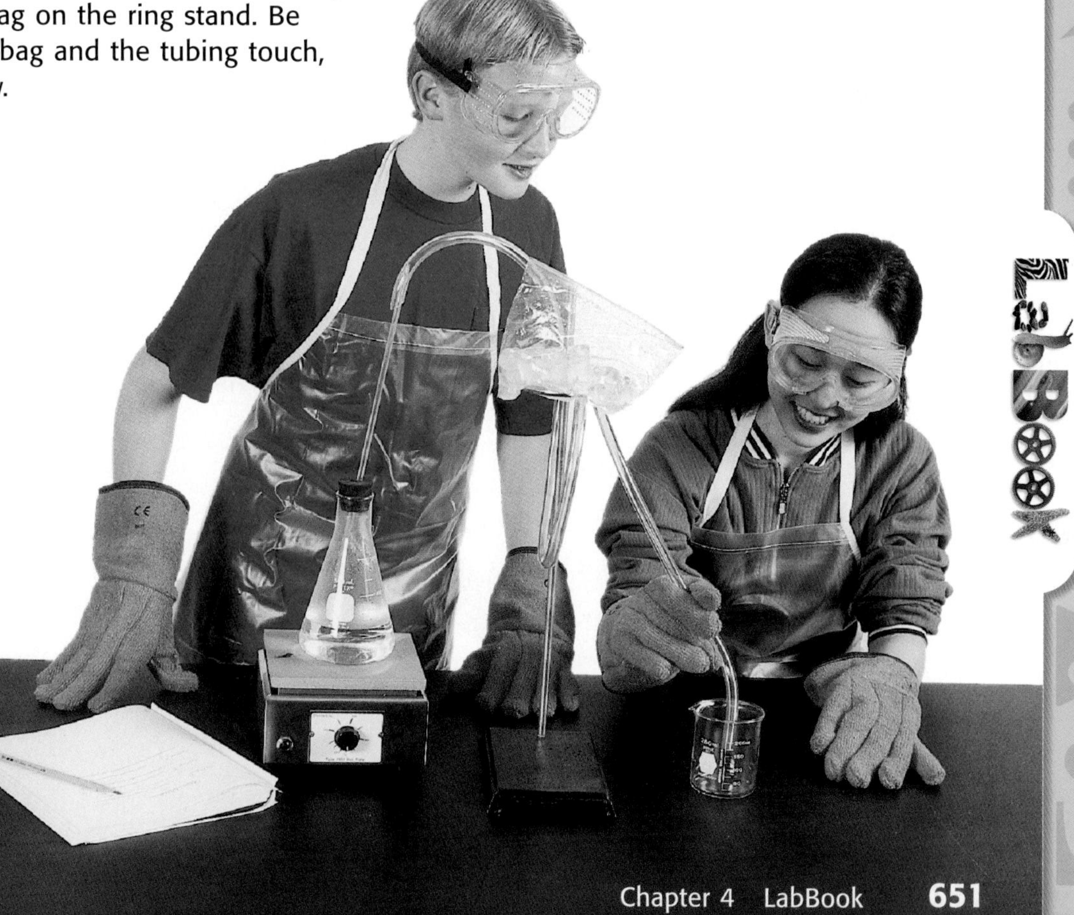

Draw Conclusions: Parts A and B

4. Which method—filtration or evaporation—removed the most pollutants from the water? Explain your reasoning.
5. Describe any changes that occurred in the clean water during this experiment.
6. What do you think are the advantages and disadvantages of each method?
7. Explain how you think each material (sand, gravel, and charcoal) used in the filtration system helped clean the water.
8. List areas of the country where you think each method of purification would be the most and the least beneficial. Explain your reasoning.

Applying Your Data

Do you think either purification method would remove oil from water? If time permits, repeat your experiment using several spoonfuls of cooking oil as the pollutant.

Filtration is only one step in the purification of water at water treatment plants. Use reference books, back issues of magazines, CD-ROMs, and computer databases to research other methods used to purify public water supplies.

Model-Making Lab

Turning the Tides

Daily tides are caused by two "bulges" on the ocean's surface—one on the side of the Earth facing the moon and the other on the opposite side of the Earth. The bulge on the side facing the moon is caused by the moon's gravitational pull on the water. But the bulge on the opposite side of the Earth is slightly more difficult to explain. Whereas the moon pulls the water on one side of the Earth, the combined rotation of the Earth and the moon "pushes" the water on the opposite side of the Earth. In this activity, you will model the motion of the Earth and the moon to investigate the tidal bulge on the side of Earth facing away from the moon.

MATERIALS

- cardboard, 1 cm × 1 cm piece
- corrugated cardboard, one large and one small, with centers marked (2 disks)
- dowel, $\frac{1}{4}$ in. in diameter and 36 cm long
- glue, white
- pencil, sharp
- stapler with staples
- string, 5 cm length

SAFETY

Procedure

1. Draw a line from the center of each disk along the folds in the cardboard to the edge of the disk. This line is the radius.
2. Place a drop of white glue on one end of the dowel. Lay the larger disk flat, and align the dowel with the line for the radius you drew in step 1. Insert about 2.5 cm of the dowel into the edge of the disk.
3. Add a drop of glue to the other end of the dowel, and push that end into the smaller disk, again along its radius. The setup should look like a large, two-headed lollipop, as shown below. This setup is a model of the Earth-moon system.
4. Staple the string to the edge of the large disk on the side opposite the dowel. Staple the cardboard square to the other end of the string. This smaller piece of cardboard represents the Earth's oceans that face away from the moon.
5. Place the tip of the pencil at the center of the large disk, as shown in the figure on the next page, and spin the model. You may poke a small hole in the bottom of the disk with your pencil, but DO NOT poke all the way through the cardboard. Record your observations. **Caution:** Be sure you are at a safe distance from other people before spinning your model.

6. Now, find your model's center of mass. The center of mass is the point at which the model can be balanced on the end of the pencil. (Hint: It might be easier to find the center of mass by using the eraser end. Then, use the sharpened end of the pencil to balance the model.) This balance point should be just inside the edge of the larger disk.

7. Place the pencil at the center of mass, and spin the model around the pencil. Again, you may wish to poke a small hole in the disk. Record your observations.

Analyze the Results

1. What happened when you tried to spin the model around the center of the large disk? This model, called the Earth-centered model, represents the incorrect view that the moon orbits the center of the Earth.

2. What happened when you tried to spin the model around its center of mass? This point, called the *barycenter,* is the point around which both the Earth and the moon rotate.

3. In each case, what happened to the string and cardboard square when the model was spun?

Draw Conclusions

4. Which model—the Earth-centered model or the barycentric model—explains why the Earth has a tidal bulge on the side opposite the moon? Explain.

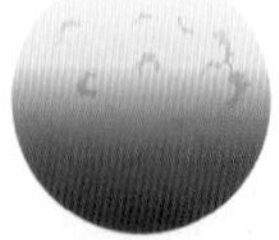

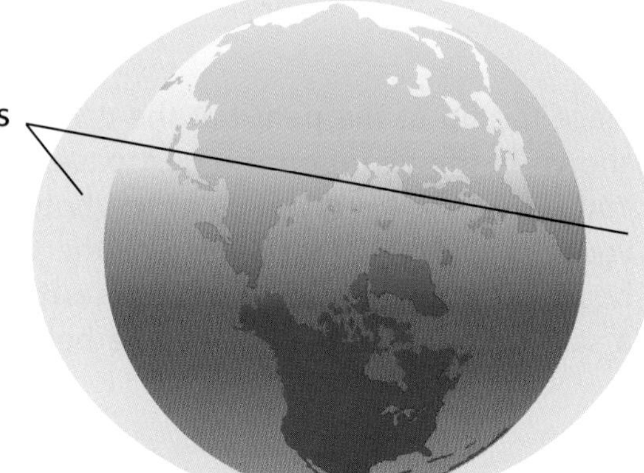

Using Scientific Methods

Skills Practice Lab

Go Fly a Bike!

Your friend Daniel just invented a bicycle that can fly! Trouble is, the bike can fly only when the wind speed is between 3 m/s and 10 m/s. If the wind is not blowing hard enough, the bike won't get enough lift to rise into the air, and if the wind is blowing too hard, the bike is difficult to control. Daniel needs to know if he can fly his bike today. Can you build a device that can estimate how fast the wind is blowing?

MATERIALS

- clay, modeling
- cups, paper, small (5)
- hole punch
- marker, colored
- pencil, sharp, with an eraser
- ruler, metric
- scissors
- stapler, small
- straws, straight plastic (2)
- tape, masking
- thumbtack
- watch (or clock) that indicates seconds

SAFETY

Ask a Question

1. How can I construct a device to measure wind speed?

Form a Hypothesis

2. Write a possible answer for the question above. Explain your reasoning.

Test the Hypothesis

3. Cut off the rolled edges of all five paper cups. They will then be lighter so that they can spin more easily.
4. Measure and place four equally spaced markings 1 cm below the rim of one of the paper cups.
5. Use the hole punch to punch a hole at each mark so that the cup has four equally spaced holes. Use the sharp pencil to carefully punch a hole in the center of the bottom of the cup.
6. Push a straw through two opposite holes in the side of the cup.
7. Repeat step 5 for the other two holes. The straws should form an X.
8. Measure 3 cm from the bottom of the remaining paper cups, and mark each spot with a dot.
9. At each dot, punch a hole in the paper cups with the hole punch.
10. Color the outside of one of the four cups.

11. Slide a cup on one of the straws by pushing the straw through the punched hole. Rotate the cup so that the bottom faces to the right.
12. Fold the end of the straw, and staple it to the inside of the cup directly across from the hole.
13. Repeat steps 11–12 for each of the remaining cups.
14. Push the tack through the intersection of the two straws.
15. Push the eraser end of a pencil through the bottom hole in the center cup. Push the tack as far as it will go into the end of the eraser.
16. Push the sharpened end of the pencil into some modeling clay to form a base. The device will then be able to stand up without being knocked over, as shown at right.
17. Blow into the cups so that they spin. Adjust the tack so that the cups can freely spin without wobbling or falling apart. Congratulations! You have just constructed an anemometer.
18. Find a suitable area outside to place the anemometer vertically on a surface away from objects that would obstruct the wind, such as buildings and trees.
19. Mark the surface at the base of the anemometer with masking tape. Label the tape "starting point."
20. Hold the colored cup over the starting point while your partner holds the watch.
21. Release the colored cup. At the same time, your partner should look at the watch or clock. As the cups spin, count the number of times the colored cup crosses the starting point in 10 s.

Analyze the Results

1. How many times did the colored cup cross the starting point in 10 s?
2. Divide your answer in step 21 by 10 to get the number of revolutions in 1 s.
3. Measure the diameter of your anemometer (the distance between the outside edges of two opposite cups) in centimeters. Multiply this number by 3.14 to get the circumference of the circle made by the cups of your anemometer.
4. Multiply your answer from step 3 by the number of revolutions per second (step 2). Divide that answer by 100 to get wind speed in meters per second.
5. Compare your results with those of your classmates. Did you get the same results? What could account for any slight differences in your results?

Draw Conclusions

6. Could Daniel fly his bicycle today? Why or why not?

Skills Practice Lab

Watching the Weather

Imagine that you own a private consulting firm that helps people plan for big occasions, such as weddings, parties, and celebrity events. One of your duties is making sure the weather doesn't put a damper on your clients' plans. In order to provide the best service possible, you have taken a crash course in reading weather maps. Will the celebrity golf match have to be delayed on account of rain? Will the wedding ceremony have to be moved inside so the blushing bride doesn't get soaked? It is your job to say yea or nay.

MATERIALS

- pencil

Procedure

1. Study the station model and legend shown on the next page. You will use the legend to interpret the weather map on the final page of this activity.
2. Weather data is represented on a weather map by a station model. A station model is a small circle that shows the location of the weather station along with a set of symbols and numbers around the circle that represent the data collected at the weather station. Study the table below.

Weather-Map Symbols

Weather conditions		Cloud cover		Wind speed (mph)	
••	Light rain	○	No clouds	◎	Calm
∴	Moderate rain	⦶	One-tenth or less		3–8
⁘	Heavy rain	◔	Two- to three-tenths		9–14
,	Drizzle	◕	Broken		15–20
∗ ∗	Light snow	◐	Nine-tenths		21–25
⁂	Moderate snow	●	Overcast		32–37
	Thunderstorm	⊗	Sky obscured		44–48
	Freezing rain	**Special Symbols**			55–60
∞	Haze		Cold front		66–71
≡	Fog		Warm front		
		H	High pressure		
		L	Low pressure		
			Hurricane		

Station Model

Wind speed is represented by whole and half tails.

A line indicates the direction the wind is coming from.

Air temperature

A symbol represents the current weather conditions. If there is no symbol, there is no precipitation.

Dew point temperature

Shading indicates the cloud coverage.

234

77

73

Atmospheric pressure in millibars (mbar). This number has been shortened on the station model. To read the number properly you must follow a few simple rules.

- If the first number is greater than 5, place a 9 in front of the number and a decimal point between the last two digits.
- If the first number is less than or equal to 5, place a 10 in front of the number and a decimal point between the last two digits.

Interpreting Station Models

The station model below is for Boston, Massachusetts. The current temperature in Boston is 42°F, and the dew point is 39°F. The barometric pressure is 1011.0 mbar. The sky is overcast, and there is moderate rainfall. The wind is coming from the southwest at 15–20 mph.

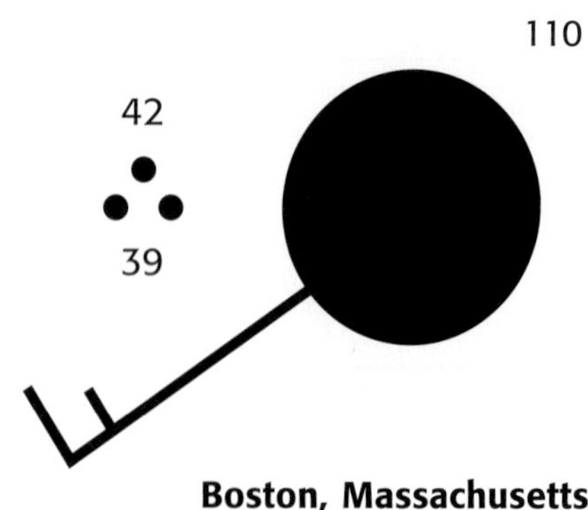

Boston, Massachusetts

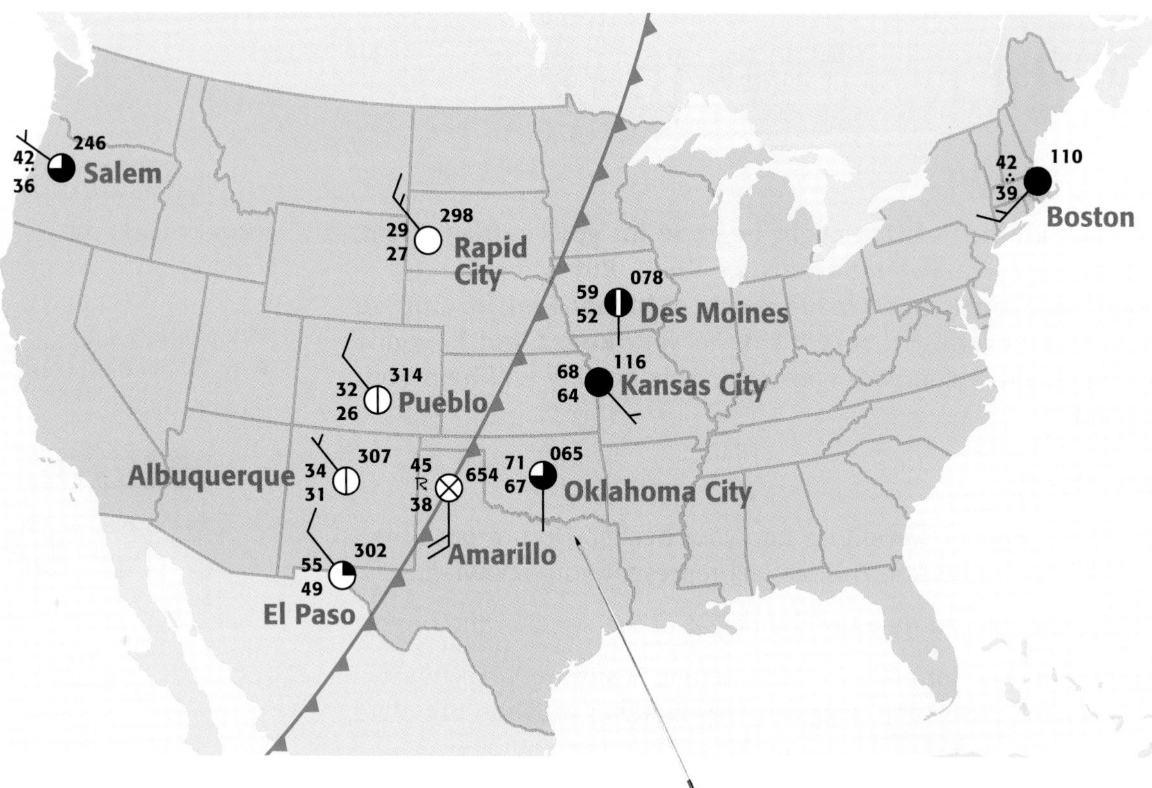

Analyze the Results

1. Based on the weather for the entire United States, what time of year is it? Explain your answer.
2. Interpret the station model for Salem, Oregon. What is the temperature, dew point, cloud coverage, wind direction, wind speed, and atmospheric pressure? Is there any precipitation? If so, what kind?
3. What is happening to wind direction, temperature, and pressure as the cold front approaches? as it passes?

Draw Conclusions

4. Interpret the station model for Amarillo, Texas.

Skills Practice Lab

Let It Snow!

Although an inch of rain might be good for your garden, 7 cm or 8 cm could cause an unwelcome flood. But what about snow? How much snow is too much? A blizzard might drop 40 cm of snow overnight. Sure it's up to your knees, but how does this much snow compare with rain? This activity will help you find out.

MATERIALS

- beaker, 100 mL
- gloves, heat-resistant
- graduated cylinder
- hot plate
- ice, shaved, 150 mL
- ruler, metric

SAFETY

Procedure

1. Pour 50 mL of shaved ice into your beaker. Do not pack the ice into the beaker. This ice will represent your snowfall.
2. Use the ruler to measure the height of the snow in the beaker.
3. Turn on the hot plate to a low setting. **Caution:** Wear heat-resistant gloves and goggles when working with the hot plate.
4. Place the beaker on the hot plate, and leave it there until all of the snow melts.
5. Pour the water into the graduated cylinder, and record the height and volume of the water.
6. Repeat steps 1–5 two more times.

Analysis

1. What was the difference in height before and after the snow melted in each of your three trials? What was the average difference?
2. Why did the volume change after the ice melted?
3. What was the ratio of snow height to water height?
4. Use the ratio you found in step 3 of the Analysis to calculate how much water 50 cm of this snow would produce. Use the following equation to help.

$$\frac{\text{measured height of snow}}{\text{measured height of water}} = \frac{\text{50 cm of snow}}{\text{? cm of water}}$$

5. Why is it important to know the water content of a snowfall?

Applying Your Data

Shaved ice isn't really snow. Research to find out how much water real snow would produce. Does every snowfall produce the same ratio of snow height to water depth?

Using Scientific Methods

Model-Making Lab

Gone with the Wind

Pilots at the Fly Away Airport need your help—fast! Last night, lightning destroyed the orange windsock. This windsock helped pilots measure which direction the wind was blowing. But now the windsock is gone with the wind, and an incoming airplane needs to land. The pilot must know which direction the wind is blowing and is counting on you to make a device that can measure wind direction.

MATERIALS

- card, index
- compass, drawing
- compass, magnetic
- pencil, sharpened
- plate, paper
- protractor
- rock, small
- ruler, metric
- scissors
- stapler
- straw, straight plastic
- thumbtack (or pushpin)

SAFETY

Ask a Question

1. How can I measure wind direction?

Form a Hypothesis

2. Write a possible answer to the question above.

Test the Hypothesis

3. Find the center of the plate by tracing around its edge with a drawing compass. The pointed end of the compass should poke a small hole in the center of the plate.
4. Use a ruler to draw a line across the center of the plate.
5. Use a protractor to help you draw a second line through the center of the plate. This new line should be at a 90° angle to the line you drew in step 4.
6. Moving clockwise, label each line "N," "E," "S," and "W."
7. Use a protractor to help you draw two more lines through the center of the plate. These lines should be at a 45° angle to the lines you drew in steps 4 and 5.

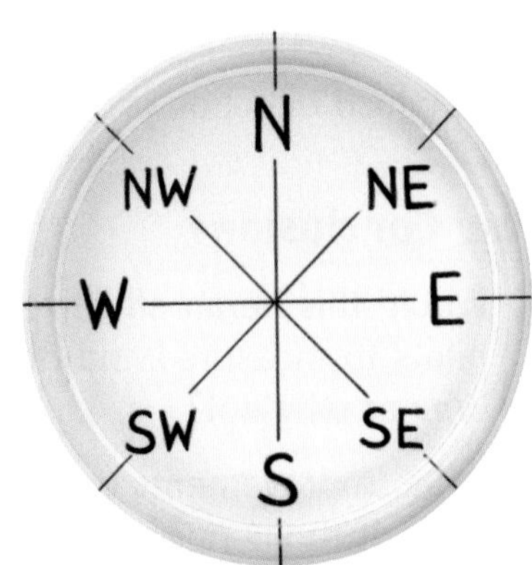

8. Moving clockwise from *N*, label these new lines "NE," "SE," "SW," and "NW." The plate now resembles the face of a magnetic compass. The plate will be the base of your wind-direction indicator. It will help you read the direction of the wind at a glance.

9. Measure and mark a 5 cm × 5 cm square on an index card, and cut out the square. Fold the square in half to form a triangle.

10. Staple an open edge of the triangle to the straw so that one point of the triangle touches the end of the straw.

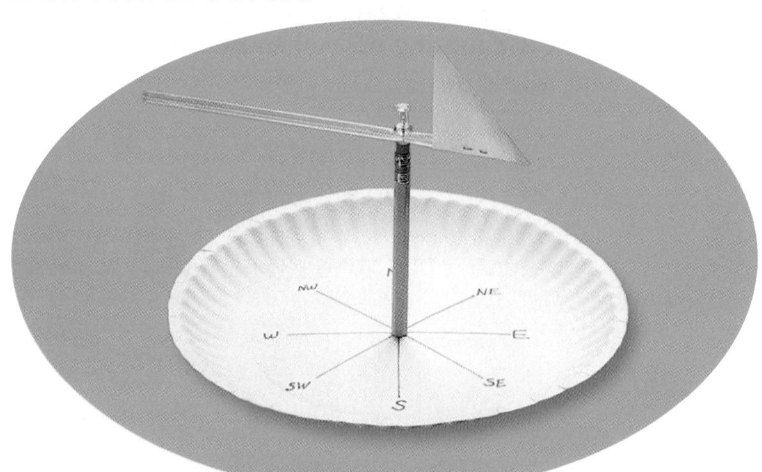

11. Hold the pencil at a 90° angle to the straw. The eraser should touch the balance point of the straw. Push a thumbtack or pushpin through the straw and into the eraser. The straw should spin without falling off.

12. Find a suitable area outside to measure the wind direction. The area should be clear of trees and buildings.

13. Press the sharpened end of the pencil through the center hole of the plate and into the ground. The labels on your paper plate should be facing the sky, as shown on this page.

14. Use a compass to find magnetic north. Rotate the plate so that the *N* on the plate points north. Place a small rock on top of the plate so that the plate does not turn.

15. Watch the straw as it rotates. The triangle will point in the direction the wind is blowing.

Analyze the Results

1. From which direction is the wind coming?
2. In which direction is the wind blowing?

Draw Conclusions

3. Would this be an effective way for pilots to measure wind direction? Why or why not?
4. What improvements would you suggest to Fly Away Airport to measure wind direction more accurately?

Applying Your Data

Use this tool to measure and record wind direction for several days. What changes in wind direction occur as a front approaches? as a front passes?

Review magnetic declination in the chapter entitled "Maps as Models of the Earth." How might magnetic declination affect your design for a tool to measure wind direction?

Using Scientific Methods

Skills Practice Lab

The Sun's Yearly Trip Through the Zodiac

During the course of a year, the sun appears to move through a circle of 12 constellations in the sky. The 12 constellations make up a "belt" in the sky called the *zodiac.* Each month, the sun appears to be in a different constellation. The ancient Babylonians developed a 12-month calendar based on the idea that the sun moved through this circle of constellations as it revolved around the Earth. They believed that the constellations of stars were fixed in position and that the sun and planets moved past the stars. Later, Copernicus developed a model of the solar system in which the Earth and the planets revolve around the sun. But how can Copernicus's model of the solar system be correct when the sun appears to move through the zodiac?

MATERIALS

- ball, inflated
- box, cardboard, large
- cards, index (12)
- chairs (12)
- tape, masking (1 roll)

Ask a Question

1. If the sun is at the center of the solar system, why does it appear to move with respect to the stars in the sky?

Form a Hypothesis

2. Write a possible answer to the question above. Explain your reasoning.

Test the Hypothesis

3. Set the chairs in a large circle so that the backs of the chairs all face the center of the circle. Make sure that the chairs are equally spaced, like the numbers on the face of a clock.
4. Write the name of each constellation in the zodiac on the index cards. You should have one card for each constellation.
5. Stand inside the circle with the masking tape and the index cards. Moving counterclockwise, attach the cards to the backs of the chairs in the following order: Aries, Taurus, Gemini, Cancer, Leo, Virgo, Libra, Scorpio, Sagittarius, Capricorn, Aquarius, and Pisces.
6. Use masking tape to label the ball "Sun."
7. Place the large, closed box in the center of the circle. Set the roll of masking tape flat on top of the box.

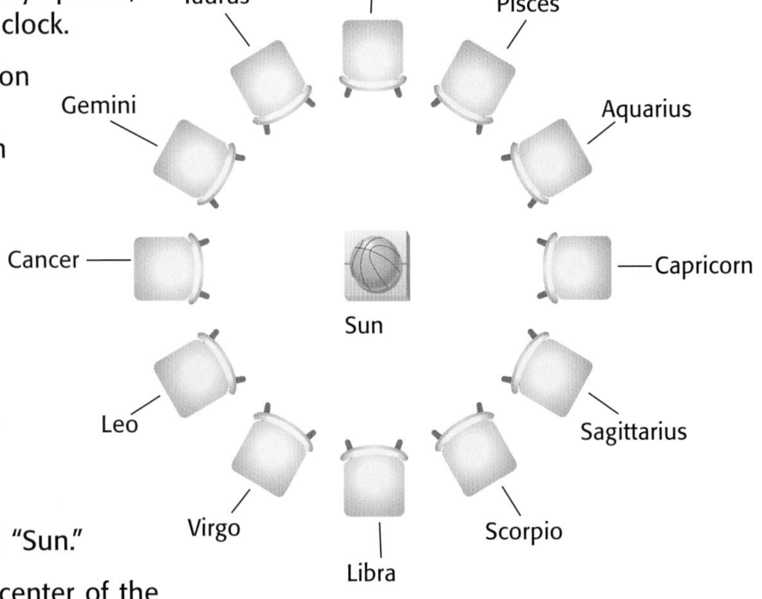

8. Place the ball on top of the roll of masking tape so that the ball stays in place.
9. Stand inside the circle of chairs. You will represent the Earth. As you move around the ball, you will model the Earth's orbit around the sun. Notice that even though only the "Earth" is moving, as seen from the Earth, the sun appears to move through the entire zodiac!
10. Stand in front of the chair labeled "Aries." Look at the ball representing the sun. Then, look past the ball to the chair at the opposite side of the circle. Where in the zodiac does the sun appear to be?
11. Move to the next chair on your right (counterclockwise). Where does the sun appear to be? Is it in the same constellation? Explain your answer.
12. Repeat step 10 until you have observed the position of the sun from each chair in the circle.

Analyze the Results

1. Did the sun appear to move through the 12 constellations, even though the Earth was orbiting around the sun? How can you explain this apparent movement?

Draw Conclusions

2. How does Copernicus's model of the solar system explain the apparent movement of the sun through the constellations of the zodiac?

Skills Practice Lab

Volumania!

You have learned how to measure the volume of a solid object that has square or rectangular sides. But there are lots of objects in the world that have irregular shapes. In this lab activity, you'll learn some ways to find the volume of objects that have irregular shapes.

MATERIALS

Part A

- graduated cylinder
- water
- various small objects supplied by your teacher

Part B

- bottle, plastic (or similar container), 2L, bottom half
- funnel
- graduated cylinder
- pan, aluminum pie
- paper towels
- water

SAFETY

Part A: Finding the Volume of Small Objects

Procedure

1. Fill a graduated cylinder half full with water. Read and record the volume of the water. Be sure to look at the surface of the water at eye level and to read the volume at the bottom of the meniscus, as shown below.

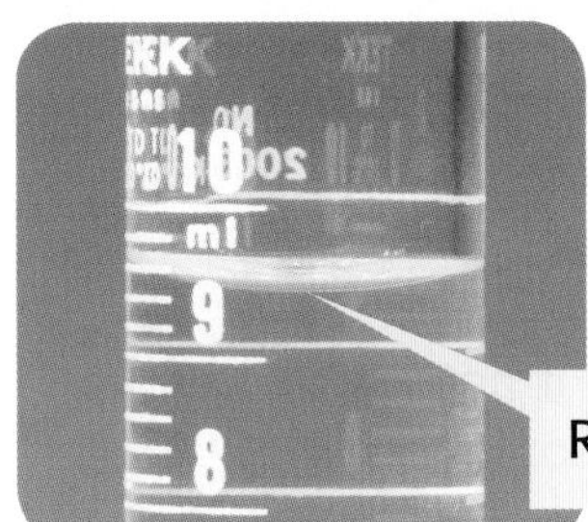

2. Carefully slide one of the objects into the tilted graduated cylinder, as shown below.
3. Read the new volume, and record it.
4. Subtract the old volume from the new volume. The resulting amount is equal to the volume of the solid object.
5. Use the same method to find the volume of the other objects. Record your results.

Analyze the Results

1. What changes do you have to make to the volumes you determine in order to express them correctly?
2. Do the heaviest objects always have the largest volumes? Why or why not?

Part B: Finding the Volume of Your Hand

Procedure

1. Completely fill the container with water. Put the container in the center of the pie pan. Be sure not to spill any of the water into the pie pan.
2. Make a fist, and put your hand into the container up to your wrist.
3. Remove your hand, and let the excess water drip into the container, not the pie pan. Dry your hand with a paper towel.
4. Use the funnel to pour the overflow water into the graduated cylinder. Measure the volume. This measurement is the volume of your hand. Record the volume. (Remember to use the
correct unit of volume for a solid object.)
5. Repeat this procedure with your other hand.

Analyze the Results

1. Was the volume the same for both of your hands? If not, were you surprised? What might account for a person's hands having different volumes?
2. Would it have made a difference if you had placed your open hand into the container instead of your fist? Explain your reasoning.
3. Compare the volume of your right hand with the volume of your classmates' right hands. Create a class graph of right-hand volumes. What is the average right-hand volume for your class?

Applying Your Data

Design an experiment to determine the volume of a person's body. In your plans, be sure to include the materials needed for the experiment and the procedures that must be followed. Include a sketch that shows how your materials and methods would be used in this experiment.

Using an encyclopedia, the Internet, or other reference materials, find out how the volumes of very large samples of matter—such as an entire planet—are determined.

Skills Practice Lab

Determining Density

The density of an object is its mass divided by its volume. But how does the density of a small amount of a substance relate to the density of a larger amount of the same substance? In this lab, you will calculate the density of one marble and of a group of marbles. Then, you will confirm the relationship between the mass and volume of a substance.

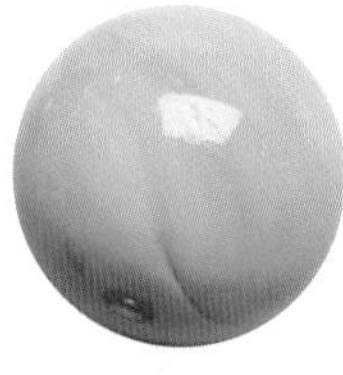

MATERIALS

- balance, metric
- graduated cylinder, 100 mL
- marbles, glass (8–10)
- paper, graph
- paper towels
- water

SAFETY

Procedure

1. Copy the table below. Include one row for each marble.

Mass of marble (g)	Total mass of marbles (g)	Total volume (mL)	Volume of marbles (mL) (total volume minus 50.0 mL)	Density of marbles (g/mL) (total mass divided by volume)
		DO NOT WRITE IN BOOK		

2. Fill the graduated cylinder with 50 mL of water. If you put in too much water, twist one of the paper towels, and use it to absorb excess water.
3. Measure the mass of a marble as accurately as you can (to at least .01 g). Record the mass in the table.
4. Carefully drop the marble in the tilted cylinder, and measure the total volume. Record the volume in the third column.
5. Measure and record the mass of another marble. Add the masses of the marbles together, and record this value in the second column of the table.
6. Carefully drop the second marble in the graduated cylinder. Complete the row of information in the table.
7. Repeat steps 5 and 6. Add one marble at a time. Stop when you run out of marbles, the water no longer completely covers the marbles, or the graduated cylinder is full.

Analyze the Results

1. Examine the data in your table. As the number of marbles increases, what happens to the total mass of the marbles? What happens to the volume of the marbles? What happens to the density of the marbles?
2. Graph the total mass of the marbles (y-axis) versus the volume of the marbles (x-axis). Is the graph a straight line?

Draw Conclusions

3. Does the density of a substance depend on the amount of substance present? Explain how your results support your answer.

Applying Your Data

Calculate the slope of the graph. How does the slope compare with the values in the column entitled "Density of marbles"? Explain.

Using Scientific Methods

Skills Practice Lab

Layering Liquids

You have learned that liquids form layers according to the densities of the liquids. In this lab, you'll discover whether it matters in which order you add the liquids.

MATERIALS

- beaker (or other small, clear container)
- funnel (3)
- graduated cylinder, 10 mL (3)
- liquid A
- liquid B
- liquid C

SAFETY

Ask a Question

1. Does the order in which you add liquids of different densities to a container affect the order of the layers formed by those liquids?

Form a Hypothesis

2. Write a possible answer to the question above.

Test the Hypothesis

3. Using the graduated cylinders, add 10 mL of each liquid to the clear container. Remember to read the volume at the bottom of the meniscus, as shown below. Record the order in which you added the liquids.
4. Observe the liquids in the container. Sketch what you see. Be sure to label the layers and the colors.
5. Add 10 mL more of liquid C. Observe what happens, and record your observations.
6. Add 20 mL more of liquid A. Observe what happens, and record your observations.

Analyze the Results

1. Which of the liquids has the greatest density? Which has the least density? How can you tell?
2. Did the layers change position when you added more of liquid C? Explain your answer.
3. Did the layers change position when you added more of liquid A? Explain your answer.
4. Find out in what order your classmates added the liquids to the container. Compare your results with those of a classmate who added the liquids in a different order. Were your results different? Explain why or why not.

Draw Conclusions

5. Based on your results, evaluate your hypothesis from step 2.

Using Scientific Methods

Skills Practice Lab

A Sugar Cube Race!

If you drop a sugar cube into a glass of water, how long will it take to dissolve? What can you do to speed up the rate at which it dissolves? Should you change something about the water, the sugar cube, or the process? In other words, what variable should you change? Before reading further, make a list of variables that could be changed in this situation. Record your list.

MATERIALS

- beakers or other clear containers (2)
- clock or stopwatch
- graduated cylinder
- sugar cubes (2)
- water
- other materials approved by your teacher

SAFETY

Ask a Question

1. Write a question you can test about factors that affect the rate sugar dissolves.

Form a Hypothesis

2. Choose one variable to test. Record your choice, and predict how changing your variable will affect the rate of dissolving.

Test the Hypothesis

3. Pour 150 mL of water into one of the beakers. Add one sugar cube, and use the stopwatch to measure how long it takes for the sugar cube to dissolve. You must not disturb the sugar cube in any way! Record this time.
4. Be sure to get your teacher's approval before you begin. You may need additional equipment.
5. Prepare your materials to test the variable you have picked. When you are ready, start your procedure for speeding up the rate at which the sugar cube dissolves. Use the stopwatch to measure the time. Record this time.

Analyze the Results

1. Compare your results with the prediction you made in step 2. Was your prediction correct? Why or why not?

Draw Conclusions

2. Why was it necessary to observe the sugar cube dissolving on its own before you tested the variable?
3. Do you think changing more than one variable would speed up the rate of dissolving even more? Explain your reasoning.
4. Discuss your results with a group that tested a different variable. Which variable had a greater effect on the rate of dissolving?

Skills Practice Lab

Making Butter

A colloid is an interesting substance. It has properties of both solutions and suspensions. Colloidal particles are not heavy enough to settle out, so they remain evenly dispersed throughout the mixture. In this activity, you will make butter—a very familiar colloid—and observe the characteristics that classify butter as a colloid.

MATERIALS

- clock or stopwatch
- container with lid, small, clear
- heavy cream
- marble

SAFETY

Procedure

1. Place a marble inside the container, and fill the container with heavy cream. Put the lid tightly on the container.
2. Take turns shaking the container vigorously and constantly for 10 min. Record the time when you begin shaking. Every minute, stop shaking the container, and hold it up to the light. Record your observations.
3. Continue shaking the container, taking turns if necessary. When you see, hear, or feel any changes inside the container, note the time and change.
4. After 10 min of shaking, you should have a lump of "butter" surrounded by liquid inside the container. Describe both the butter and the liquid in detail.
5. Let the container sit for about 10 min. Observe the butter and liquid again, and record your observations.

Analyze the Results

1. When you noticed the change inside the container, what did you think was happening at that point?
2. Based on your observations, explain why butter is classified as a colloid.
3. What kind of mixture is the liquid that is left behind? Explain.

LabBook

Model-Making Lab

Unpolluting Water

In many cities, the water supply comes from a river, lake, or reservoir. This water may include several mixtures, including suspensions (with suspended dirt, oil, or living organisms) and solutions (with dissolved chemicals). To make the water safe to drink, your city's water supplier must remove impurities. In this lab, you will model the procedures used in real water treatment plants.

MATERIALS

- beaker, 250 mL (4)
- charcoal, activated, washed
- cup, plastic-foam, 8 oz (2)
- graduated cylinder
- nail, small
- paper, filter (2 pieces)
- rubber band
- ruler, metric
- sand, fine, washed
- scissors
- spoon, plastic (2)
- water, "polluted"

Part A: Untreated Water

Procedure

1. Measure 100 mL of "polluted" water into a graduated cylinder. Be sure to shake the bottle of water before you pour so your sample will include all the impurities.
2. Pour the contents of the graduated cylinder into one of the beakers.
3. Copy the table below, and record your observations of the water in the "Before treatment" row.

Observations						
	Color	Clearness	Odor	Any layers?	Any solids?	Water volume
Before treatment						
After oil separation						
After sand filtration			DO NOT WRITE IN BOOK			
After charcoal						

Part B: Settling In

If a suspension is left standing, the suspended particles will settle to the top or bottom. You should see a layer of oil at the top.

Procedure

1. Separate the oil by carefully pouring the oil into another beaker. You can use a plastic spoon to get the last bit of oil from the water. Record your observations.

Part C: Filtration

Cloudy water can be a sign of small particles still in suspension. These particles can usually be removed by filtering. Water treatment plants use sand and gravel as filters.

Procedure

1. Make a filter as follows:
   - **a.** Use the nail to poke 5 to 10 small holes in the bottom of one of the cups.
   - **b.** Cut a circle of filter paper to fit inside the bottom of the cup. (This filter will keep the sand in the cup.)
   - **c.** Fill the cup to 2 cm below the rim with wet sand. Pack the sand tightly.
   - **d.** Set the cup inside an empty beaker.
2. Pour the polluted water on top of the sand, and let the water filter through. Do not pour any of the settled mud onto the sand. (Dispose of the mud as instructed by your teacher.) In your table, record your observations of the water collected in the beaker.

Part D: Separating Solutions

Something that has been dissolved in a solvent cannot be separated using filters. Water treatment plants use activated charcoal to absorb many dissolved chemicals.

Procedure

1. Place activated charcoal about 3 cm deep in the unused cup. Pour the water collected from the sand filtration into the cup, and stir with a spoon for 1 min.
2. Place a piece of filter paper over the top of the cup, and fasten it in place with a rubber band. With the paper securely in place, pour the water through the filter paper and back into a clean beaker. Record your observations in your table.

Analyze the Results

1. Is your unpolluted water safe to drink? Why or why not?
2. When you treat a sample of water, do you get out exactly the same amount of water that you put in? Explain your answer.
3. Some groups may still have cloudy water when they finish. Explain a possible cause for this.

Skills Practice Lab

Energy of a Pendulum

A pendulum clock is a compound machine that uses stored energy to do work. A spring stores energy, and with each swing of the pendulum, some of that stored energy is used to move the hands of the clock. In this lab, you will take a close look at the energy conversions that occur as a pendulum swings.

MATERIALS

- marker
- mass, hooked, 100 g
- meterstick
- string, 1 m

SAFETY

Procedure

1. Make a pendulum by tying the string around the hook of the mass. Use the marker and the meterstick to mark points on the string that are 50 cm, 70 cm, and 90 cm away from the mass.
2. Hold the string at the 50 cm mark. Gently pull the mass to the side, and release it without pushing it. Observe at least 10 swings of the pendulum.
3. Record your observations. Be sure to note how fast and how high the pendulum swings.
4. Repeat steps 2 and 3 while holding the string at the 70 cm mark and again while holding the string at the 90 cm mark.

Analyze the Results

1. List similarities and differences in the motion of the pendulum during all three trials.
2. At which point (or points) of the swing was the pendulum moving the slowest? the fastest?

Draw Conclusions

3. In each trial, at which point (or points) of the swing did the pendulum have the greatest potential energy? the least potential energy? (Hint: Think about your answers to question 2.)
4. At which point (or points) of the swing did the pendulum have the greatest kinetic energy? the least kinetic energy? Explain your answers.
5. Describe the relationship between the pendulum's potential energy and its kinetic energy on its way down. Explain.
6. What improvements might reduce the amount of energy used to overcome friction so that the pendulum would swing for a longer period of time?

Skills Practice Lab

Wave Speed, Frequency, and Wavelength

Wave speed, frequency, and wavelength are three related properties of waves. In this lab, you will make observations and collect data to determine the relationship among these properties.

MATERIALS

- meterstick
- stopwatch
- toy, coiled spring

SAFETY

Part A: Wave Speed

Procedure

1. Copy Table 1.

Table 1 Wave Speed Data			
Trial	Length of spring (m)	Time for wave (s)	Speed of wave (m/s)
1			
2			
3		DO NOT WRITE IN BOOK	
Average			

2. Two students should stretch the spring to a length of 2 m to 4 m on the floor or on a table. A third student should measure the length of the spring. Record the length in Table 1.
3. One student should pull part of the spring sideways with one hand, as shown at right, and release the pulled-back portion. This action will cause a wave to travel down the spring.
4. Using a stopwatch, the third student should measure how long it takes for the wave to travel down the length of the spring and back. Record this time in Table 1.
5. Repeat steps 3 and 4 two more times.

Part B: Wavelength and Frequency

Procedure

1. Keep the spring the same length that you used in Part A.
2. Copy Table 2.

***Table 2* Wavelength and Frequency Data**

Trial	Length of spring (m)	Time for 10 cycles (s)	Wave frequency (Hz)	Wavelength (m)
1				
2				
3				
Average				

3. One of the two students holding the spring should start shaking the spring from side to side until a wave pattern appears that resembles one of those shown.
4. Using the stopwatch, the third student should measure and record how long it takes for 10 cycles of the wave pattern to occur. (One back-and-forth shake is 1 cycle.) Keep the pattern going so that measurements for three trials can be made.

Analyze the Results

Part A

1. Calculate and record the wave speed for each trial. (Speed equals distance divided by time; distance is twice the spring length.)
2. Calculate and record the average time and the average wave speed.

Part B

3. Calculate the frequency for each trial by dividing the number of cycles (10) by the time. Record the answers in Table 2.
4. Determine the wavelength using the equation at right that matches your wave pattern. Record your answer in Table 2.
5. Calculate and record the average time and frequency.

Draw Conclusions: Parts A and B

6. Analyze the relationship among speed, wavelength, and frequency. Multiply or divide any two of them to see if the result equals the third. (Use the averages from your data tables.) Write the equation that shows the relationship.

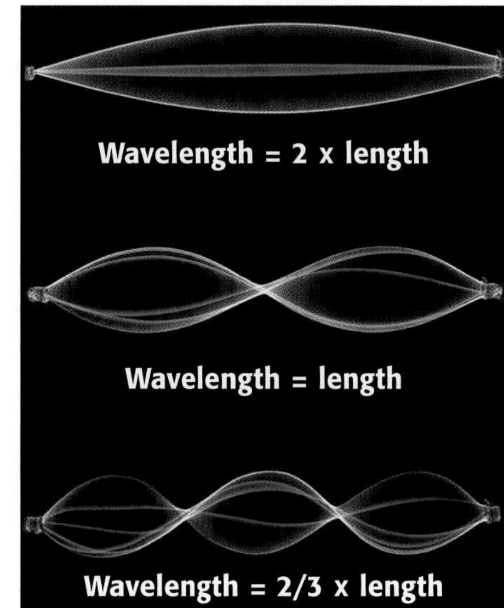

Skills Practice Lab

Cells Alive!

You have probably used a microscope to look at single-celled organisms such as those shown below. They can be found in pond water. In the following exercise, you will look at *Protococcus*—algae that form a greenish stain on tree trunks, wooden fences, flowerpots, and buildings.

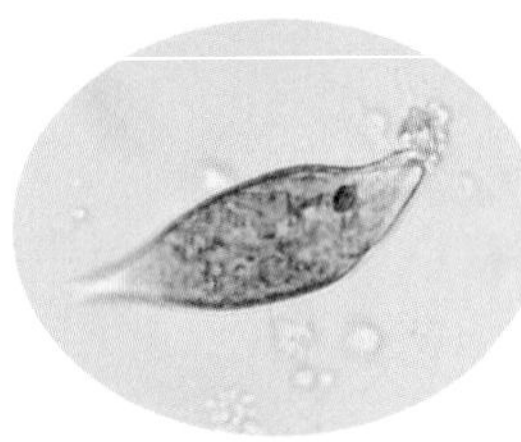

Euglena

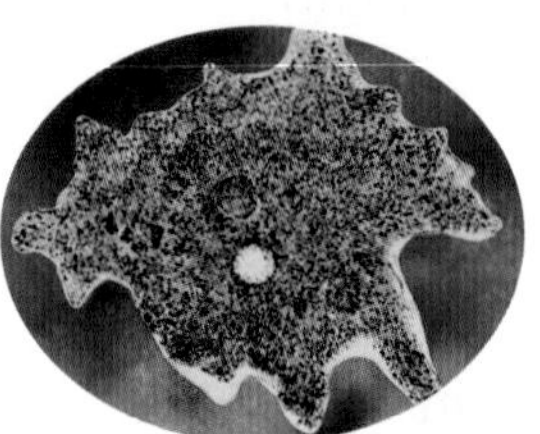

Amoeba

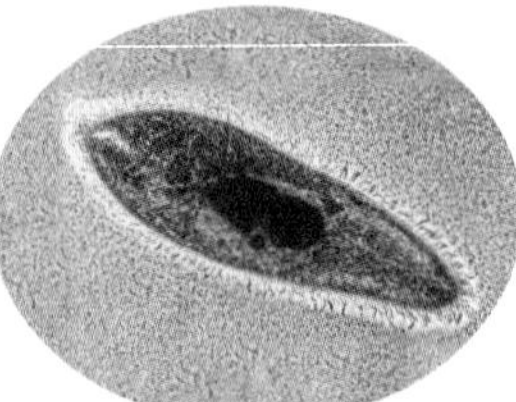

Paramecium

MATERIALS

- eyedropper
- microscope
- microscope slide and coverslip
- *Protococcus* (or other algae)
- water

SAFETY

Procedure

1. Locate some *Protococcus*. Scrape a small sample into a container. Bring the sample to the classroom, and make a wet mount of it as directed by your teacher. If you can't find *Protococcus* outdoors, look for algae on the glass in an aquarium. Such algae may not be *Protococcus,* but it will be a very good substitute.
2. Set the microscope on low power to examine the algae. On a separate sheet of paper, draw the cells that you see.
3. Switch to high power to examine a single cell. Draw the cell.
4. You will probably notice that each cell contains several chloroplasts. Label a chloroplast on your drawing. What is the function of the chloroplast?
5. Another structure that should be clearly visible in all the algae cells is the nucleus. Find the nucleus in one of your cells, and label it on your drawing. What is the function of the nucleus?
6. What does the cytoplasm look like? Describe any movement you see inside the cells.

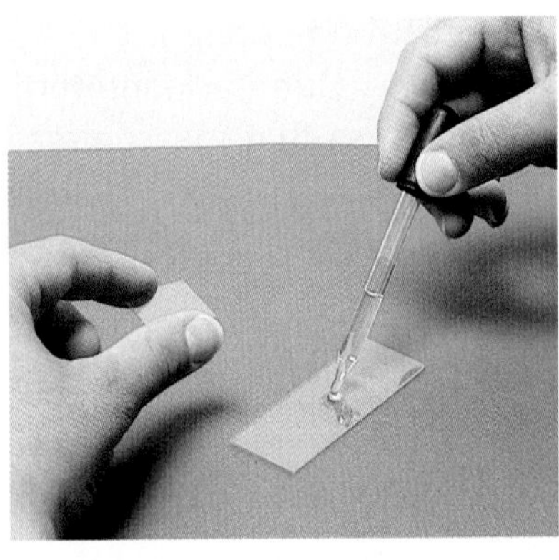

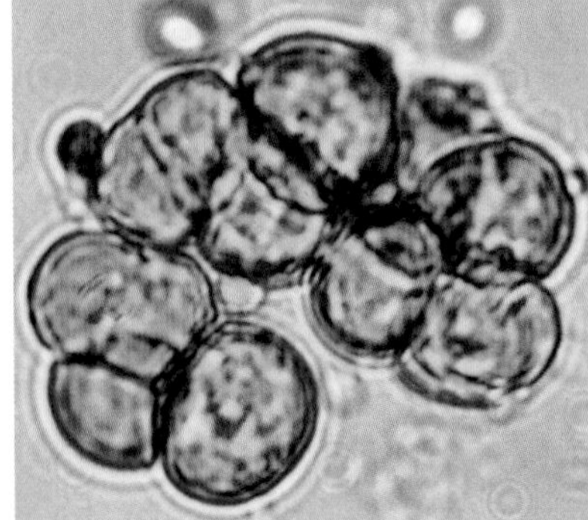

Protococcus

Analyze the Results

1. Are *Protococcus* single-celled organisms or multicellular organisms?
2. How are *Protococcus* different from amoebas?

Skills Practice Lab

Voyage of the USS *Adventure*

You are a crew member on the USS *Adventure*. The *Adventure* has been on a 5-year mission to collect life-forms from outside the solar system. On the voyage back to Earth, your ship went through a meteor shower, which ruined several of the compartments containing the extraterrestrial life-forms. Now it is necessary to put more than one life-form in the same compartment.

You have only three undamaged compartments in your starship. You and your crewmates must stay in one compartment, and that compartment should be used for extraterrestrial life-forms only if absolutely necessary. You and your crewmates must decide which of the life-forms could be placed together. It is thought that similar life-forms will have similar needs. You can use only observable characteristics to group the life-forms.

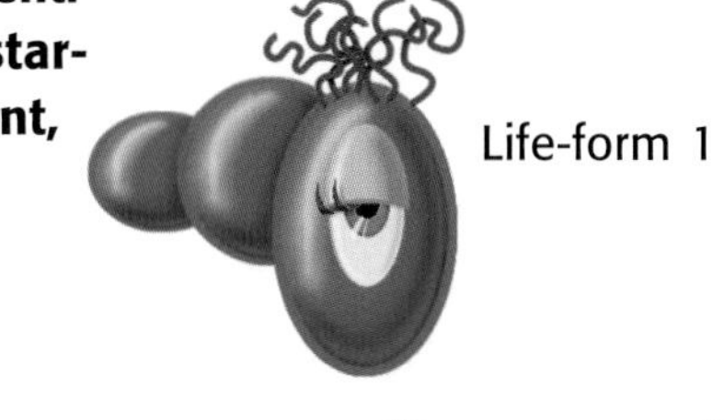

Life-form 2

Life-form 3

Life-form 4

Life-form 5

Procedure

1. Make a data table similar to the one below. Label each column with as many characteristics of the various life-forms as possible. Leave enough space in each square to write your observations. The life-forms are pictured on this page.

Life-form Characteristics				
	Color	Shape	Legs	Eyes
Life-form 1				
Life-form 2				
Life-form 3				
Life-form 4				

2. Describe each characteristic as completely as you can. Based on your observations, determine which of the life-forms are most alike.

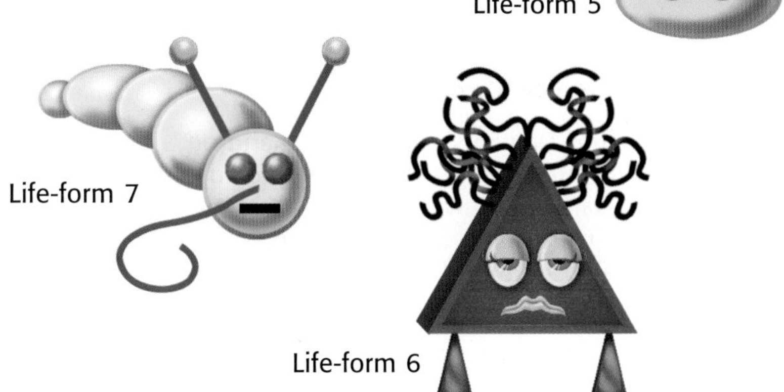

3. Make a data table like the one below. Fill in the table according to the decisions you made in step 2. State your reasons for the way you have grouped your life-forms.

Life-form Room Assignments		
Compartment	**Life-forms**	**Reasons**
1		
2		
3		DO NOT WRITE IN BOOK

4. The USS *Adventure* has to make one more stop before returning home. On planet X437 you discover the most interesting life-form ever found outside of Earth—the CC9, shown at right. Make a decision, based on your previous grouping of life-forms, about whether you can safely include CC9 in one of the compartments for the trip to Earth.

CC9

Analyze the Results

1. Describe the life-forms in compartment 1. How are they similar? How are they different?
2. Describe the life-forms in compartment 2. How are they similar? How do they differ from the life-forms in compartment 1?
3. Are there any life-forms in compartment 3? If so, describe their similarities. In which compartment will you and your crewmates remain for the journey home?

Draw Conclusions

4. Are you able to transport life-form CC9 safely back to Earth? If so, in which compartment will it be placed? How did you decide?

Applying Your Data

In 1831, Charles Darwin sailed from England on a ship called the HMS *Beagle*. You have studied the finches that Darwin observed on the Galápagos Islands. What were some of the other unusual organisms he found there? For example, find out about the Galápagos tortoise.

LabBook

Skills Practice Lab

Travelin' Seeds

You have learned from your study of plants that there are some very interesting and unusual plant adaptations. Some of the most interesting adaptations are modifications that allow plant seeds and fruits to be dispersed, or scattered, away from the parent plant. This dispersal enables the young seedlings to obtain the space, sun, and other resources they need without directly competing with the parent plant. In this activity, you will use your own creativity to disperse a seed.

MATERIALS

- bean seed
- seed-dispersal challenge card
- various household or recycled materials (examples: glue, tape, paper, paper clips, rubber bands, cloth, paper cups and plates, paper towels, and cardboard)

Procedure

1. Obtain a seed and a dispersal challenge card from your teacher. On a sheet of paper, record the type of challenge card you have been given.
2. Create a plan for using the available materials to disperse your seed, as described on the challenge card. Record your plan. Get your teacher's approval before proceeding.
3. With your teacher's permission, test your seed-dispersal method. Perform several trials. Make a data table, and record the results of your trials.

Analyze the Results

1. Were you able to complete the seed-dispersal challenge successfully? Explain.
2. Are there any modifications you could make to your method to improve the dispersal of your seed?

Draw Conclusions

3. Describe some plants that disperse their seeds in a way similar to your seed-dispersal method.

◀ Mangrove seed

◀ Cottonwood

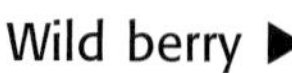

Wild berry ▶

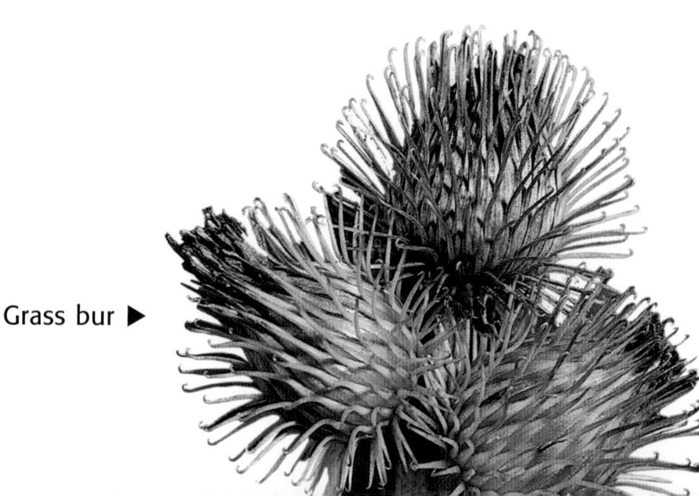

Grass bur ▶

Skills Practice Lab

Enzymes in Action

You know how important enzymes are in the process of digestion. This lab will help you see enzymes at work. Hydrogen peroxide is continuously produced by your cells. If it is not quickly broken down, hydrogen peroxide will kill your cells. Luckily, your cells contain an enzyme that converts hydrogen peroxide into two nonpoisonous substances. This enzyme is also present in the cells of beef liver. In this lab, you will observe the action of this enzyme on hydrogen peroxide.

MATERIALS

- beef liver, 1 cm cubes (3)
- gloves, protective
- graduated cylinder, 10 mL
- hydrogen peroxide, fresh (4 mL)
- mortar and pestle (or fork and watch glass)
- plate, small
- spatula
- test tube (3)
- test-tube rack
- tweezers
- water

SAFETY

Procedure

1. Draw a data table similar to the one below. Be sure to leave enough space to write your observations.

Data Table		
Size and condition of liver	**Experimental liquid**	**Observations**
1 cm cube beef liver	2 mL water	
1 cm cube beef liver	2 mL hydrogen peroxide	DO NOT WRITE IN BOOK
1 cm cube beef liver (mashed)	2 mL hydrogen peroxide	

2. Get three equal-sized pieces of beef liver from your teacher, and use your forceps to place them on your plate.
3. Pour 2 mL of water into a test tube labeled "Water and liver."
4. Using the tweezers, carefully place one piece of liver in the test tube. Record your observations in your data table.
5. Pour 2 mL of hydrogen peroxide into a second test tube labeled "Liver and hydrogen peroxide."
Caution: Do not splash hydrogen peroxide on your skin. If you do get hydrogen peroxide on your skin, rinse the affected area with running water immediately, and tell your teacher.
6. Using the tweezers, carefully place one piece of liver in the test tube. Record your observations of the second test tube in your data table.
7. Pour another 2 mL of hydrogen peroxide into a third test tube labeled "Ground liver and hydrogen peroxide."
8. Using a mortar and pestle (or fork and watch glass), carefully grind the third piece of liver.
9. Using the spatula, scrape the ground liver into the third test tube. Record your observations of the third test tube in your data table.

Analyze the Results

1. What was the purpose of putting the first piece of liver in water? Why was this a necessary step?
2. Describe the difference you observed between the liver and the ground liver when each was placed in the hydrogen peroxide. How can you account for this difference?

Applying Your Data

Do plant cells contain enzymes that break down hydrogen peroxide? Try this experiment using potato cubes instead of liver to find out.

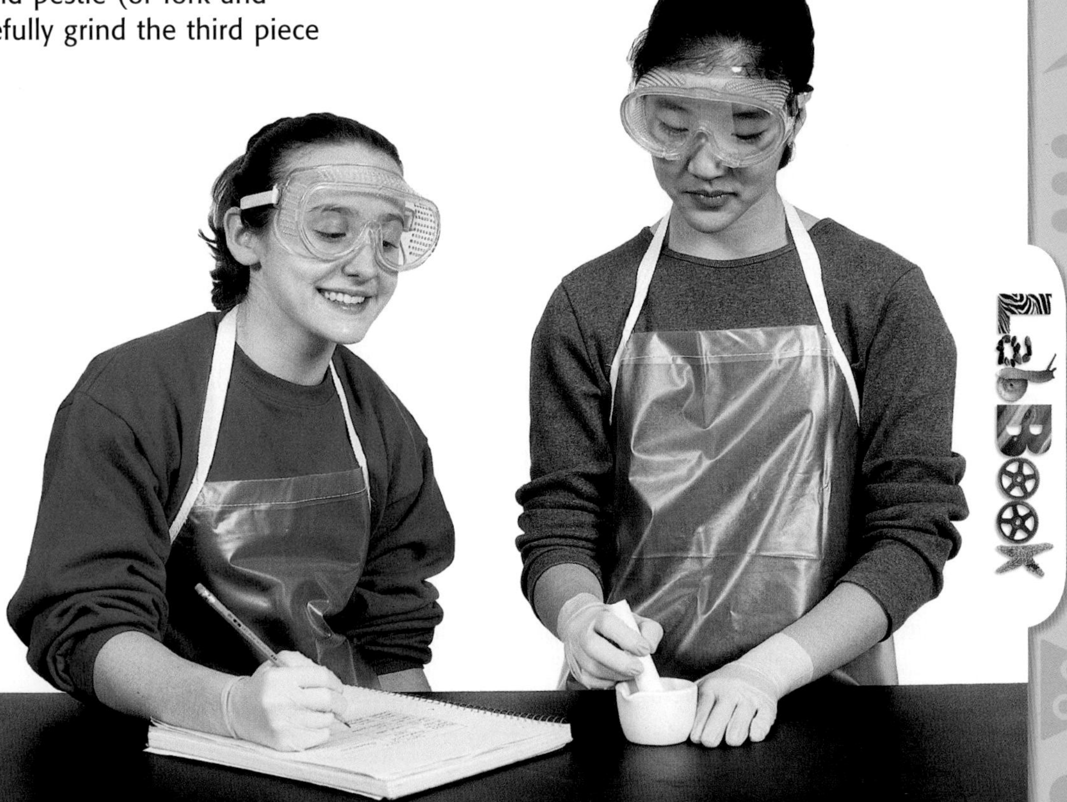

Skills Practice Lab

My, How You've Grown!

In humans, the process of development that takes place between fertilization and birth lasts about 266 days. In 4 weeks, the new individual grows from a single fertilized cell to an embryo whose heart is beating and pumping blood. All of the organ systems and body parts are completely formed by the end of the seventh month. During the last 2 months before birth, the baby grows, and its organ systems mature. At birth, the average mass of a baby is about 33,000 times as much as that of an embryo at 2 weeks of development! In this activity, you will discover just how fast a fetus grows.

MATERIALS

- paper, graph
- pencils, colored

Procedure

1. Using graph paper, make two graphs—one entitled "Length" and one entitled "Mass." On the length graph, use intervals of 25 mm on the *y*-axis. Extend the *y*-axis to 500 mm. On the mass graph, use intervals of 100 g on the *y*-axis. Extend this *y*-axis to 3,300 g. Use 2-week intervals for time on the *x*-axes for both graphs. Both *x*-axes should extend to 40 weeks.
2. Examine the data table at right. Plot the data in the table on your graphs. Use a colored pencil to draw the curved line that joins the points on each graph.

Increase of Mass and Length of Average Human Fetus

Time (weeks)	Mass (g)	Length (mm)
2	0.1	1.5
3	0.3	2.3
4	0.5	5.0
5	0.6	10.0
6	0.8	15.0
8	1.0	30.0
13	15.0	90.0
17	115.0	140.0
21	300.0	250.0
26	950.0	320.0
30	1,500.0	400.0
35	2,300.0	450.0
40	3,300.0	500.0

Analyze the Results

1. Describe the change in mass of a developing fetus. How can you explain this change?
2. Describe the change in length of a developing fetus. How does the change in mass compare to the change in length?

Applying Your Data

Using the information in your graphs, estimate how tall a child would be at age 3 if he or she continued to grow at the same average rate that a fetus grows.

LabBook

Model-Making Lab

Antibodies to the Rescue

Some cells of the immune system, called *B cells,* make antibodies that attack and kill invading viruses and microorganisms. These antibodies help make you immune to disease. Have you ever had chickenpox? If you have, your body has built up antibodies that can recognize that particular virus. Antibodies will attach themselves to the virus, tagging it for destruction. If you are exposed to the same disease again, the antibodies remember that virus. They will attack the virus even quicker and in greater number than they did the first time. This is the reason that you will probably never have chickenpox more than once.

In this activity, you will construct simple models of viruses and their antibodies. You will see how antibodies are specific for a particular virus.

MATERIALS

- craft materials, such as buttons, fabric scraps, pipe cleaners, and recycled materials
- paper, colored
- scissors
- tape (or glue)

Procedure

1. Draw the virus patterns shown on this page on a separate piece of paper, or design your own virus models from the craft supplies. Remember to design different receptors on each of your virus models.
2. Write a few sentences describing how your viruses are different.
3. Cut out the viruses, and attach them to a piece of colored paper with tape or glue.

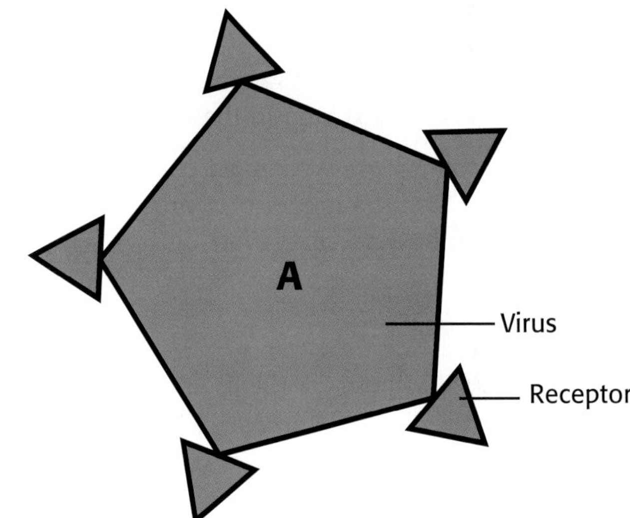

Viruses

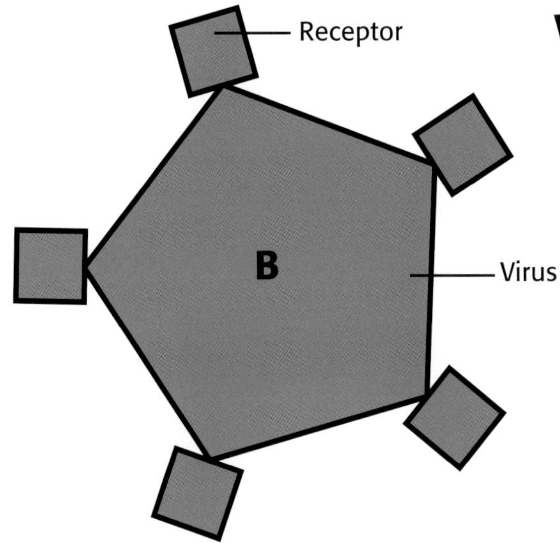

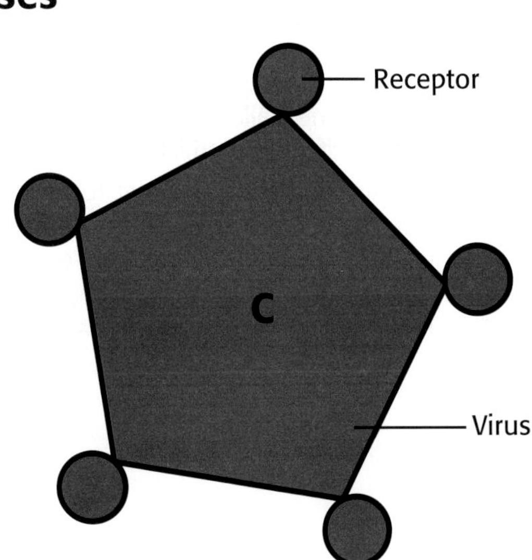

4. Select the antibodies drawn below, or design your own antibodies that will exactly fit on the receptors on your virus models. Draw or create each antibody enough times to attach one to each receptor site on the virus.

Antibodies

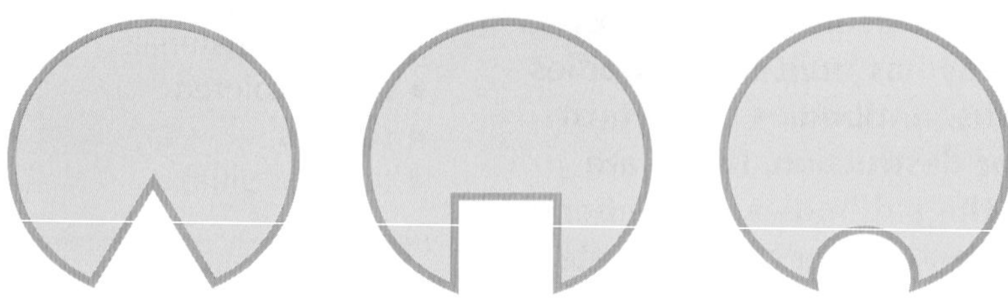

5. Cut out the antibodies you have drawn. Arrange the antibodies so that they bind to the virus at the appropriate receptor. Attach them to the virus with tape or glue.

Analyze the Results

1. Explain how an antibody "recognizes" a particular virus.
2. After the attachment of antibodies to the receptors, what would be the next step in the immune response?
3. Many vaccines use weakened copies of the virus to protect the body. Use the model of a virus and its specific antibody to explain how vaccines work.

Draw Conclusions

4. Use your model of a virus to demonstrate to the class how a receptor might change or mutate so that a vaccine would no longer be effective.

Applying Your Data

Research in the library or on the Internet to find information about the discovery of the Salk vaccine for polio. Include information on how polio affects people today.

Research in the library or on the Internet to find information and write a report about filoviruses. What do they look like? What diseases do they cause? Why are they especially dangerous? Is there an effective vaccine against any filovirus? Explain.

Model-Making Lab

Adaptation: It's a Way of Life

Since the beginning of life on Earth, species have had special characteristics called *adaptations* that have helped them survive changes in environmental conditions. Changes in a species' environment include climate changes, habitat destruction, or the extinction of prey. These things can cause a species to die out unless the species has a characteristic that helps it survive. For example, a species of bird may have an adaptation for eating sunflower seeds and ants. If the ant population dies out, the bird can still eat seeds and can therefore survive.

In this activity, you will explore several adaptations and design an organism with adaptations you choose. Then, you will describe how these adaptations help the organism survive.

MATERIALS

- arts-and-crafts materials, various
- markers, colored
- magazines for cutouts
- poster board
- scissors

SAFETY

Procedure

1. Study the chart below. Choose one adaptation from each column. For example, an organism might be a scavenger that burrows underground and has spikes on its tail!

Adaptations

Diet	Type of transportation	Special adaptation
carnivore	flies	uses sensors to detect heat
herbivore	glides through the air	is active only at night and has excellent night vision
omnivore	burrows underground	changes colors to match its surroundings
scavenger	runs fast	has armor
decomposer	swims	has horns
	hops	can withstand extreme temperature changes
	walks	secretes a terrible and sickening scent
	climbs	has poison glands
	floats	has specialized front teeth
	slithers	has tail spikes
		stores oxygen in its cells so it does not have to breathe continuously
		one of your own invention

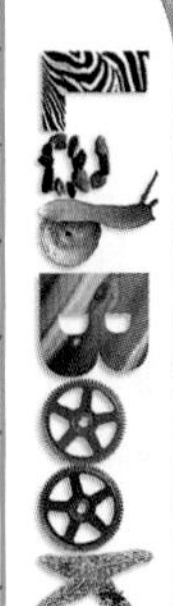

2. Design an organism that has the three adaptations you have chosen. Use poster board, colored markers, picture cutouts, or craft materials of your choosing to create your organism.
3. Write a caption on your poster describing your organism. Describe its appearance, its habitat, its niche, and the way its adaptations help it survive. Give your organism a two-part "scientific" name that is based on its characteristics.
4. Display your creation in your classroom. Share with classmates how you chose the adaptations for your organism.

Analyze the Results

1. What does your imaginary organism eat?
2. In what environment or habitat would your organism be most likely to survive—in the desert, tropical rain forest, plains, icecaps, mountains, or ocean? Explain your answer.
3. Is your creature a mammal, a reptile, an amphibian, a bird, or a fish? What modern organism (on Earth today) or ancient organism (extinct) is your imaginary organism most like? Explain the similarities between the two organisms. Do some research outside the lab, if necessary, to find out about a real organism that may be similar to your imaginary organism.

Draw Conclusions

4. If there were a sudden climate change, such as daily downpours of rain in a desert, would your imaginary organism survive? What adaptations for surviving such a change does it have?

Applying Your Data

Call or write to an agency such as the U.S. Fish and Wildlife Service to get a list of endangered species in your area. Choose an organism on that list. Describe the organism's niche and any special adaptations it has that help it survive. Find out why it is endangered and what is being done to protect it. Examine the illustration of the animal at right. Based on its physical characteristics, describe its habitat and niche. Is this a real animal?

Using Scientific Methods

Inquiry Lab

Life in the Desert

Organisms that live in the desert have some unusual methods for conserving water. Conserving water is a special challenge for animals that live in the desert. In this activity you will invent a water-conserving "adaptation" for a desert animal, represented by a piece of sponge. You will protect your wet desert sponge so it will dry out as little as possible over a 24 h period.

MATERIALS

- balance
- sponge, dry, 8 cm × 8 cm × 2 cm (2 pieces)
- water
- other materials as needed

Ask a Question

1. How can an animal conserve water in the desert?

Form a Hypothesis

2. Plan a method for keeping your "desert animal" from drying out. Your "animal" must be in the open for at least 4 h during the 24 h period. Real desert animals expose themselves to the dry desert heat to search for food. Write your plan and predictions about the outcome of your experiment.
3. Design and draw data tables, if necessary. Have your teacher approve your plan before you begin.

Test the Hypothesis

4. Soak two pieces of sponge in water until they begin to drip. Place each piece on a balance, and record its mass.
5. Immediately protect one sponge according to your plan. Place both pieces in an area where they will not be disturbed. You should take your protected "animal" out for feeding for a total of at least 4 h.
6. At the end of 24 h, place each piece of sponge on the balance again, and record its mass.

Analyze the Results

1. Describe the adaptation you used to help your "animal" survive. Was it effective? Explain.
2. What was the purpose of leaving one of the sponges unprotected? How did the water loss in each of your sponges compare?

Communicating Your Data

Conduct a class discussion about other adaptations and results. How can you relate these invented adaptations to adaptations for desert survival among real organisms?

Using Scientific Methods

Inquiry Lab

Discovering Mini-Ecosystems

In your study of ecosystems, you learned that a biome is a very large ecosystem that includes a set of smaller, related ecosystems. For example, a coniferous forest biome may include a river ecosystem, a wetland ecosystem, and a lake ecosystem. Each of those ecosystems may include several other smaller, related ecosystems. Even cities have mini-ecosystems! You may find a mini-ecosystem on a patch of sidewalk, in a puddle of rainwater, under a leaky faucet, in a shady area, or under a rock. In this activity, you will design a method for comparing two different mini-ecosystems found near your school.

MATERIALS

- items to be determined by the students and approved by the teacher

SAFETY

Ask a Question

1. Examine the grounds around your school, and select two different areas you wish to investigate. Decide what you want to learn about your mini-ecosystems. For example, you may want to know what kind of living things each area contains. Be sure to get your teacher's approval before you begin.

Form a Hypothesis

2. For each mini-ecosystem, make data tables for recording your observations.

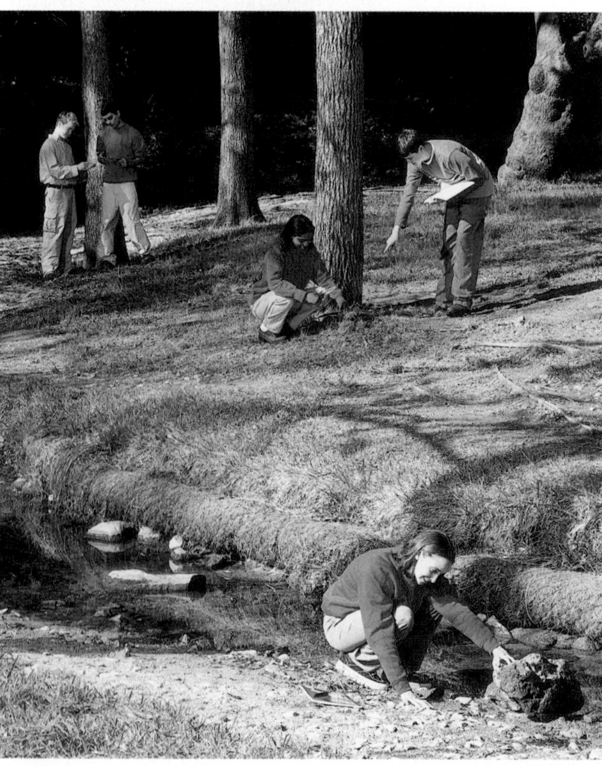

Test the Hypothesis

3. Observe your mini-ecosystem according to your plan at several different time points throughout the day. It may be helpful to use a camera to capture your observations. Record your observations.

4. Wait 24 h and observe your mini-ecosystem again at the same times that you observed it the day before. Record your observations.

5. Wait 1 week, and observe your mini-ecosystem again at the same times. Record your observations.

Analyze the Results

1. What factors determine the differences between your mini-ecosystems? Identify the factors that set each mini-ecosystem apart from its surrounding area.

2. How do the populations of your mini-ecosystems compare?

3. Identify some of the adaptations that the organisms living in your two mini-ecosystems have. Describe how the adaptations help the organisms survive in their environment.

Draw Conclusions

4. Write a report describing and comparing your mini-ecosystems with those of your classmates.

Contents

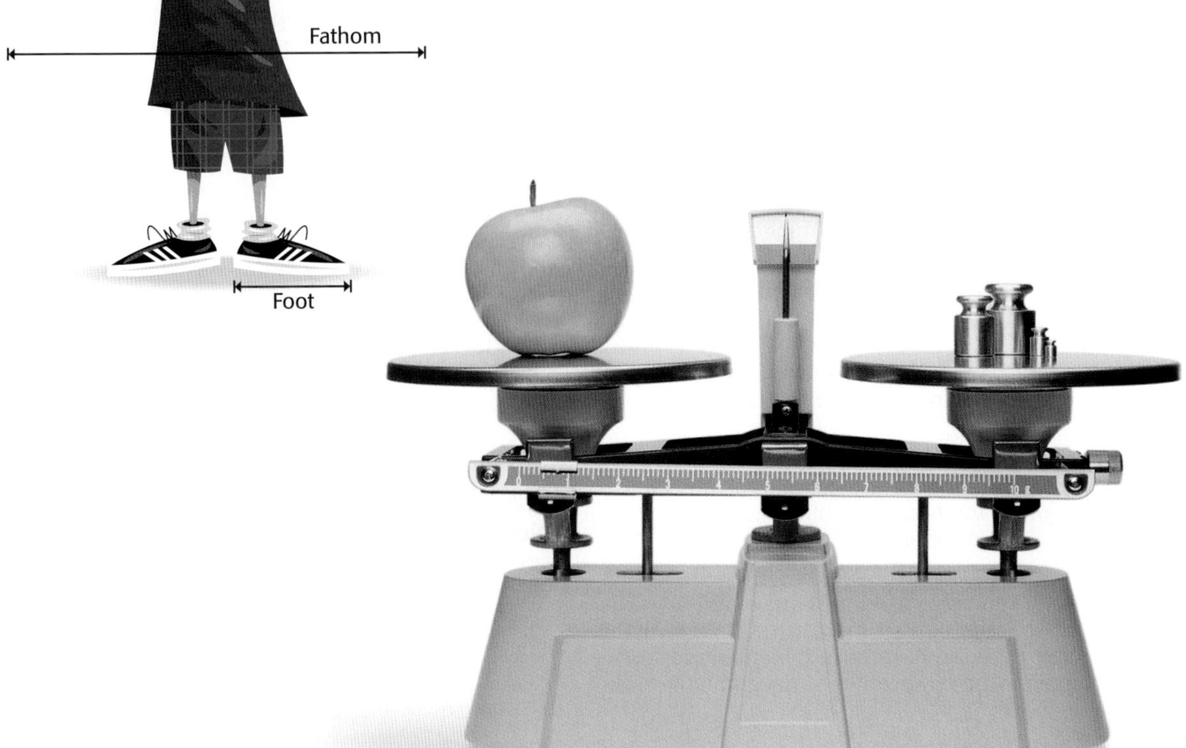

Reading Check Answers

Chapter 1 Science in Our World

Section 1

Page 4: the knowledge gained by observing the natural world

Page 6: Recycling paper protects forests and saves fuel and chemicals from being used to make paper from trees.

Page 9: Science educators work in schools, zoos, aquariums, and national parks.

Section 2

Page 11: Scientific methods help scientists get reliable answers.

Page 13: A variable is the only factor that is changed in a controlled experiment.

Page 14: Scientists can make tables or graphs to organize their data.

Page 16: Scientists can write reports for scientific journals, give talks on their results, or put their results on the Internet.

Section 3

Page 19: Three kinds of models are physical, mathematical, and conceptual models.

Page 20: Models can represent both very large and very small objects at a size that you can easily see.

Section 4

Page 22: a tube that has lenses at each end, a stage, and a light

Page 25: Area measures how much surface area an object has.

Page 27: When you don't understand a safety symbol, you should ask your teacher for help.

Chapter 2 Minerals of the Earth's Crust

Section 1

Page 41: An element is a pure substance that cannot be broken down into simpler substances by ordinary chemical means. A compound is a substance made of two or more elements that have been chemically bonded.

Page 42: Answers may vary. Silicate minerals contain a combination of silicon and oxygen; nonsilicate minerals do not contain a combination of silicon and oxygen.

Section 2

Page 45: A mineral's streak is not affected by air or water, but a mineral's color may be affected by air or water.

Page 46: Scratch the mineral with a series of 10 reference minerals. If the reference mineral scratches the unidentified mineral, the reference mineral is harder than the unidentified mineral.

Section 3

Page 51: Surface mining is used to remove mineral deposits that are at or near the Earth's surface. Subsurface mining is used to remove mineral deposits that are too deep to be removed by surface mining.

Page 53: Sample answer: Gemstones are nonmetallic minerals that are valued for their beauty and rarity rather than for their usefulness.

Chapter 3 Weathering and Soil Formation

Section 1

Page 65: Wind, water, and gravity can cause abrasion.

Page 66: Answers may vary. Sample answer: ants, worms, mice, coyotes, and rabbits.

Page 69: Oxidation occurs when oxygen combines with an element to form an oxide.

Section 2

Page 71: As the surface area increases, the rate of weathering also increases.

Page 72: Warm, humid climates have higher rates of weathering because oxidation happens faster when temperatures are higher and when water is present.

Page 73: Mountains weather faster because they are exposed to more wind, rain, and ice, which are agents of weathering.

Section 3

Page 74: Soil is formed from parent rock, organic material, water, and air.

Page 77: Heavy rains leach precious nutrients into deeper layers of soil, resulting in a very thin layer of topsoil.

Page 78: Temperate climates have the most productive soil.

Section 4

Page 80: Soil provides nutrients to plants, houses for animals, and stores water.

Page 83: They restore important nutrients to the soil and provide cover to prevent erosion.

Chapter 4 The Flow of Fresh Water

Section 1

Page 94: The Colorado River eroded the rock over millions of years.

Page 96: A divide is the boundary that separates drainage areas, whereas a watershed is the area of land that is drained by a water system.

Page 97: An increase in a stream's gradient and discharge can cause the stream to flow faster.

Page 99: A mature river erodes its channel wider rather than deeper. It is not steep and has fewer falls and rapids. It also has good drainage and more discharge than a youthful river does.

Page 100: Rejuvenated rivers form when the land is raised by tectonic forces.

Section 2

Page 103: Deltas are made of the deposited load of the river, which is mostly mud.

Page 105: The flow of water can be controlled by dams and levees.

Section 3

Page 106: The zone of aeration is located underground. It is the area above the water table.

Page 108: The size of the recharge zone depends on how permeable rock is at the surface.

Page 109: A well must be deeper than the water table for it to be able to reach water.

Page 110: Deposition is the process that causes the formation of stalactites and stalagmites.

Section 4

Page 112: Nonpoint-source pollution is the hardest to control.

Page 115: Less than 8% of water in our homes is used for drinking.

Page 116: Drip irrigation systems deliver small amounts of water directly to the roots of the plant so that the plant absorbs the water before it can evaporate or runoff.

Page 117: Answers may vary. Sample answer: taking shorter showers, avoiding running water while brushing your teeth, and using the dishwasher only when it is full.

Chapter 5 The Ocean

Section 1

Page 129: The first oceans began to form sometime before 4 billion years ago as the Earth cooled enough for water vapor to condense and fall as rain.

Page 130: Coastal water in places with hotter, drier climates has a higher salinity because less fresh water runs into the ocean in drier areas and because heat increases the evaporation rate.

Page 132: Parts of the ocean along the equator are warmer because they receive more sunlight per year.

Page 134: If the ocean did not release thermal energy so slowly, the air temperature on land would vary greatly from above 100°C during the day to below 100°C at night.

Section 2

Page 136: Heyerdahl theorized that the inhabitants of Polynesia originally sailed from Peru on rafts powered only by the wind and ocean currents. Heyerdahl proved his theory by sailing from Peru to Polynesia on a raft powered only by wind and ocean currents.

Page 138: The Earth's rotation causes surface currents to move in curved paths rather than in straight lines.

Page 139: The three factors that form a pattern of surface currents on Earth are global winds, the Coriolis effect, and continental deflections.

Page 140: Density causes variations in the movement of deep currents.

Section 3

Page 143: Cold-water currents keep coastal climates cooler than inland climates all year long.

Page 145: Answers may vary. Sample answer: It is important to study El Niño because El Niño can greatly affect organisms and land. One way that scientists study El Niño is through a network of buoys located along the equator. These buoys record information that helps scientists predict when an El Niño is likely to occur.

Section 4

Page 146: The lowest point of a wave is called a *trough*.

Page 148: Deep-water waves become shallow-water waves as they move toward the shore and reach water that is shallower than one-half their wavelength.

Page 151: A storm surge is a local rise in sea level near the shore and is caused by strong winds from a storm, such as a hurricane. Storm surges are difficult to study because they disappear as quickly as they form.

Section 5

Page 152: The gravity of the moon pulls on every particle of the Earth.

Page 154: A tidal range is the difference between levels of ocean water at high tide and low tide.

Chapter 6 The Atmosphere

Section 1

Page 166: Water can be liquid (rain), solid (snow or ice), or gas (water vapor).

Page 168: The troposphere is the layer of turning or change. The stratosphere is the layer in which gases are layered and do not mix vertically. The mesosphere is the middle layer. The thermosphere is the layer in which temperatures are highest.

Page 170: The thermosphere does not feel hot because air molecules are spaced far apart and cannot collide to transfer much thermal energy.

Section 2

Page 173: Cold air is more dense than warm air, so cold air sinks and warm air rises. This produces convection currents.

Page 175: A greenhouse gas is a gas that absorbs thermal energy in the atmosphere.

Section 3

Page 177: Sinking air causes areas of high pressure because sinking air presses down on the air beneath it.

Page 178: the westerlies

Page 181: At night, the air along the mountain slopes cools. This cool air moves down the slopes into the valley and produces a mountain breeze.

Section 4

Page 182: Sample answer: smoke, dust and sea salt

Page 185: Answers may vary. Acid precipitation may decrease the soil nutrients that are available to plants.

Page 186: Powdered limestone is used to counteract the effects of acidic snowmelt from snow that accumulated during the winter.

Page 188: Allowance trading establishes allowances for a certain type of pollutant. Companies are permitted to release their allowance of the pollutant, but if they exceed the allowance, they must buy additional allowances or pay a fine.

Chapter 7 Climate and Weather

Section 1

Page 200: Climate is the average weather condition in an area over a long period of time. Weather is the condition of the atmosphere at a particular time.

Page 202: Locations near the equator have less seasonal variation because the tilt of the Earth does not change the amount of energy these locations receive from the sun.

Page 204: The atmosphere becomes less dense and loses its ability to absorb and hold thermal energy at higher elevations.

Page 205: The Gulf Stream current carries warm water past Iceland, which heats the air and causes milder temperatures.

Page 206: Each biome has a different climate and different plant and animal communities.

Section 2

Page 208: The water cycle is the continuous movement of water from Earth's oceans and rivers into the atmosphere, into the ground, and back into the oceans and rivers.

Page 210: A psychrometer is used to measure relative humidity.

Page 211: The bulb of a wet-bulb thermometer is covered with moistened material. The bulb cools as water evaporates from the material. If the air is dry, more water will evaporate from the material, and the temperature recorded by the thermometer will be low. If the air is humid, less water will evaporate from the material, and the temperature recorded by the thermometer will be higher.

Page 213: Altostratus clouds form at middle altitudes.

Section 3

Page 217: A maritime tropical air mass causes hot and humid summer weather in the midwestern United States.

Page 219: An occluded front produces cool temperatures and large amounts of rain.

Page 221: A cyclone can produce stormy weather. An anticyclone can produce dry, clear weather.

Section 4

Page 223: A severe thunderstorm is a thunderstorm that produces high winds, hail, flash floods, or tornadoes.

Page 225: Hurricanes are also called *typhoons* or *cyclones.*

Page 226: Hurricanes get their energy from the condensation of water vapor.

Section 5

Page 230: Meteorologists use weather balloons to collect atmospheric data above Earth's surface.

Chapter 8 Studying Space

Section 1

Page 245: Copernicus believed in a sun-centered universe.

Page 246: Newton's law of gravity helped explain why the planets orbit the sun and moons orbit planets.

Section 2

Page 248: The objective lens collects light and forms an image at the back of the telescope. The eyepiece magnifies the image produced by the objective lens.

Page 250: The motion of air pollution, water vapor, and light pollution distort the images produced by optical telescopes.

Page 253: X-ray telescopes are placed in space because Earth's atmosphere blocks most X-ray radiation from space.

Section 3

Page 255: Different constellations are visible in the Northern and Southern Hemispheres because different portions of the sky are visible from the Northern and Southern Hemispheres.

Page 257: The apparent movement of the sun and stars is caused by the Earth's rotation on its axis.

Page 258: 9.46 trillion kilometers

Page 260: One might conclude that all of the galaxies are traveling toward the Earth and that the universe is contracting.

Section 4

Page 263: Answers may vary. LEO is much closer to the Earth than GEO.

Page 265: Information from one location is transmitted to a communications satellite. The satellite then sends the information to another location on Earth.

Page 267: Satellites in the EOS program are designed to work together so that many different types of data can be integrated.

Chapter 9 A Family of Planets

Section 1

Page 279: Light travels about 300,000 km/s.

Page 281: Jupiter, Saturn, Uranus, Neptune, and Pluto are in the outer solar system.

Section 2

Page 283: Radar technology was used to map the surface of Venus.

Page 284: Earth's global system includes the atmosphere, the oceans, and the biosphere.

Page 286: Mars' crust is chemically different from Earth's crust, so the Martian crust does not move. As a result, volcanoes build up in the same spots on Mars.

Section 3

Page 289: Saturn's rings are made of icy particles ranging in size from a few centimeters to several meters wide.

Page 291: Neptune's interior releases energy to its outer layers, which creates belts of clouds in Neptune's atmosphere.

Section 4

Page 295: The moon formed from a piece of Earth's mantle, which broke off during a collision between Earth and a large object.

Page 297: During a solar eclipse, the moon blocks out the sun and casts a shadow on Earth.

Page 298: We don't see solar and lunar eclipses every month because the moon's orbit around Earth is tilted.

Page 299: Because Titan's atmosphere is similar to the atmosphere on Earth before life evolved, scientists can study Titan's atmosphere to learn how life began.

Page 300: Pluto is eclipsed by Charon every 120 years.

Section 5

Page 303: Comets come from the Oort cloud and the Kuiper belt.

Page 305: The major types of meteorites are stony, metallic, and stony-iron meteorites.

Page 306: Large objects strike Earth every few thousand years.

Chapter 10 The Properties of Matter

Section 1

Page 321: liters (L) and milliliters (mL)

Page 322: You could measure the volume of an apple by submerging the apple in a container of water and measuring the volume of the water that the apple displaces.

Page 324: kilograms (kg), grams (g), and milligrams (mg)

Section 2

Page 326: Some physical properties are color, shape, odor, weight, volume, texture, state, and density.

Page 328: If the object's density is less than the water's density, the object will float.

Page 330: A physical change is a change that occurs to a substance or object that does not change the identity of the substance.

Section 3

Page 332: Reactivity describes the ability of two or more substances to combine and form one or more new substances.

Page 334: Chemical changes occur when one or more substances are changed into entirely new substances that have different properties. A chemical property of a substance determines whether a chemical change will occur.

Chapter 11 Elements, Compounds, and Mixtures

Section 1

Page 348: An element is a pure substance because it contains only one type of particle.

Page 350: Metals are shiny, conduct heat energy, and conduct electric current.

Section 2

Page 353: Three physical properties used to identify compounds are melting point, density, and color.

Page 354: Compounds can be broken down into elements or simpler compounds.

Section 3

Page 356: Substances in a mixture keep their identities because no chemical change takes place when a mixture is made.

Page 359: An alloy is a solid solution of metal or nonmetal dissolved in another metal.

Page 361: As temperature increases, the solubility of a gas decreases.

Page 362: The particles of a suspension can be separated by passing the suspension through a filter.

Section 4

Page 365: Ionic compounds are made up of a metal and a nonmetal.

Page 366: Reactants are the starting substances in a chemical reaction, and products are the substances that are formed.

Page 368: 4

Chapter 12 Energy

Section 1

Page 380: Energy is the ability to do work.

Page 383: kinetic energy and potential energy

Page 385: Sound energy consists of vibrations carried through the air.

Page 386: Nuclear energy comes from changes in the nucleus of an atom.

Section 2

Page 389: Elastic potential energy can be stored by stretching a rubber band. Elastic potential energy is released when the rubber band goes back to its original shape.

Page 390: Plants get their energy from the sun.

Page 392: Machines can change the size or direction of the input force.

Chapter 13 The Energy of Waves

Section 1

Page 404: All waves are disturbances that transmit energy.

Page 406: Electromagnetic waves do not require a medium.

Page 408: A sound wave is a longitudinal wave.

Section 2

Page 411: Shaking the rope faster makes the wavelength shorter; shaking the rope more slowly makes the wavelength longer.

Page 412: 3 Hz

Section 3

Page 415: It refracts.

Page 417: Constructive interference occurs when the crests of one wave overlap the crests of another wave.

Page 418: A standing wave results from a wave that is reflected between two fixed points. Interference from the wave and reflected waves cause certain points to remain at rest and certain points to remain at a large amplitude.

Section 4

Page 420: The law of reflection states that the angle of incidence equals the angle of reflection.

Page 421: Sample answer: Four light sources are a television screen, a fluorescent light in the classroom, a light bulb, and the tail of a firefly.

Page 422: You can see things outside of a beam of light because light is scattered outside of the beam.

Page 425: The amount that a wave diffracts depends on the wavelength of the wave and the size of the barrier or opening.

Page 426: Constructive interference is interference in which the resulting wave has a greater amplitude than the original waves had.

Chapter 14 Cells: The Basic Units of Life

Section 1

Page 441: Sample answer: All organisms are made of one or more cells, the cell is the basic unit of all living things, and all cells come from existing cells.

Page 442: If a cell's volume gets too large, the cell's surface area will not be able to take in enough nutrients or get rid of wastes fast enough to keep the cell alive.

Page 443: Organelles are structures within a cell that perform specific functions for the cell.

Page 445: One difference between eubacteria and archaea is that bacterial ribosomes are different from archaebacterial ribosomes.

Page 446: The main difference between prokaryotes and eukaryotes is that eukaryotic cells have a nucleus and membrane-bound organelles and prokaryotic cells do not.

Section 2

Page 448: Plant, algae, and fungi cells have cell walls.

Page 449: A cell membrane encloses the cell and separates and protects the cell's contents from the cell's environment. The cell wall also controls the movement of materials into and out of the cell.

Page 450: The cytoskeleton is a web of proteins in the cytoplasm. It gives the cell support and structure.

Page 452: Most of a cell's ATP is made in the cell's mitochondria.

Page 454: Lysosomes destroy worn-out organelles, attack foreign invaders, and get rid of waste material from inside the cell.

Section 3

Page 456: Sample answer: larger size, longer life, and cell specialization

Page 457: An organ is a structure of two or more tissues working together to perform a specific function in the body.

Page 458: cell, tissue, organ, organ system

Chapter 15 Classification

Section 1

Page 470: Sample answer: How many known species are there? What are the defining characteristics of each species? and What are the relationships between these species?

Page 473: genus and species

Page 474: A dichotomous key is an identification aid that uses a series of descriptive statements.

Section 2

Page 477: *Escherichia coli*

Page 479: Sample answer: Plants make energy through photosynthesis. Some members of the kingdoms Fungi, Protista, and Eubacteria consume plants. When these organisms digest the plant material, they get energy and nutrients made by the plants.

Page 481: Sponges don't have sense organs, and they usually can't move around.

Chapter 16 Structure and Function

Section 1

Page 493: Sexual reproduction is reproduction in which the sex cells (egg and sperm) of two parents unite to form a new individual.

Page 494: External fertilization is when sex cells unite outside of the female's body. Internal fertilization is when sex cells unite inside the female's body.

Page 495: All mammals reproduce sexually and nurture their young with milk.

Section 2

Page 497: Sample answer: Animals may eat fruits and discard the seeds away from the parent plant. Other fruits, such as burrs, get caught in an animal's fur. Some fruits are carried by the wind.

Page 498: plantlets, tubers, and runners

Section 3

Page 500: Consumers cannot make their own food and must eat other organisms. Producers can make their own food.

Page 502: Chelicerae help a spider get food by holding the spider's prey and by injecting venom into the prey.

Section 4

Page 504: Chlorophyll reflects more wavelengths of green light than wavelengths of other colors of light. So, most plants look green.

Page 506: Sample answer: Stomata are openings in the leaf's epidermis and cuticle through which carbon dioxide enters the leaf. Plants combine this carbon dioxide with water to make food.

Chapter 17 Human Body Systems

Section 1

Page 519: The stomach works with other organs, such as the small and large intestines, to digest food.

Page 520: Sample answer: The cardiovascular and circulatory systems work together to deliver the materials cells need to survive and help remove cell wastes.

Section 2

Page 523: Enzymes cut proteins into amino acids that the body can use.

Page 525: Chyme is a soupy mixture of partially digested food in the stomach.

Page 527: Bile breaks large fat droplets into very small droplets. This process allows more fat molecules to be exposed to digestive enzymes.

Page 528: Fiber keeps the stool soft and keeps material moving through the large intestine.

Section 3

Page 530: plasma, red blood cells, white blood cells, and platelets

Page 531: White blood cells identify and attack pathogens that may make you sick.

Page 532: Systolic pressure is the pressure inside arteries when the ventricles contract. Diastolic pressure is the pressure inside the arteries when the ventricles are relaxed.

Section 4

Page 535: Sample answer: The thyroid gland increases the rate at which the body uses energy. The thymus gland regulates the immune system, which helps your body fight disease.

Page 536: Insulin helps regulate the amount of glucose in the blood.

Chapter 18 Reproduction and Development

Section 1

Page 548: testes, epididymis, vas deferens, urethra, penis

Page 550: Twins happen about 30 times in every 1,000 births.

Section 2

Page 552: Fertilization happens when the nucleus of a sperm unites with the nucleus of an egg. Implantation happens after the fertilized egg travels down the fallopian tube to the uterus and embeds itself in the wall of the uterus.

Page 553: The placenta is important because it provides the embryo with oxygen and nutrients from the mother's blood. Wastes from the embryo also travel to the placenta, where they are carried to the mother so that she can excrete them.

Page 554: The embryo is now called a *fetus*. The fetus's face begins to look more human, and the fetus can swallow, grows rapidly (triples in size), and begins to make movements that the mother can feel.

Page 556: A person's reproductive system becomes mature.

Chapter 19 Body Defenses and Disease

Section 1

Page 569: Cooking kills dangerous bacteria or parasites living in meat, fish, and eggs.

Page 571: Frank's doctor did not prescribe antibiotics because Frank had a cold. Colds are caused by viruses. Antibiotics can't stop viruses.

Section 2

Page 573: Macrophages engulf, or eat, any microorganisms or viruses that enter your body.

Page 574: If a virus particle enters the body, it may pass into body cells and begin to replicate. Or it may be engulfed and broken up by macrophages.

Page 577: rheumatoid arthritis, diabetes, multiple sclerosis, and lupus

Page 578: HIV causes AIDS.

Chapter 20 Interactions of Living Things

Section 1

Page 593: The biosphere is the part of Earth where life exists.

Section 2

Page 595: Organisms that eat other organisms are called *consumers*.

Page 597: An energy pyramid is a diagram that shows an ecosystem's loss of energy.

Page 598: Other animals in the park were affected by the disappearance of the gray wolf because the food web was interrupted. The animals that would normally be prey for the gray wolf were more plentiful. These larger populations ate more vegetation.

Section 3

Page 601: The main ways that organisms affect each other are through competition, predator and prey relationships, symbiotic relationships, and coevolution.

Page 603: Camouflage helps an organism blend in with its surroundings because of its coloring. It is harder for a predator to find a camouflaged prey.

Page 604: In a mutualistic relationship, both organisms benefit from the relationship.

Page 606: Flowers need to attract pollinators to help the flowers reproduce with other members of their species.

Chapter 21 The Earth's Ecosystems

Section 1

Page 619: Sample answer: *Deciduous* comes from a Latin word that means "to fall off." In temperate deciduous forests, the trees lose their leaves in the fall.

Page 620: evergreen trees; squirrels, insects, finches, chickadees, jays, porcupines, elk, and moose

Page 622: During the dry season, grasses on the savanna dry out and turn yellow. But their deep roots survive for many months without water.

Page 623: Sample answer: Desert plants grow far apart. Some plants have shallow, widespread roots to take up water after a storm. Some desert plants have fleshy stems and leaves to store water. They also have waxy coatings to prevent water loss.

Page 624: Sample answer: Alpine tundra is tundra found at the top of tall mountains, above the tree line.

Section 2

Page 626: Sample answer: Plankton are tiny organisms that float near the surface of the water. They form the base of the ocean's feeding relationships.

Page 627: Sample answer: Fishes that live near the poles have adaptations for the near-freezing water. Animals in coral reefs need warm water to live. Some animals migrate to warmer waters to reproduce. Water temperature affects whether some animals can eat.

Page 629: Sample answer: Some animals get food from material that sinks to the bottom from the surface. Other animals get energy from chemicals released by thermal vents.

Page 630: Sample answer: When corals die, they leave behind their skeletons. Other corals grow on these remains. Over time, the layers build up to form a coral reef.

Section 3

Page 633: Sample answer: The littoral zone is the zone closest to shore in which light reaches the lake bottom. The open zone extends from the littoral zone and goes as deep as sunlight can reach. The deep-water zone lies beneath the open-water zone.

Page 634: A swamp is a wetland ecosystem in which trees and vines grow.

Page 635: Sample answer: Many fishes will die as the pond fills in because bacteria that decompose material in the pond use up the oxygen in the water.

Study Skills

FoldNote Instructions

Have you ever tried to study for a test or quiz but didn't know where to start? Or have you read a chapter and found that you can remember only a few ideas? Well, FoldNotes are a fun and exciting way to help you learn and remember the ideas you encounter as you learn science!

FoldNotes are tools that you can use to organize concepts. By focusing on a few main concepts, FoldNotes help you learn and remember how the concepts fit together. They can help you see the "big picture." Below you will find instructions for building 10 different FoldNotes.

Pyramid

1. Place a sheet of paper in front of you. Fold the lower left-hand corner of the paper diagonally to the opposite edge of the paper.
2. Cut off the tab of paper created by the fold (at the top).
3. Open the paper so that it is a square. Fold the lower right-hand corner of the paper diagonally to the opposite corner to form a triangle.
4. Open the paper. The creases of the two folds will have created an X.
5. Using scissors, cut along one of the creases. Start from any corner, and stop at the center point to create two flaps. Use tape or glue to attach one of the flaps on top of the other flap.

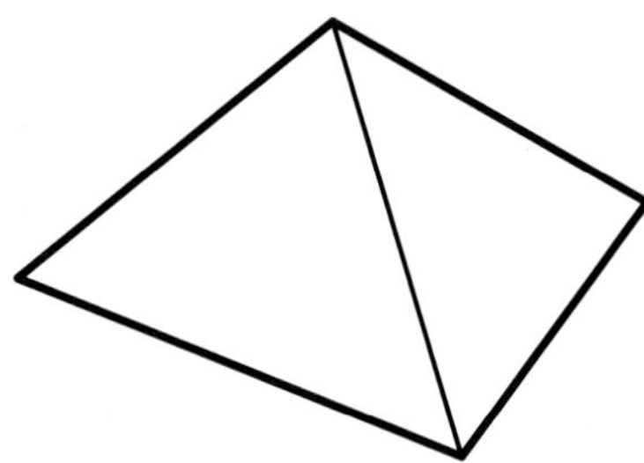

Double Door

1. Fold a sheet of paper in half from the top to the bottom. Then, unfold the paper.
2. Fold the top and bottom edges of the paper to the crease.

Appendix

Booklet

1. Fold a sheet of paper in half from left to right. Then, unfold the paper.
2. Fold the sheet of paper in half again from the top to the bottom. Then, unfold the paper.
3. Refold the sheet of paper in half from left to right.
4. Fold the top and bottom edges to the center crease.
5. Completely unfold the paper.
6. Refold the paper from top to bottom.
7. Using scissors, cut a slit along the center crease of the sheet from the folded edge to the creases made in step 4. Do not cut the entire sheet in half.
8. Fold the sheet of paper in half from left to right. While holding the bottom and top edges of the paper, push the bottom and top edges together so that the center collapses at the center slit. Fold the four flaps to form a four-page book.

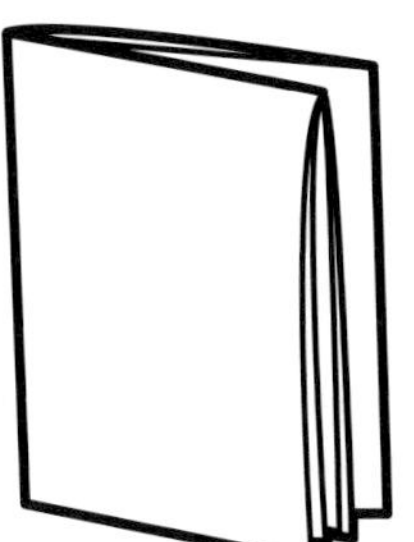

Layered Book

1. Lay one sheet of paper on top of another sheet. Slide the top sheet up so that 2 cm of the bottom sheet is showing.
2. Hold the two sheets together, fold down the top of the two sheets so that you see four 2 cm tabs along the bottom.
3. Using a stapler, staple the top of the FoldNote.

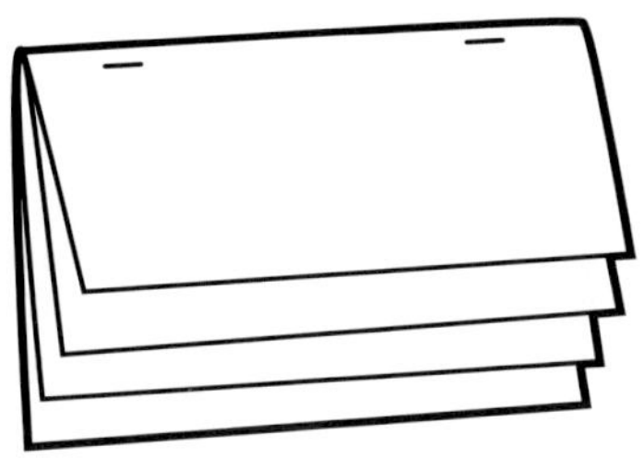

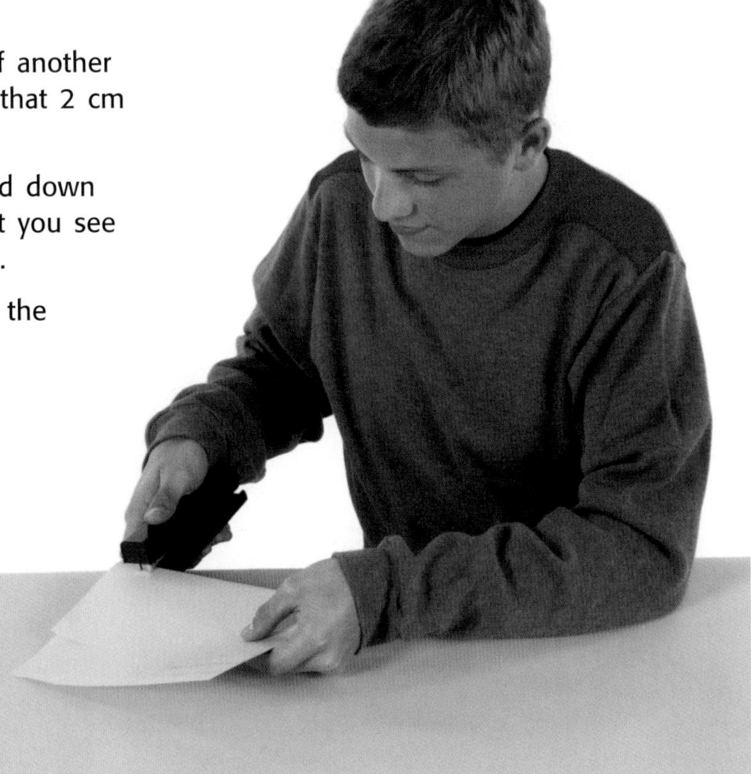

Appendix

Key-Term Fold

1. Fold a sheet of lined notebook paper in half from left to right.
2. Using scissors, cut along every third line from the right edge of the paper to the center fold to make tabs.

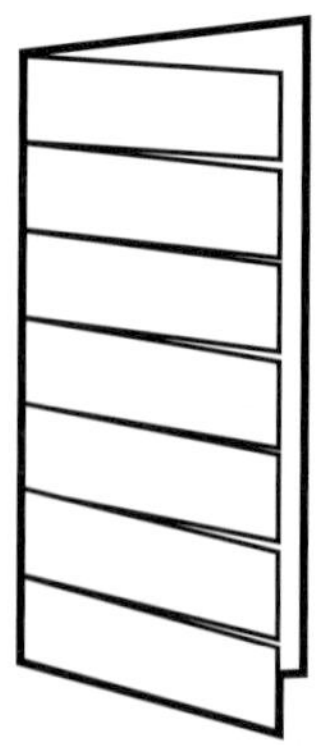

Four-Corner Fold

1. Fold a sheet of paper in half from left to right. Then, unfold the paper.
2. Fold each side of the paper to the crease in the center of the paper.
3. Fold the paper in half from the top to the bottom. Then, unfold the paper.
4. Using scissors, cut the top flap creases made in step 3 to form four flaps.

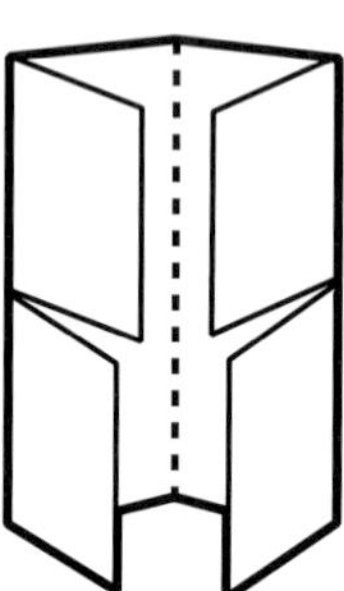

Three-Panel Flip Chart

1. Fold a piece of paper in half from the top to the bottom.
2. Fold the paper in thirds from side to side. Then, unfold the paper so that you can see the three sections.
3. From the top of the paper, cut along each of the vertical fold lines to the fold in the middle of the paper. You will now have three flaps.

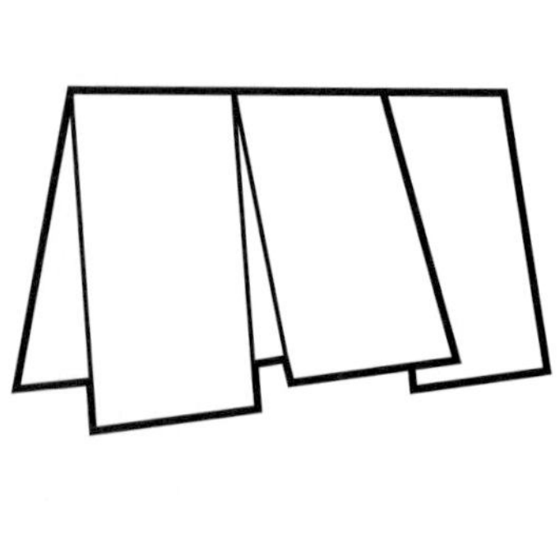

Appendix

Table Fold

1. Fold a piece of paper in half from the top to the bottom. Then, fold the paper in half again.
2. Fold the paper in thirds from side to side.
3. Unfold the paper completely. Carefully trace the fold lines by using a pen or pencil.

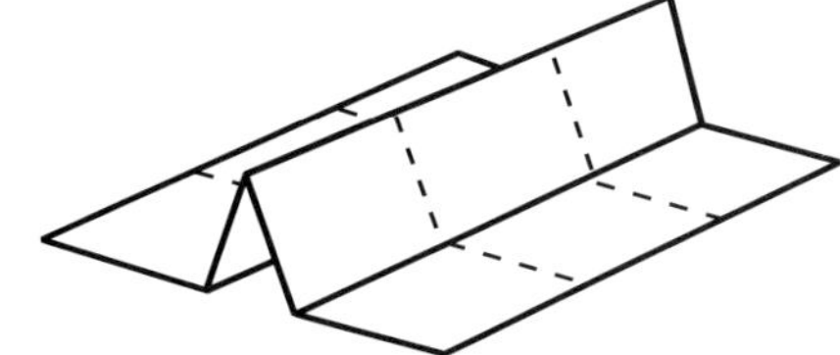

Two-Panel Flip Chart

1. Fold a piece of paper in half from the top to the bottom.
2. Fold the paper in half from side to side. Then, unfold the paper so that you can see the two sections.
3. From the top of the paper, cut along the vertical fold line to the fold in the middle of the paper. You will now have two flaps.

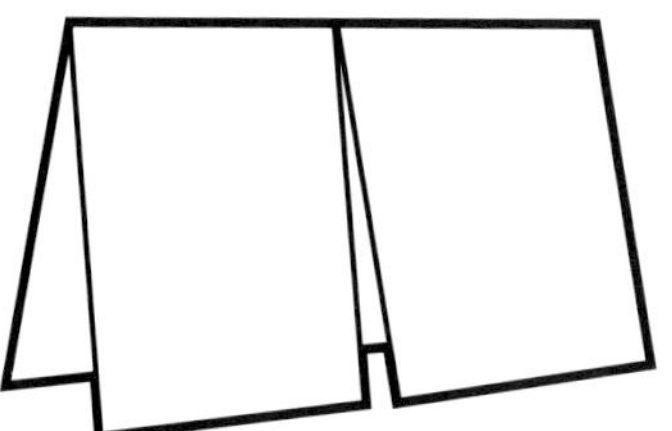

Tri-Fold

1. Fold a piece a paper in thirds from the top to the bottom.
2. Unfold the paper so that you can see the three sections. Then, turn the paper sideways so that the three sections form vertical columns.
3. Trace the fold lines by using a pen or pencil. Label the columns "Know," "Want," and "Learn."

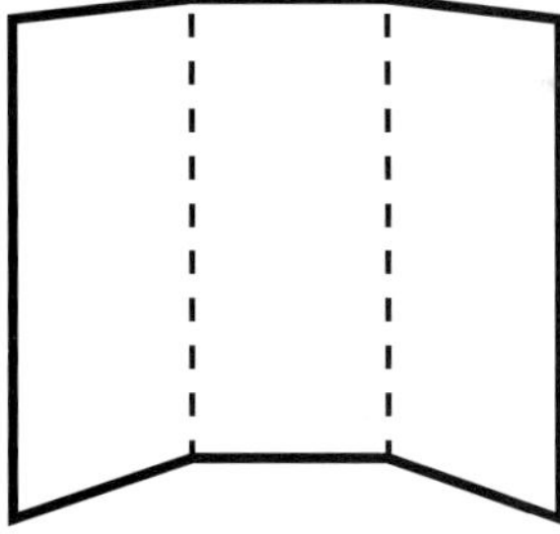

Graphic Organizer Instructions

Have you ever wished that you could "draw out" the many concepts you learn in your science class? Sometimes, being able to *see* how concepts are related really helps you remember what you've learned. Graphic Organizers do just that! They give you a way to draw or map out concepts.

All you need to make a Graphic Organizer is a piece of paper and a pencil. Below you will find instructions for four different Graphic Organizers designed to help you organize the concepts you'll learn in this book.

Spider Map

1. Draw a diagram like the one shown. In the circle, write the main topic.
2. From the circle, draw legs to represent different categories of the main topic. You can have as many categories as you want.
3. From the category legs, draw horizontal lines. As you read the chapter, write details about each category on the horizontal lines.

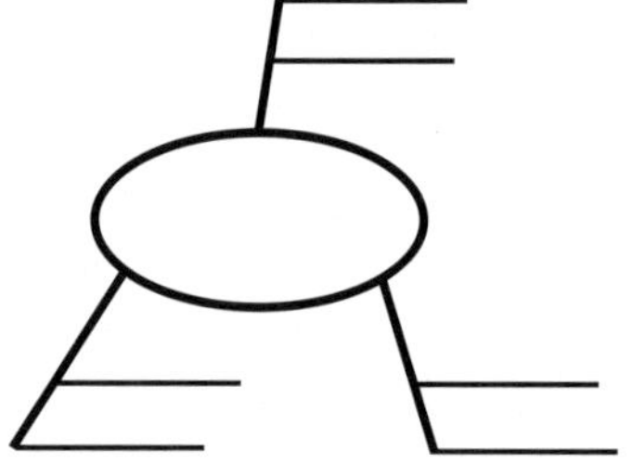

Comparison Table

1. Draw a chart like the one shown. Your chart can have as many columns and rows as you want.
2. In the top row, write the topics that you want to compare.
3. In the left column, write characteristics of the topics that you want to compare. As you read the chapter, fill in the characteristics for each topic in the appropriate boxes.

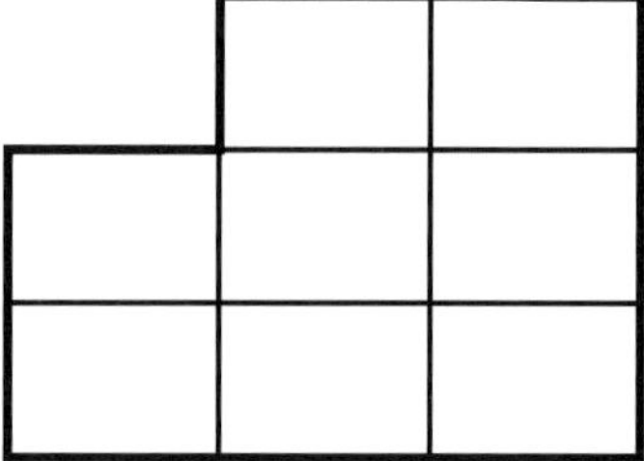

Appendix

Chain-of-Events-Chart

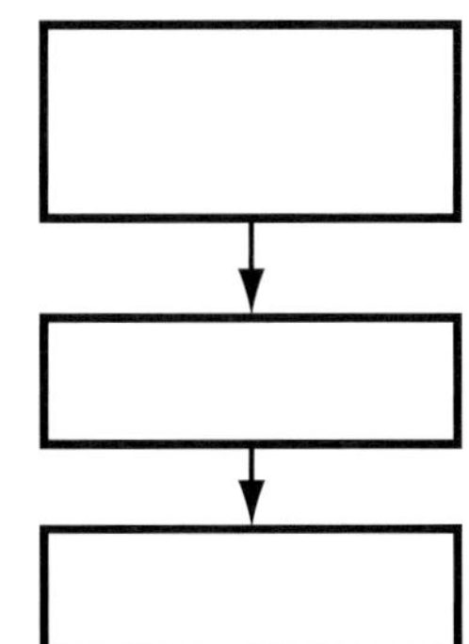

1. Draw a box. In the box, write the first step of a process or the first event of a timeline.
2. Under the box, draw another box, and use an arrow to connect the two boxes. In the second box, write the next step of the process or the next event in the timeline.
3. Continue adding boxes until the process or timeline is finished.

Concept Map

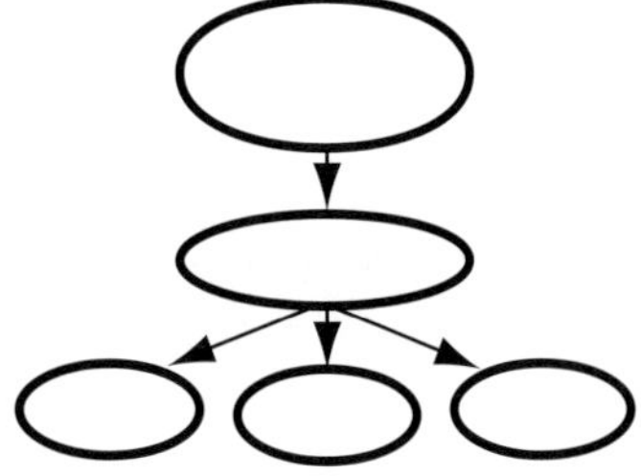

1. Draw a circle in the center of a piece of paper. Write the main idea of the chapter in the center of the circle.
2. From the circle, draw other circles. In those circles, write characteristics of the main idea. Draw arrows from the center circle to the circles that contain the characteristics.
3. From each circle that contains a characteristic, draw other circles. In those circles, write specific details about the characteristic. Draw arrows from each circle that contains a characteristic to the circles that contain specific details. You may draw as many circles as you want.

SI Measurement

The International System of Units, or SI, is the standard system of measurement used by many scientists. Using the same standards of measurement makes it easier for scientists to communicate with one another.

SI works by combining prefixes and base units. Each base unit can be used with different prefixes to define smaller and larger quantities. The table below lists common SI prefixes.

SI Prefixes			
Prefix	**Symbol**	**Factor**	**Example**
kilo-	k	1,000	kilogram, 1 kg = 1,000 g
hecto-	h	100	hectoliter, 1 hL = 100 L
deka-	da	10	dekameter, 1 dam = 10 m
		1	meter, liter, gram
deci-	d	0.1	decigram, 1 dg = 0.1 g
centi-	c	0.01	centimeter, 1 cm = 0.01 m
milli-	m	0.001	milliliter, 1 mL = 0.001 L
micro-	μ	0.000 001	micrometer, 1 μm = 0.000 001 m

SI Conversion Table		
SI units	**From SI to English**	**From English to SI**
Length		
kilometer (km) = 1,000 m	1 km = 0.621 mi	1 mi = 1.609 km
meter (m) = 100 cm	1 m = 3.281 ft	1 ft = 0.305 m
centimeter (cm) = 0.01 m	1 cm = 0.394 in.	1 in. = 2.540 cm
millimeter (mm) = 0.001 m	1 mm = 0.039 in.	
micrometer (μm) = 0.000 001 m		
nanometer (nm) = 0.000 000 001 m		
Area		
square kilometer (km^2) = 100 hectares	1 km^2 = 0.386 mi^2	1 mi^2 = 2.590 km^2
hectare (ha) = 10,000 m^2	1 ha = 2.471 acres	1 acre = 0.405 ha
square meter (m^2) = 10,000 cm^2	1 m^2 = 10.764 ft^2	1 ft^2 = 0.093 m^2
square centimeter (cm^2) = 100 mm^2	1 cm^2 = 0.155 in.^{2}	1 in.^{2} = 6.452 cm^2
Volume		
liter (L) = 1,000 mL = 1 dm^3	1 L = 1.057 fl qt	1 fl qt = 0.946 L
milliliter (mL) = 0.001 L = 1 cm^3	1 mL = 0.034 fl oz	1 fl oz = 29.574 mL
microliter (μL) = 0.000 001 L		
Mass		
kilogram (kg) = 1,000 g	1 kg = 2.205 lb	1 lb = 0.454 kg
gram (g) = 1,000 mg	1 g = 0.035 oz	1 oz = 28.350 g
milligram (mg) = 0.001 g		
microgram (μg) = 0.000 001 g		

Temperature Scales

Temperature can be expressed by using three different scales: Fahrenheit, Celsius, and Kelvin. The SI unit for temperature is the kelvin (K).

Although 0 K is much colder than 0°C, a change of 1 K is equal to a change of 1°C.

Three Temperature Scales

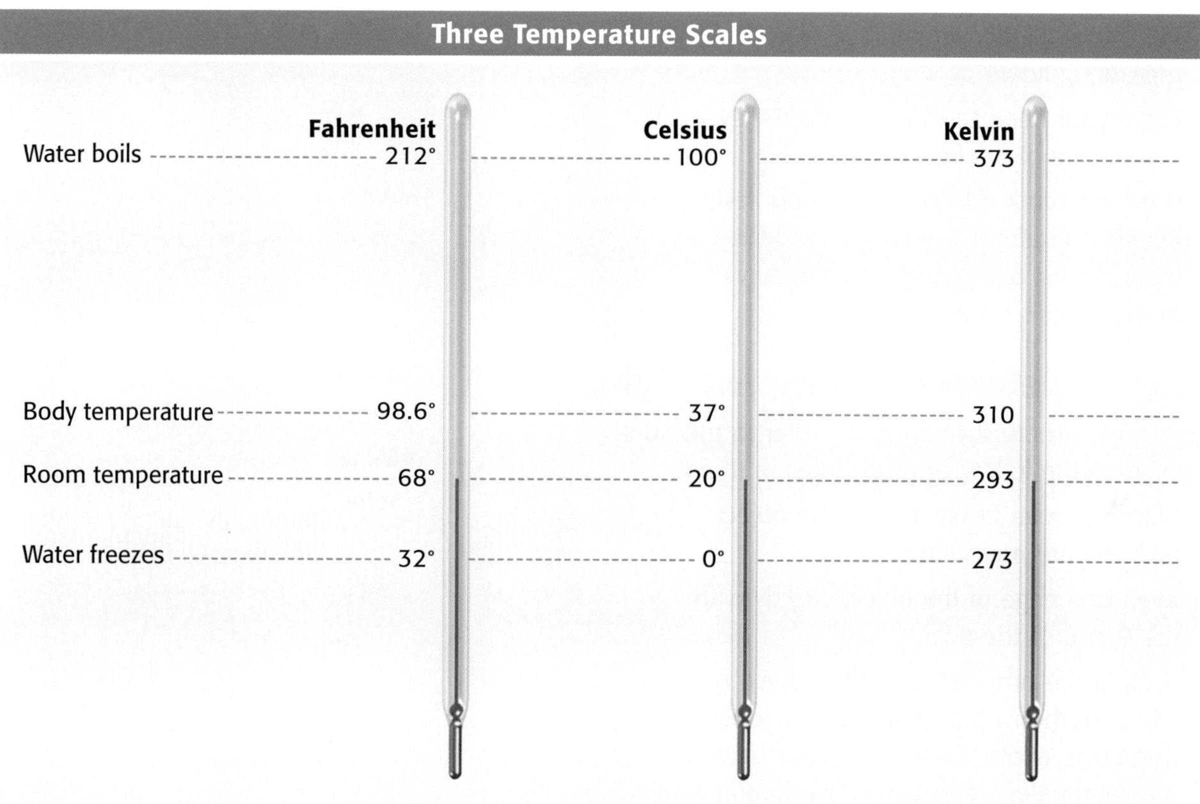

Temperature Conversions Table		
To convert	**Use this equation:**	**Example**
Celsius to Fahrenheit °C → °F	$°F = \left(\frac{9}{5} \times °C\right) + 32$	Convert 45°C to °F. $°F = \left(\frac{9}{5} \times 45°C\right) + 32 = 113°F$
Fahrenheit to Celsius °F → °C	$°C = \frac{5}{9} \times (°F - 32)$	Convert 68°F to °C. $°C = \frac{5}{9} \times (68°F - 32) = 20°C$
Celsius to Kelvin °C → K	$K = °C + 273$	Convert 45°C to K. $K = 45°C + 273 = 318\ K$
Kelvin to Celsius K → °C	$°C = K - 273$	Convert 32 K to °C. $°C = 32K - 273 = -241°C$

Measuring Skills

Using a Graduated Cylinder

When using a graduated cylinder to measure volume, keep the following procedures in mind:

1. Place the cylinder on a flat, level surface before measuring liquid.
2. Move your head so that your eye is level with the surface of the liquid.
3. Read the mark closest to the liquid level. On glass graduated cylinders, read the mark closest to the center of the curve in the liquid's surface.

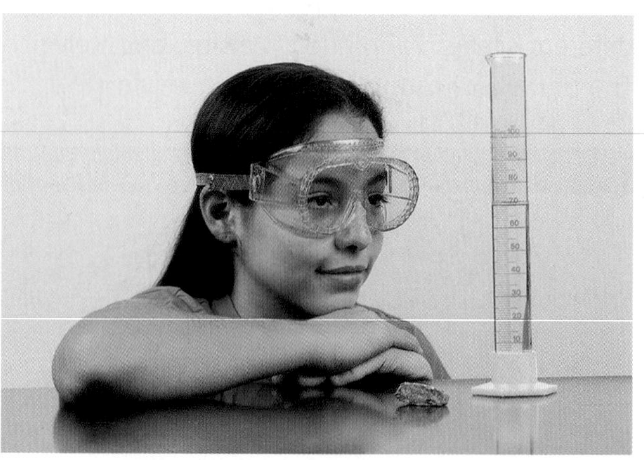

Using a Meterstick or Metric Ruler

When using a meterstick or metric ruler to measure length, keep the following procedures in mind:

1. Place the ruler firmly against the object that you are measuring.
2. Align one edge of the object exactly with the 0 end of the ruler.
3. Look at the other edge of the object to see which of the marks on the ruler is closest to that edge. (Note: Each small slash between the centimeters represents a millimeter, which is one-tenth of a centimeter.)

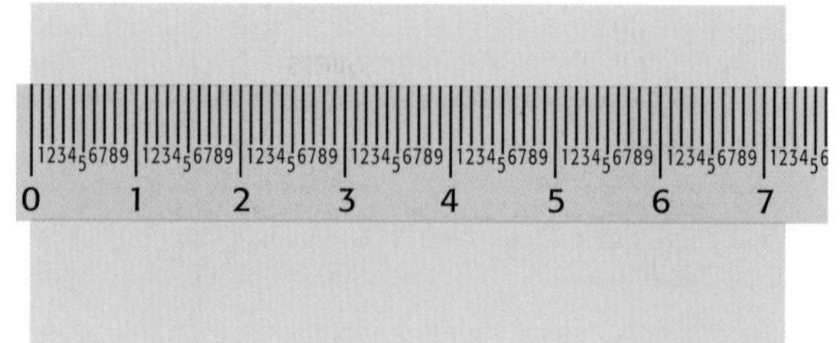

Using a Triple-Beam Balance

When using a triple-beam balance to measure mass, keep the following procedures in mind:

1. Make sure the balance is on a level surface.
2. Place all of the countermasses at 0. Adjust the balancing knob until the pointer rests at 0.
3. Place the object you wish to measure on the pan. **Caution:** Do not place hot objects or chemicals directly on the balance pan.
4. Move the largest countermass along the beam to the right until it is at the last notch that does not tip the balance. Follow the same procedure with the next-largest countermass. Then, move the smallest countermass until the pointer rests at 0.
5. Add the readings from the three beams together to determine the mass of the object.
6. When determining the mass of crystals or powders, first find the mass of a piece of filter paper. Then, add the crystals or powder to the paper, and remeasure. The actual mass of the crystals or powder is the total mass minus the mass of the paper. When finding the mass of liquids, first find the mass of the empty container. Then, find the combined mass of the liquid and container. The mass of the liquid is the total mass minus the mass of the container.

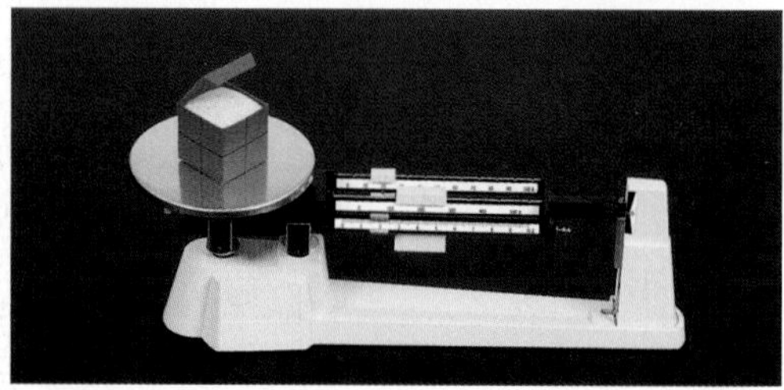

Scientific Methods

The ways in which scientists answer questions and solve problems are called **scientific methods.** The same steps are often used by scientists as they look for answers. However, there is more than one way to use these steps. Scientists may use all of the steps or just some of the steps during an investigation. They may even repeat some of the steps. The goal of using scientific methods is to come up with reliable answers and solutions.

Six Steps of Scientific Methods

Good questions come from careful **observations.** You make observations by using your senses to gather information. Sometimes, you may use instruments, such as microscopes and telescopes, to extend the range of your senses. As you observe the natural world, you will discover that you have many more questions than answers. These questions drive investigations.

Questions beginning with *what, why, how,* and *when* are important in focusing an investigation. Here is an example of a question that could lead to an investigation.

Question: How does acid rain affect plant growth?

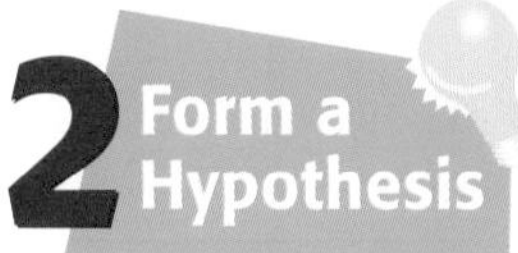

After you ask a question, you need to form a **hypothesis.** A hypothesis is a clear statement of what you expect the answer to your question to be. Your hypothesis will represent your best "educated guess" based on what you have observed and what you already know. A good hypothesis is testable. Otherwise, the investigation can go no further. Here is a hypothesis based on the question, "How does acid rain affect plant growth?"

Hypothesis: Acid rain slows plant growth.

The hypothesis can lead to predictions. A prediction is what you think the outcome of your experiment or data collection will be. Predictions are usually stated in an if-then format. Here is a sample prediction for the hypothesis that acid rain slows plant growth.

Prediction: If a plant is watered with only acid rain (which has a pH of 4), then the plant will grow at half its normal rate.

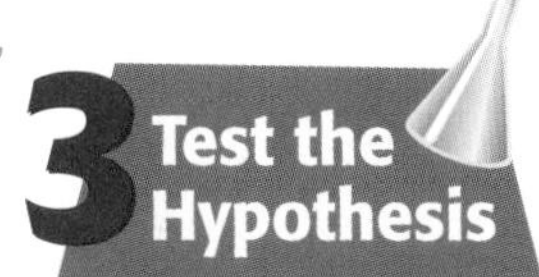

After you have formed a hypothesis and made a prediction, your hypothesis should be tested. One way to test a hypothesis is with a controlled experiment. A **controlled experiment** tests only one factor at a time. In an experiment to test the effect of acid rain on plant growth, the **control group** would be watered with normal rain water. The **experimental group** would be watered with acid rain. All of the plants should receive the same amount of sunlight and water each day. The air temperature should be the same for all groups. However, the acidity of the water will be a variable. In fact, any factor that is different from one group to another is a **variable.** If your hypothesis is correct, then the acidity of the water and plant growth are *dependant variables.* The amount a plant grows is dependent on the acidity of the water. However, the amount of water each plant receives and the amount of sunlight each plant receives are *independent variables.* Either of these factors could change without affecting the other factor.

Sometimes, the nature of an investigation makes a controlled experiment impossible. For example, the Earth's core is surrounded by thousands of meters of rock. Under such circumstances, a hypothesis may be tested by making detailed observations.

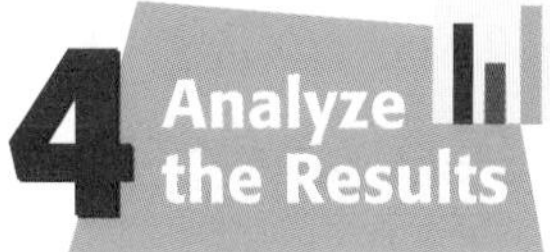

After you have completed your experiments, made your observations, and collected your data, you must analyze all the information you have gathered. Tables and graphs are often used in this step to organize the data.

Appendix

After analyzing your data, you can determine if your results support your hypothesis. If your hypothesis is supported, you (or others) might want to repeat the observations or experiments to verify your results. If your hypothesis is not supported by the data, you may have to check your procedure for errors. You may even have to reject your hypothesis and make a new one. If you cannot draw a conclusion from your results, you may have to try the investigation again or carry out further observations or experiments.

After any scientific investigation, you should report your results. By preparing a written or oral report, you let others know what you have learned. They may repeat your investigation to see if they get the same results. Your report may even lead to another question and then to another investigation.

Scientific Methods in Action

Scientific methods contain loops in which several steps may be repeated over and over again. In some cases, certain steps are unnecessary. Thus, there is not a "straight line" of steps. For example, sometimes scientists find that testing one hypothesis raises new questions and new hypotheses to be tested. And sometimes, testing the hypothesis leads directly to a conclusion. Furthermore, the steps in scientific methods are not always used in the same order. Follow the steps in the diagram, and see how many different directions scientific methods can take you.

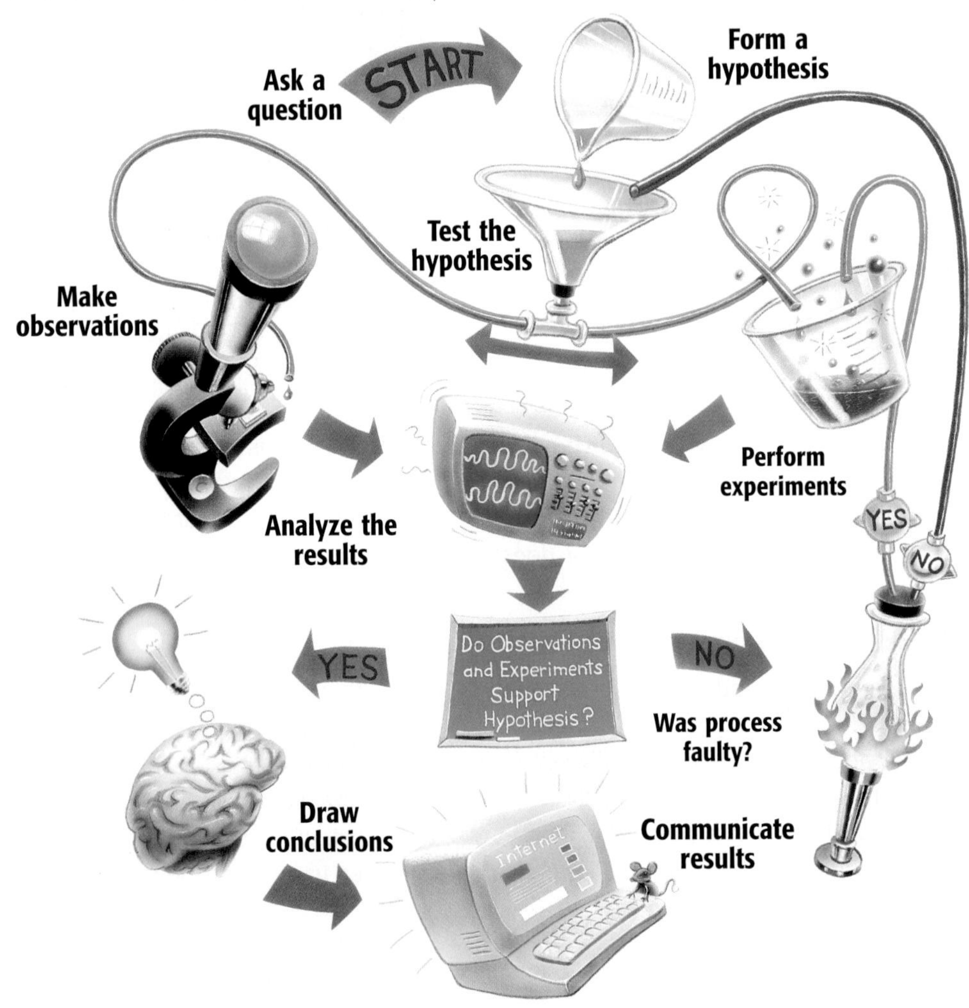

Appendix

Making Charts and Graphs

Pie Charts

A pie chart shows how each group of data relates to all of the data. Each part of the circle forming the chart represents a category of the data. The entire circle represents all of the data. For example, a biologist studying a hardwood forest in Wisconsin found that there were five different types of trees. The data table at right summarizes the biologist's findings.

Wisconsin Hardwood Trees	
Type of tree	**Number found**
Oak	600
Maple	750
Beech	300
Birch	1,200
Hickory	150
Total	3,000

How to Make a Pie Chart

1. To make a pie chart of these data, first find the percentage of each type of tree. Divide the number of trees of each type by the total number of trees, and multiply by 100.

$$\frac{\text{600 oak}}{\text{3,000 trees}} \times 100 = 20\%$$

$$\frac{\text{750 maple}}{\text{3,000 trees}} \times 100 = 25\%$$

$$\frac{\text{300 beech}}{\text{3,000 trees}} \times 100 = 10\%$$

$$\frac{\text{1,200 birch}}{\text{3,000 trees}} \times 100 = 40\%$$

$$\frac{\text{150 hickory}}{\text{3,000 trees}} \times 100 = 5\%$$

2. Now, determine the size of the wedges that make up the pie chart. Multiply each percentage by 360°. Remember that a circle contains 360°.

$20\% \times 360° = 72°$ $25\% \times 360° = 90°$
$10\% \times 360° = 36°$ $40\% \times 360° = 144°$
$5\% \times 360° = 18°$

3. Check that the sum of the percentages is 100 and the sum of the degrees is 360.

$20\% + 25\% + 10\% + 40\% + 5\% = 100\%$

$72° + 90° + 36° + 144° + 18° = 360°$

4. Use a compass to draw a circle and mark the center of the circle.
5. Then, use a protractor to draw angles of 72°, 90°, 36°, 144°, and 18° in the circle.
6. Finally, label each part of the chart, and choose an appropriate title.

A Community of Wisconsin Hardwood Trees

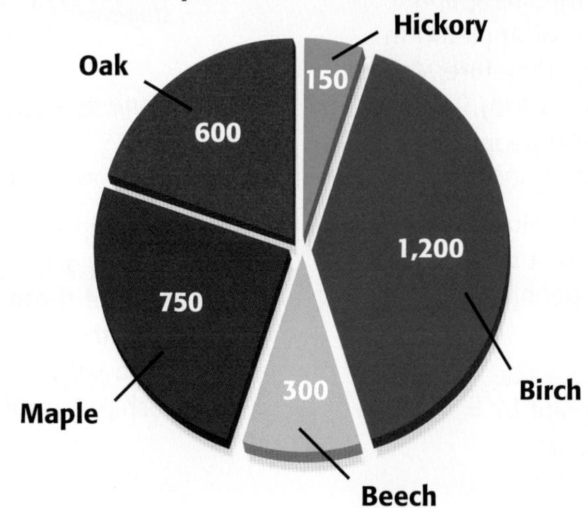

Appendix

Line Graphs

Line graphs are most often used to demonstrate continuous change. For example, Mr. Smith's students analyzed the population records for their hometown, Appleton, between 1900 and 2000. Examine the data at right.

Because the year and the population change, they are the *variables*. The population is determined by, or dependent on, the year. Therefore, the population is called the **dependent variable,** and the year is called the **independent variable.** Each set of data is called a **data pair.** To prepare a line graph, you must first organize data pairs into a table like the one at right.

Population of Appleton, 1900–2000

Year	Population
1900	1,800
1920	2,500
1940	3,200
1960	3,900
1980	4,600
2000	5,300

How to Make a Line Graph

1. Place the independent variable along the horizontal (*x*) axis. Place the dependent variable along the vertical (*y*) axis.
2. Label the *x*-axis "Year" and the *y*-axis "Population." Look at your largest and smallest values for the population. For the *y*-axis, determine a scale that will provide enough space to show these values. You must use the same scale for the entire length of the axis. Next, find an appropriate scale for the *x*-axis.
3. Choose reasonable starting points for each axis.
4. Plot the data pairs as accurately as possible.
5. Choose a title that accurately represents the data.

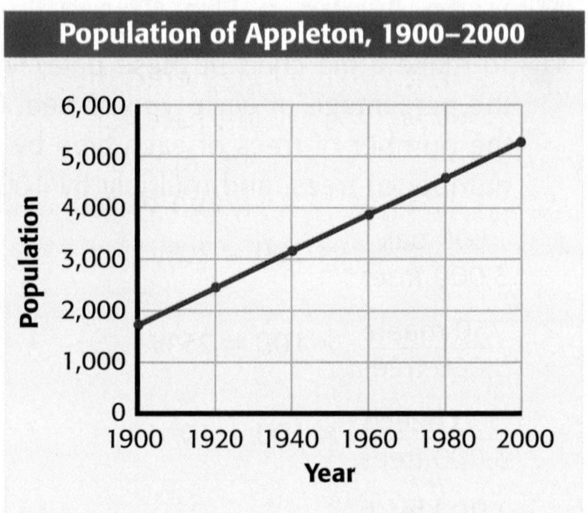

How to Determine Slope

Slope is the ratio of the change in the *y*-value to the change in the *x*-value, or "rise over run."

1. Choose two points on the line graph. For example, the population of Appleton in 2000 was 5,300 people. Therefore, you can define point *a* as (2000, 5,300). In 1900, the population was 1,800 people. You can define point *b* as (1900, 1,800).
2. Find the change in the *y*-value.
(*y* at point *a*) − (*y* at point *b*) =
5,300 people − 1,800 people =
3,500 people
3. Find the change in the *x*-value.
(*x* at point *a*) − (*x* at point *b*) =
2000 − 1900 = 100 years
4. Calculate the slope of the graph by dividing the change in *y* by the change in *x*.

$$slope = \frac{change\ in\ y}{change\ in\ x}$$

$$slope = \frac{3{,}500\ \text{people}}{100\ \text{years}}$$

$$slope = 35\ \text{people per year}$$

In this example, the population in Appleton increased by a fixed amount each year. The graph of these data is a straight line. Therefore, the relationship is **linear.** When the graph of a set of data is not a straight line, the relationship is **nonlinear.**

Topic: **Periodic Table**
Go To: **go.hrw.com**
Keyword: **HNO PERIODIC**
Visit the HRW Web site for updates on the periodic table.

This zigzag line reminds you where the metals, nonmetals, and metalloids are.

Group 10	Group 11	Group 12	Group 13	Group 14	Group 15	Group 16	Group 17	Group 18
								2 **He** Helium 4.0
			5 **B** Boron 10.8	6 **C** Carbon 12.0	7 **N** Nitrogen 14.0	8 **O** Oxygen 16.0	9 **F** Fluorine 19.0	10 **Ne** Neon 20.2
			13 **Al** Aluminum 27.0	14 **Si** Silicon 28.1	15 **P** Phosphorus 31.0	16 **S** Sulfur 32.1	17 **Cl** Chlorine 35.5	18 **Ar** Argon 39.9
28 **Ni** Nickel 58.7	29 **Cu** Copper 63.5	30 **Zn** Zinc 65.4	31 **Ga** Gallium 69.7	32 **Ge** Germanium 72.6	33 **As** Arsenic 74.9	34 **Se** Selenium 79.0	35 **Br** Bromine 79.9	36 **Kr** Krypton 83.8
46 **Pd** Palladium 106.4	47 **Ag** Silver 107.9	48 **Cd** Cadmium 112.4	49 **In** Indium 114.8	50 **Sn** Tin 118.7	51 **Sb** Antimony 121.8	52 **Te** Tellurium 127.6	53 **I** Iodine 126.9	54 **Xe** Xenon 131.3
78 **Pt** Platinum 195.1	79 **Au** Gold 197.0	80 **Hg** Mercury 200.6	81 **Tl** Thallium 204.4	82 **Pb** Lead 207.2	83 **Bi** Bismuth 209.0	84 **Po** Polonium (209)	85 **At** Astatine (210)	86 **Rn** Radon (222)
110 **Ds** Darmstadtium (269)†	111 **Uuu** Unununium (272)†	112 **Uub** Ununbium (277)†		114 **Uuq** Ununquadium (285)†				

The names and three-letter symbols of elements are temporary. They are based on the atomic numbers of the elements. Official names and symbols will be approved by an international committee of scientists.

63 **Eu** Europium 152.0	64 **Gd** Gadolinium 157.2	65 **Tb** Terbium 158.9	66 **Dy** Dysprosium 162.5	67 **Ho** Holmium 164.9	68 **Er** Erbium 167.3	69 **Tm** Thulium 168.9	70 **Yb** Ytterbium 173.0	71 **Lu** Lutetium 175.0
95 **Am** Americium (243)	96 **Cm** Curium (247)	97 **Bk** Berkelium (247)	98 **Cf** Californium (251)	99 **Es** Einsteinium (252)	100 **Fm** Fermium (257)	101 **Md** Mendelevium (258)	102 **No** Nobelium (259)	103 **Lr** Lawrencium (262)

Physical Science Laws and Equations

Law of Conservation of Energy

The law of conservation of energy states that energy can be neither created nor destroyed.

The total amount of energy in a closed system is always the same. Energy can be changed from one form to another, but all of the different forms of energy in a system always add up to the same total amount of energy no matter how many energy conversions occur.

Law of Universal Gravitation

The law of universal gravitation states that all objects in the universe attract each other by a force called *gravity*. The size of the force depends on the masses of the objects and the distance between objects.

The first part of the law explains why a bowling ball is much harder to lift than a table-tennis ball. Because the bowling ball has a much larger mass than the table-tennis ball does, the amount of gravity between the Earth and the bowling ball is greater than the amount of gravity between the Earth and the table-tennis ball.

The second part of the law explains why a satellite can remain in orbit around the Earth. The satellite is carefully placed at a distance great enough to prevent the Earth's gravity from immediately pulling the satellite down but small enough to prevent the satellite from completely escaping the Earth's gravity and wandering off into space.

Newton's Laws of Motion

Newton's first law of motion states that an object at rest remains at rest and an object in motion remains in motion at constant speed and in a straight line unless acted on by an unbalanced force.

The first part of the law explains why a football will remain on a tee until it is kicked off or until a gust of wind blows it off.

The second part of the law explains why a bike rider will continue moving forward after the bike comes to an abrupt stop. Gravity and the friction of the sidewalk will eventually stop the rider.

Newton's second law of motion states that the acceleration of an object depends on the mass of the object and the amount of force applied.

The first part of the law explains why the acceleration of a 4 kg bowling ball will be greater than the acceleration of a 6 kg bowling ball if the same force is applied to both.

The second part of the law explains why the acceleration of a bowling ball will be larger if a larger force is applied to the bowling ball.

The relationship of acceleration (a) to mass (m) and force (F) can be expressed mathematically by the following equation:

$$acceleration = \frac{force}{mass}, \text{ or } a = \frac{F}{m}$$

This equation is often rearranged to the form

$$force = mass \times acceleration$$

or

$$F = m \times a$$

Newton's third law of motion states that whenever one object exerts a force on a second object, the second object exerts an equal and opposite force on the first.

This law explains that a runner is able to move forward because of the equal and opposite force that the ground exerts on the runner's foot after each step.

Appendix

Useful Equations

Average speed

$$\textit{average speed} = \frac{\textit{total distance}}{\textit{total time}}$$

Example: A bicycle messenger traveled a distance of 136 km in 8 h. What was the messenger's average speed?

$$\frac{136 \text{ km}}{8 \text{ h}} = 17 \text{ km/h}$$

The messenger's average speed was **17 km/h.**

Average acceleration

$$\textit{average acceleration} = \frac{\textit{final velocity} - \textit{starting velocity}}{\textit{time it takes to change velocity}}$$

Example: Calculate the average acceleration of an Olympic 100 m dash sprinter who reaches a velocity of 20 m/s south at the finish line. The race was in a straight line and lasted 10 s.

$$\frac{20 \text{ m/s} - 0 \text{ m/s}}{10 \text{ s}} = 2 \text{ m/s/s}$$

The sprinter's average acceleration is **2 m/s/s south.**

Net force

Forces in the Same Direction

When forces are in the same direction, add the forces together to determine the net force.

Example: Calculate the net force on a stalled car that is being pushed by two people. One person is pushing with a force of 13 N northwest, and the other person is pushing with a force of 8 N in the same direction.

$$13 \text{ N} + 8 \text{ N} = 21 \text{ N}$$

The net force is **21 N northwest.**

Forces in Opposite Directions

When forces are in opposite directions, subtract the smaller force from the larger force to determine the net force. The net force will be in the direction of the larger force.

Net force (continued)

Example: Calculate the net force on a rope that is being pulled on each end. One person is pulling on one end of the rope with a force of 12 N south. Another person is pulling on the opposite end of the rope with a force of 7 N north.

$$12 \text{ N} - 7 \text{ N} = 5 \text{ N}$$

The net force is **5 N south.**

Density

$$\textit{density} = \frac{\textit{mass}}{\textit{volume}}$$

Example: Calculate the density of a sponge that has a mass of 10 g and a volume of 40 cm^3.

$$\frac{10 \text{ g}}{40 \text{ cm}^3} = \frac{0.25 \text{g}}{\text{cm}^3}$$

The density of the sponge is **0.25 g/cm^3.**

Pressure

Pressure is the force exerted over a given area. The SI unit for pressure is the pascal, whose symbol is Pa.

$$\textit{pressure} = \frac{\textit{force}}{\textit{area}}$$

Example: Calculate the pressure of the air in a soccer ball if the air exerts a force of 10 N over an area of 0.5 m^2.

$$\textit{pressure} = \frac{10 \text{ N}}{0.5 \text{ m}^2} = \frac{20 \text{ N}}{\text{m}^2} = 20 \text{ Pa}$$

The pressure of the air inside the soccer ball is **20 Pa.**

Concentration

$$\textit{concentration} = \frac{\textit{mass of solute}}{\textit{volume of solvent}}$$

Example: Calculate the concentration of a solution in which 10 g of sugar is dissolved in 125 mL of water.

$$\frac{10 \text{ g of sugar}}{125 \text{ mL of water}} = \frac{0.08 \text{ g}}{\text{mL}}$$

The concentration of this solution is **0.08 g/mL.**

Appendix

Properties of Common Minerals

	Mineral	Color	Luster	Streak	Hardness
Silicate Minerals	**Beryl**	deep green, pink, white, bluish green, or yellow	vitreous	white	7.5–8
	Chlorite	green	vitreous to pearly	pale green	2–2.5
	Garnet	green, red, brown, black	vitreous	white	6.5–7.5
	Hornblende	dark green, brown, or black	vitreous	none	5–6
	Muscovite	colorless, silvery white, or brown	vitreous or pearly	white	2–2.5
	Olivine	olive green, yellow	vitreous	white or none	6.5–7
	Orthoclase	colorless, white, pink, or other colors	vitreous	white or none	6
	Plagioclase	colorless, white, yellow, pink, green	vitreous	white	6
	Quartz	colorless or white; any color when not pure	vitreous or waxy	white or none	7
Nonsilicate Minerals	**Native Elements**				
	Copper	copper-red	metallic	copper-red	2.5–3
	Diamond	pale yellow or colorless	adamantine	none	10
	Graphite	black to gray	submetallic	black	1–2
	Carbonates				
	Aragonite	colorless, white, or pale yellow	vitreous	white	3.5–4
	Calcite	colorless or white to tan	vitreous	white	3
	Halides				
	Fluorite	light green, yellow, purple, bluish green, or other colors	vitreous	none	4
	Halite	white	vitreous	white	2.0–2.5
	Oxides				
	Hematite	reddish brown to black	metallic to earthy	dark red to red-brown	5.6–6.5
	Magnetite	iron-black	metallic	black	5.5–6.5
	Sulfates				
	Anhydrite	colorless, bluish, or violet	vitreous to pearly	white	3–3.5
	Gypsum	white, pink, gray, or colorless	vitreous, pearly, or silky	white	2.0
	Sulfides				
	Galena	lead-gray	metallic	lead-gray to black	2.5–2.8
	Pyrite	brassy yellow	metallic	greenish, brownish, or black	6–6.5

Appendix

Density (g/cm^3)	Cleavage, Fracture, Special Properties	Common Uses
2.6–2.8	1 cleavage direction; irregular fracture; some varieties fluoresce in ultraviolet light	gemstones, ore of the metal beryllium
2.6–3.3	1 cleavage direction; irregular fracture	
4.2	no cleavage; conchoidal to splintery fracture	gemstones, abrasives
3.0–3.4	2 cleavage directions; hackly to splintery fracture	
2.7–3	1 cleavage direction; irregular fracture	electrical insulation, wallpaper, fireproofing material, lubricant
3.2–3.3	no cleavage; conchoidal fracture	gemstones, casting
2.6	2 cleavage directions; irregular fracture	porcelain
2.6–2.7	2 cleavage directions; irregular fracture	ceramics
2.6	no cleavage; conchoidal fracture	gemstones, concrete, glass, porcelain, sandpaper, lenses
8.9	no cleavage; hackly fracture	wiring, brass, bronze, coins
3.5	4 cleavage directions; irregular to conchoidal fracture	gemstones, drilling
2.3	1 cleavage direction; irregular fracture	pencils, paints, lubricants, batteries
2.95	2 cleavage directions; irregular fracture; reacts with hydrochloric acid	no important industrial uses
2.7	3 cleavage directions; irregular fracture; reacts with weak acid; double refraction	cements, soil conditioner, whitewash, construction materials
3.0–3.3	4 cleavage directions; irregular fracture; some varieties fluoresce	hydrofluoric acid, steel, glass, fiberglass, pottery, enamel
2.1–2.2	3 cleavage directions; splintery to conchoidal fracture; salty taste	tanning hides, salting icy roads, food preservation
5.2–5.3	no cleavage; splintery fracture; magnetic when heated	iron ore for steel, pigments
5.2	no cleavage; splintery fracture; magnetic	iron ore
3.0	3 cleavage directions; conchoidal to splintery fracture	soil conditioner, sulfuric acid
2.3	3 cleavage directions; conchoidal to splintery fracture	plaster of Paris, wallboard, soil conditioner
7.4–7.6	3 cleavage directions; irregular fracture	batteries, paints
5	no cleavage; conchoidal to splintery fracture	sulfuric acid

Sky Maps

Spring

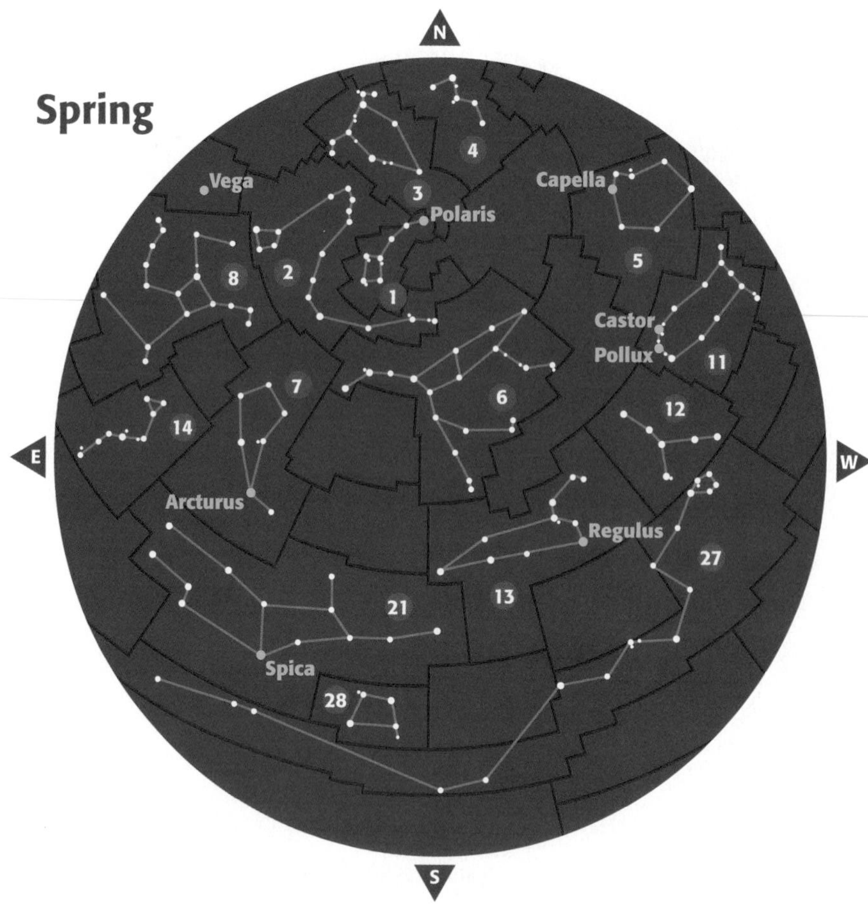

Summer

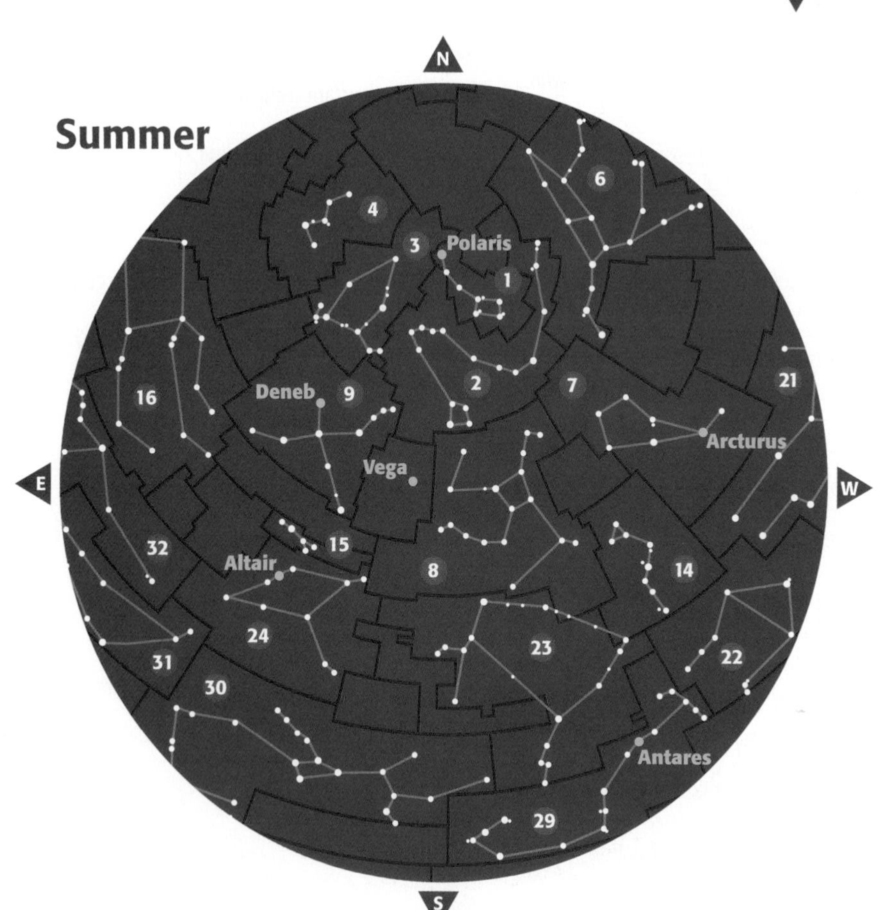

Constellations

1 Ursa Minor
2 Draco
3 Cepheus
4 Cassiopeia
5 Auriga
6 Ursa Major
7 Bootes
8 Hercules
9 Cygnus
10 Perseus
11 Gemini
12 Cancer
13 Leo
14 Serpens
15 Sagitta
16 Pegasus
17 Pisces

Appendix

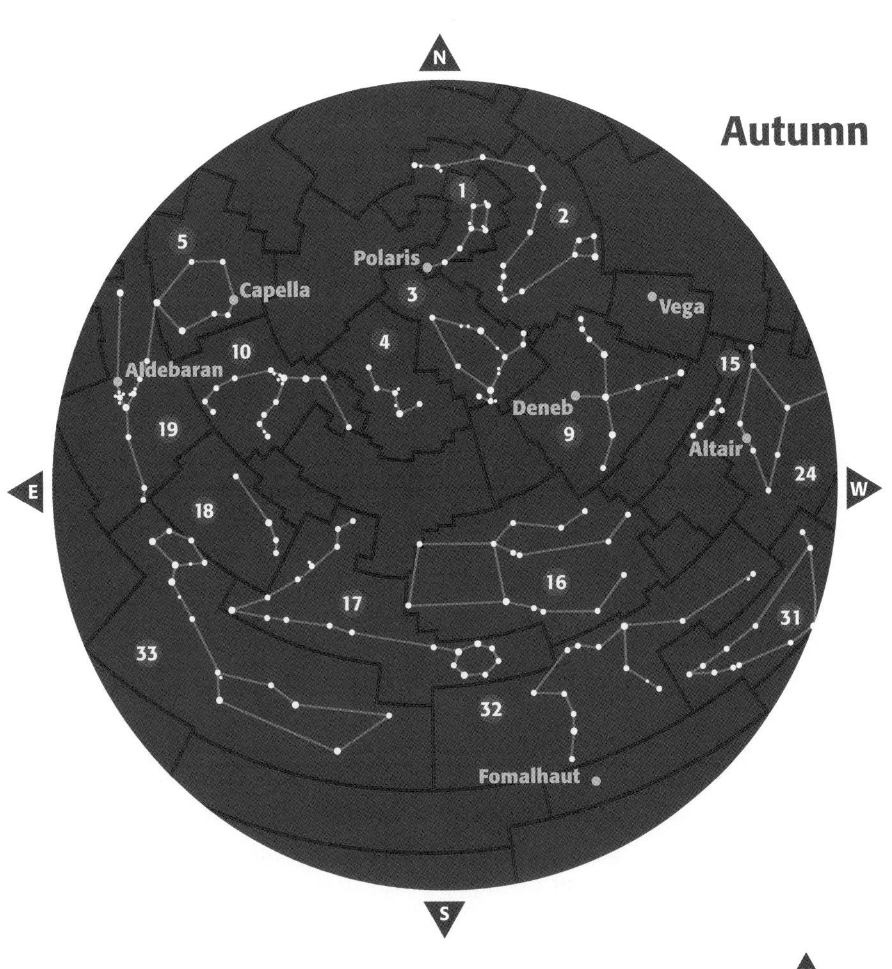

Constellations

18 Aries
19 Taurus
20 Orion
21 Virgo
22 Libra
23 Ophiuchus
24 Aquila
25 Lepus
26 Canis Major
27 Hydra
28 Corvus
29 Scorpius
30 Sagittarius
31 Capricornus
32 Aquarius
33 Cetus
34 Columba

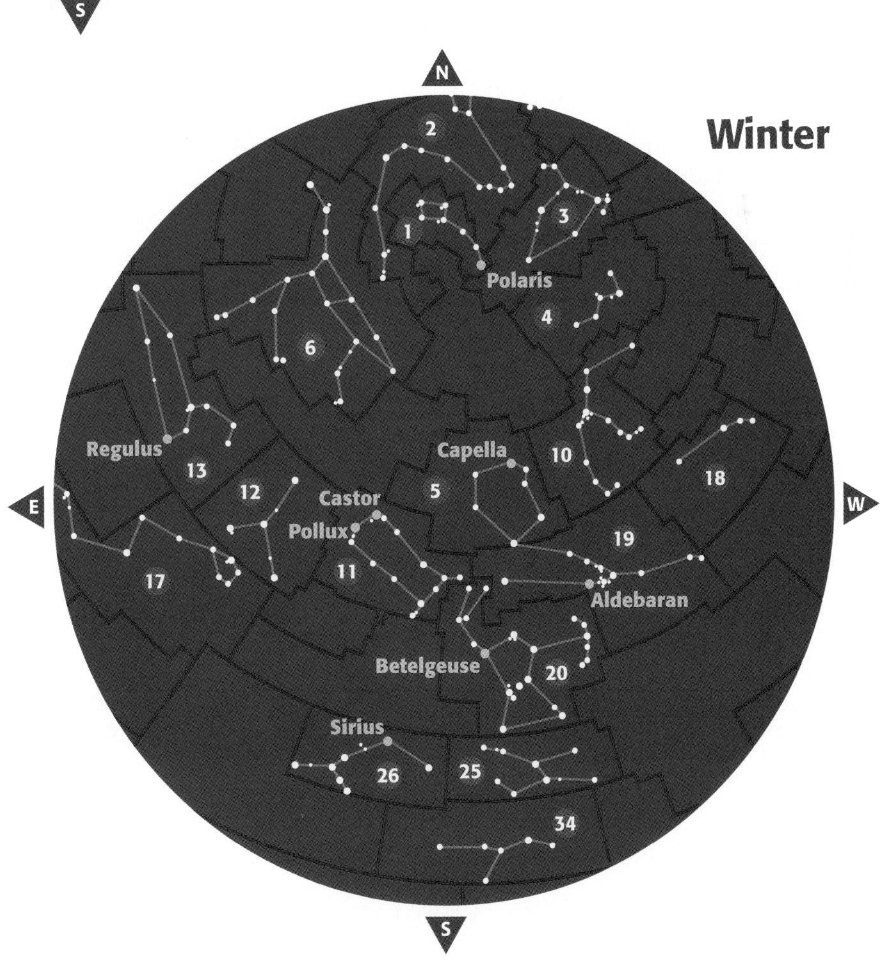

Appendix

Glossary

A

abiotic describes the nonliving part of the environment, including water, rocks, light, and temperature (590)

abrasion the grinding and wearing away of rock surfaces through the mechanical action of other rock or sand particles (65)

absorption in optics, the transfer of light energy to particles of matter (422)

acid precipitation rain, sleet, or snow that contains a high concentration of acids (67, 185)

air mass a large body of air where temperature and moisture content are similar throughout (216)

air pollution the contamination of the atmosphere by the introduction of pollutants from human and natural sources (182)

air pressure the measure of the force with which air molecules push on a surface (167)

allergy a reaction to a harmless or common substance by the body's immune system (577)

alluvial fan a fan-shaped mass of material deposited by a stream when the slope of the land decreases sharply (104)

altitude the angle between an object in the sky and the horizon (256)

amplitude the maximum distance that the particles of a wave's medium vibrate from their rest position (410)

anemometer an instrument used to measure wind speed (231)

Animalia a kingdom made up of complex, multicellular organisms that lack cell walls, can usually move around, and quickly respond to their environment (480)

antibody a protein made by B cells that binds to a specific antigen (573)

anticyclone the rotation of air around a high-pressure center in the direction opposite to Earth's rotation (220)

aquifer a body of rock or sediment that stores groundwater and allows the flow of groundwater (107)

Archaebacteria (AHR kee bak TEER ee uh) a kingdom made up of bacteria that live in extreme environments (477)

area a measure of the size of a surface or a region (25)

artesian spring a spring whose water flows from a crack in the cap rock over the aquifer (109)

artificial satellite any human-made object placed in orbit around a body in space (262)

asexual reproduction reproduction that does not involve the union of sex cells and in which a single parent produces offspring that are genetically identical to the parent (492)

asteroid a small, rocky object that orbits the sun, usually in a band between the orbits of Mars and Jupiter (304)

asteroid belt the region of the solar system that is between the orbits of Mars and Jupiter and in which most asteroids orbit (304)

astronomical unit the average distance between the Earth and the sun; approximately 150 million kilometers (symbol, AU) (279)

astronomy the study of the universe (244)

atmosphere a mixture of gases that surrounds a planet or moon (166)

autoimmune disease a disease in which the immune system attacks the organism's own cells (577)

B

barometer an instrument that measures atmospheric pressure (231)

B cell a white blood cell that makes antibodies (573)

bedrock the layer of rock beneath soil (74)

biome (BIE OHM) a large region characterized by a specific type of climate and certain types of plant and animal communities (206, 618)

biosphere the part of Earth where life exists (593)

biotic describes living factors in the environment (590)

blood the fluid that carries gases, nutrients, and wastes through the body and that is made up of platelets, white blood cells, red blood cells, and plasma (530)

blood pressure the force that blood exerts on the walls of the arteries (532)

C

carnivore an organism that eats animals (595)

carrying capacity the largest population that an environment can support at any given time (601)

cell in biology, the smallest unit that can perform all life processes; cells are covered by a membrane and contain DNA and cytoplasm (440)

cell membrane a phospholipid layer that covers a cell's surface and acts as a barrier between the inside of a cell and the cell's environment (443)

cellular respiration the process by which cells use oxygen to produce energy from food (505)

cell wall a rigid structure that surrounds the cell membrane and provides support to the cell (448)

channel the path that a stream follows (97)

chemical change a change that occurs when one or more substances change into entirely new substances with different properties (334)

chemical equation a representation of a chemical reaction that uses symbols to show the relationship between the reactants and the products (366)

chemical formula a combination of chemical symbols and numbers to represent a substance (364)

chemical property a property of matter that describes a substance's ability to participate in chemical reactions (332)

chemical weathering the process by which rocks break down as a result of chemical reactions (67)

chlorophyll (KLAWR uh FIL) a green pigment that captures light energy for photosynthesis (504)

classification the division of organisms into groups, or classes, based on specific characteristics (470)

cleavage the splitting of a mineral along smooth, flat surfaces (45)

climate the average weather conditions in an area over a long period of time (200)

cloud a collection of small water droplets or ice crystals suspended in the air, which forms when the air is cooled and condensation occurs (212)

coelom (SEE luhm) a body cavity that contains the internal organs (501)

coevolution the evolution of two species that is due to mutual influence, often in a way that makes the relationship more beneficial to both species (605)

colloid (KAHL OYD) a mixture consisting of tiny particles that are intermediate in size between those in solutions and those in suspensions and that are suspended in a liquid, solid, or gas (362)

comet a small body of ice, rock, and cosmic dust that follows an elliptical orbit around the sun and that gives off gas and dust in the form of a tail as it passes close to the sun (302)

commensalism a relationship between two organisms in which one organism benefits and the other is unaffected (604)

community all of the populations of species that live in the same habitat and interact with each other (592)

compound a substance made up of atoms of two or more different elements joined by chemical bonds (41, 352)

concentration the amount of a particular substance in a given quantity of a mixture, solution, or ore (360)

condensation the change of state from a gas to a liquid (211)

constellation a region of the sky that contains a recognizable star pattern and that is used to describe the location of objects in space (254)

consumer an organism that eats other organisms or organic matter (500)

convection the transfer of thermal energy by the circulation or movement of a liquid or gas (173)

Coriolis effect the apparent curving of the path of a moving object from an otherwise straight path due to the Earth's rotation (138, 178)

crystal a solid whose atoms, ions, or molecules are arranged in a definite pattern (41)

cyclone an area in the atmosphere that has lower pressure than the surrounding areas and has winds that spiral toward the center (220)

D

data any pieces of information acquired through observation or experimentation (13)

day the time required for Earth to rotate once on its axis (244)

deep current a streamlike movement of ocean water far below the surface (139)

delta a fan-shaped mass of material deposited at the mouth of a stream (103)

density the ratio of the mass of a substance to the volume of the substance (46, 327)

deposition the process in which material is laid down (102)

desert an area that has little or no plant life, long periods without rain, and extreme temperatures; usually found in hot climates (623)

dichotomous key (die KAHT uh muhs KEE) an aid that is used to identify organisms and that consists of the answers to a series of questions (474)

differential weathering the process by which softer, less weather resistant rocks wear away and leave harder, more weather resistant rocks behind (70)

diffraction a change in the direction of a wave when the wave finds an obstacle or an edge, such as an opening (416, 425)

digestive system the organs that break down food so that it can be used by the body (522)

divide the boundary between drainage areas that have streams that flow in opposite directions (96)

dormant describes the inactive state of a seed or other plant part when conditions are unfavorable to growth (498)

E

eclipse an event in which the shadow of one celestial body falls on another (297)

ecology the study of the interactions of living organisms with one another and with their environment (590)

ecosystem a community of organisms and their abiotic, or nonliving, environment (593)

egg a sex cell produced by a female (493)

electromagnetic spectrum all of the frequencies or wavelengths of electromagnetic radiation (251)

element a substance that cannot be separated or broken down into simpler substances by chemical means (40, 348)

elevation the height of an object above sea level (204)

El Niño a change in the surface water temperature in the Pacific Ocean that produces a warm current (144)

embryo (EM bree OH) a developing human, from fertilization through the first 8 weeks of development (the 10th week of pregnancy) (552)

endocrine system a collection of glands and groups of cells that secrete hormones that regulate growth, development, and homeostasis; includes the pituitary, thyroid, parathyroid, and adrenal glands, the hypothalamus, the pineal body, and the gonads (534)

endoplasmic reticulum (EN doh PLAZ mik ri TIK yuh luhm) a system of membranes that is found in a cell's cytoplasm and that assists in the production, processing, and transport of proteins and in the production of lipids (451)

energy the capacity to do work (380)

energy conversion a change from one form of energy to another (388)

energy pyramid a triangular diagram that shows an ecosystem's loss of energy, which results as energy passes through the ecosystem's food chain (597)

erosion the process by which wind, water, ice, or gravity transports soil and sediment from one location to another (81, 94)

esophagus (i SAHF uh guhs) a long, straight tube that connects the pharynx to the stomach (524)

estuary (ES tyoo er ee) an area where fresh water from rivers mixes with salt water from the ocean (630)

Eubacteria (YOO bak TEER ee uh) a kingdom that contains all prokaryotes except archaebacteria (477)

eukaryote an organism made up of cells that have a nucleus enclosed by a membrane; eukaryotes include animals, plants, and fungi but not archaebacteria or eubacteria (446)

external fertilization the union of sex cells outside the bodies of the parents (494)

F

fetus (FEET uhs) a developing human from seven or eight weeks after fertilization until birth (554)

floodplain an area along a river that forms from sediments deposited when the river overflows its banks (104)

food chain the pathway of energy transfer through various stages as a result of the feeding patterns of a series of organisms (596)

food web a diagram that shows the feeding relationships between organisms in an ecosystem (596)

fracture the manner in which a mineral breaks along either curved or irregular surfaces (45)

frequency the number of waves produced in a given amount of time (412)

front the boundary between air masses of different densities and usually different temperatures (218)

function the special, normal, or proper activity of an organ or part (459)

Fungi (FUHN JIE) a kingdom made up of nongreen, eukaryotic organisms that have no means of movement, reproduce by using spores, and get food by breaking down substances in their surroundings and absorbing the nutrients (478)

G

gallbladder a sac-shaped organ that stores bile produced by the liver (527)

gas giant a planet that has a deep, massive atmosphere, such as Jupiter, Saturn, Uranus, or Neptune (288)

geostationary orbit an orbit that is about 36,000 km above the Earth's surface and in which a satellite is above a fixed spot on the equator (263)

gland a group of cells that make special chemicals for the body (534)

global warming a gradual increase in average global temperature (175)

Golgi complex (GOHL jee KAHM PLEKS) cell organelle that helps make and package materials to be transported out of the cell (453)

greenhouse effect the warming of the surface and lower atmosphere of Earth that occurs when water vapor, carbon dioxide, and other gases absorb and reradiate thermal energy (174)

gut the digestive tract (501)

H

hardness a measure of the ability of a mineral to resist scratching (46)

herbivore an organism that eats only plants (595)

homeostasis (HOH mee OH STAY sis) the maintenance of a constant internal state in a changing environment (518)

horizon the line where the sky and the Earth appear to meet (256)

hormone a substance that is made in one cell or tissue and that causes a change in another cell or tissue in a different part of the body (534)

humidity the amount of water vapor in the air (209)

humus dark, organic material formed in soil from the decayed remains of plants and animals (76)

hurricane a severe storm that develops over tropical oceans and whose strong winds of more than 120 km/h spiral in toward the intensely low-pressure storm center (225)

hypothesis (hie PAHTH uh sis) an explanation that is based on prior scientific research or observations and that can be tested (12)

I

immune system the cells and tissues that recognize and attack foreign substances in the body (573)

immunity the ability to resist an infectious disease (570)

inertia (in UHR shuh) the tendency of an object to resist being moved or, if the object is moving, to resist a change in speed or direction until an outside force acts on the object (324)

infectious disease a disease that is caused by a pathogen and that can be spread from one individual to another (568)

interference the combination of two or more waves that results in a single wave (417, 426)

internal fertilization fertilization of an egg by sperm that occurs inside the body of a female (494)

J

jet stream a narrow belt of strong winds that blow in the upper troposphere (180)

K

kinetic energy (ki NET ik EN uhr jee) the energy of an object that is due to the object's motion (381)

L

La Niña a change in the eastern Pacific Ocean in which the surface water temperature becomes unusually cool (144)

large intestine the wider and shorter portion of the intestine that removes water from mostly digested food and that turns the waste into semisolid feces, or stool (528)

latitude the distance north or south from the equator; expressed in degrees (201)

law a summary of many experimental results and observations; a law tells how things work (21)

law of conservation of mass the law that states that mass cannot be created or destroyed in ordinary chemical and physical changes (367)

leaching the removal of substances that can be dissolved from rock, ore, or layers of soil due to the passing of water (76)

lightning an electric discharge that takes place between two oppositely charged surfaces, such as between a cloud and the ground, between two clouds, or between two parts of the same cloud (223)

light-year the distance that light travels in one year; about 9.46 trillion kilometers (258)

liver the largest organ in the body; it makes bile, stores and filters blood, and stores excess sugars as glycogen (527)

load the materials carried by a stream; *also* the mass of rock overlying a geological structure (98)

longitudinal wave a wave in which the particles of the medium vibrate parallel to the direction of wave motion (408)

longshore current a water current that travels near and parallel to the shoreline (149)

low Earth orbit an orbit that is less than 1,500 km above the Earth's surface (263)

luster the way in which a mineral reflects light (44)

lysosome (LIE suh SOHM) a cell organelle that contains digestive enzymes (454)

M

macrophage (MAK roh FAYJ) an immune system cell that engulfs pathogens and other materials (573)

marsh a treeless wetland ecosystem where plants such as grasses grow (634)

mass a measure of the amount of matter in an object (25, 323)

matter anything that has mass and takes up space (320)

mechanical energy the amount of work an object can do because of the object's kinetic and potential energies (383)

mechanical weathering the breakdown of rock into smaller pieces by physical means (64)

medium a physical environment in which phenomena occur (405)

memory B cell a B cell that responds to an antigen more strongly when the body is reinfected with an antigen than it does during its first encounter with the antigen (576)

meniscus (muh NIS kuhs) the curve at a liquid's surface by which one measures the volume of the liquid (321)

mesosphere the layer of the atmosphere between the stratosphere and the thermosphere and in which temperature decreases as altitude increases (169)

metal an element that is shiny and that conducts heat and electricity well (350)

metalloid an element that has properties of both metals and nonmetals (350)

meteor a bright streak of light that results when a meteoroid burns up in the Earth's atmosphere (305)

meteorite a meteoroid that reaches the Earth's surface without burning up completely (305)

meteoroid a relatively small, rocky body that travels through space (305)

meter the basic unit of length in the SI (symbol, m) (25)

mineral a naturally formed, inorganic solid that has a definite chemical structure (40)

mitochondrion (MIET oh KAHN dree uhn) in eukaryotic cells, the cell organelle that is surrounded by two membranes and that is the site of cellular respiration (452)

mixture a combination of two or more substances that are not chemically combined (356)

model a pattern, plan, representation, or description designed to show the structure or workings of an object, system, or concept (18)

month a division of the year that is based on the orbit of the moon around the Earth (244)

mutualism (MYOO choo uhl IZ uhm) a relationship between two species in which both species benefit (604)

N

neap tide a tide of minimum range that occurs during the first and third quarters of the moon (154)

noninfectious disease a disease that cannot spread from one individual to another (568)

nonmetal an element that conducts heat and electricity poorly (350)

nonpoint-source pollution pollution that comes from many sources rather than from a single, specific site (112)

nonsilicate mineral a mineral that does not contain compounds of silicon and oxygen (42)

nucleus in a eukaryotic cell, a membrane-bound organelle that contains the cell's DNA and that has a role in processes such as growth, metabolism, and reproduction (443)

O

observation the process of obtaining information by using the senses (11)

ocean current a movement of ocean water that follows a regular pattern (136)

omnivore an organism that eats both plants and animals (595)

ore a natural material whose concentration of economically valuable minerals is high enough for the material to be mined profitably (50)

organ a collection of tissues that carry out a specialized function of the body (457, 519)

organelle one of the small bodies in a cell's cytoplasm that are specialized to perform a specific function (443)

organism a living thing; anything that can carry out life processes independently (458)

organ system a group of organs that work together to perform body functions (458)

ovary in the female reproductive system of animals, an organ that produces eggs (549)

P

pancreas the organ that lies behind the stomach and that makes digestive enzymes and hormones that regulate sugar levels (526)

parasitism (PAR uh SIET IZ uhm) a relationship between two species in which one species, the parasite, benefits from the other species, the host, which is harmed (605)

parent rock a rock formation that is the source of soil (74)

pathogen a virus, microorganism, or other organism that causes disease (568)

penis the male organ that transfers sperm to a female and that carries urine out of the body (548)

permeability the ability of a rock or sediment to let fluids pass through its open spaces, or pores (107)

phase the change in the sunlit area of one celestial body as seen from another celestial body (296)

photosynthesis (FOHT oh SIN thuh sis) the process by which plants, algae, and some bacteria use sunlight, carbon dioxide, and water to make food (504)

physical change a change of matter from one form to another without a change in chemical properties (330)

physical property a characteristic of a substance that does not involve a chemical change, such as density, color, or hardness (326)

placenta (pluh SEN tuh) the partly fetal and partly maternal organ by which materials are exchanged between a fetus and the mother (553)

plankton the mass of mostly microscopic organisms that float or drift freely in freshwater and marine environments (626)

Plantae a kingdom made up of complex, multicellular organisms that are usually green, have cell walls made of cellulose, cannot move around, and use the sun's energy to make sugar by photosynthesis (479)

point-source pollution pollution that comes from a specific site (112)

polar easterlies prevailing winds that blow from east to west between 60° and 90° latitude in both hemispheres (178)

population a group of organisms of the same species that live in a specific geographical area (592)

porosity the percentage of the total volume of a rock or sediment that consists of open spaces (107)

potential energy the energy that an object has because of the position, shape, or condition of the object (382)

precipitation any form of water that falls to the Earth's surface from the clouds (214)

predator an organism that eats all or part of another organism (602)

prevailing winds winds that blow mainly from one direction during a given period (203)

prey an organism that is killed and eaten by another organism (60)

product a substance that forms in a chemical reaction (366)

prograde rotation the counterclockwise spin of a planet or moon as seen from above the planet's North Pole; rotation in the same direction as the sun's rotation (283)

prokaryote (pro KAR ee OHT) an organism that consists of a single cell that does not have a nucleus (444)

Protista (proh TIST uh) a kingdom of mostly one-celled eukaryotic organisms that are different from plants, animals, bacteria, and fungi (478)

pure substance a sample of matter, either a single element or a single compound, that has definite chemical and physical properties (348)

R

radiation the transfer of energy as electromagnetic waves (172)

reactant (ree AK tuhnt) a substance or molecule that participates in a chemical reaction (366)

recharge zone an area in which water travels downward to become part of an aquifer (108)

reclamation the process of returning land to its original condition after mining is completed (51)

reflecting telescope a telescope that uses a curved mirror to gather and focus light from distant objects (249)

reflection the bouncing back of a ray of light, sound, or heat when the ray hits a surface that it does not go through (414, 420)

refracting telescope a telescope that uses a set of lenses to gather and focus light from distant objects (249)

refraction the bending of a wave as the wave passes between two substances in which the speed of the wave differs (415, 423)

relative humidity the ratio of the amount of water vapor in the air to the maximum amount of water vapor the air can hold at a set temperature (209)

resonance a phenomenon that occurs when two objects naturally vibrate at the same frequency; the sound produced by one object causes the other object to vibrate (419)

retrograde rotation the clockwise spin of a planet or moon as seen from above the planet's North Pole (283)

ribosome a cell organelle composed of RNA and protein; the site of protein synthesis (451)

S

salinity a measure of the amount of dissolved salts in a given amount of liquid (130)

satellite a natural or artificial body that revolves around a planet (294)

savanna a grassland that often has scattered trees and that is found in tropical and subtropical areas where seasonal rains, fires, and drought happen (622)

scattering an interaction of light with matter that causes light to change its energy, direction of motion, or both (422)

science the knowledge obtained by observing natural events and conditions in order to discover facts and formulate laws or principles that can be verified or tested (4)

scientific methods a series of steps followed to solve problems (10)

septic tank a tank that separates solid waste from liquids and that has bacteria that break down the solid waste (115)

sewage treatment plant a facility that cleans the waste materials found in water that comes from sewers or drains (114)

sexual reproduction reproduction in which sex cells from two parents unite to produce offspring that share traits from both parents (493)

silicate mineral a mineral that contains a combination of silicon, oxygen, and one or more metals (42)

small intestine the organ between the stomach and the large intestine where most of the breakdown of food happens and most of the nutrients from food are absorbed (526)

soil a loose mixture of rock fragments, organic material, water, and air that can support the growth of vegetation (74)

soil conservation a method to maintain the fertility of the soil by protecting the soil from erosion and nutrient loss (80)

soil structure the arrangement of soil particles (75)

soil texture the soil quality that is based on the proportions of soil particles (75)

solubility the ability of one substance to dissolve in another at a given temperature and pressure (360)

solute in a solution, the substance that dissolves in the solvent (358)

solution a homogeneous mixture of two or more substances uniformly dispersed throughout a single phase (358)

solvent in a solution, the substance in which the solute dissolves (358)

sperm the male sex cell (493)

spring tide a tide of increased range that occurs two times a month, at the new and full moons (154)

standing wave a pattern of vibration that simulates a wave that is standing still (418)

stoma one of many openings in a leaf or a stem of a plant that enable gas exchange to occur (plural, *stomata*) (506)

stomach the saclike, digestive organ between the esophagus and the small intestine that breaks down food by the action of muscles, enzymes, and acids (525)

storm surge a local rise in sea level near the shore that is caused by strong winds from a storm, such as those from a hurricane (151)

stratosphere the layer of the atmosphere that is above the troposphere and in which temperature increases as altitude increases (169)

streak the color of the powder of a mineral (45)

structure the arrangement of parts in an organism (459)

surface current a horizontal movement of ocean water that is caused by wind and that occurs at or near the ocean's surface (137, 205)

suspension a mixture in which particles of a material are more or less evenly dispersed throughout a liquid or gas (362)

swamp a wetland ecosystem in which shrubs and trees grow (634)

swell one of a group of long ocean waves that have steadily traveled a great distance from their point of generation (150)

symbiosis a relationship in which two different organisms live in close association with each other (604)

T

taxonomy (taks AHN uh mee) the science of describing, naming, and classifying organisms (471)

T cell an immune system cell that coordinates the immune system and attacks many infected cells (573)

telescope an instrument that collects electromagnetic radiation from the sky and concentrates it for better observation (248)

temperature a measure of how hot (or cold) something is; specifically, a measure of the average kinetic energy of the particles in an object (26)

terrestrial planet one of the highly dense planets nearest to the sun; Mercury, Venus, Mars, and Earth (282)

testes the primary male reproductive organs, which produce sperm cells and testosterone (singular, *testis*) (548)

theory an explanation that ties together many hypotheses and observations (20)

thermal conduction the transfer of energy as heat through a material (173)

thermometer an instrument that measures and indicates temperature (231)

thermosphere the uppermost layer of the atmosphere, in which temperature increases as altitude increases (170)

thunder the sound caused by the rapid expansion of air along an electrical strike (223)

thunderstorm a usually brief, heavy storm that consists of rain, strong winds, lightning, and thunder (222)

tidal range the difference in levels of ocean water at high tide and low tide (154)

tide the periodic rise and fall of the water level in the oceans and other large bodies of water (152)

tissue a group of similar cells that perform a common function (457, 518)

tornado a destructive, rotating column of air that has very high wind speeds, is visible as a funnel-shaped cloud, and touches the ground (224)

trade winds prevailing winds that blow from east to west from 30° latitude to the equator in both hemispheres (178)

transpiration the process by which plants release water vapor into the air through stomata (506)

transverse wave a wave in which the particles of the medium move perpendicularly to the direction the wave is traveling (407)

tributary a stream that flows into a lake or into a larger stream (96)

troposphere the lowest layer of the atmosphere, in which temperature decreases at a constant rate as altitude increases (169)

tsunami a giant ocean wave that forms after a volcanic eruption, submarine earthquake, or landslide (150)

tundra a treeless plain found in the Arctic, in the Antarctic, or on the tops of mountains that is characterized by very low winter temperatures and short, cool summers (624)

U

umbilical cord (uhm BIL i kuhl KAWRD) the structure that connects an embryo and then the fetus to the placenta and through which blood vessels pass (553)

undertow a subsurface current that is near shore and that pulls objects out to sea (149)

upwelling the movement of deep, cold, and nutrient-rich water to the surface (143)

uterus in female mammals, the hollow, muscular organ in which a fertilized egg is embedded and in which the embryo and fetus develop (549)

V

vagina the female reproductive organ that connects the outside of the body to the uterus (549)

vesicle (VES i kuhl) a small cavity or sac that contains materials in a eukaryotic cell; forms when part of the cell membrane surrounds the materials to be taken into the cell or transported within the cell (453)

volume a measure of the size of a body or region in three-dimensional space (26, 320)

W

water cycle the continuous movement of water from the ocean to the atmosphere to the land and back to the ocean (95, 133)

watershed the area of land that is drained by a water system (96)

water table the upper surface of underground water; the upper boundary of the zone of saturation (106)

wave a periodic disturbance in a solid, liquid, or gas as energy is transmitted through a medium (404)

wavelength the distance from any point on a wave to an identical point on the next wave (411)

wave speed the speed at which a wave travels through a medium (412)

weather the short-term state of the atmosphere, including temperature, humidity, precipitation, wind, and visibility (200)

weathering the process by which rock materials are broken down by the action of physical or chemical processes (64)

weight a measure of the gravitational force exerted on an object; its value can change with the location of the object in the universe (323)

westerlies prevailing winds that blow from west to east between 30° and 60° latitude in both hemispheres (178)

wetland an area of land that is periodically underwater or whose soil contains a great deal of moisture (634)

whitecap the bubbles in the crest of a breaking wave (150)

wind the movement of air caused by differences in air pressure (176)

Y

year the time required for the Earth to orbit once around the sun (244)

Z

zenith the point in the sky directly above an observer on Earth (256)

Spanish Glossary

A

abiotic/abiótico término que describe la parte sin vida del ambiente, incluyendo el agua, las rocas, la luz y la temperatura (590)

abrasion/abrasión proceso por el cual las superficies de las rocas se muelen o desgastan por medio de la acción mecánica de otras rocas y partículas de arena (65)

absorption/absorción en la óptica, la transferencia de energía luminosa a las partículas de materia (422)

acid precipitation/precipitación ácida lluvia, aguanieve o nieve que contiene una alta concentración de ácidos (67, 185)

air mass/masa de aire un gran volumen de aire que tiene una temperatura y contenido de humedad similar en toda su extensión (216)

air pollution/contaminación del aire la contaminación de la atmósfera debido a la introducción de contaminantes provenientes de fuentes humanas y naturales (182)

air pressure/presión del aire la medida de la fuerza con la que las moléculas del aire empujan contra una superficie (167)

allergy/alergia una reacción del sistema inmunológico del cuerpo a una substancia inofensiva o común (577)

alluvial fan/abanico aluvial masa de materiales rocosos en forma de abanico, depositados por un arroyo cuando la pendiente del terreno disminuye bruscamente (104)

altitude/altitud el ángulo que se forma entre un objeto en el cielo y el horizonte (256)

amplitude/amplitud la distancia máxima a la que vibran las partículas del medio de una onda a partir de su posición de reposo (410)

anemometer/anemómetro un instrumento que se usa para medir la rapidez del viento (231)

Animalia/Animalia un reino formado por organismos pluricelulares complejos que no tienen pared celular, normalmente son capaces de moverse y reaccionan rápidamente a su ambiente (480)

antibody/anticuerpo una proteína producida por las células B que se une a un antígeno específico (573)

anticyclone/anticiclón la rotación del aire alrededor de un centro de alta presión en dirección opuesta a la rotación de la Tierra (220)

aquifer/acuífero un cuerpo rocoso o sedimento que almacena agua subterránea y permite que fluya (107)

Archaebacteria/arqueobacteria un reino formado por bacterias que viven en ambientes extremos (477)

area/área una medida del tamaño de una superficie o región (25)

artesian spring/manantial artesiano un manantial en el que el agua fluye a partir de una grieta en la capa de rocas que se encuentra sobre el acuífero (109)

artificial satellite/satélite artificial cualquier objeto hecho por los seres humanos y colocado en órbita alrededor de un cuerpo en el espacio (262)

asexual reproduction/reproducción asexual reproducción que no involucra la unión de células sexuales, en la que un solo progenitor produce descendencia que es genéticamente igual al progenitor (492)

asteroid/asteroide un objeto pequeño y rocoso que se encuentra en órbita alrededor del Sol, normalmente en una banda entre las órbitas de Marte y Júpiter (304)

asteroid belt/cinturón de asteroides la región del Sistema Solar que está entre las órbitas de Marte y Júpiter, en la que la mayoría de los asteroides se encuentran en órbita (304)

astronomical unit/unidad astronómica la distancia promedio entre la Tierra y el Sol; aproximadamente 150 millones de kilómetros (símbolo: UA) (279)

astronomy/astronomía el estudio del universo (244)

atmosphere/atmósfera una mezcla de gases que rodea un planeta o una luna (166)

autoimmune disease/enfermedad autoinmune una enfermedad en la que el sistema inmunológico ataca las células del propio organismo (577)

B

barometer/barómetro un instrumento que mide la presión atmosférica (231)

B cell/célula B un glóbulo blanco de la sangre que fabrica anticuerpos (573)

bedrock/lecho de roca la capa de rocas que está debajo del suelo (74)

biome/bioma una región extensa caracterizada por un tipo de clima específico y ciertos tipos de comunidades de plantas y animales (206, 618)

biosphere/biosfera la parte de la Tierra donde existe la vida (593)

biotic/biótico término que describe los factores vivientes del ambiente (590)

blood/sangre el líquido que lleva gases, nutrientes y desechos por el cuerpo y que está formado por plaquetas, glóbulos blancos, glóbulos rojos y plasma (530)

blood pressure/presión sanguínea la fuerza que la sangre ejerce en las paredes de las arterias (532)

C

carnivore/carnívoro un organismo que se alimenta de animales (595)

carrying capacity/capacidad de carga la población más grande que un ambiente puede sostener en cualquier momento dado (601)

cell/célula en biología, la unidad más pequeña que puede realizar todos los procesos vitales; las células están cubiertas por una membrana y tienen ADN y citoplasma (440)

cell membrane/membrana celular una capa de fosfolípidos que cubre la superficie de la célula y funciona como una barrera entre el interior de la célula y el ambiente de la célula (443)

cellular respiration/respiración celular el proceso por medio del cual las células utilizan oxígeno para producir energía a partir de los alimentos (505)

cell wall/pared celular una estructura rígida que rodea la membrana celular y le brinda soporte a la célula (448)

channel/canal el camino que sigue un arroyo (97)

chemical change/cambio químico un cambio que ocurre cuando una o más substancias se transforman en substancias totalmente nuevas con propiedades diferentes (334)

chemical equation/ecuación química una representación de una reacción química que usa símbolos para mostrar la relación entre los reactivos y los productos (366)

chemical formula/fórmula química una combinación de símbolos químicos y números que se usan para representar una substancia (364)

chemical property/propiedad química una propiedad de la materia que describe la capacidad de una substancia de participar en reacciones químicas (332)

chemical weathering/desgaste químico el proceso por medio del cual las rocas se fragmentan como resultado de reacciones químicas (67)

chlorophyll/clorofila un pigmento verde que capta la energía luminosa para la fotosíntesis (504)

classification/clasificación la división de organismos en grupos, o clases, en función de características específicas (470)

cleavage/exfoliación el agrietamiento de un mineral en sus superficies lisas y planas (45)

climate/clima las condiciones promedio del tiempo en un área durante un largo período de tiempo (200)

cloud/nube un conjunto de pequeñas gotitas de agua o cristales de hielo suspendidos en el aire, que se forma cuando el aire se enfría y ocurre condensación (212)

coelom/celoma una cavidad del cuerpo que contiene los órganos internos (501)

coevolution/coevolución la evolución de dos especies que se debe a su influencia mutua, a menudo de un modo que hace que la relación sea más beneficiosa para ambas (605)

colloid/coloide una mezcla formada por partículas diminutas que son de tamaño intermedio entre las partículas de las soluciones y las de las suspensiones y que se encuentran suspendidas en un líquido, sólido o gas (362)

comet/cometa un cuerpo pequeño formado por hielo, roca y polvo cósmico que sigue una órbita elíptica alrededor del Sol y que libera gas y polvo, los cuales forman una cola al pasar cerca del Sol (302)

commensalism/comensalismo una relación entre dos organismos en la que uno se beneficia y el otro no es afectado (604)

community/comunidad todas las poblaciones de especies que viven en el mismo hábitat e interactúan entre sí (592)

compound/compuesto una substancia formada por átomos de dos o más elementos diferentes unidos por enlaces químicos (41, 352)

concentration/concentración la cantidad de una cierta substancia en una cantidad determinada de mezcla, solución o mena (360)

condensation/condensación el cambio de estado de gas a líquido (211)

constellation/constelación una región del cielo que contiene un patrón reconocible de estrellas y que se utiliza para describir la ubicación de los objetos en el espacio (254)

consumer/consumidor un organismo que se alimenta de otros organismos o de materia orgánica (500)

convection/convección la transferencia de energía térmica mediante la circulación o el movimiento de un líquido o gas (173)

Coriolis effect/efecto de Coriolis la desviación aparente de la trayectoria recta que experimentan los objetos en movimiento debido a la rotación de la Tierra (138, 178)

crystal/cristal un sólido cuyos átomos, iones o moléculas están ordenados en un patrón definido (41)

cyclone/ciclón un área de la atmósfera que tiene una presión menor que la de las áreas circundantes y que tiene vientos que giran en espiral hacia el centro (220)

D

data/datos cualquier parte de la información que se adquiere por medio de la observación o experimentación (13)

day/día el tiempo que se requiere para que la Tierra rote una vez sobre su eje (244)

deep current/corriente profunda un movimiento del agua del océano que es similar a una corriente y ocurre debajo de la superficie (139)

delta/delta un depósito de materiales rocosos en forma de abanico ubicado en la desembocadura de un río (103)

density/densidad la relación entre la masa de una substancia y su volumen (46, 327)

deposition/deposición el proceso por medio del cual un material se deposita (102)

desert/desierto una región con poca vegetación o sin vegetación, largos períodos sin lluvia y temperaturas extremas; generalmente se ubica en climas calientes (623)

dichotomous key/clave dicotómica una ayuda para identificar organismos, que consiste en las respuestas a una serie de preguntas (474)

differential weathering/desgaste diferencial el proceso por medio cual las rocas más suaves y menos resistentes al clima se desgastan y las rocas más duras y resistentes al clima permanecen (70)

diffraction/difracción un cambio en la dirección de una onda cuando ésta se encuentra con un obstáculo o un borde, tal como una abertura (416, 425)

digestive system/aparato digestivo los órganos que descomponen la comida de modo que el cuerpo la pueda usar (522)

divide/división el límite entre áreas de drenaje que tienen corrientes que fluyen en direcciones opuestas (96)

dormant/aletargado término que describe el estado inactivo de una semilla u otra parte de las plantas cuando las condiciones son desfavorables para el crecimiento (498)

E

eclipse/eclipse un suceso en el que la sombra de un cuerpo celeste cubre otro cuerpo celeste (297)

ecology/ecología el estudio de las interacciones de los seres vivos entre sí mismos y entre sí mismos y su ambiente (590)

ecosystem/ecosistema una comunidad de organismos y su ambiente abiótico o no vivo (593)

egg/óvulo una célula sexual producida por una hembra (493)

electromagnetic spectrum/espectro electromagnético todas las frecuencias o longitudes de onda de la radiación electromagnética (251)

element/elemento una substancia que no se puede separar o descomponer en substancias más simples por medio de métodos químicos (40, 348)

elevation/elevación la altura de un objeto sobre el nivel del mar (204)

El Niño/El Niño un cambio en la temperatura del agua superficial del océano Pacífico que produce una corriente caliente (144)

embryo/embrión un ser humano desde la fecundación hasta las primeras 8 semanas de desarrollo (décima semana del embarazo) (552)

endocrine system/sistema endocrino un conjunto de glándulas y grupos de células que secretan hormonas que regulan el crecimiento, el desarrollo y la homeostasis; incluye las glándulas pituitaria, tiroides, paratiroides y suprarrenal, el hipotálamo, el cuerpo pineal y las gónadas (534)

endoplasmic reticulum/retículo endoplásmico un sistema de membranas que se encuentra en el citoplasma de la célula y que tiene una función en la producción, procesamiento y transporte de proteínas y en la producción de lípidos (451)

energy/energía la capacidad de realizar un trabajo (380)

energy conversion/transformación de energía un cambio de un tipo de energía a otro (388)

energy pyramid/pirámide de energía un diagrama triangular que muestra la pérdida de energía en un ecosistema, producida a medida que la energía pasa a través de la cadena alimenticia del ecosistema (597)

erosion/erosión el proceso por medio del cual el viento, el agua, el hielo o la gravedad transporta tierra y sedimentos de un lugar a otro (81, 94)

esophagus/esófago un conducto largo y recto que conecta la faringe con el estómago (524)

estuary/estuario un área donde el agua dulce de los ríos se mezcla con el agua salada del océano (630)

Eubacteria/Eubacteria un reino que agrupa a todos los procariotes, excepto a las arqueobacterias (477)

eukaryote/eucariote un organismo cuyas células tienen un núcleo rodeado por una membrana; entre los eucariotes se encuentran los animales, las plantas y los hongos, pero no las arqueobacterias ni las eubacterias (446)

external fertilization/fecundación externa la unión de células sexuales fuera del cuerpo de los progenitores (494)

F

fetus/feto un ser humano en desarrollo de las semanas siete a ocho después de la fecundación hasta el nacimiento (554)

floodplain/llanura de inundación un área a lo largo de un río formada por sedimentos que se depositan cuando el río se desborda (104)

food chain/cadena alimenticia la vía de transferencia de energía través de varias etapas, que ocurre como resultado de los patrones de alimentación de una serie de organismos (596)

food web/red alimenticia un diagrama que muestra las relaciones de alimentación entre los organismos de un ecosistema (596)

fracture/fractura la forma en la que se rompe un mineral a lo largo de superficies curvas o irregulares (45)

frequency/frecuencia el número de ondas producidas en una cantidad de tiempo determinada (412)

front/frente el límite entre masas de aire de diferentes desidades y, normalmente, diferentes temperaturas (218)

function/función la actividad especial, normal o adecuada de un órgano o parte (459)

Fungi/Fungi un reino formado por organismos eucarióticos no verdes que no tienen capacidad de movimiento, se reproducen por esporas y obtienen alimento al descomponer substancias de su entorno y absorber los nutrientes (478)

G

gallbladder/vesícula biliar un órgano que tiene la forma de una bolsa y que almacena la bilis producida por el hígado (527)

gas giant/gigante gaseoso un planeta con una atmósfera masiva y profunda, como por ejemplo, Júpiter, Saturno, Urano o Neptuno (288)

geostationary orbit/órbita geoestacionaria una órbita que está a aproximadamente 36,000 km de la superficie terrestre, en la que un satélite permanece sobre un punto fijo en el ecuador (263)

gland/glándula un grupo de células que elaboran ciertas substancias químicas para el cuerpo (534)

global warming/calentamiento global un aumento gradual de la temperatura global promedio (175)

Golgi complex/aparato de Golgi un organelo celular que ayuda a hacer y a empacar los materiales que serán transportados al exterior de la célula (453)

greenhouse effect/efecto de invernadero el calentamiento de la superficie y de la parte más baja de la atmósfera, el cual se produce cuando el vapor de agua, el dióxido de carbono y otros gases absorben y vuelven a irradiar la energía térmica (174)

gut/tripa el tracto digestivo (501)

H

hardness/dureza una medida de la capacidad de un mineral de resistir ser rayado (46)

herbivore/herbívoro un organismo que sólo come plantas (595)

homeostasis/homeostasis la capacidad de mantener un estado interno constante en un ambiente en cambio (518)

horizon/horizonte la línea donde parece que el cielo y la Tierra se unen (256)

hormone/hormona una substancia que es producida en una célula o tejido, la cual causa un cambio en otra célula o tejido ubicado en una parte diferente del cuerpo (534)

humidity/humedad la cantidad de vapor de agua que hay en el aire (209)

humus/humus material orgánico obscuro que se forma en la tierra a partir de restos de plantas y animales en descomposición (76)

hurricane/huracán tormenta severa que se desarrolla sobre océanos tropicales, con vientos fuertes que soplan a más de 120 km/h y que se mueven en espiral hacia el centro de presión extremadamente baja de la tormenta (225)

hypothesis/hipótesis una explicación que se basa en observaciones o investigaciones científicas previas y que se puede probar (12)

I

immune system/sistema inmunológico las células y tejidos que reconocen y atacan substancias extrañas en el cuerpo (573)

immunity/inmunidad la capacidad de resistir una enfermedad infecciosa (570)

inertia/inercia la tendencia de un objeto a no moverse o, si el objeto se está moviendo, la tendencia a resistir un cambio en su rapidez o dirección hasta que una fuerza externa actúe en el objeto (324)

infectious disease/enfermedad infecciosa una enfermedad que es causada por un patógeno y que puede transmitirse de un individuo a otro (568)

interference/interferencia la combinación de dos o más ondas que resulta en una sola onda (417, 426)

internal fertilization/fecundación interna fecundación de un óvulo por un espermatozoide, la cual ocurre dentro del cuerpo de la hembra (494)

J

jet stream/corriente en chorro un cinturón delgado de vientos fuertes que soplan en la parte superior de la troposfera (180)

K

kinetic energy/energía cinética la energía de un objeto debido al movimiento del objeto (381)

L

La Niña/La Niña un cambio en el océano Pacífico oriental por el cual el agua superficial se vuelve más fría que de costumbre (144)

large intestine/intestino grueso la porción más ancha y más corta del intestino, que elimina el agua de los alimentos casi totalmente digeridos y convierte los desechos en heces semisólidas o excremento (528)

latitude/latitud la distancia hacia el norte o hacia el sur del ecuador; se expresa en grados (201)

law/ley un resumen de muchos resultados y observaciones experimentales; una ley dice cómo funcionan las cosas (21)

law of conservation of mass/ley de la conservación de la masa la ley que establece que la masa no se crea ni se destruye por cambios químicos o físicos comunes (367)

leaching/lixiviación la remoción de substancias que pueden disolverse de rocas, menas o capas de suelo debido al paso del agua (76)

lightning/relámpago una descarga eléctrica que ocurre entre dos superficies que tienen carga opuesta, como por ejemplo, entre una nube y el suelo, entre dos nubes o entres dos partes de la misma nube (223)

light-year/año luz la distancia que viaja la luz en un año; aproximadamente 9.46 trillones de kilómetros (258)

liver/hígado el órgano más grande del cuerpo; produce bilis, almacena y filtra la sangre, y almacena el exceso de azúcares en forma de glucógeno (527)

load/carga los materiales que lleva un arroyo; también, la masa de rocas que recubre una estructura geológica (98)

longitudinal wave/onda longitudinal una onda en la que las partículas del medio vibran paralelamente a la dirección del movimiento de la onda (408)

longshore current/corriente de ribera una corriente de agua que se desplaza cerca de la costa y paralela a ella (149)

low Earth orbit/órbita terrestre baja una órbita ubicada a menos de 1,500 km sobre la superficie terrestre (263)

luster/brillo la forma en que un mineral refleja la luz (44)

lysosome/lisosoma un organelo celular que contiene enzimas digestivas (454)

M

macrophage/macrófago una célula del sistema inmunológico que envuelve a los patógenos y otros materiales (573)

marsh/pantano un ecosistema pantanoso sin árboles, donde crecen plantas tales como el pasto (634)

mass/masa una medida de la cantidad de materia que tiene un objeto (25, 323)

matter/materia cualquier cosa que tiene masa y ocupa un lugar en el espacio (320)

mechanical energy/energía mecánica la cantidad de trabajo que un objeto realiza debido a las energías cinética y potencial del objeto (383)

mechanical weathering/desgaste mecánico el rompimiento de una roca en pedazos más pequeños mediante medios físicos (64)

medium/medio un ambiente físico en el que ocurren fenómenos (405)

memory B cell/célula B de memoria una célula B que responde con mayor eficacia a un antígeno cuando el cuerpo vuelve a infectarse con él que cuando lo encuentra por primera vez (576)

meniscus/menisco la curva que se forma en la superficie de un líquido, la cual sirve para medir el volumen de un líquido (321)

mesosphere/mesosfera la capa de la atmósfera que se encuentra entre la estratosfera y la termosfera, en la cual la temperatura disminuye al aumentar la altitud (169)

metal/metal un elemento que es brillante y conduce bien el calor y la electricidad (350)

metalloid/metaloides elementos que tienen propiedades tanto de metales como de no metales (350)

meteor/meteoro un rayo de luz brillante que se produce cuando un meteoroide se quema en la atmósfera de la Tierra (305)

meteorite/meteorito un meteoroide que llega a la superficie de la Tierra sin quemarse por completo (305)

meteoroid/meteoroide un cuerpo rocoso relativamente pequeño que viaja en el espacio (305)

meter/metro la unidad fundamental de longitud en el sistema internacional de unidades (símbolo: m) (25)

mineral/mineral un sólido natural e inorgánico que tiene una estructura química definida (40)

mitochondrion/mitocondria en las células eucarióticas, el organelo celular rodeado por dos membranas que es el lugar donde se lleva a cabo la respiración celular (452)

mixture/mezcla una combinación de dos o más substancias que no están combinadas químicamente (356)

model/modelo un diseño, plan, representación o descripción cuyo objetivo es mostrar la estructura o funcionamiento de un objeto, sistema o concepto (18)

month/mes una división del año que se basa en la órbita de la Luna alrededor de la Tierra (244)

mutualism/mutualismo una relación entre dos especies en la que ambas se benefician (604)

N

neap tide/marea muerta una marea que tiene un rango mínimo, la cual ocurre durante el primer y el tercer cuartos de la Luna (154)

noninfectious disease/enfermedad no infecciosa una enfermedad que no se contagia de una persona a otra (568)

nonmetal/no metal un elemento que es mal conductor del calor y la electricidad (350)

nonpoint-source pollution/contaminación no puntual contaminación que proviene de muchas fuentes, en lugar de provenir de un solo sitio específico (112)

nonsilicate mineral/mineral no-silicato un mineral que no contiene compuestos de sílice y oxígeno (42)

nucleus/núcleo en una célula eucariótica, un organelo cubierto por una membrana, el cual contiene el ADN de la célula y participa en procesos tales como el crecimiento, metabolismo y reproducción (443)

O

observation/observación el proceso de obtener información por medio de los sentidos (11)

ocean current/corriente oceánica un movimiento del agua del océano que sigue un patrón regular (136)

omnivore/omnívoro un organismo que come tanto plantas como animales (595)

ore/mena un material natural cuya concentración de minerales con valor económico es suficientemente alta como para que el material pueda ser explotado de manera rentable (50)

organ/órgano un conjunto de tejidos que desempeñan una función especializada en el cuerpo (457, 519)

organelle/organelo uno de los cuerpos pequeños del citoplasma de una célula que están especializados para llevar a cabo una función específica (443)

organism/organismo un ser vivo; cualquier cosa que pueda llevar a cabo procesos vitales independientemente (458)

organ system/aparato (o sistema) de órganos un grupo de órganos que trabajan en conjunto para desempeñar funciones corporales (458)

ovary/ovario en el aparato reproductor femenino de los animales, un órgano que produce óvulos (549)

P

pancreas/páncreas el órgano que se encuentra detrás del estómago y que produce las enzimas digestivas y las hormonas que regulan los niveles de azúcar (526)

parasitism/parasitismo una relación entre dos especies en la que una, el parásito, se beneficia de la otra, el huésped, que resulta perjudicada (605)

parent rock/roca precursora una formación rocosa que es la fuente a partir de la cual se origina el suelo (74)

pathogen/patógeno un virus, microorganismo u otra substancia que causa enfermedades (568)

penis/pene el órgano masculino que transfiere espermatozoides a una hembra y que lleva la orina hacia el exterior del cuerpo (548)

permeability/permeabilidad la capacidad de una roca o sedimento de permitir que los fluidos pasen a través de sus espacios abiertos o poros (107)

phase/fase el cambio en el área iluminada de un cuerpo celeste según se ve desde otro cuerpo celeste (296)

photosynthesis/fotosíntesis el proceso por medio del cual las plantas, las algas y algunas bacterias utilizan la luz solar, el dióxido de carbono y el agua para producir alimento (504)

physical change/cambio físico un cambio de materia de una forma a otra sin que ocurra un cambio en sus propiedades químicas (330)

physical property/propiedad física una característica de una substancia que no implica un cambio químico, tal como la densidad, el color o la dureza (326)

placenta/placenta el órgano parcialmente fetal y parcialmente materno por medio del cual se intercambian materiales entre el feto y la madre (553)

plankton/plancton la masa de organismos en su mayoría microscópicos que flotan o se encuentran a la deriva en ambientes de agua dulce o marina (626)

Plantae/Plantae un reino formado por organismos pluricelulares complejos que normalmente son verdes, tienen una pared celular de celulosa, no tienen capacidad de movimiento y utilizan la energía del Sol para producir azúcar mediante la fotosíntesis (479)

point-source pollution/contaminación puntual contaminación que proviene de un lugar específico (112)

polar easterlies/vientos polares del este vientos preponderantes que soplan de este a oeste entre los 60° y los 90° de latitud en ambos hemisferios (178)

population/población un grupo de organismos de la misma especie que viven en un área geográfica específica (592)

porosity/porosidad el porcentaje del volumen total de una roca o sedimento que está formado por espacios abiertos (107)

potential energy/energía potencial la energía que tiene un objeto debido a su posición, forma o condición (382)

precipitation/precipitación cualquier forma de agua que cae de las nubes a la superficie de la Tierra (214)

predator/depredador un organismo que se alimenta de otro organismo o de parte de él (602)

prevailing winds/vientos prevalecientes vientos que soplan principalmente de una dirección durante un período de tiempo determinado (203)

prey/presa un organismo al que otro organismo mata para alimentarse de él (60)

product/producto una substancia que se forma en una reacción química (366)

prograde rotation/rotación progresiva el giro en contra de las manecillas del reloj de un planeta o de una luna según lo vería un observador ubicado encima del Polo Norte del planeta; rotación en la misma dirección que la rotación del Sol (283)

prokaryote/procariote un organismo que está formado por una sola célula y que no tiene núcleo (444)

Protista/Protista un reino compuesto principalmente por organismo eucarióticos unicelulares que son diferentes de las plantas, animales, bacterias y hongos (478)

pure substance/substancia pura una muestra de materia, ya sea un solo elemento o un solo compuesto, que tiene propiedades químicas y físicas definidas (348)

R

radiation/radiación la transferencia de energía en forma de ondas electromagnéticas (172)

reactant/reactivo una substancia o molécula que participa en una reacción química (366)

recharge zone/zona de recarga un área en la que el agua se desplaza hacia abajo para convertirse en parte de un acuífero (108)

reclamation/restauración el proceso de hacer que la tierra vuelva a su condición original después de que se terminan las actividades de explotación minera (51)

reflecting telescope/telescopio reflector un telescopio que utiliza un espejo curvo para captar y enfocar la luz de objetos lejanos (249)

reflection/reflexión el rebote de un rayo de luz, sonido o calor cuando el rayo golpea una superficie pero no la atraviesa (414, 420)

refracting telescope/telescopio refractante un telescopio que utiliza un conjunto de lentes para captar y enfocar la luz de objetos lejanos (249)

refraction/refracción el curvamiento de una onda cuando ésta pasa entre dos substancias en las que su velocidad difiere (415, 423)

relative humidity/humedad relativa la proporción de la cantidad de vapor de agua que hay en el aire respecto a la cantidad máxima de vapor de agua que el aire puede contener a una temperatura dada (209)

resonance/resonancia un fenómeno que ocurre cuando dos objetos vibran naturalmente a la misma frecuencia; el sonido producido por un objeto hace que el otro objeto vibre (419)

retrograde rotation/rotación retrógrada el giro en el sentido de las manecillas del reloj de un planeta o de una luna según lo vería un observador ubicado encima del Polo Norte del planeta (283)

ribosome/ribosoma un organelo celular compuesto de ARN y proteína; el sitio donde ocurre la síntesis de proteínas (451)

S

salinity/salinidad una medida de la cantidad de sales disueltas en una cantidad determinada de líquido (130)

satellite/satélite un cuerpo natural o artificial que gira alrededor de un planeta (294)

savanna/sabana una región de pastizales que, a menudo, tiene árboles dispersos; se encuentra en áreas tropicales y subtropicales donde se producen lluvias, incendios y sequías estacionales (622)

scattering/dispersión una interacción de la luz con la materia que hace que la luz cambie su energía, la dirección del movimiento o ambas (422)

science/ciencia el conocimiento que se obtiene por medio de la observación natural de acontecimientos y condiciones con el fin de descubrir hechos y formular leyes o principios que puedan ser verificados o probados (4)

scientific methods/métodos científicos una serie de pasos que se siguen para solucionar problemas (10)

septic tank/tanque séptico un tanque que separa los desechos sólidos de los líquidos y que tiene bacterias que descomponen los desechos sólidos (115)

sewage treatment plant/planta de tratamiento de residuos una instalación que limpia los materiales de desecho que se encuentran en el agua procedente de cloacas o alcantarillas (114)

sexual reproduction/reproducción sexual reproducción en la que se unen las células sexuales de los dos progenitores para producir descendencia que comparte caracteres de ambos progenitores (493)

silicate mineral/mineral silicato un mineral que contiene una combinación de sílice, oxígeno y uno o más metales (42)

small intestine/intestino delgado el órgano que se encuentra entre el estómago y el intestino grueso en el cual se produce la mayor parte de la descomposición de los alimentos y se absorben la mayoría de los nutrientes (526)

soil/suelo una mezcla suelta de fragmentos de roca, material orgánico, agua y aire en la que puede crecer vegetación (74)

soil conservation/conservación del suelo un método para mantener la fertilidad del suelo protegiéndolo de la erosión y la pérdida de nutrientes (80)

soil structure/estructura del suelo la organización de las partículas del suelo (75)

soil texture/textura del suelo la cualidad del suelo que se basa en las proporciones de sus partículas (75)

solubility/solubilidad la capacidad de una substancia de disolverse en otra a una temperatura y una presión dadas (360)

solute/soluto en una solución, la sustancia que se disuelve en el solvente (358)

solution/solución una mezcla homogénea de dos o más sustancias dispersas de manera uniforme en una sola fase (358)

solvent/solvente en una solución, la sustancia en la que se disuelve el soluto (358)

sperm/espermatozoide la célula sexual masculina (493)

spring tide/marea muerta una marea de mayor rango que ocurre dos veces al mes, durante la luna nueva y la luna llena (154)

standing wave/onda estacionaria un patrón de vibración que simula una onda que está parada (418)

stoma/estoma una de las muchas aberturas de una hoja o de un tallo de una planta, la cual permite que se lleve a cabo el intercambio de gases (506)

stomach/estómago el órgano digestivo con forma de bolsa ubicado entre el esófago y el intestino delgado, que descompone los alimentos por la acción de músculos, enzimas y ácidos (525)

storm surge/marea de tempestad un levantamiento local del nivel del mar cerca de la costa, el cual es resultado de los fuertes vientos de una tormenta, como por ejemplo, los vientos de un huracán (151)

stratosphere/estratosfera la capa de la atmósfera que se encuentra encima de la troposfera y en la que la temperatura aumenta al aumentar la altitud (169)

streak/veta el color del polvo de un mineral (45)

structure/estructura el orden y distribución de las partes de un organismo (459)

surface current/corriente superficial un movimiento horizontal del agua del océano que es producido por el viento y que ocurre en la superficie del océano o cerca de ella (137, 205)

suspension/suspensión una mezcla en la que las partículas de un material se encuentran dispersas de manera más o menos uniforme a través de un líquido o de un gas (362)

swamp/ciénaga un ecosistema de pantano en el que crecen arbustos y árboles (634)

swell/mar de leva un grupo de olas oceánicas grandes que se han desplazado una gran distancia desde el punto en el que se originaron (150)

symbiosis/simbiosis una relación en la que dos organismos diferentes viven estrechamente asociados uno con el otro (604)

T

taxonomy/taxonomía la ciencia de describir, nombrar y clasificar organismos (471)

T cell/célula T una célula del sistema inmunológico que coordina el sistema inmunológico y ataca a muchas células infectadas (573)

telescope/telescopio un instrumento que capta la radiación electromagnética del cielo y la concentra para mejorar la observación (248)

temperature/temperatura una medida de qué tan caliente (o frío) está algo; específicamente, una medida de la energía cinética promedio de las partículas de un objeto (26)

terrestrial planet/planeta terrestre uno de los planetas muy densos que se encuentran más cerca del Sol; Mercurio, Venus, Marte y la Tierra (282)

testes/testículos los principales órganos reproductores masculinos, los cuales producen espermatozoides y testosterona (548)

theory/teoría una explicación que relaciona muchas hipótesis y observaciones (20)

thermal conduction/conducción térmica la transferencia de energía en forma de calor a través de un material (173)

thermometer/termómetro un instrumento que mide e indica la temperatura (231)

thermosphere/termosfera la capa más alta de la atmósfera, en la cual la temperatura aumenta a medida que la altitud aumenta (170)

thunder/trueno el sonido producido por la expansión rápida del aire a lo largo de una descarga eléctrica (223)

thunderstorm/tormenta eléctrica una tormenta fuerte y normalmente breve que consiste en lluvia, vientos fuertes, relámpagos y truenos (222)

tidal range/rango de marea la diferencia en los niveles del agua del océano entre la marea alta y la marea baja (154)

tide/marea el ascenso y descenso periódico del nivel del agua en los océanos y otras masas grandes de agua (152)

tissue/tejido un grupo de células similares que llevan a cabo una función común (457, 518)

tornado/tornado una columna destructiva de aire en rotación cuyos vientos se mueven a velocidades muy altas; se ve como una nube con forma de embudo y toca el suelo (224)

trade winds/vientos alisios vientos prevalecientes que soplan de este a oeste desde los 30° de latitud hacia el ecuador en ambos hemisferios (178)

transpiration/transpiración el proceso por medio del cual las plantas liberan vapor de agua al aire por medio de los estomas; *también,* la liberación de vapor de agua al aire por otros organismos (506)

transverse wave/onda transversal una onda en la que las partículas del medio se mueven perpendicularmente respecto a la dirección en la que se desplaza la onda (407)

tributary/afluente un arroyo que fluye a un lago o a otro arroyo más grande (96)

troposphere/troposfera la capa inferior de la atmósfera, en la que la temperatura disminuye a una tasa constante a medida que la altitud aumenta (169)

tsunami/tsunami una ola gigante del océano que se forma después de una erupción volcánica, terremoto submarino o desprendimiento de tierras (150)

tundra/tundra una llanura sin árboles situada en la región ártica o antártica o en la cumbre de las montañas; se caracteriza por temperaturas muy bajas en el invierno y veranos cortos y frescos (624)

U

umbilical cord/cordón umbilical la estructura que une al embrión y después al feto con la placenta, a través de la cual pasan vasos sanguíneos (553)

undertow/resaca un corriente subsuperficial que está cerca de la orilla y que arrastra los objetos hacia el mar (149)

upwelling/surgencia el movimiento de las aguas profundas, frías y ricas en nutrientes hacia la superficie (143)

uterus/útero en los mamíferos hembras, el órgano hueco y muscular en el que se incrusta el óvulo fecundado y en el que se desarrollan el embrión y el feto (549)

V

vagina/vagina el órgano reproductivo femenino que conecta la parte exterior del cuerpo con el útero (549)

vesicle/vesícula una cavidad o bolsa pequeña que contiene materiales en una célula eucariótica; se forma cuando parte de la membrana celular rodea los materiales que van a ser llevados al interior la célula o transportados dentro de ella (453)

volume/volumen una medida del tamaño de un cuerpo o región en un espacio de tres dimensiones (26, 320)

W

water cycle/ciclo del agua el movimiento continuo del agua: del océano a la atmósfera, de la atmósfera a la tierra y de la tierra al océano (95, 133)

watershed/cuenca hidrográfica el área del terreno que es drenada por un sistema de agua (96)

water table/capa freática el nivel más alto del agua subterránea; el límite superior de la zona de saturación (106)

wave/onda una perturbación periódica en un sólido, líquido o gas que se transmite a través de un medio en forma de energía (404)

wavelength/longitud de onda la distancia entre cualquier punto de una onda y un punto idéntico en la onda siguiente (411)

wave speed/rapidez de onda la rapidez a la cual viaja una onda a través de un medio (412)

weather/tiempo el estado de la atmósfera a corto plazo que incluye la temperatura, la humedad, la precipitación, el viento y la visibilidad (200)

weathering/meteorización el proceso por el cual se desintegran los materiales que forman las rocas debido a la acción de procesos físicos o químicos (64)

weight/peso una medida de la fuerza gravitacional ejercida sobre un objeto; su valor puede cambiar en función de la ubicación del objeto en el universo (323)

westerlies/vientos del oeste vientos preponderantes que soplan de oeste a este entre 30° y 60° de latitud en ambos hemisferios (178)

wetland/pantano un área de tierra que está periódicamente bajo el agua o cuyo suelo contiene una gran cantidad de humedad (634)

whitecap/cabrillas las burbujas de la cresta de una ola rompiente (150)

wind/viento el movimiento de aire producido por diferencias en la presión barométrica (176)

Y

year/año el tiempo que se requiere para que la Tierra le dé la vuelta al Sol una vez (244)

Z

zenith/cenit el punto del cielo situado directamente sobre un observador en la Tierra (256)

Index

Boldface page numbers refer to illustrative material, such as figures, tables, margin elements, photographs, and illustrations.

A

B

Index

D

E

Index

Index

J

K

L

Index

M

N

P

Index

Q

R

Index

T

U

V

W

Z

Index

Acknowledgments

continued from page ii

Academic Reviewers
continued

Kenneth H. Brink, Ph.D.
Senior Scientist and Physical Oceanography Director
Coastal Ocean Institute and Rinehart Coastal Research Center
Woods Hole Oceanographic Institution
Woods Hole, Massachusetts

John Brockhaus, Ph.D.
Professor of Geospatial Information Science and Director of Geospatial Information Science Program
Department of Geography and Environmental Engineering
United States Military Academy
West Point, New York

Howard L. Brooks, Ph.D.
Professor of Physics and Astronomy
Department of Physics and Astronomy
DePauw University
Greencastle, Indiana

Dan Bruton, Ph.D.
Associate Professor
Department of Physics and Astronomy
Stephen F. Austin State University
Nacogdoches, Texas

Michael Carleton, Ph.D.
Curator of Mammals
Smithsonian Museum of Natural History
Washington, D.C.

Wesley N. Colley, Ph.D.
Lecturer
Department of Astronomy
University of Virginia
Charlottesville, Virginia

Joe W. Crim, Ph.D.
Professor and Head of Cellular Biology
Department of Cellular Biology
University of Georgia
Athens, Georgia

Scott Darveau, Ph.D.
Associate Professor of Chemistry
Chemistry Department
University of Nebraska at Kearney
Kearney, Nebraska

William E. Dunscombe
Chairman
Biology Department
Union County College
Cranford, New Jersey

Turgay Ertekin, Ph.D.
Professor and Chairman of Petroleum and Natural Gas Engineering
Energy and Geo-Environmental Engineering
Pennsylvania State University
University Park, Pennsylvania

Simonetta Frittelli, Ph.D.
Associate Professor
Department of Physics
Duquesne University
Pittsburgh, Pennsylvania

Linda K. Gaul
Epidemiologist
Texas Department of Health
Austin, Texas

William Grisham, Ph.D.
Lecturer
Psychology Department
University of California, Los Angeles
Los Angeles, California

David S. Hall, Ph.D.
Assistant Professor of Physics
Department of Physics
Amherst College
Amherst, Massachusetts

Deborah Hanley, Ph.D.
Meteorologist
State of Florida
Department of Agriculture and Consumer Services
Division of Forestry
Tallahassee, Florida

Mary Kay Hemenway, Ph.D.
Research Associate and Senior Lecturer
Astronomy Department
The University of Texas
Austin, Texas

David Hershey, Ph.D.
Education Consultant
Hyattsville, Maryland

Steven A. Jennings, Ph.D.
Associate Professor
Geography and Environmental Studies
University of Colorado at Colorado Springs
Colorado Springs, Colorado

Ping H. Johnson, M.D., Ph.D., CHES
Assistant Professor of Health Education
Department of Health, Physical Education and Sport Science
Kennesaw State University
Kennesaw, Georgia

Jamie Kneitel, Ph.D.
Postdoctoral Associate
Department of Biology
Washington University
St. Louis, Missouri

John Krenz, Ph.D.
Associate Professor
Biological Sciences
Minnesota State University
Mankato, Minnesota

David Lamp, Ph.D.
Associate Professor of Physics
Physics Department
Texas Tech University
Lubbock, Texas

Madeline Micceri Mignone, Ph.D.
Assistant Professor
Natural Science
Dominican College
Orangeburg, New York

Richard F. Niedziela, Ph.D.
Assistant Professor of Chemistry
Department of Chemistry
DePaul University
Chicago, Illinois

Gerald J. Niemi, Ph.D.
Professor and Center Director
Biology and Center for Water and the Environment
Natural Resources Research Institute
University of Minnesota
Duluth, Minnesota

Eva Oberdoerster, Ph.D.
Lecturer
Department of Biology
Southern Methodist University
Dallas, Texas

Kenneth K. Peace
Manager of Transportation
WestArch Coal, Inc.
St. Louis, Missouri

Kate Queeney, Ph.D.
Assistant Professor of Chemistry
Chemistry Department
Smith College
Northampton, Massachusetts

Michael H. Renfroe, Ph.D.
Professor of Biology
Department of Biology
James Madison University
Harrisonburg, Virginia

Kenneth H. Rubin, Ph.D.
Associate Professor
Department of Geology and Geophysics
University of Hawaii at Manoa
Honolulu, Hawaii

Dork Sahagian, Ph.D.
Research Professor
Department of Earth Sciences
Institute for the Study of Earth, Oceans, and Space
University of New Hampshire
Durham, New Hampshire

Laurie Santos, Ph.D.
Assistant Professor
Department of Psychology
Yale University
New Haven, Connecticut

Patrick K. Schoff, Ph.D.
Research Associate
Natural Resources Research Institute
University of Minnesota—Duluth
Duluth, Minnesota

H. Michael Sommermann, Ph.D.
Professor of Physics
Physics Department
Westmont College
Santa Barbara, California

Vatche P. Tchakerian, Ph.D.
Professor
Department of Geography and Geology
Texas A&M University
College Station, Texas

Richard S. Treptow, Ph.D.
Professor of Chemistry
Department of Chemistry and Physics
Chicago State University
Chicago, Illinois

Richard P. Vari, Ph.D.
Research Scientist and Curator
Division of Fishes
National Museum of Natural History
Washington, D.C.

Dale Wheeler
Assistant Professor of Chemistry
A. R. Smith Department of Chemistry
Appalachian State University
Boone, North Carolina

Ross Whitwam, Ph.D.
Assistant Professor of Biology
Division of Science and Mathematics
Mississippi University for Women
Columbus, Mississippi

Lab Testing

Barry L. Bishop
Science Teacher and Department Chair
San Rafael Junior High School
Ferron, Utah

James Chin
Science Teacher
Frank A. Day Middle School
Newtonville, Massachusetts

Randy Christian
Science Teacher
Stovall Junior High School
Houston, Texas

Kenneth Creese
Science Teacher
White Mountain Junior High
Rock Springs, Wyoming

Georgiann Delgadillo
Science Teacher
East Valley Continuous Curriculum School
Spokane, Washington

Alonda Droege
Biology Teacher
Evergreen High School
Seattle, Washington

Rebecca Ferguson
Science Teacher
North Ridge Middle School
North Richland Hills, Texas

Jennifer Ford
Science Teacher and Department Chair
North Ridge Middle School
North Richland Hills, Texas

Norman E. Holcomb
Science Teacher
Marion Local Schools
Maria Stein, Ohio

Kenneth J. Horn
Science Teacher and Department Chair
Fallston Middle School
Fallston, Maryland

Tracy Jahn
Science Teacher
Berkshire Junior-Senior High School
Canaan, New York

David Jones
Science Teacher
Andrew Jackson Middle School
Cross Lanes, West Virginia

M. R. Penny Kisiah
Science Teacher and Department Chair
Fairview Middle School
Tallahassee, Florida

Michael E. Kral
Science Teacher
West Hardin Middle School
Cecilia, Kentucky

Kathy LaRoe
Science Teacher
East Valley Middle School
East Helena, Montana

Jane M. Lemons
Science Teacher
Western Rockingham Middle School
Madison, North Carolina

Maurine O. Marchani
Science Teacher and Department Chair
Raymond Park Middle School
Indianapolis, Indiana

Jason P. Marsh
Biology Teacher
Montevideo High School and Montevideo Country School
Montevideo, Minnesota

Edith C. McAlanis
Science Teacher and Department Chair
Socorro Middle School
El Paso, Texas

Kevin McCurdy, Ph.D.
Science Teacher
Elmwood Junior High School
Rogers, Arkansas

Alyson Mike
Science Teacher
East Valley Middle School
East Helena, Montana

Jan Nelson
Science Teacher
East Valley Middle School
East Helena, Montana

Joseph W. Price
Science Teacher and Department Chair
H.M. Browne Junior High School
Washington, D.C.

Terry J. Rakes
Science Teacher
Elmwood Junior High School
Rogers, Arkansas

David M. Sparks
Science Teacher
Redwater Junior High School
Redwater, Texas

Larry Tackett
Science Teacher and Department Chair
R. H. Terrell Junior High School
Washington, D.C.

Walter Woolbaugh
Science Teacher
Manhattan School System
Manhattan, Montana

Gordon Zibelman
Science Teacher
Drexel Hill Middle School
Drexel Hill, Pennsylvania

Teacher Reviewers

Diedre S. Adams
Physical Science Instructor
Science Department
West Vigo Middle School
West Terre Haute, Indiana

Barbara Gavin Akre
Teacher of Biology, Anatomy-Physiology, and Life Science
Duluth Independent School District
Duluth, Minnesota

Laura Buchanan
Science Teacher and Department Chairperson
Corkran Middle School
Glen Burnie, Maryland

Sarah Carver
Science Teacher
Jackson Creek Middle School
Bloomington, Indiana

Robin K. Clanton
Science Department Head
Berrien Middle School
Nashville, Georgia

Hilary Cochran
Science Teacher
Indian Crest Junior High School
Souderton, Pennsylvania

Karen Dietrich, S.S.J., Ph.D.
Principal and Biology Instructor
Mount Saint Joseph Academy
Flourtown, Pennsylvania

Trisha Elliott
Science and Math Teacher
Chain of Lakes Middle School
Orlando, Florida

Liza M. Guasp
Science Teacher
Celebration K–8 School
Celebration, Florida

Meredith Hanson
Science Teacher
Westside Middle School
Rocky Face, Georgia

Ronald W. Hudson
Science Teacher
Batchelor Middle School
Bloomington, Indiana

James Kerr
Oklahoma Teacher of the Year 2002–2003
Oklahoma State Department of Education
Union Public Schools
Tulsa, Oklahoma

Laura Kitselman
Science Teacher and Coordinator
Loudoun Country Day School
Leesburg, Virginia

Debra S. Kogelman, MAed.
Science Teacher
University of Chicago Laboratory Schools
Chicago, Illinois

Deborah L. Kronsteiner
Teacher
Science Department
Spring Grove Area Middle School
Spring Grove, Pennsylvania

Jennifer L. Lamkie
Science Teacher
Thomas Jefferson Middle School
Edison, New Jersey

Sally M. Lesley
ESL Science Teacher
Burnet Middle School
Austin, Texas

Stacy Loeak
Science Teacher and Department Chair
Baker Middle School
Columbus, Georgia

Augie Maldonado
Science Teacher
Grisham Middle School
Round Rock, Texas

Jean Pletchette
Health Educator
Winterset Community Schools
Winterset, Iowa

Thomas Lee Reed
Science Teacher
Rising Starr Middle School
Fayetteville, Georgia

Shannon Ripple
Science Teacher
Science Department
Canyon Vista Middle School
Round Rock, Texas

Susan H. Robinson
Science Teacher
Oglethorpe County Middle School
Lexington, Georgia

Elizabeth Rustad
Science Teacher
Higley School District
Gilbert, Arizona

Helen Schiller
Instructional Coach
Greenville County Schools
Greenville, South Carolina

Stephanie Snowden
Science Teacher
Canyon Vista Middle School
Round Rock, Texas

Marci L. Stadiem
Department Head
Science Department
Cascade Middle School, Highline School District
Seattle, Washington

Bruce A. Starek
Department Chairperson, Science Teacher
Baker Middle School
Michigan City, Indiana

Florence Vaughan
Science Teacher
University of Chicago Laboratory Schools
Chicago, Illinois

Larry A. Weber, M.S.
Science Teacher
Marshall School
Duluth, Minnesota

Angie Williams
Teacher
Riversprings Middle School
Crawfordville, Florida

Answer Checking

Hatim Belyamani
Austin, Texas

John A. Benner
Austin, Texas

Catherine Podeszwa
Duluth, Minnesota

Staff Credits

Editorial

Leigh Ann García, *Executive Editor*
Kelly Rizk, *Senior Editor*
David Westerberg, *Senior Editor*
Laura Zapanta, *Senior Editor*

Editorial Development Team

Karin Akre
Monica Brown
Jen Driscoll
Shari Husain
Michael Mazza
Karl Pallmeyer
Laura Prescott
Bill Rader
Jim Ratcliffe
Dennis Rathnaw
Betsy Roll
Kenneth Shepardson

Copyeditors

Dawn Marie Spinozza, *Copyediting Manager*
Simon Key
Jane A. Kirschman
Kira J. Watkins

Editorial Support Staff

Debbie Starr, *Managing Editor*
Kristina Bigelow
Suzanne Krejci
Shannon Oehler

Online Products

Bob Tucek, *Executive Editor*
Wesley M. Bain

Design

Book Design

Kay Selke, *Director of Book Design*
Mercedes Newman, *Page Designer*
Holly Whittaker, *Project Administrator*

Media Design

Richard Metzger, *Design Director*
Chris Smith, *Developmental Designer*

Image Acquisitions

Curtis Riker, *Director*
Jeannie Taylor, *Photo Research Manager*
Diana Goetting, *Senior Photo Researcher*
Elaine Tate, *Art Buyer Supervisor*
Angela Boehm, *Senior Art Buyer*

Publishing Services

Carol Martin, *Director*

Graphic Services

Bruce Bond, *Director*
Jeff Bowers, *Graphic Services Manager*
Katrina Gnader, *Graphics Specialist*
Cathy Murphy, *Senior Graphics Specialist*
Nanda Patel, *Graphics Specialist*
JoAnn Stringer, *Senior Graphics Specialist II*

Technology Services

Laura Likon, *Director*
Juan Baquera, *Technology Services Manager*
Lana Kaupp, *Senior Technology Services Analyst*
Margaret Sanchez, *Senior Technology Services Analyst*
Sara Buller, *Technology Services Analyst*
Patty Zepeda, *Technology Services Analyst*
Jeff Robinson, *Ancillary Design Manager*

New Media

Armin Gutzmer, *Director*
Melanie Baccus, *New Media Coordinator*
Lydia Doty, *Senior Project Manager*
Cathy Kuhles, *Technical Assistant*
Marsh Flournoy, *Quality Assurance Analyst*
Tara F. Ross, *Senior Project Manager*

Design New Media

Ed Blake, *Director*
Kimberly Cammerata, *Design Manager*
Michael Rinella, *Senior Designer*

Production

Eddie Dawson, *Production Manager*
Sherry Sprague, *Project Manager*
Suzanne Brooks, *Production Coordinator*

Teacher Edition

Alicia Sullivan
David Hernandez
April Litz

Manufacturing and Inventory

Jevara Jackson
Ivania Quant Lee
Wilonda Ieans

Ancillary Development and Production

General Learning Communications, Northbrook, Illinois

Credits

Abbreviations used: (t) top, (c) center, (b) bottom, (l) left, (r) right, (bkgd) background

PHOTOGRAPHY

Front Cover (tl) Andy Small/CORBIS; (tr) Andy Small/CORBIS; (b) Yva Momatiuk/ John Eastcott/Minden Pictures; (c) JH Carmicheal/Getty Images

Skills Practice Lab Teens SamDudgeon/HRW

Connection to Astrology Corbis Images; **Connection to Biology** David M. Phillips/ Visuals Unlimited; **Connection to Chemistry** Digital Image copyright © 2005 PhotoDisc; **Connection to Environment** Digital Image copyright © 2005 PhotoDisc; Connection to Geology Letraset Phototone; **Connection to Language Arts** Digital Image copyright © 2005 PhotoDisc; **Connection to Meteorology** Digital Image copyright © 2005 PhotoDisc; **Connection to Oceanography** © ICONOTEC; **Connection to Physics** Digital Image copyright © 2005 PhotoDisc

Table of Contents iii (t), Sam Dudgeon/HRW; iii (b), NASA; iv (t), Howard B. Bluestein; iv (bl), Tom Pantages Photography; v (t), E. R. Degginger/Color-Pic, Inc.; v (green), Dr. E.R. Degginger/Bruce Coleman Inc.; v (purple), Mark A. Schneider/ Photo Researchers, Inc.; v, CORBIS Images/HRW; vi, Laurent Gillieron/Keystone/AP/ Wide World Photos; vi (b), The G.R. "Dick" Roberts Photo Library; viii (t), National Geographic Image Collection/Robert W. Madden; viii (b), Bob Krueger/Photo Researchers, Inc.; ix (t), Glenn M. Oliver/Visuals Unlimited; ix (b) Tom Bean/CORBIS; x (t), Stuart Westmorland/CORBIS; xi (t), Goddard Space Flight Center Scientific Visualization Studio/NASA; xi (b), NASA; xii (tl), Index Stock; xii (c), MSFC/NASA; xii (bl), Peter Van Steen/HRW; xiii (t), Bill & Sally Fletcher/Tom Stack & Associates; xiii (b), NASA/TSADO/Tom Stack & Associates; xiv (t), NASA/Peter Arnold, Inc.; xv; Sam Dudgeon/HRW; xvi, Victoria Smith/HRW; xviii, xix, xx, xxii, Victoria Smith/HRW; xxvi, Sam Dudgeon/HRW; xxvii (t), John Langford/HRW; xxvii (b), xxviii (t, bl), Sam Dudgeon/HRW; xxviii (bl), Stephanie Morris/HRW; xxix (tl), Sam Dudgeon/HRW; xxix (tr), Jana Birchum/HRW; xxix (b), Sam Dudgeon/HRW

Chapter One 4 Peter Van Steen/HRW Photo; 5 (t) Peter Van Steen/HRW; 5 (b) Victoria Smith/HRW; 7(t) Mike Segar/Reuters Photo Archive; 7(b) CORBIS/ Annie Griffiths Belt; 8 (t) Annie Griffiths/Westlight/Corbis; 8 (b) AP Photo/Knoxville News-Sentinel; 9 Aurora Photos; 11 Peter Van Steen/HRW; 12 Courtesy of Dr. David Gillette; 16 Paul Fraughton/HRW; 18 (l) Sam Dudgeon/HRW; 18 (r) Jim Sugar Photography/CORBIS; 20 (l) AKG-Images; 20 (r) Image Copyright ©2001 PhotoDisc, Inc.; 21 Victoria Smith/HRW; 22 CENCO; 22 (zoom) Robert Brons/Getty Images/ Stone; 23 Victoria Smith/HRW; 25 (t) (b) Peter Van Steen/HRW; 26 (l) Peter Van Steen/HRW; 26(r) Peter Van Steen/HRW; 30 Paul Fraughton/HRW 31 (R) Image Copyright ©2001 PhotoDisc, Inc.34 (tr), The Stuart News, Carl Rivenbark/AP/Wide World Photos; 35, AFP/CORBIS; 35 (b), AFP/CORBIS

Unit One 36 (tl), Ed Reschke/Peter Arnold, Inc.; 36 (c), Francois Gohier; 36 (b), Smithsonian Air and Space Museum; 36 (tl), T.A. Wiewandt/DRK Photo; 37 (tl), Uwe Fink/University of Arizona, Department of Planetary Sciences, Lunar & Planetary Laboratory; 37 (tr), Hulton Archive/Getty Images; 37 (stone), Adam Woolfitt/British Museum/Woodfin Camp & Associtès, Inc.; 37, (volcano), K. Segerstrom/USGS; 37 (bl), NASA; 37 (br), Iziko Museums of Cape Town

Chapter Two 38-39, Terry Wilson; 66, Sam Dudgeon/HRW; 41, Dr. Rainer Bode/ Bode-Verlag Gmb; 42 (tr), Victoria Smith/HRW; 42 (bc), Sam Dudgeon/HRW; 42 (tl), Sam Dudgeon/HRW; 43, (copper), E. R. Degginger/Color-Pic, Inc.; 43, (calcite), E. R. Degginger/Color-Pic, Inc.; 43, (fluorite), E. R. Degginger/Color-Pic, Inc.; 43, (corundum), E. R. Degginger/Color-Pic, Inc.; 43, (gypsum), SuperStock; 43, (galena), Visuals Unlimited/Ken Lucas; 44, (vitreous), Biophoto Associates/Photo Researchers, Inc.; 44, (waxy), Biophoto Associates/Photo Researchers, Inc.; 44, (silky), Dr. E.R. Degginger/ Bruce Coleman Inc.; 44, (submetallic), John Cancalosi 1989/DRK Photo; 44 (bl), Kosmatsu Mining Systems; 44, (resinous), Charles D. Winters/Photo Researchers, Inc.; 44, (pearly), Victoria Smith/HRW; 44, (metallic), Victoria Smith/HRW; 44, (earthy), Sam Dudgeon/HRW; 45 (tr, c, bl), Sam Dudgeon/HRW; 45, Tom Pantages; 46, (1), Visuals Unlimited/Ken Lucas; 46, (3), Visuals Unlimited/Dane S. Johnson; 46, (7), Carlyn Iverson/Absolute Science Illustration and Photography; 46, (8), Mark A. Schneider/Visuals Unlimited; 46, (9), Charles D. Winters/Photo Researchers, Inc.; 46, (10), Bard Wrisley; 46, (5), Biophoto Associates/Photo Researchers, Inc.; 46, (6), Victoria Smith/HRW; 46, (4), Mark A. Schneider/Photo Researchers, Inc.; 46, (2), Sam Dudgeon/HRW; 47 (tc), Sam Dudgeon/HRW; 47 (tr), Sam Dudgeon/HRW, Courtesy Science Stuff, Austin, TX; 47 (br), Tom Pantages Photography; 47 (bc), Sam Dudgeon/ HRW; 47 (tl), Mark A. Schneider/Photo Researchers, Inc.; 47 (tl), Mark A. Schneider/ Photo Researchers, Inc.; 47 (bl), 74 (t), Sam Dudgeon/HRW; 48 (bl), Victoria Smith/ HRW Photo, Courtesy Science Stuff, Austin, TX; 48 (c), Breck P. Kent; 49 (br), Sam Dudgeon/HRW; 49 (c), Breck P. Kent; 49 (t), Visuals Unlimited/Ken Lucas; 50 (br), Wernher Krutein; 51, Stewart Cohen/Index Stock Photography, Inc.; 52, Digital Image copyright © 2005 PhotoDisc; 53, Historic Royal Palaces; 54 (c), Russell Dian/HRW; 54 (b), 55 (tr), Sam Dudgeon/HRW; 56, Digital Image copyright © 2005 PhotoDisc; 57 (b), E. R. Degginger/Color-Pic, Inc.; 60 (t), Stephan Edelbroich; 61 (t), Will & Dennie McIntyre/McIntyre Photography; 61 (b), Mark Schneider/Visuals Unlimited

Chapter Three 62-63, Johny Sundby/Zuma Press/NewsCom; 64, SuperStock; 65 (tc), Visuals Unlimited/Martin G. Miller; 65 (tl), Ron Niebrugge/Niebrugge Images; 65 (tr), Grant Heilman/Grant Heilman Photography; 66 (t), John Sohlden/Visuals Unlimited; 68 (t), Laurence Parent; 68 (b), C. Campbell/Westlight/Corbis; 69, Bob Krueger/ Photo Researchers, Inc.; 70 (b), B. Ross/Westlight/Corbis; 72 (bl), Digital Image copyright © 2005 EyeWire ; 72 (br), David Cumming; Eye Ubiquitous/CORBIS; 73, Corbis Images; 74, The G.R. "Dick" Roberts Photo Library; 77, Tom Bean/Getty Images/Stone; 78 (t), Bill Ross/Westlight/Corbis; 78 (b), Bruce Coleman, Inc.; 79, Lee Rentz/Bruce Coleman, Inc.; 80 (bl), Grant Heilman Photography, Inc.; 80 (br), Charlton Photos, Inc.; 81, Kevin Fleming/CORBIS; 82 (tr), Mark Lewis/ImageState; 82 (tl), Paul Chesley/Getty Images/Stone; 82 (br), Tom Hovland/Grant Heilman Photography, Inc.; 82 (bl), AgStockUsa; 83, Bettmann/CORBIS; 84 (bl), 299 Sam Dudgeon/HRW; 86, B. Ross/Westlight/Corbis; 87, Bob Krueger/Photo Researchers, Inc.; 90 (tr), M.A. Kessler/ Earth Sciences Department, University of California at Santa Cruz; 90 (tl), © W. Ming/ UNEP/Peter Arnold, Inc.; 91 (t), Michael Murphy/By permission of Selah, Bamberger Ranch; 91 (b), Michael Murphy/By permission of Selah, Bamberger Ranch

Chapter Four 92-93, Owen Franklin/CORBIS; 94, Tom Bean/DRK Photo; 96, E.R.I.M./ Stone; 97, Jim Wark/Peter Arnold; 97 (tl), Nancy Simmerman/Getty Images/Stone; 99, Frans Lanting/Minden Pictures; 99 (cr), Laurence Parent; 100 (t), The G.R. "Dick" Roberts Photo Library; 100, Galen Rowell/Peter Arnold, Inc.; 101 (t), Nancy Simmerman/Getty Images/Stone; 102, Glenn M. Oliver/Visuals Unlimited; 103 (t), The Huntington Library/SuperStock; 103 (b), Earth Satellite Corporation/Science Photo Library/Photo Researchers, Inc.; 104 (t), Visuals Unlimited/Martin G. Miller; 104 (b), Earth Satellite Corporation; 105, Jerry Laizure/AP/Wide World Photos; 110, Rich Reid/Animals Animals/Earth Scenes; 111, Leif Skoogfers/Woodfin Camp & Associates, Inc.; 112, Digital Image © 2005, Eyewire/Getty Images; 113, Morton Beebe/CORBIS; 117, Getty Images/Stone; 118, Victoria Smith/HRW; 120, Martin Harvey; Gallo Images/ CORBIS; 121 (t), The Huntington Library/SuperStock; 121 (b), Jim Wark/Peter Arnold; 124 (t), David R. Parks; 124 (br), Martin Harvey; Gallo Images/CORBIS; 125 (tr), Photo by Sam Kittner, courtesy of Rita Colwell/National Science Foundation; 125 (b), Anwar Huq, UMBI

Chapter Five 126-127, Tom Salyer/Reuters NewMedia Inc./CORBIS; 128, Tom Van Sant, Geosphere Project/Planetary Visions/Science Photo Library; 132 (l), U.S. Navy; 132 (r), U.S. Navy; 134, Rosentiel School of Marine and Atmospheric Science, University of Miami; 135, Courtesy of Robert Cantor/Christian Grantham; 136, Hulton Archive/Getty Images; 137 (r), Sam Dudgeon/HRW; 137 (t), Rosentiel School of Marine and Atmospheric Science, University of Miami; 144, Lacy Atkins/ San Francisco Examiner/AP/Wide World Photos; 149 (b), CC Lockwood/Bruce Coleman, Inc.; 150 (tl), Darrell Wong/Getty Images/Stone; 150 (tr), August Upitis/ Getty Images/Taxi; 155 (tl), VOSCAR/The Maine Photographer; 155 (tr), VOSCAR/ The Maine Photographer; 156, Andy Christiansen/HRW; 162 (t), J.A.L. Cooke/Oxford Scientific Films/Animals Animals/Earth Scenes; 163 (t), Pacific Whale Foundation; 163 (b), Flip Nicklin/Minden Pictures

Chapter Six 164-165, Robert Holmes/CORBIS; 167, Peter Van Steen/HRW; 169 (t), SuperStock; 169 (b), NASA; 452, Image Copyright ©2005 PhotoDisc, Inc.; 171, Patrick J. Endres/Alaskaphotographics.com; 176, Terry Renna/AP/Wide World Photos; 177 (b), Moredun Animal Health Ltd./Science Photo Library/Photo Researchers, Inc.; 180 (t), NASA/Science Photo Library/Photo Researchers, Inc.; 182 (c), Argus Fotoarchiv/ Peter Arnold, Inc.; 182 (r), David Weintraub/Photo Researchers, Inc; 182 (l), Digital Image copyright © 2005 PhotoDisc/Getty Images; 183 (bl), Steve Starr/CORBIS; 183 (r), Corbis Images; 185, Simon Fraser/SPL/Photo Researchers, Inc.; 186 (t), Goddard Space Flight Center Scientific Visualization Studio/NASA; 186 (b), Goddard Space Flight Center Scientific Visualization Studio/NASA; 187, Tampa Electric; 188, Francis Dean/The Image Works; 189, Tampa Electric; 190, 191, Sam Dudgeon/HRW; 193 (t), Goddard Space Flight Center Scientific Visualization Studio/NASA; 196 (b), James McInnis/Los Alamos National Laboratories; 196 (t), Jonathan Blair/CORBIS; 197 (r), Fred Hirschmann; 197 (bl), Fred Hirschmann

Chapter Seven 198-199, Tim Chapman/Miami Herald/NewsCom; 200 (bkgd), Tom Van Sant, Geosphere Project/Planetary Visions/Science Photo Library/Photo Researchers, Inc.; 200 (tl), G.R. Roberts Photo Library; 200 (tr), Index Stock; 200 (c), Yva Momatiuk & John Eastcott; 200 (bl), Gary Retherford/Photo Researchers, Inc.; 200 (br), SuperStock; 201 (tr), CALLER-TIMES/AP/Wide World Photos; 201 (tc), Doug Mills/AP/Wide World Photos; 203 (b), Tom Van Sant, Geosphere Project/Planetary Visions/Science Photo Library/Photo Researchers, Inc.; 204 (bl), Larry Ulrich Photography; 204 (br), Paul Wakefield/Getty Images/Stone; 207, Index Stock; 208, Sam Dudgeon/HRW; 211, Victoria Smith/HRW; 212 (tc), NOAA; 212 (tr), Joyce Photographics/Photo Researchers, Inc.; 212 (tl), Corbis Images; 214, Gene E. Moore; 488 (tl), Gerben Oppermans/Getty Images/Stone; 215 (c), Corbis Images; 215 (t), Victoria Smith/HRW; 217, Image Copyright ©2005 PhotoDisc, Inc.; 217 (t), Reuters/Gary Wiepert/NewsCom; 220, NASA; 222, William H. Edwards/Getty Images/The Image Bank; 223 (br), Jean-Loup Charmet/Science Photo Library/Photo Researchers, Inc.; 224 (all), Howard B. Bluestein/Photo Researchers, Inc.; 225 (t), Red Huber/Orlando Sentinel/SYGMA/CORBIS; 225 (b), NASA; 226 (tl), NASA/Science Photo Library/Photo Researchers, Inc.; 227, Dave Martin/AP/Wide World Photos; 228 (b), Joe Raedle/NewsCom; 228 (t), Will Chandler/Anderson Independent-Mail/AP/Wide World Photos; 229 (t), Jean-Loup Charmet/Science Photo Library/Photo Researchers, Inc.; 229 (c), NASA/Science Photo Library/Photo Researchers, Inc.; 230, Graham Neden/Ecoscene/CORBIS; 231, Sam Dudgeon/HRW; 231 (br), G.R. Roberts Photo Library; 231 (t), Guido Alberto Rossi/Getty Images/The Image Bank; 232, National Weather Service/NOAA; 236, Sam Dudgeon/HRW; 237 (tl), Corbis Images; 237 (b), Joyce Photographics/Photo Researchers, Inc.; 240 (tr), Lightscapes Photography, Inc./CORBIS; 241 (t), Michael Lyon; 241 (bl), Corbis Images

Chapter Eight 242-243, Roger Ressmeyer/CORBIS; 244, David L. Brown/Tom Stack & Associates; 246, The Bridgeman Art Library; 247, Roger Ressmeyer/Corbis; 248 (bl), Peter Van Steen/HRW; 248 (r), Fred Espenek; 250 (tl), Simon Fraser/Science Photo Library/Photo Researchers, Inc.; 250 (b), NASA; 250 (inset), Roger Ressmeyer/Corbis; 251 (radio), Sam Dudgeon/HRW; 251 (microwave) Sam Dudgeon/HRW; 251 (keyboard), Chuck O'Rear/Woodfin Camp & Associates, Inc.; 251 (sunburn), HRW; 251 (x-ray), David M. Dennis/Tom Stack & Associates; 251 (head), Michael Scott/Getty Images/Stone; 251 (tea), Tony McConnell/SPL/Photo Researchers, Inc.; 252 (gamma), NASA; 252 (radio), NASA; 252 (x-ray), NASA; 252 (infrared), NASA; 253, MSFC/NASA; 256, Peter Van Steen/HRW; 256 (bkgd), Frank Zullo/Photo Researchers, Inc.; 259 (tl), Jim Cummings/Getty Images/Taxi; 259 (tc), Mike Yamashita/Woodfin Camp/Picture Quest; 259 (tr), NASA; 259 (cr), Nozomi MSI Team/ISAS; 259 (bc), Jerry Lodriguss/Photo Researchers, Inc.; 259 (br), Tony & Daphne Hallas/Science Photo Library/Photo Researchers, Inc.; 260 (b), Jane C. Charlton, Penn State/HST/ESA/NASA; 260 (tc), NCAR/Tom Stack & Associates; 262 (bl), Brian Parker/Tom Stack & Associates; 262 (br), Sam Dudgeon/HRW; 264, Aerial Images, Inc. and SOVINFORMSPUTNIK; 265, NASA Marshall/National Space Science and Technology Center; 266 (bl, br), USGS; 268, Peter Van Steen/HRW; 269, Peter Van Steen/HRW; 270 (t), MSFC/NASA; 270 (tea),Tony McConnell/SPL/Photo Researchers, Inc.; 274 (t), Craig Matthew and Robert Simmon/NASA/GSFC/DMSP; 275 (t), American Museum of Natural History; 275 (bl), Richard Berenholtz/CORBIS

Chapter Nine 276-277, NASA/CORBIS; 278 (Mercury), NASA; 278 (Venus), NASA/Peter Arnold, Inc; 278 (Earth), Paul Morrell/Getty Images/Stone; 278 (Mars), USGS/TSADO/Tom Stack & Associates; 278 (Jupiter), Reta Beebe (New Mexico State University)/NASA; 278, NASA/Mark S. Robinson; 283, NASA; 650 (b), NASA; 650 (tl), Frans Lanting/Minden Pictures; 285, World Perspective/Getty Images/Stone; 285 (b), 286 (b), 652 (inset), NASA; 287, ESA; 288, NASA/Peter Arnold, Inc.; 289 (t), 289 (br), 289 (Saturn), 289 (Uranus), 289, (Neptune), 289 (Pluto), 290 (t), 291, 292 (t), 294, NASA; 296 (moons), John Bova/Photo Researchers, Inc.; 297, Fred Espenek; 298 (tl), Jerry Lodriguss/Photo Researchers, Inc.; 299 (b), NASA; 300 (t), USGS/Science Photo Library/Photo Researchers, Inc.; 300 (b), World Perspective/Getty Images/Stone; 302 (t), NASA; 302, Bill & Sally Fletcher/Tom Stack & Associates; 305 (bc), Breck P. Kent/Animals Animals/Earth Scenes; 305 (bl), E.R. Degginger/Bruce Coleman Inc.; 305 (br), Ken Nichols/Institute of Meteorites/University of New Mexico; 305 (t), Dennis Wilson/Science Photo Library/Photo Researhers, Inc.; 306, NASA; 307, Ken Nichols/Institute of Meteorites/University of New Mexico; 310, NASA; 311, ESA; 311 (b), NASA; 314 (tr), Richard Murrin; 315 (t), NASA; 315 (bl), Mehau Kulyk/Science Photo Library/Photo Researchers, Inc.

Unit Two 316 (t), Corbis-Bettmann; 316 (bl), Enrico Tedeschi; 316 (c), UPI/CORBIS/Bettman; 317 (cr), Getty Images; 317 (cl), Sam Dudgeon/HRW; 317 (tr), Brown Brothers/HRW Photo Library; 317 (bl), ©Natalie Fobes/Getty Images; 317 (br), REUTERS/Charles W. Luzier/NewsCom

Chapter Ten 318-319 (all), Mark Renders/Getty Images; 320 (b), Sam Dudgeon/HRW; 320 (bc), Digital Image copyright © 2005 PhotoDisc; 321 (cr), Sam Dudgeon/HRW; 322 (cl), Sam Dudgeon/HRW; 322 (cl), Victoria Smith/HRW; 323 (all), Sam Dudgeon/HRW; 324 (tl), John Langford/HRW; 324 (br), Corbis Images; 326 (b), Sam Dudgeon/HRW; 327 (tl), Victoria Smith/HRW; 327 (tr, tc, c), Sam Dudgeon/HRW; 327 (cl), Peter Van Steen/HRW; 327 (cr, bl), John Morrison/Morrison Photography; 328 (tl), Richard Megna/Fundamental Photographs; 328 (bl), Victoria Smith/HRW; 330 (tr), Lance Schriner/HRW; 330 (tl), John Langford/HRW; 331 (tr), Victoria Smith/HRW; 331 (inset), Sam Dudgeon/HRW; 332 (br), Rob Boudreau/Getty Images; 333 (cl, cr), Charlie Winters/HRW; 333 (tl, tr), Sam Dudgeon/HRW; 334 (c, cr), Morrison Photography; 334 (bl), Joseph Drivas/Getty Images; 334 (br), © SuperStock; 335 (all), Sam Dudgeon/HRW; 336 (all), Charlie Winters/HRW; 337 (tr), CORBIS Images/HRW; 338 (b), Sam Dudgeon/HRW; 340 (bc), Richard Megna/Fundamental Photographs; 341 (cr), Lance Schriner/HRW; 344 (tl), © David Young-Wolff/PhotoEdit; 345 (cr), Courtesy Mimi So; 345 (b), Steve Cole/PhotoDisc/PictureQuest

Chapter Eleven 346-347 (all), Scott Van Osdol/HRW; 348 (br), Jonathan Blair/Woodfin Camp & Associates, Inc.; 348 (bl), Victoria Smith/HRW; 349 (br), Russ Lappa/Photo Researchers, Inc.; 349 (bl, bc), Charles D. Winters/Photo Researchers, Inc.; 350 (tl), © Zack Burris/Zack Burris, Inc.; 350 (tcl), Yann Arthus-Bertrand/CORBIS; 350 (tcr, tr), Walter Chandoha; 351 (lead), Victoria Smith/HRW; 351 (copper, tin, sulfur), Sam Dudgeon/HRW; 351 (neon), Runk/Shoenberger/Grant Heilman Photography Inc.; 351 (silicon), Joyce Photographics/Photo Researchers, Inc.; 351 (boron), Russ Lappa/Photo Researchers, Inc.; 351 (antimony), Charles D. Winters/Photo Researchers, Inc.; 351 (iodine), Larry Stepanowicz; 352 (bl), Runk/Schoenberger/Grant Heilman Photography Inc.; 353 (bl), Runk/Shoenberger/Grant Heilman Photography; 353 (bc), Richard Megna/Fundamental Photographs; 353 (br), Sam Dudgeon/HRW; 354 (tl), Richard Megna/Fundamental Photographs; 355 (tr), John Kaprielian/Photo Researchers, Inc.; 356 (br), Sam Dudgeon/HRW; 357 (tl), Charles D. Winters; 357 (cl), Sam Dudgeon/HRW; 357 (bc), Charles D. Winters/Photo Researchers, Inc.; 357 (bl), Klaus Guldbrandsen/Science Photo Library/Photo Researchers, Inc.; 357 (tr, cr, br), John Langford/HRW; 358 (tl), Sam Dudgeon/HRW; 359 (bl), Richard Haynes/HRW; 360 (tr), Sam Dudgeon/HRW; 361 (all), John Langford/HRW; 362 (bl), HRW; 362 (br), Lance Schriner/HRW; 363 (tr), Sam Dudgeon/HRW; 366 (tl), John Langford/HRW; 366 (bl), Richard Haynes/HRW; 367 (tr), Charles D. Winters/Photo Researchers, Inc.; 367 (tc), John Langford/HRW; 367 (tl), © Ingram Publishing; ; 370 (bl), © Stuart Westmoreland/Getty Images; 371 (b), Sam Dudgeon/HRW; 372 (tr), Sam Dudgeon/HRW; 372 (tl), Walter Chandoha; 373 (tr), Sam Dudgeon/HRW; 376 (tl), Peter Van Steen/HRW; 377 (tr), Courtesy of Aundra Nix; 377 (cr), Astrid & Hans-Frieder Michler/SPL/Photo Researchers, Inc.

Chapter Twelve 378-379 Wayne Source; 380 (br), Tim Kiusalaas/Masterfile; 381 (cr), Sam Dudgeon/HRW; 382 (tl), Earl Kowall/CORBIS; 383 (br), Sam Dudgeon/HRW; 384 (tl), John Langford/HRW; 384 (tc), Corbis Images; 384 (tr), David Phillips/HRW; 385 (br), Sam Dudgeon/HRW; 385 (cr), Peter Van Steen/HRW; 386 (tr), John Langford/HRW; 386 (bl), NASA; 387 (cr), Peter Van Steen/HRW; 387 (t), Sam Dudgeon/HRW; 388 (br), © Duomo/CORBIS; 389 (bl, br), John Langford/HRW; 389 (tr), Peter Van Steen/HRW; 392 (all), John Langford/HRW; 393 (tr), © Martin Bond/Photo Researchers, Inc.; 396 (tl), Courtesy of Honda; 396 (bc), Digital Image copyright © 2005 PhotoDisc; 397 (bl), Mike Powell/Allsport/Getty Images; 400 (bl), Courtesy Pursuit Dynamics; 400 (tr), © Bettman/CORBIS; 401 (all), Robert Wolf/HRW

Chapter Thirteen 402-403 (all), © Jason Childs/Getty Images; 405 (tr), Robert Mathena/Fundamental Photographs, New York; 405 (bl), © Albert Copley/Visuals Unlimited; 406 (t), NASA; 413 (tr), © Steve Kaufman/CORBIS; 414 (br), Erich Schrempp/Photo Researchers, Inc.; 415 (tl), Richard Megna/Fundamental Photographs; 416 (tc), Educational Development Center; 418 (tl), Richard Megna/Fundamental Photographs; 418 (bl), John Langford/HRW; 421 (br), © Darwin Dale/Photo Researchers, Inc.; 422 (bl), Sovfoto/Eastfoto; 423 (bl), Richard Megna/Fundamental Photographs; 425 (br), Ken Kay/Fundamental Photographs; 427 (cr), Ken Kay/Fundamental Photographs; 428 (br), James H. Karales/Peter Arnold, Inc.; 429 (b), Sam Dudgeon/HRW; 430 (bl), Richard Megna/Fundamental Photographs; 431 (bl), Martin Bough/Fundamental Photographs; 434 (tl), Pete Saloutos/The Stock Market; 434 (tr), The Granger Collection, New York; 435 (all), Peter Van Steen/HRW

Unit Three 436 (c), The National Archives/Corbis; 436 (b), Cold Spring Harbor Laboratory; 436 (t), © Burstein Collection/CORBIS; 437 (t), Ed Reschke/Peter Arnold; 437 (tcr), Keith Porter/Photo Researchers; 437 (bcl), Ed Reschke/Peter Arnold, Inc.; 437 (br), © Dr. Ian Wilmut/Liaison/Getty News Images; 437 (bl), Dan McCoy/Rainbow; 437 (bcr), © Glen Allison/Getty Images/Stone; 437 (tcl), © Bettmann/CORBIS

Chapter Fourteen 438-439, Dennis Kunkel/Phototake; 440 (l), Visuals Unlimited/Kevin Collins; 440 (r), Leonard Lessin/Peter Arnold; 441 (r), T.E. Adams/Visuals Unlimited; 441 (cl), Roland Birke/Peter Arnold, Inc.; 441 (bkgd), Jerome Wexler/Photo Researchers, Inc.; 441 (cr), Biophoto Associates/Photo Researchers, Inc.; 441 (l), M.I. Walker/Photo Researchers, Inc.; 442 Photodisc, Inc.; 443 (t), William Dentler/BPS/Stone; 443 (b), Dr. Gopal Murti/Science Photo Library/Photo Researchers, Inc.; 445 Wolfgang Baumeister/Science Photo Library/Photo Researchers, Inc.; 446 (l), Biophoto Associates/Photo Researchers, Inc.; 450 (bl), Don Fawcett/Visuals Unlimited; 450 (t), Dr. Peter Dawson/Science Photo Library/Photo Researchers, Inc.; 451 (r), R. Bolender-D. Fawcett/Visuals Unlimited; 452 (cl), Don Fawcett/Visuals Unlimited; 452 (bl), Newcomb & Wergin/BPS/Tony Stone Images; 453 (br), Garry T Cole/BPS/Stone; 454 (tl), Dr. Gopal Murti/Science Photo Library/Photo Researchers, Inc.; 454 (cl), Dr. Jeremy Burgess/Science PhotoLibrary/Science Source/Photo Researchers; 456 Quest/Science Photo Library/Photo Researchers, Inc.; 457 Manfred Kage/Peter Arnold, Inc. ; 460 (b), Sam Dudgeon/HRW; 466 (r), Photo Researchers, Inc.; 466 (l), Science Photo Library/Photo Researchers, Inc.; 467 (b), Digital Image copyright © 2005 Artville; 467 (t), Courtesy Caroline Schooley

Chapter Fifteen 468-469 Frans Lanting/Minden Pictures; 470 Gerry Ellis/ENP Images; 476 Biophoto Associates/Photo Researchers; 477 (t), Sherrie Jones/Photo Researchers; 477 (br), Dr. Tony Brian & David Parker/Science Photo Library/Photo Researchers; 477 (inset), Dr. Tony Brian & David Parker/Science Photo Library/Photo Researchers; 478 (t), Visuals Unlimited/Stanley Flegler; 478 (b), © Phil A. Dotson/Photo Researchers, Inc.; 479 (l), © Royalty-free/CORBIS; 479 (r), David R. Frazier/Photo Researchers, Inc.; 480 (tl), SuperStock; 480 (tr), © G. Randall/Getty Images/FPG International; 480 (bl), SuperStock; 481, Corbis Images; 481 Dr. Tony Brian & David Parker/Science Photo Library/Photo Researchers; 484 (b), Dr. Tony Brian & David Parker/Science Photo Library/Photo Researchers; 485 (b), SuperStock; 488 (r), Piotr Naskrecki/Conservation International; 489 (r), © National Geographic Image Collection/Michael Nichols; 489 (l), © National Geographic Image Collection/Michael Fay

Chapter Sixteen 490-491 © Chris Mattison; Frank Lane Picture Agency/CORBIS; 494 (l), Dr. Jeremy Burgess/Science Photo Library/Photo Researchers; 497 (b), Visuals Unlimited/W. Ormerod; 499 (c), Paul Hein/Unicorn; 499 (l), Jerome Wexler/Photo Researchers; 499 (r), George Bernard/Earth Scenes; 500 (b)© Keren Su/Getty Images/Stone; 502 (b) Gary Gaugler/ Visuals Unlimited; 502 (t) © Keren Su/Getty Images/Stone; 503 (t) © Tom Tietz/Getty Images/Stone; 503 (t) Sylvain Cordier/Photo Researchers; 504 (r), Visuals Unlimited/Cabisco; 504 (l), Innerspace Visions; 506 (b), Photo Researchers; 506 (t), Digital Image copyright © 2005 PhotoDisc Green; 507 © Charles Phillip/CORBIS; 509 (b), Sam Dudgeon/HRW; 511 (t) Sylvain Cordier/Photo Researchers; 511 (b) Jerome Wexler/Photo Researchers; 514 (r), © Tim Rock/Lonely Planet Images; 514 (l), © Bill Beatty/Visuals Unlimited; 515 Photo courtesy The International Crane Foundation

Chapter Seventeen 516-517 AFP/CORBIS; 518-519 (b-bkgd), © David Madison/Getty Images/Stone; 520 Sam Dudgeon/HRW; 529 (t), Victoria Smith/HRW; 530 Susumu Nishinaga/Science Photo Library/Photo Researchers, Inc.; 531 (b), Don Fawcett/Photo Researchers; 533 © Getty Images/The Image Bank; 536 (c), Sam Dudgeon/HRW; 537 Will & Deni McIntyre/Photo Researchers; 539 Sam Dudgeon/HRW; 544 (l), © Dan McCoy/Rainbow; 544 (r), Reuters/David Gray/NewsCom; 545 (t), Peter Van Steen/HRW

Chapter Eighteen 546-547 Photo Lennart Nilsson/Albert Bonniers Forlag AB, A Child Is Born, Dell Publishing Company; 550 Chip Henderson; 555 (tl), Petit Format/Nestle/Science Source/Photo Researchers, Inc.; 555 (cl), Photo Lennart Nilsson/Albert Bonniers Forlag AB, A Child Is Born, Dell Publishing Company; 555 (cr), Photo Lennart Nilsson/Albert Bonniers Forlag AB, A Child Is Born, Dell Publishing Company; 555 (br), Keith/Custom Medical Stock Photo; 555 (tr), David M. Phillips/Photo Researchers, Inc.; 556 (l), Peter Van Steen/HRW; 556 (cl), Peter Van Steen/HRW; 556 (c), Peter Van Steen/HRW; 556 (cr), Peter Van Steen/HRW; 556 (r), Peter Van Steen/HRW; 557 © Mark Harmel/Getty Images/FPG International; 559 Digital Image copyright © 2005 PhotoDisc; 560 Peter Van Steen/HRW; 561 Photo Lennart Nilsson/Albert Bonniers Forlag AB, A Child Is Born, Dell Publishing Company; 564 (r), Jim Tunell/Zuma Press/NewsCom; 564 (l), © Michael Clancy; 565 (l), ZEPHYR/Science Photo Library/Photo Researchers, Inc.; 565 (r), Salem Community College

Chapter Nineteen 566-567 (t), © K. Kjeldsen/Photo Researchers, Inc.; 568 (br), CNRI/Science Photo Library/Photo Researchers; 568 (bl), Tektoff-RM/CNRI/Science Photo Library/Photo Researchers; 569 (t), Kent Wood/Photo Researchers; 570 (b), Peter Van Steen/HRW ; 572 (b), Peter Van Steen/HRW; 576 (t), John Langford/HRW Photo; 577 (b), Clinical Radiology Dept., Salisbury District Hospital/Science Photo Library/Photo Researchers; 577 (t), SuperStock; 578 (b), Photo Lennart Nilsson/Albert Bonniers Forlag AB; 578 (tl), Dr. A. Liepins/Science Photo Library/Photo Researchers; 578 (tr), Dr. A. Liepins/Science Photo Library/Photo Researchers; 580 Sam Dudgeon/HRW; 583 (t), Peter Van Steen/HRW ; 586 (l), E. R. Degginger/Bruce Coleman; 586 (r), Chris Rogers/Index Stock Imagery, Inc.; 587 (t), Peter Van Steen/HRW; 587 (b), Corbis

Chapter Twenty 588-589 © Roine Magnusson/Getty Images/The Image Bank; 595 (r), © David M. Phillips/Visuals Unlimited; 597 (t), © George H. H. Huey/CORBIS; 597 (c), © D. Robert & Lorri Franz/CORBIS; 597 (b), © Jason Brindel Photography/Alamy Photos; 598 (t), Laguna Photo/Liaison International/Getty News Images; 598 (b), Jeff Lepore/Photo Researchers; 600 Jeff Foott/AUSCAPE; 601 © Ross Hamilton/Getty Images/Stone; 602 (l), Visuals Unlimited/Gerald & Buff Corsi; 602 (cr), Hans Pfletschinger/Peter Arnold; 603 (r), W. Peckover/Academy of Natural Sciences Philadelphia/VIREO; 603 (l), Leroy Simon/Visuals Unlimited; 604 (b), Ed Robinson/Tom Stack & Associates; 604 (tl), © Telegraph Color Library/Getty Images/FPG International; 604 (tr), OSF/Peter Parks/Animals Animals Earth Scenes; 605 (t), © Gay Bumgarner/Getty Images/Stone; 605 (b), Carol Hughes/Bruce Coleman; 606 (tl), CSIRO Wildlife & Ecology; 606 (r), © Rick & Nora Bowers/Visuals Unlimited; 607 Leroy Simon/Visuals Unlimited; 608 Sam Dudgeon/HRW; 609 Sam Dudgeon/HRW; 609 Sam Dudgeon/HRW; 610 Leroy Simon/Visuals Unlimited; 614 (r), © National Geographic Image Collection/Darlyne Murawski; 614 (l), Digital Image copyright © 2005 PhotoDisc; 615 (r), Photo from the Dept. of Communication Services, North Carolina State University; 615 (l), Digital Image copyright © 2005 Artville

Chapter Twenty-One 616-617 © Studio Carlo Dani/Animals Animals/Earth Scenes; 622 (t), Grant Heilman; 622 (b), Tom Brakefield/Bruce Coleman; 624 (t), © Kathy Bushue/Getty Images/Stone; 626 (inset), Manfred Kage/Peter Arnold; 626-627 (b), Stuart Westmorland/Getty Images/Stone; 630 (b), © Jeff Hunter/Getty Images/The Image Bank; 634 (t), Dwight Kuhn; 634 (b), Hardie Truesdale/International Stock; 637 Sam Dudgeon/HRW; 642 (r), Dr. Verena Tunnicliffe; 642 (l), © Raymond Gehman/CORBIS; 643 (t), Lincoln P. Brower; 643 (b), © Royalty-Free/CORBIS

Lab Book 647 (tr), Victoria Smith/HRW, Courtesy of Science Stuff, Austin, TX; 647, (galena), Ken Lucas/Visuals Unlimited Inc.; 647 (cr), Charlie Winters/HRW; 648, Sam Dudgeon/HRW; 651, Victoria Smith/HRW; 652, Andy Christiansen/HRW; 654, Victoria Smith/HRW; 655, Sam Dudgeon/HRW; 658, Kuni Stringer/AP/Wide World Photos; 659, Victoria Smith/HRW; 660, Jay Malonson/AP/Wide World Photos; 662, Sam Dudgeon/HRW; 663, Victoria Smith/HRW; 664, Peter Van Steen/HRW; 665-668, Sam Dudgeon/HRW; 669 (all), Sam Dudgeon/HRW; 670 (tr), John Langford/HRW; 670 (cr), NASA; 671 (all), Sam Dudgeon/HRW; 672 (br), Sam Dudgeon/HRW; 674 (bc), Sam Dudgeon/HRW; 675 (br), Gareth Trevor/Getty Images; 676 (tr), Sam Dudgeon/HRW; 677 (br), Victoria Smith/HRW; 678 (all), Richard Megna/Fundamental Photographs; 680 (tl), Runk/Schoenberger/Grant Heilman; 683 (b), Breck P. Kent; 683 (br), Stephen J. Krasemann/Photo Researchers; 683 (c), Visuals Unlimited/R. Calentine; 683 (t), Runk/Schoenberger/Grant Heilman; 684 Sam Dudgeon/HRW; 685 Sam Dudgeon/HRW; 692 Peter Van Steen/HRW